THE

# INTERNATIONAL SERIES
OF
# MONOGRAPHS ON PHYSICS

# THE INTERNATIONAL SERIES OF MONOGRAPHS ON PHYSICS

*Already Published*

THE THEORY OF ELECTRIC AND MAGNETIC SUSCEPTIBILITIES. By J. H. VAN VLECK. 1932

THE THEORY OF ATOMIC COLLISIONS. By N. F. MOTT and H. S. W. MASSEY. *Third edition.* 1965

RELATIVITY, THERMODYNAMICS, AND COSMOLOGY. By R. C. TOLMAN. 1934

KINEMATIC RELATIVITY. A sequel to *Relativity, Gravitation, and World-Structure.* By E. A. MILNE. 1948

THE PRINCIPLES OF STATISTICAL MECHANICS. By R. C. TOLMAN. 1938

ELECTRONIC PROCESSES IN IONIC CRYSTALS. By N. F. MOTT and R. W. GURNEY. *Second edition.* 1948

GEOMAGNETISM. By S. CHAPMAN and J. BARTELS. 1940. 2 vols.

THE SEPARATION OF GASES. By M. RUHEMANN. *Second edition.* 1949

THE PRINCIPLES OF QUANTUM MECHANICS. By P. A. M. DIRAC. *Fourth edition.* 1958

THEORY OF ATOMIC NUCLEUS AND NUCLEAR ENERGY SOURCES. By G. GAMOW and C. L. CRITCHFIELD. 1949. *Being the third edition of* STRUCTURE OF ATOMIC NUCLEUS AND NUCLEAR TRANSFORMATIONS.

THE PULSATION THEORY OF VARIABLE STARS. By S. ROSSELAND. 1949

THEORY OF PROBABILITY. By HAROLD JEFFREYS. *Third edition.* 1961

THE FRICTION AND LUBRICATION OF SOLIDS. By F. P. BOWDEN and D. TABOR. Part I. 1950. Part II. 1963

ELECTRONIC AND IONIC IMPACT PHENOMENA. By H. S. W. MASSEY and E. H. S. BURHOP. 1952

MIXTURES. By E. A. GUGGENHEIM. 1952

THE THEORY OF RELATIVITY. By C. MØLLER. 1952

THE OUTER LAYERS OF A STAR. By R. v. d. R. WOOLLEY and D. W. N. STIBBS. 1953

DISLOCATIONS AND PLASTIC FLOW IN CRYSTALS. By A. H. COTTRELL. 1953

ELECTRICAL BREAKDOWN OF GASES. By J. M. MEEK and J. D. CRAGGS. 1953

GEOCHEMISTRY. By the late V. M. GOLDSCHMIDT. Edited by ALEX MUIR. 1954

THE QUANTUM THEORY OF RADIATION. By W. HEITLER. *Third edition.* 1954

ON THE ORIGIN OF THE SOLAR SYSTEM. By H. ALFVÉN. 1954

DYNAMICAL THEORY OF CRYSTAL LATTICES. By M. BORN and K. HUANG. 1954

METEOR ASTRONOMY. By A. C. B. LOVELL. 1954

RECENT ADVANCES IN OPTICS. By E. H. LINFOOT. 1955

QUANTUM THEORY OF SOLIDS. By R. E. PEIERLS. 1955

MOLECULAR BEAMS. By NORMAN F. RAMSEY. 1956

NEUTRON TRANSPORT THEORY. By B. DAVISON with the collaboration of J. B. SYKES. 1957

RECTIFYING SEMI-CONDUCTOR CONTACTS. By H. K. HENISCH. 1957

THE THEORY OF ELEMENTARY PARTICLES. By J. HAMILTON. 1959

ELECTRONS AND PHONONS. The Theory of Transport Phenomena in Solids. By J. M. ZIMAN. 1960

HYDRODYNAMIC AND HYDROMAGNETIC STABILITY. By S. CHANDRASEKHAR. 1961

THE PRINCIPLES OF NUCLEAR MAGNETISM. By A. ABRAGAM. 1961

COSMICAL ELECTRODYNAMICS: Fundamental Principles. By H. ALFVÉN and C.-G. FÄLTHAMMAR. *Second edition.* 1963

THEORY AND PRACTICE OF THE EVALUATION OF MEASUREMENTS. By L. JÁNOSSY. 1964

# THE THEORY OF BETA RADIOACTIVITY

BY

E. J. KONOPINSKI
PROFESSOR OF PHYSICS
INDIANA UNIVERSITY

OXFORD
AT THE CLARENDON PRESS
1966

PHYSICS

*Oxford University Press, Ely House, London W. 1*

GLASGOW NEW YORK TORONTO MELBOURNE WELLINGTON

CAPE TOWN SALISBURY IBADAN NAIROBI LUSAKA ADDIS ABABA

BOMBAY CALCUTTA MADRAS KARACHI LAHORE DACCA

KUALA LUMPUR HONG KONG



PRINTED IN GREAT BRITAIN

# PREFACE

THE presentation here will bear the marks of its origins in lectures to various audiences having various degrees of acquaintance with the formal languages of physics. The lectures to undergraduates with knowledge of no more than the most elementary quantum-mechanical ideas seemed appropriate for introducing the data on which the theory is based. They set the tone for the first chapter, which demonstrates that quite a complete description of allowed nuclear $\beta$-decay can be constructed without even mentioning a 'spinor'.

The second and third chapters present elements of the quantum-relativistic description of spin-$\frac{1}{2}$ particles. Such preliminaries were found to be needed even for audiences acquainted with the textbook versions, but without experience in detailed applications. A novel approach is used, based on the 'Zitterbewegung', because this seemed particularly helpful for understanding the degrees of 'handedness' characteristic of $\beta$-decay products. Special attention is given to the distinction between 'helicity' and 'chirality' because of dissatisfactions, expressed to the author by experimentalists, with having too many essentials hidden behind the formal usage of 'gamma-five'.

Fermi's theoretical framework, as modified by the Yang and Lee discovery of parity non-conservation, is presented in Chapter IV. A description of the Fermi and Gamow–Teller emissions as radiations of singlet and triplet waves is developed there. The complete theoretical expectations for allowed nuclear $\beta$-emissions are worked out in Chapter V. The elements of nuclear structure theory most essential to an understanding of the nuclear $\beta$-moments are also presented. A new development is the determination of phases needed for predicting interferences between singlet and triplet emissions.

The formal development of $\beta$-multipole expansions to arbitrary order, in Chapter VI, yields another set of results new to the literature. A fresh approach is used, modelled on the parallelism between the generation of Dirac and Maxwell fields. A discussion of the reality of $\beta$-moments not explicitly dependent on time-reversal invariance was found possible.

The 'exact' evaluations of Chapter VI provide a systematic basis for the classifications and evaluations of 'forbidden' emissions in Chapter VII. The theory of the forbidden $\beta$-moments is reviewed, and extended to 'forbidden effects on allowed emissions'. The latter treatment enables distinguishing 'non-anomalous weak-magnetism' which exists irrespective of whether the Vector current is conserved or not. A contribution to the weak-magnetism by orbital motions, apparently not explicitly recognized heretofore, is isolated. All this serves to set the stage for a particularly clean-cut distinction of the 'anomalous' weak-magnetism arising from the Conserved Vector Current, which is introduced after the evidence from muon decay in Chapter XII. The pion $\beta$-decay arising from the Conserved Current is also presented there.

Like the expectations for $\beta$-emissions in Chapter VII, those for the electron captures discussed in Chapter VIII are presented for arbitrary degrees of forbiddenness. New types of $\beta$-moments, not essentially involved in the emission phenomena but important for the forbidden captures, are isolated. Chapter VIII also presents the expectations for neutrino capture, making explicit the effects of the neutrino helicity on the size of the cross-section.

Quantized field descriptions are not introduced until Chapter IX, when they provide advantages in the anti-symmetrizations among the products of double $\beta$-decay. The role of the latter in determining the appropriate description of the neutrino is discussed, together with other evidence on this point, in the last section of Chapter X.

The bearing of the neutrino description adopted on the 'Principle of Lepton Conservation' is also discussed in Chapter X. Detailed constructions of neutrino beam descriptions under failures of the lepton conservation are undertaken there for the first time.

The greater part of Chapter X is devoted to the symmetry principles implicit in the theories of four-fermion interactions. The alternative forms of the latter are discussed, and new evidence, based on interference effects in allowed emissions, is adduced against the existence of a Pseudoscalar coupling.

The last three chapters complete a review of the 'strangeness-conserving' $\beta$-phenomena. The pion, the muon, and the 'neutretto' are introduced in Chapter XI. The name for the last of these particles is adopted so as to avoid the preconceptions implicit in 'muon's neutrino', pending evidence that the particle is actually massless. The possible identification of the neutretto with the 'other two components' of the neutrino is discussed in the final chapter.

Muon decay, the subject of Chapter XII, is first discussed apart from any formal coupling law. It is indicated how a quite complete description of all the muon decay phenomena follows from conservation principles as they apply to emissions from a point. The general Michel family of spectra is derived on that basis, and then the actual observations are accounted for when the particles are restricted to specific helicities. When specific interaction laws are introduced, the evidence for a unique one is also discussed.

The effects of the strong interactions of nucleons on their general behaviour in the weak interaction phenomena (i.e. the nucleon 'form-factors') are discussed in the last chapter, as a preliminary to the understanding of the muon and neutretto capture processes.

The present conclusions about the weak interactions as couplings between transformation currents are perhaps most succinctly expressed in equations (12.63) and (12.86).

The various references quoted in this work are simply those which the author happened to consult in some degree. He found the scholarly task of attributing precise credit wherever credit is due to be so time-consuming that it was put beyond his powers. He hastens to acknowledge that only very minor parts of the vast development are original with him.

The author is indebted to the National Science Foundation for support during summer periods used for the preparation of this treatise.

E. J. K.

*Indiana University*
*April 1964*

# CONTENTS

# I

# THE CRITICAL DATA

## 1.1. An introduction to nuclear β-decay

A DIAGRAM which illustrates numberless accounts of radioactivity is shown in Fig. 1.1. It is meant to represent the behaviour of emanations from a naturally radioactive material, in the presence of a magnetic field directed normally to the plane of the diagram. It serves to classify the emanations according to the electrical charge borne by each. The positive, negative, and neutral emanations were named $\alpha$-, $\beta$-, and $\gamma$-rays, respectively. This is the origin of the name '$\beta$-radioactivity'.

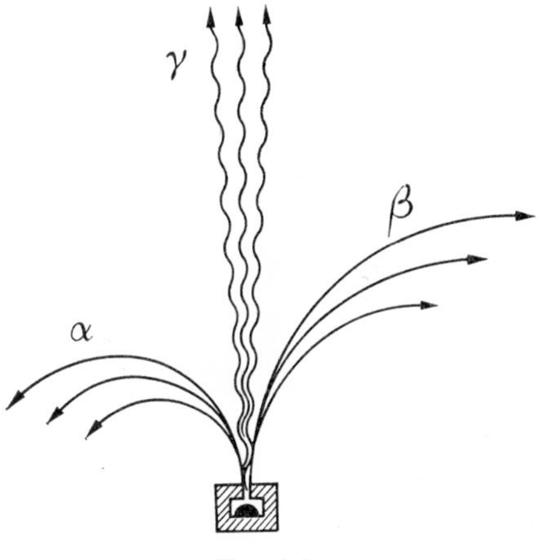


FIG. 1.1

Each of the three types of processes is found to entail a characteristic change in the state of some atomic nucleus. Usually, only mixtures of distinct nuclear species will produce all three types of emanations, in the way implied by the above diagram. A given type of nucleus will usually emit only $\alpha$-rays or $\beta$-rays, not both. On the other hand, spontaneous $\gamma$-radiation rarely occurs except in the company of $\alpha$- or $\beta$-rays.

The $\alpha$-emanations have been identified as nuclei of helium. They are successfully understood as fragments of nuclear matter which are thrown off when this results in a stabler structure.

The $\gamma$-rays have been identified as electromagnetic radiation. Emissions of radiation during motions within systems of charges are commonplace. $\gamma$-rays are then to be expected whenever an $\alpha$- or $\beta$-process leaves the product nucleus in an excited state, requiring internal redistributions of charge before it is settled into a finally stable state.

The $\beta$-emanations have been identified as ordinary electrons. The understanding of how these arise required a radical enlargement of conceptions about physical processes.

*The $\beta$-radiation process*

That the $\beta$-electrons are extruded from the nuclei themselves is confirmed by chemical analyses which show that the parent and daughter nuclei differ in charge by one unit. Yet nuclei are successfully understood as composed of neutrons and protons only; there is no room for pre-existent electrons, waiting to emerge. Despite their 'material' character, the electrons must be presumed to be created in the act of emission, in much the way that photons come into existence in the electromagnetic radiation process. The alteration of the nuclear charge must be the result of the conversion of a neutron into a proton during the $\beta$-radiation process.

The transformation of neutrons into protons is directly observed in the free neutron decay, $\mathrm{n} \to \mathrm{p}+\mathrm{e}^-$. This might lead one to regard neutrons merely as closer combinations of protons and electrons than are hydrogen atoms. To quell that idea is the finding that also protons decay into neutrons, with the emission of positrons: $\mathrm{p} \to \mathrm{n}+\mathrm{e}^+$.

It is true that *free* protons cannot spontaneously decay; they are less massive than neutrons ($M_\mathrm{p}\,c^2 < M_\mathrm{n}\,c^2$ by 1·293 MeV), hence the energy is not available. However, when the transforming proton, and the neutron to be produced, is each a part of a nuclear structure into which it is bound, then the energy may become available. A bound particle may be attributed a mass-energy which is smaller than it is in the particle's free state, by the energy of binding.‡ If a nuclear structure is such that the replacement of a proton in it by a neutron results in a deeper binding (smaller mass), then the excess mass-energy becomes available for positron emission. A large number of such cases have been discovered, among artificially produced, rather than naturally occurring, nuclei.

The considerations here suggest that $\beta$-radioactivity should be treated as a radiation process, much like electromagnetic emission. The primary difference is that massive, charge-bearing quanta are radiated,

‡ For example, the energy of an electron bound in a hydrogen atom is $m'c^2 = mc^2(1-\alpha^2)^{\frac{1}{2}}$, where $m$ is its rest-mass and $\alpha = e^2/\hbar c$. Since $\alpha \approx 1/137 \ll 1$, the energy is approximately $m'c^2 \approx mc^2 - me^4/2\hbar^2$. The last term is just the well-known Balmer formula for the binding energy of normal hydrogen.

rather than the chargeless and massless photons. This idea was formulated in detail by Fermi,‡ and the ultimate development of his formulation successfully encompasses current knowledge concerning $\beta$-radioactivity and allied phenomena.

Before the formulation can be properly developed, certain critical pieces of observational information about the $\beta$-processes must be available. Some of these were not yet available at the time of Fermi's initial effort. Indeed, the very existence of some of the most informative phenomena was not even suspected until much later, after Yang and Lee§ pointed out that previous attempts at observations had been unwarrantedly restricted, by the presumption that only results with reflectional symmetry were to be expected.

The objective of this chapter will be to assemble the critical pieces of data in as economical a form as is consistent with an appreciation of their significance. The data will not merely be listed but the immediate inferences which give them significance will also be discussed.

*$\beta$-decay lifetimes*

Systematic observations on the $\beta$-processes must ostensibly start with the isolation of each species of $\beta$-radioactive nuclei (the specific 'isotopes'). The isolation can usually be done literally, by physico-chemical procedures, but can often also be done sufficiently well merely by restricting the observations to $\beta$-electrons found to appear at a rate characteristic of the isotope. The latter circumstance is a significant one. It stems from the finding that the rate is simply proportional to the number, $N$, of the undecayed, parent nuclei present at any moment, i.e. $-dN/dt = \lambda N$, where $\lambda$ is a 'decay constant' characteristic of the isotope. Its constancy is shown by the fact that the activity decays exponentially with time, $-dN/dt = \lambda N_0 \exp(-\lambda t)$, a result which follows from $\lambda = -dN/N\,dt$ constant.

The finding that the number of $\beta$-processes undergone by a collection of nuclear systems is proportional to the number of them present implies that the sudden $\beta$-emission by any individual system is a matter of chance. This provided one of the earliest indications that the behaviour of elementary systems is to be interpreted statistically, in conformity with quantum mechanical principles. The inferences from the observations on $\beta$-decay must be made on that basis.

The number of nuclei of a given $\beta$-radioactive isotope, $N = N_0 \exp(-\lambda t)$, is cut down to a fraction $1/e$ in each time interval $\tau = 1/\lambda$, hence $\tau$ is

‡ E. Fermi, *Z. Phys.* **88**, 254 (1934).
§ T. D. Lee and C. N. Yang, *Phys. Rev.* **104**, 254 (1956).

called the 'mean life' of the isotope. The time for decrease by one-half, $t_{\frac{1}{2}} = \tau \ln 2 = 0{\cdot}693\tau$, is known as the 'half-life' of the decay.

A survey of observed $\beta$-decay rates shows, first, that they have an enormous range of variation from isotope to isotope. The nuclei of ${}_5B_7^{12}$ (a boron isotope having 5 protons and 7 neutrons) have a half-life of only 0·027 seconds, while ${}_{19}K_{21}^{40}$ has a lifetime of $1{\cdot}5(10)^9$ years! We must seek to correlate such variations with other observable characteristics of the decays.

What is immediately observed is that the more rapidly decaying nuclei tend to emit the more energetic electrons. However, making this correlation quantitative is complicated by a curious fact. It is found that ostensibly identical nuclei, forming a population with a characteristic decay rate, transforming into products which are again unseparable from each other, may yet emit electrons of widely different energies. A given type of nucleus sometimes emits a $\beta$-particle with one energy, sometimes with another. It may emit any one of a *continuous spectrum* of electron energies. This is perhaps the most striking feature of $\beta$-decay. It contrasts sharply with the $\alpha$- or $\gamma$-rays, each of which always bear the definite, discrete energy by which the initial and final nuclear states differ.

## 1.2. Introduction of the neutrino

*The continuous spectrum*

A given type of $\beta$-radioactive nucleus has a definite mass, $M_i$, and its daughter, differing from the parent by an n $\leftrightarrow$ p substitution, also has a definite mass, $M_f$. Every case of decay of that isotope therefore releases the definite energy, $W_0 = (M_i - M_f)c^2$. Part of this energy is used up in forming the electron's rest-mass, $m$, and the remainder should appear as kinetic energy of the emitted particles. However, only a vanishingly small minority of the electrons are actually found to have a full 'end-point' kinetic energy, $W_0 - mc^2$. A typical energy-distribution or 'spectrum', as it is observed, is shown in Fig. 1.2. Plotted is $d\lambda/\lambda\, dT$, the fraction of the decay rate devoted to producing electrons with kinetic energy $T$, per unit of the energy scale. The mystery is: what happens to the remainder, $W_0 - mc^2 - T$, of the energy in all cases in which the electron only receives the kinetic energy $T < W_0 - mc^2$?

Sometimes additional energy does appear in the form of $\gamma$-radiation, but then it is separately accounted for by the mass difference, $M_f^* - M_f$, between excited and ground states of the daughter nucleus. There is still an energy $W_0^* - T - mc^2$ to account for, with $W_0^* = (M_i - M_f^*)c^2$. Moreover, there are many cases in which no appreciable electromagnetic energy appears at all, yet the phenomenon of a continuous $\beta$-spectrum persists.

The 'missing energy' cannot be accounted for by assuming that the electron loses part of its initial kinetic energy while passing out of the solid material of the source. Changing the source thickness, in a range of thin sources, affects only a small, low-energy, portion of the spectrum.

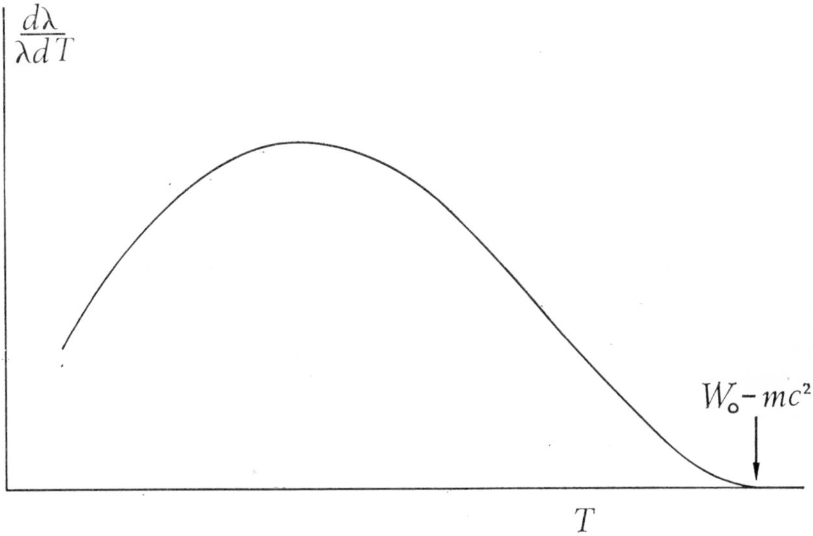


FIG. 1.2

The observed effect is commensurate with known rates of energy loss for electrons penetrating through matter, and the latter are not at all adequate to explain the amounts of energy found to be 'missing'.

A quite conclusive demonstration that the 'missing energy' escapes the source entirely was provided by the Ellis–Wooster calorimetric experiment. A sample of RaE was placed within a calorimeter massive enough to stop, within itself, all known types of emanations; the consequent rise of temperature was measured, and found to correspond to what is expected if each $\beta$-electron deposits an *average* value of the RaE spectrum of energies, rather than the end-point value, $W_0 - mc^2$. The 'missing energy' was still missing. It had escaped the calorimeter.

Pauli offered the explanation which has since been confirmed. The 'missing energy' must be carried away by a hitherto unknown type of particle, at least one of which must be presumed to be emitted together with each $\beta$-electron. Since the electrons account for all the charge carried away, the new particles must be chargeless. They must also have practically no other means of interacting with matter, in order to have escaped detection through energy interchanges, as in the calorimeter. Fermi dubbed the hypothetical particles 'neutrinos'.

*Neutrino momentum*

According to relativistic principles, any energy, including that attributed to the neutrino, should be treated as only one of the components of an energy-momentum four-vector. For example, the total energy, $W = T+mc^2$, of a free electron behaves like a fourth component, $p_4 = iW/c$, of a four-vector having the electron's momentum $\mathbf{p}$, as its three 'spatial' components. The entity is called a four-vector because it is the sum of the squares of all four components which is expected to be a constant independent of the reference frame:

$$p^2 - W^2/c^2 = -m^2c^2. \tag{1.1}$$

The constant is identified from the fact that the relationship is to persist even in the frame moving with the particle, in which $\mathbf{p} = 0$ and $W = mc^2$. These considerations emphasize that basic physical principles make it impossible to attribute energy without also attributing momentum to the neutrino. They become interchangeable merely by being viewed from different ones of relatively moving reference frames.

Separate detection of the effects of neutrino momentum was difficult to achieve, but was done eventually, when it became feasible to make measurements on the individual nuclear recoils from $\beta$-emission. The electron and recoil momenta were found not to balance by themselves; it was necessary to assume that their non-vanishing resultant momentum was balanced against that of a third, invisible body.

*Neutrino capture*

For many years, the only evidence for the existence of the neutrino was limited to the moment of its emission in $\beta$-decay. It was simply the hypothetical carrier of whatever energy-momentum was 'missing'. To make its detection as satisfactory as that of the neutron, or of $\gamma$-rays, it seemed necessary to find effects it produces after leaving the $\beta$-source. That was finally achieved by Reines, Cowan, Harrison, Kruse, and MacGuire.‡ These investigators took advantage of the presumed huge fluxes of neutrinos which should emerge from a nuclear reactor, with its large quantities of radioactivity. The effects sought were reversals of the neutron decay. Since neutrons transform into protons with the

‡ Work summarized in a paper by F. Reines and C. Cowan, *Phys. Rev.* **113**, 273 (1959).

emission of electrons and, presumably, neutrinos as well, the recapture of neutrinos by protons may well be expected to reproduce neutrons, together with positrons. Accordingly, huge quantities of hydrogen-rich liquid were placed near a reactor and the simultaneous detection of neutrons and positrons was arranged for. The processes were found, and in about the expected intensity. Details of the findings will be better discussed after a basis for the expectations has been developed (§ 8.2).

Long before such direct evidences for the neutrino were garnered, Fermi incorporated the conception into his theory of $\beta$-decay. The theory had many immediate successes which testified to the usefulness of the conception. Among the successes was the demonstration that the observed electron spectra are just such as are to be expected from the sharing of a given amount of energy, $W_0$, between two light particles. This particular success depends very little on the precise form given to the theory. It can be understood on a quite elementary, 'statistical' basis, implicit in any quantum mechanical theory, to be discussed next.

## 1.3. The statistical β-spectrum

*Energy-momentum conservation*

Consider a nucleus at rest which suddenly explodes into three fragments. Designate by $\mathbf{p}$, $\mathbf{q}$, and $\mathbf{P}$ the respective momenta attained by the fragments in some one such event. They must balance according to:

$$0 = \mathbf{P}+\mathbf{p}+\mathbf{q}. \tag{1.2}$$

Energy conservation imposes the further restriction:

$$M_i c^2 \equiv M_f c^2+W_0 = M_f c^2+E+W+K, \tag{1.3}$$

in which $E$ is the recoil kinetic energy of the nucleus, while $W$ and $K$ are energies of the electron and neutrino, corresponding to the momenta $\mathbf{p}$ and $\mathbf{q}$, inclusive of rest-energies:

$$W = c(p^2+m^2c^2)^{\frac{1}{2}} \quad \text{and} \quad K = c(q^2+\mu^2c^2)^{\frac{1}{2}}. \tag{1.4}$$

Here $\mu$ designates whatever rest-mass the neutrino may have.

We may first assure ourselves that the recoil energy $E$ may be neglected in the energy balance (1.3). The recoil momentum, $\mathbf{P}$, may be of the same order as $\mathbf{p}$ and $\mathbf{q}$, in the momentum balance (1.2), but

$$E \approx P^2/2M_f = (\mathbf{p}+\mathbf{q})^2/2M_f.$$

The energy conservation relation (1.3) shows that $W+K < W_0$, hence $c^2(\mathbf{p}+\mathbf{q})^2 < W_0^2$, and $$E < (W_0/2M_f c^2)W_0.$$

One of the most appreciable recoils occurs in the $B^{12}$ decay, which releases $W_0 \approx 27{\cdot}2mc^2$. Since $M_f \approx 12(1836)m$ in that case, $E/W_0 < (10)^{-3}$, which makes the recoil negligible in the energy balance. The heavy nucleus absorbs any momentum which the light particles are given without absorbing appreciable energy, hence only the energy restriction

$$W+K = W_0 \tag{1.5}$$

needs to be observed in further considerations of the energy sharing between the electron and the neutrino.

*'Statistical' sharing of the energy*

Lacking further information about details of the decay, we assume that the electron and neutrino share the energy 'statistically'. By this we shall mean that the chance for a specific subgroup of states to emerge is proportional to the number of these states. The number of states of motion for an electron freed with a momentum $\mathbf{p}$, in the range

$$(d\mathbf{p}) \equiv dp_x\, dp_y\, dp_z,$$

is proportional to the size of this range $(d\mathbf{p})$, while the number of neutrino states in the range $(d\mathbf{q})$ is proportional to $(d\mathbf{q})$. If $d\lambda/\lambda$ stands for the fraction of the decays in which the momenta in the stated ranges are attained, then

$$\frac{d\lambda}{\lambda} = \frac{(d\mathbf{p})(d\mathbf{q})}{\int \dots \int (d\mathbf{p})(d\mathbf{q})}. \tag{1.6}$$

The integral in the denominator represents the whole of the 'available momentum space' consistent with the energy restriction (1.5). In order to enforce this restriction, put $(d\mathbf{q}) = q^2\, dq\, d\Omega_\nu$ where $d\Omega_\nu$ is the solid angle element into which the momenta in the range $(d\mathbf{q})$ are directed. Then we replace $q\, dq$ by $K\, dK/c^2$, according to (1.4). Now the energy restriction, $K+W = W_0$, requires that, for a given electron energy $W$, the integration range $dK$ of the neutrino energy be limited to a vanishing element, $dK \to 0$. This element occurs in both numerator and denominator of (1.6), hence cancels out. Also put $(d\mathbf{p}) = p^2\, dp d\Omega_e$, and then integrate over all neutrino and electron directions. The result is a new‡ ratio replacing (1.6),

$$\frac{d\lambda}{\lambda} = \frac{qKp^2\, dp}{\int\limits_0^{p_0} qKp^2\, dp}, \tag{1.7}$$

giving the fraction of the decays devoted to producing electrons of momentum magnitude in the range $dp$. The integration limit

$$p_0 = c^{-1}[(W_0-\mu c^2)^2-m^2c^4]^{\frac{1}{2}}$$

‡ Here, and throughout this treatise, $d\lambda$ will be treated as a differential of variable order, defined through other differentials which occur in its expression. It will always denote a 'partial' decay rate per nucleus, but the restrictions on the decays counted in the rates will vary in a way which should be clear from the context.

is the maximum electron momentum, attained when the neutrino has a vanishing momentum, so that $K \to \mu c^2$.

The decay fraction which produces electrons of energy in the range $dW$ follows from substituting $p\,dp = W dW/c^2$ into (1.7), with the result:

$$d\lambda/dW = (\lambda/f_0)W(W_0-W)[W^2-m^2c^4]^{\frac{1}{2}}[(W_0-W)^2-\mu^2c^4]^{\frac{1}{2}}/(mc^2)^5. \tag{1.8}$$

Here $f_0$ stands for the dimensionless integral:

$$f_0(p_0) = \int_0^{p_0} dp\, p^2 qK/(mc)^5 c. \tag{1.9}$$

The spectrum (1.8) vanishes in the limit at which the electron receives no kinetic energy, $W = mc^2$, and again when the neutrino gets none, $W = W_0-\mu c^2$. It rises to a maximum between these limits in much the way observed experimentally, according to the example of Fig. 1.2. The detailed behaviour depends on the size of the neutrino rest-mass, $\mu$.

*The neutrino mass*

The fact that most of the electrons are observed to get less than half the end-point kinetic energy shows immediately that the neutrino must have a smaller rest-mass than the electron. The lightest of three decay fragments participating in a 'random' momentum balance must, on the average, be given more energy to have a comparable momentum. Fig. 1.3 shows plots of the spectrum (1.8) for various masses $0 \leqslant \mu \leqslant m$. The specific end-point kinetic energy $W_0-(m+\mu)c^2 = 0{\cdot}036mc^2$ was chosen for the plots because this is characteristic of $H^3$, one of the least energetic decays known. The lower the energy release is, the greater is its sensitivity to the size of the neutrino mass.

A detailed comparison of the measured $H^3$ spectrum, near its end-point, with the expectations for various values of the neutrino rest-mass, led Langer and Moffat to conclude that $\mu < 0{\cdot}0005m$. This conclusion is consistent with independent measurements of the $H^3$ and $He^3$ masses, through their participation in nuclear reactions. The natural conclusion is that the neutrino rest-mass is negligibly small and can be presumed to be zero.

## 1.4. The coulombic distortion of the spectrum

There is an important respect in which the simple statistical spectrum (1.8), with $\mu = 0$, disagrees with observed spectra, especially those of heavier nuclei. It is illustrated by the two diagrams of Fig. 1.4. The solid curves represent the statistical spectrum (1.8). The experimental points are typical of a negatron and a positron emitter, respectively. Clearly the coulomb force due to the positive charge on the nucleus is at work here. This should slow down the outward bound negatrons, and accelerate positrons outwards, creating, respectively, surpluses and deficiencies of slow particles, just as observed. The faster particles should be comparatively less influenced by the electrostatic force, also as observed.

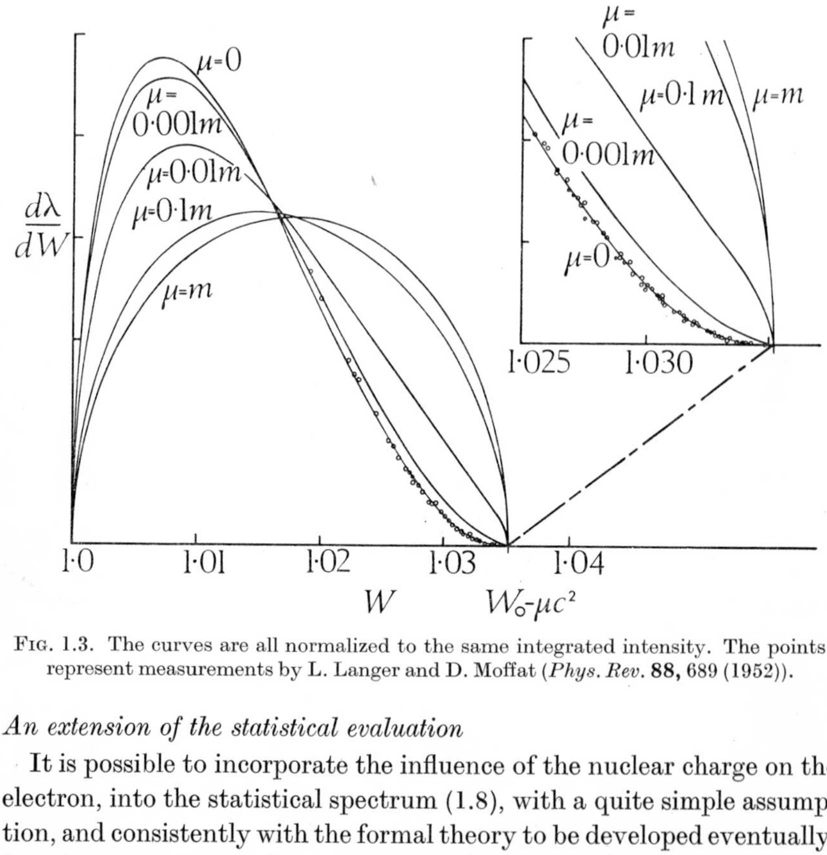


FIG. 1.3. The curves are all normalized to the same integrated intensity. The points represent measurements by L. Langer and D. Moffat (*Phys. Rev.* **88,** 689 (1952)).

*An extension of the statistical evaluation*

It is possible to incorporate the influence of the nuclear charge on the electron, into the statistical spectrum (1.8), with a quite simple assumption, and consistently with the formal theory to be developed eventually. For this purpose, we discuss the spatial density, $|\psi_c|^2$, of the electron, in a state of motion in which the electron emerges at the point, $r = 0$, of the nuclear charge $+Ze$, and attains its final momentum only outside the range of the electrostatic force, at $r = \infty$. It is to be compared with the 'free particle' density, $|\psi_0|^2$, in a state in which that momentum exists unchanged, as was effectively presumed in the statistical considerations, when the effect of the electrostatic force was ignored. Fig. 1.5 shows a qualitative picture of the density ratio, $|\psi_c/\psi_0|^2$, as a function of the radial distance from the nucleus, for negatrons and for positrons

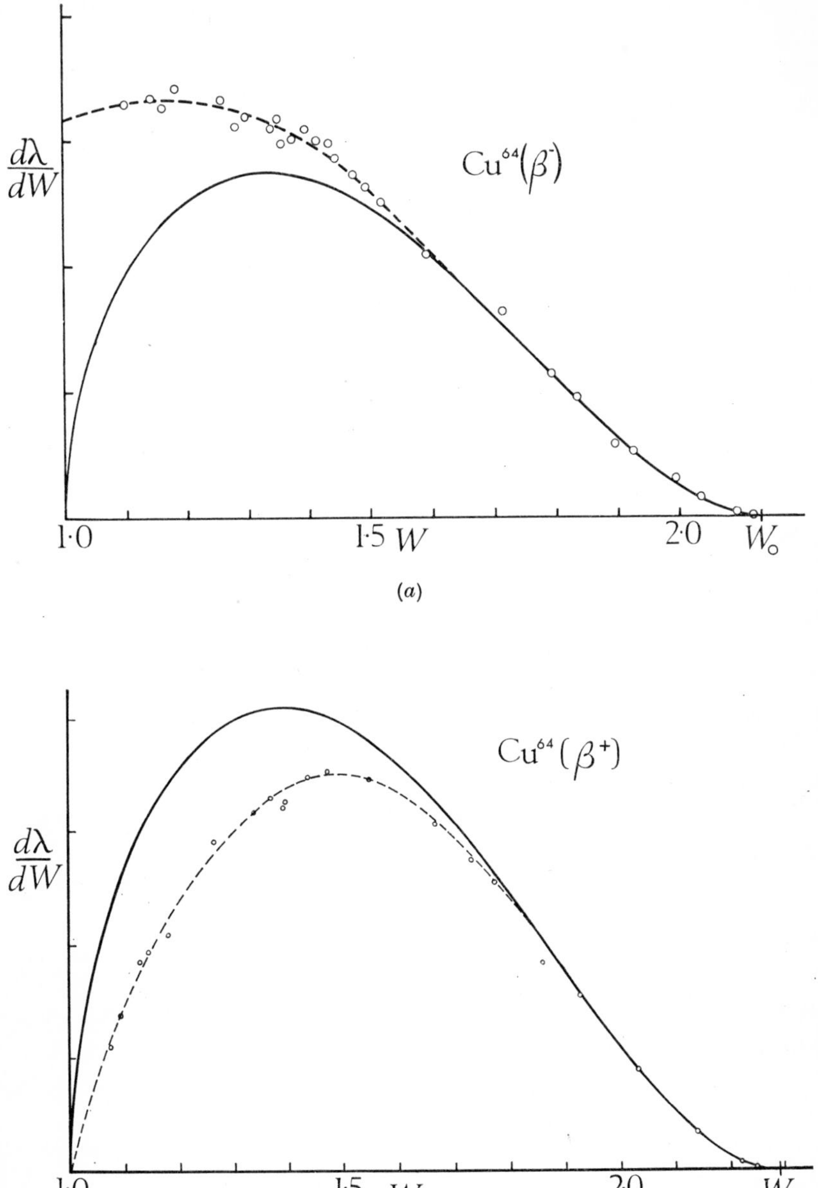


FIG. 1.4 (*a*) and (*b*). The solid curves are examples of statistical spectra (1.8) with $\mu = 0$. The dashed curves include the coulomb correction of equation (1.10). The points represent measurements by L. M. Langer, R. D. Moffat, and H. C. Price, *Phys. Rev.* **76**, 1725 (1949).

(a quantitative picture requires specification of the nuclear charge and the energy). The important point that this illustrates is that the density at the nucleus varies with the nuclear charge present, per electron emerging at infinity. The ratio $|\psi_c/\psi_0|^2$ approaches unity at infinite distances because $|\psi_c| \to |\psi_0|$ where the influence of the electrostatic force dies out.

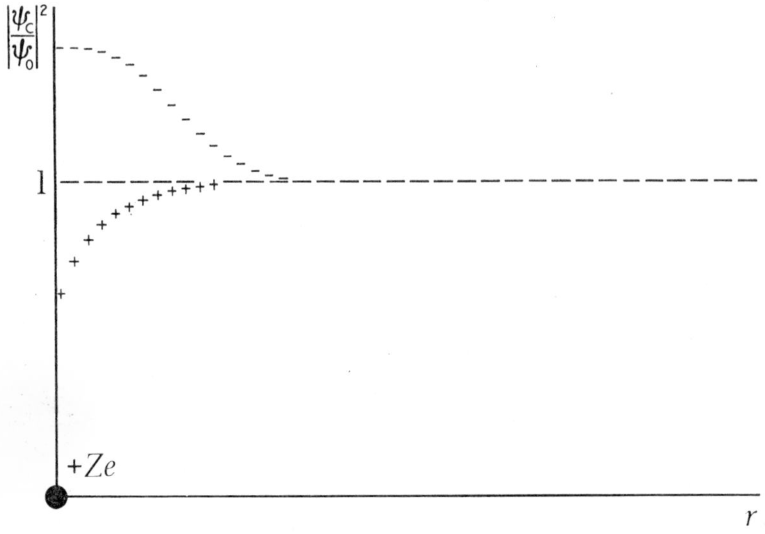


FIG. 1.5

The simple assumption now introduced is that various electron waves are excited in proportion to their density at the nucleus. This seems the most reasonable extension of the statistical evaluation, whatever the mechanism of excitation, when that is localized in the nucleus. Accordingly, we define the electron density ratio $F(Z, W) = |\psi_c(0)/\psi_0|^2$ and assume $d\lambda \sim F(Z, W)$ so that the statistical energy distribution (1.8) is corrected, in this ratio, to

$$d\lambda/\lambda\, dW = cpW(W_0 - W)^2 F(Z, W)/f(Z, W_0).(mc^2)^5, \tag{1.10}$$

where

$$f(Z, W_0) = \int_{mc^2}^{W_0} dW.cpW(W_0 - W)^2 F(Z, W)/(mc^2)^5 \tag{1.11}$$

is the appropriate modification of (1.9). We have at the same time incorporated the result $\mu = 0$ for the neutrino mass, in this modification of (1.8). It is the coulomb-modified spectrum (1.10) which will henceforth be referred to as having the 'statistical shape'.

*The electron density ratio, $F(Z, W)$*

Specific evaluations of $F(Z, W) = |\psi_c(0)|^2/|\psi_0|^2$ can be obtained from well-known solutions of the Schrödinger or Dirac equation for an electron in an electrostatic field. $\beta$-electron wavelengths are very long compared to nuclear dimensions, hence it is usually adequate to treat the nucleus as a point charge. At the same time, these wavelengths are small compared to atomic dimensions for almost all the $\beta$-spectrum, hence screening by atomic electrons can usually be ignored. Further, for cases in which the nuclear charge is not too large, the electrons which are appreciably influenced by it can be treated as non-relativistic and we may use the solution of the Schrödinger equation for an electron in the point-charge field, $Ze^2/r$. This gives‡

$$F(Z, W) = 2\pi\nu/(1-e^{-2\pi\nu}), \tag{1.12}$$

where

$$\nu = \pm Ze^2/\hbar v \quad \text{for } e^{\mp}, \tag{1.13}$$

$v$ is the electron's velocity and $Z$ is the charge number of the product nucleus. Clearly, $F = 1$ for $Z = 0$ or $v = \infty$, as it should be. For not too small a charge $Ze$ and/or low velocities,

$$F \approx 2\pi\nu = 2\pi\alpha Z.(c/v) \quad \text{for } e^-, \tag{1.12 a}$$

a quantity which must be substantially larger than unity to be a valid approximation. The corresponding approximation for positrons is

$$F \approx 2\pi|\nu|e^{-2\pi|\nu|} \quad (\text{for } e^+), \tag{1.12 b}$$

smaller by a factor $\exp(-2\pi Ze^2/\hbar v)$ than for negatrons. This factor is the well-known Gamow 'penetrability', which gives the probability that a positive charge will penetrate from $r = 0$ to $\infty$ through the 'Coulomb barrier'. (Such a factor explains the delay of the $\alpha$-emissions, mentioned in § 1.1, to periods as long as observed.)

Relativistic corrections may become important despite the fact that the high velocity particles ($v \rightarrow c$), usually considered the only ones subject to appreciable relativistic effects, should also be the ones least affected by electrostatic forces. This is because the electrons observed to emerge with a given velocity actually have that velocity only at infinity; near a large charge, negatrons have a much higher velocity, positrons an 'imaginary' one. The relativistic effects may be taken into account by using a solution of the Dirac, rather than Schrödinger,

‡ See, for example, L. Schiff, *Quantum Mechanics* (McGraw-Hill 1949), formula (20.13). Multiplied by $v$, that formula gives $|\psi_c(0)|^2$ normalized so that

$$|\psi_c(\infty)|^2 = |\psi_0|^2 = 1.$$

equation. This‡ substitutes for (1.13) the expression:

$$F(Z, W) = 2(1+\gamma_0)(2pR/\hbar)^{-2(1-\gamma_0)}e^{\pi\nu}|\Gamma(\gamma_0+i\nu)|^2/[\Gamma(2\gamma_0+1)]^2 \quad (1.14)$$

in which $\Gamma(\zeta) \equiv (\zeta-1)!$ stands for the gamma-function,

$$\gamma_0 = [1-(\alpha Z)^2]^{\frac{1}{2}}, \quad (1.15)$$

and $R$ is the radius at which $\psi_c$ is evaluated, rather than at $r = 0$, as in (1.12). Evaluation at $r = 0$ must be avoided because, as (1.14) shows, the Dirac solution diverges for $R \to 0$, although integrably, so that the density still is part of a finite total electron distribution. The divergence occurs only when the nucleus is over-idealized as a point charge; when the finite spread of the nuclear charge is taken into account, the electron density distribution is essentially unchanged outside a nuclear radius, $R$, and then remains quite flat within this radius. Accordingly, we can, with good accuracy, retain the point-charge result (1.14), evaluated at the nuclear radius. Notice that the precise value of this radius is not critical since $R$ appears in the nearly vanishing power, $2(\gamma_0-1)$. When $(\alpha Z)^2 \ll 1$, as is the case for all but the heaviest nuclei, $\gamma_0 \approx 1$, and the gamma function is well approximated§ by

$$|\Gamma(1+i\nu)|^2 = (i\nu)!(-i\nu)! = \pi\nu/\sinh \pi\nu.$$

Since, moreover, $\Gamma(3) \equiv 2!$, the expression (1.14) comes to coincide with the non-relativistic result (1.12), for $(\alpha Z)^2 \ll 1$.

*Kurie plots*

Comparisons of the theoretical, statistical spectrum (1.10) with observed $\beta$-electron energy distributions are customarily made in the following way. Let $n(W)$ be the number of electrons *observed* to have the energy $W$, per unit of the energy scale, from a source of arbitrary strength. The experimental data are then plotted as a function of $W$ in the form of the calculable quantity $[n(W)/pWF]^{\frac{1}{2}}$, a so-called 'Kurie plot'. If the observed $n(W)$ is indeed proportional to the statistical spectrum (1.10), then the 'Kurie plot' should yield a straight line, $\sim (W_0-W)$, having an intercept with the energy axis at $W = W_0$. The advantage of this procedure is that the energy release, $W_0$, need not be known beforehand. The spectrum measurement is frequently the most accurate way of determining it.

The majority of the well-measured spectra do yield straight-line Kurie plots, testifying to the accuracy of the simple theory introduced so far. An example is shown in Fig. 1.6. There frequently are deviations

‡ See, for example, M. E. Rose, *Relativistic Electron Theory* (Wiley, New York 1960).
§ E. Jahnke and F. Emde, *Funktionentafeln* (Teubner 1933), p. 12.

from the linearity at low energies; most of these prove attributable to scattering and energy losses, by the vulnerable, low-energy electrons, in the material of the source and its surroundings.

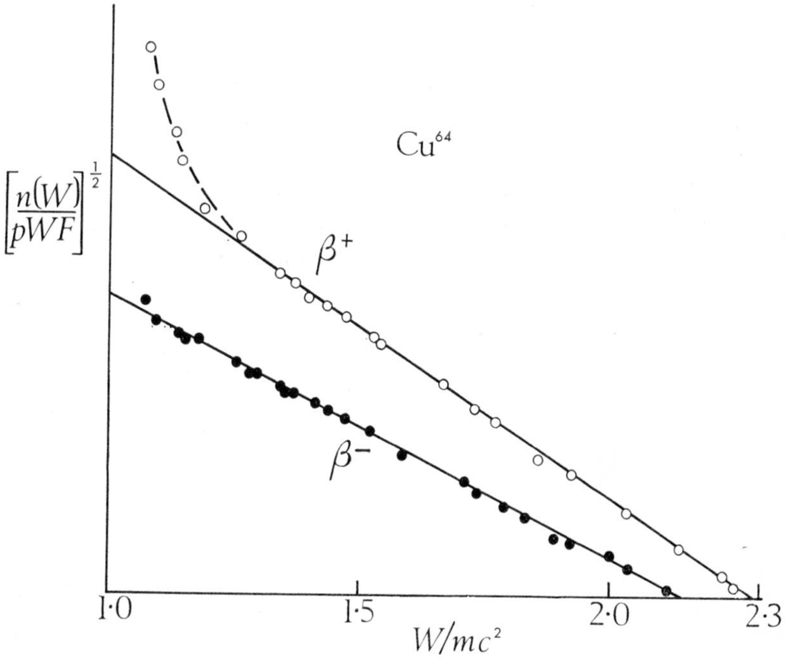


FIG. 1.6. Kurie plots of the observed $Cu^{64}$ spectra (courtesy of L. M. Langer). Most of the low-energy deviation from the straight line, of the positron spectrum, can be ascribed to the effects of screening of the nuclear charge by atomic electrons.

There are also cases of significant deviation from the statistical spectrum shape, and these must be accounted for by refinements of the theory (Chapter VII). For these cases, the Kurie plot has the valuable attribute that it separates out the relatively superficial effects included in the theory so far; the deviations from linearity are then indications of deeper properties of the $\beta$-radiation mechanism.

## 1.5. Comparative half-lives

The discussion so far has largely been confined to the *relative* decay rates, $d\lambda/\lambda$, of any one isotope, into $\beta$-particles of various energies. It was found that, in at least the majority of cases, the energy distribution can be understood in terms of rather superficial 'statistical' considerations. Thus, the spectrum for a given case of decay seems usually to be determined simply by how much energy happens to be available, and how great a nuclear charge is present to perturb the electrons. It will be instructive to see whether these simple effects are also sufficient for understanding the difference in *absolute* decay rates, $\lambda$, of the various isotopes.

*ft-values*

If only the energy release and the nuclear charge influence the decay rates, and do so in the same way as they influence the spectrum, then it may be expected that

$$d\lambda = C.F(Z, W)pWq^2\,dW/(mc)^5c^2, \tag{1.16}$$

with a proportionality constant $C$ common to all cases of $\beta$-decay. This expression corresponds to $d\lambda/\lambda$ as given by (1.10), with the abbreviation $W_0 - W = cq$ for the neutrino energy. Integration over the energy yields the total decay ~~rate~~ constant.

$$\lambda \equiv 1/\tau \equiv \ln 2/t = Cf(Z, W_0), \tag{1.17}$$

where $f(Z, W_0)$ is given by (1.11). If it were actually true that only the energy release and the nuclear charge influence the decay rate, then the quantity

$$ft = \ln 2/C$$

should be the same for all cases of $\beta$-decay. However, failures of this rule must be expected at least for that minority of cases which exhibit deviations from the statistical spectrum shape, for then $C$ in (1.16) cannot be energy-independent. We shall also see that the experimental '*ft*-values' have a wide range of variation even among cases which do have statistical spectra.

Although it is too much to expect that the simple considerations so far introduced will suffice for an understanding of the decay rates, it is still useful to calculate the *ft*-values for each case of $\beta$-decay that is studied. The reason for this is suggested by the name 'comparative half-life' which has been given to the *ft*-value. It is a way of 'correcting' the observed half-lives for the incidental effects of energy release and nuclear charge, as these enter into the merely statistical considerations, so that any remaining variations of the *ft*-values reflect further effects more explicitly.

The rate-function $f(Z, W_0)$ can be evaluated for any case of $\beta$-decay as soon as the energy release and the nuclear charge are known. Curves are shown in Figs. 1.7 and 1.8. In the limit $Z = 0$, the density ratio $F(0, W) = 1$ and the integral (1.11) becomes elementary:

$$f(0, x.mc^2) \equiv f_0 = \tfrac{1}{60}(x^2-1)^{\frac{1}{2}}[2x^4-9x^2-8]+\tfrac{1}{4}x\ln[x+(x^2-1)^{\frac{1}{2}}]. \tag{1.18}$$

This simplifies to $f_0 \approx W_0^5/30(mc^2)^5$ for very high energies, exhibiting the extremely rapid increase of decay rate with energy release to be expected on the statistical basis. For lower energies, the variation is even more rapid, as Figs. 1.7 and 1.8 show. The coulomb effect changes the magnitudes without changing the rates of variation with energy significantly. For negatrons, the coulomb attraction enhances the rate,

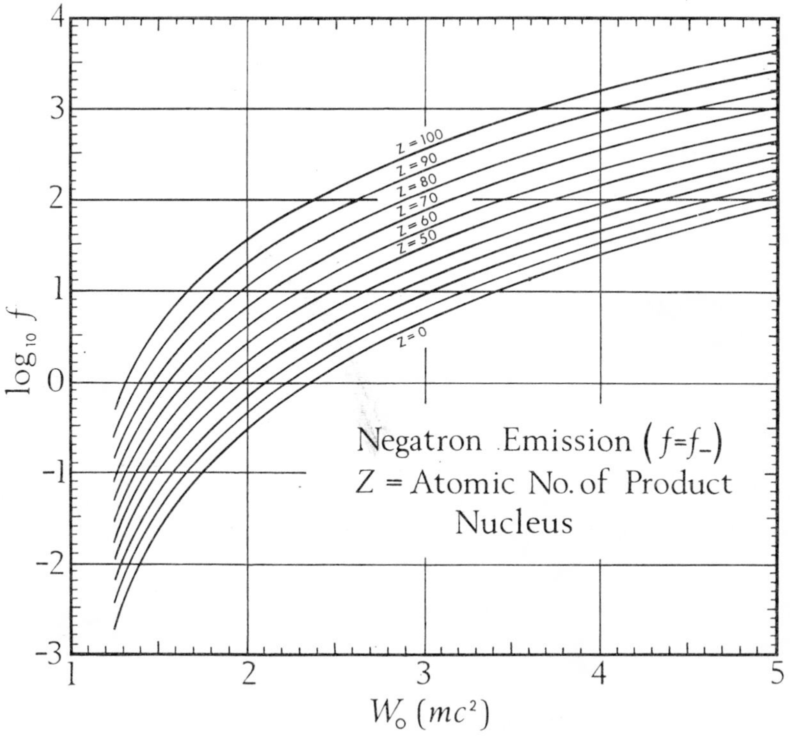


FIG. 1.7. The statistical rate function $f(Z, W_0)$ defined by (1.11), for negatrons, as computed by E. Feenberg and G. Trigg, *Rev. Mod. Phys.* **22,** 399 (1950).

in keeping with the greater relative density, $F(Z, W)$, of negatrons near the nucleus. For positrons, the effect is opposite, and more moderate, as is to be expected for particles which are pushed out of the range of greatest influence.

Comparative half-lives, $ft$, have been computed from energy and half-life measurements in some hundreds of cases of $\beta$-decay. The best determined of them are tabulated in Chapters V and VII, and readers who insist on immediate documentation of the assertions about them to be made here may consult those tables.

It first becomes evident that, far from being constant, the *ft*-values vary from $10^3$ sec to $10^{18}$ sec, and are even higher in isolated cases. There are variations from $10^3$ sec to $10^8$ sec even for cases in which the statistical spectrum shape has been observed. It will be significant that

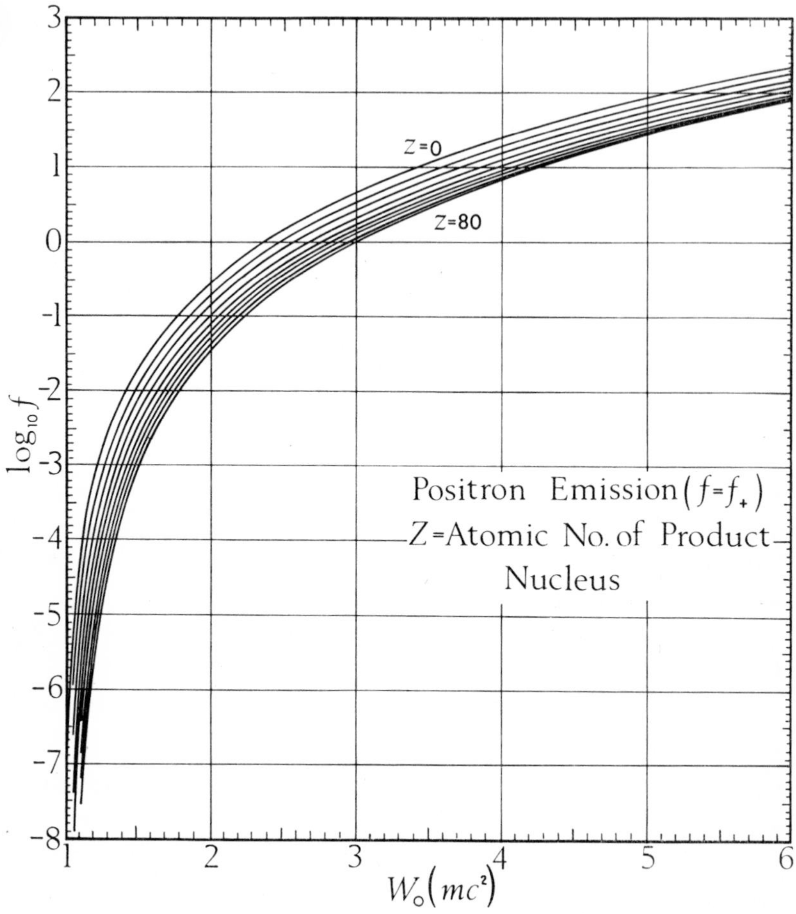


FIG. 1.8. $f(-Z, W_0)$, the statistical rate function for positrons.

all cases of marked deviation from the statistical shape have rates much smaller than the norm, with $ft \geqslant 10^7$ sec.

*The ejection of angular momentum*

To account for the differences among comparative half-lives, we must look for other characteristics than just energy release and nuclear charge, by which the decays are distinguished. As basic a distinctive characteristic as that provided by the conserved energy-momentum follows from the universal conservation of angular momentum.

The near-isolated nuclear systems one has before and after the $\beta$-process must each have a conserved, hence well-defined,‡ angular momentum, $\mathbf{I}$. This quantity is known for many of the nuclear states, from evidence culled from all types of nuclear processes; the $\beta$-processes themselves have been useful in helping determine many of the nuclear spins, but a sufficient number are known from independent evidence to keep our arguments here from 'circularity'. We now expect that if there is a difference, $\mathbf{I}_i - \mathbf{I}_f = \mathbf{J}$, between the angular momenta of the initial and final nuclear states, then this difference must be carried off by the electron-neutrino pair. How it can do this will be discussed in the next section. Here we point out correlations between known nuclear spin changes and the comparative half-lives which can be discerned in any tabulation of $ft$-values:

(1) The fastest decays, having $ft \approx 10^3$–$10^4$ sec, all eject one unit of angular momentum or less ($\Delta I \equiv |I_i - I_f| \leqslant 1$).

(2) Nuclear spin changes of more than one unit never have comparative half-lives shorter than about $10^7$ sec. Thus, an ejection of more than one unit of angular momentum seems to retard the decay.

(3) No obvious distinction is detectable between the decay rates for cases of no spin change and those with one unit of spin change.

(4) Some cases radiate one unit, or no angular momentum at all, yet have distinctly retarded rates compared to the fastest (1).

*The parity restriction*

There is one other feature, besides charge, energy, and angular momentum, which can be assigned a definite value in any nuclear state: a 'parity'. This refers to the evenness (represented as $\pi = +1$) or oddness ($\pi = -1$) in spatial variables of the nuclear state description. A more

‡ For this initial chapter, only the rudiments of the quantum mechanical description of angular momentum will be needed. It will be presumed known that (1) the maximal definition obtainable for any angular momentum, $\mathbf{j}$, is the specification of its magnitude, $j$, together with its projection, $j_z$, on some one direction in space (an arbitrarily choosable 'quantization-axis'); (2) the magnitude can have only one of the discrete values determined from $\mathbf{j}^2 = j(j+1)\hbar^2$, where $j = 0, 1, 2, 3,\ldots$ or $j = \frac{1}{2}, \frac{3}{2}, \frac{5}{2},\ldots$. The same symbol is frequently used for the quantum number, $j$, as for the angular momentum itself, for reasons of economy; (3) the projection can have only the values $j_z = \mu\hbar$, where $\mu = 0, \pm 1, \pm 2,\ldots, \pm j$, when $j$ is whole-integral and $\mu = \pm\frac{1}{2}, \pm\frac{3}{2},\ldots, \pm j$, when $j$ is half-integral.

*Orbital* angular momenta, $\mathbf{j} \equiv \mathbf{l}$, which arise from spatial distribution of linear momenta, can have only whole-integer values: $l = 0, 1, 2,\ldots$. Half-integer magnitudes arise only when the 'intrinsic spins' of fermions (spin-$\frac{1}{2}$ particles) form part of the total angular momentum.

extended discussion of 'parity conservation' is left until later (Chapter X). For the present, it will suffice to assert that definite parities have been assigned to most of the nuclear states participating in $\beta$-decay, from evidence independent of $\beta$-decay. It is then possible to speak of no parity change ($\pi_i \pi_f = +1$) or a parity change ($\pi_i \pi_f = -1$) in the nuclear transitions $i \rightarrow f$.

The last completes the list of generally definable nuclear features which can be assigned to any case of $\beta$-decay:

$$Z,\, W_0,\, \Delta I \equiv |I_i - I_f|,\, \pi_i \pi_f. \tag{1.19}$$

More detailed characteristics of the nuclear states may also influence their $\beta$-decay, but are not as generally identifiable.

The study of the comparative half-lives, *ft*, allows the following immediate conclusions about the influence of parity changes:

(*a*) The fastest decays ($ft \approx 10^{3-4}$ sec, as in the observation (1) above) join nuclear states of the same parity: $\pi_i \pi_f = +1$.

(*b*) No decay with change of parity is faster than some $10^{5\cdot 5}$ sec in *ft*-value, i.e. cases of $\pi_i \pi_f = -1$ are always retarded relative to the fastest possible decays.

Thus, the cases concerned in the observation (4) above may owe their retardation to parity mismatches of the initial and final nuclear states.

*Allowed and forbidden transitions*

The preliminary studies of comparative half-lives, *ft*, lead to conclusions just reviewed, that a $\beta$-transition is retarded unless the nuclear spin is not required to change by more than one unit (in making the energy available) and also if the nucleus is required to reverse its parity. This has led to the empirical classification of $\beta$-decays into 'allowed' and 'forbidden' transitions. The allowed cases are defined as those for which

$$\Delta I \equiv |I_i - I_f| = 0 \text{ or } 1, \quad \pi_i \pi_f = +1. \tag{1.20}$$

Cases which violate these selection rules are said to be 'forbidden' in some degree (Chapter VII).

It should be emphasized that not all cases obedient to the selection rules (1.20), hence classified as allowed, escape retardation. That should not be surprising, once it is admitted that the characters of the participating nuclear states can affect the decay rate. Nuclei are complex structures, composed of many nucleons, and the energy, angular momentum, and parity (1.19) cannot be sufficient to characterize more than superficially the great variety of internal motions which is possible to them. We may still hope to make significant comparisons of $\beta$-radiation from different nuclei by grouping them into ostensible 'families' according to some criterion or other.

*The mirror decays*

One group of isotopes which forms a homogeneous family, in the light of general nuclear theory, consists of the so-called 'mirror nuclei' (listed in Table 5.1). Each of these has one nucleon extra to an 'inert core' which is composed of equal numbers of neutrons and protons. It is the extra nucleon‡ which is transformed in making the energy available for the 'mirror decays'. These decays all obey the allowed selection rules. Examination of their comparative half-lives reveals that they vary from $ft = 1137$ sec for $H^3$ to $ft = 5680$ sec for $A^{35}$. For comparison, the 'uncorrected' half-lives vary from $t = 0{\cdot}6$ sec for $Ti^{43}$ to $t = 12{\cdot}4$ years for $H^3$, a variation by a factor of about $6(10)^8$. Relative to this the $ft$-values are constant to about one part in $10^8$!

*The $0^+ \rightarrow 0^+$ decays*

Next simplest, from certain points of view, are nuclei which differ from the 'mirrors' by having *two* nucleons extra to an 'inert core' composed of equal *even* numbers of neutrons and protons. The three isotopes with the same core, but having two neutrons, a neutron-proton pair, and two protons outside it, respectively, are said to form an 'isobaric triad'; examples for which measurements exist are listed in Table 5.4. The two extra nucleons may have opposite angular momenta, to produce a state of no resultant spin ($0^+$), but their individual angular momenta may also couple to produce states of higher spin. In order to form a homogeneous family of decays, we restrict attention to just the better measured $0^+ \rightarrow 0^+$ transitions which occur among the isobaric triads. These then are found to have the $ft$-values:

| | $O^{14} \rightarrow N^{14}$ | $Al^{26} \rightarrow Mg^{26}$ | $Cl^{34} \rightarrow S^{34}$ | $K^{38} \rightarrow A^{38}$ | $Sc^{42} \rightarrow Ca^{42}$ |
|---|---|---|---|---|---|
| $ft$ (sec) = | 3060§ ($\pm 10$) | 3050 ($\pm 60$) | 3110 ($\pm 70$) | 3140 ($\pm 400$) | 2800 ($\pm 600$) |
| $t$ (sec) = | $72{\cdot}1 \pm 0{\cdot}4$ | $6{\cdot}36 \pm 0{\cdot}08$ | $1{\cdot}54 \pm 0{\cdot}02$ | $0{\cdot}935 \pm 0{\cdot}025$ | $0{\cdot}62 \pm 0{\cdot}05$ |

The best measured values are especially uniform.

There is an extra factor 2 to be expected in the rates of decay in these cases, relative to the mirrors, which have only one nucleon the transformation of which makes the decay energy available. Among the triads,

‡ Or 'nucleon hole' (see Chapter V).
§ D. Hendrie and J. Gerhart, *Phys. Rev.* **121**, 846 (1961).

either of two protons may transform ($O^{14}$), or else the transforming proton can become either of two neutrons.

The discernment of further homogeneous families of nuclei requires making more sophisticated distinctions among nucleonic structures.

## 1.6. Spin and antiparticle states

We next consider how the electron–neutrino pair may carry away the angular momentum, $\mathbf{J} = \mathbf{I}_i - \mathbf{I}_f$, by which the initial and final nuclear states may differ.

*The orbital angular momentum*

Any ejected particles, or radiated waves, may bear away orbital angular momentum, which is $\mathbf{l} = \mathbf{r} \times \mathbf{p}$ for a particle of momentum $\mathbf{p}$,

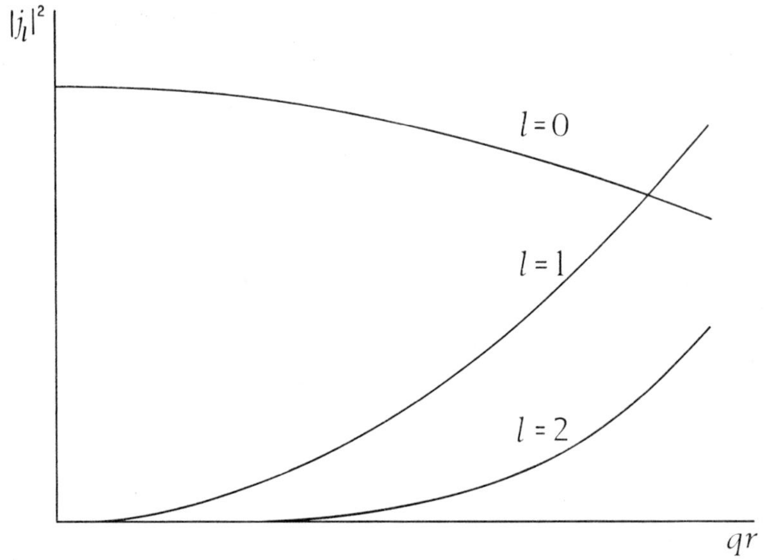


FIG. 1.9. Radial distributions exhibiting the centrifugal effects of increasing the orbital momentum from $l = 0$ to $l = 1$ or 2. (See equation (7.3).)

when at position $\mathbf{r}$ relative to the centre about which the angular momenta are gauged. To carry away a non-vanishing orbital momentum, a particle must be ejected 'off-centre', with a finite 'lever-arm', $\mathbf{r}$. The corresponding wave picture is that of a density distribution which vanishes at the centre, having its main mass at radial distances proportional to the orbital momentum. Figure 1.9 shows plots of radial densities near a nucleus, in states with $l = 0, 1, 2,...$ units of orbital momentum; such distributions are characteristic of particles subject solely to centrifugal force, as neutrinos are expected to be. If $\mathbf{q}$ is the neutrino momentum, then the various densities start at the centre in proportion to $(qr/\hbar)^{2l}$. Thus, the effect of the orbital momentum is to push the density away from the centre, as under the influence of centrifugal repulsion.

The property of a density vanishing at the centre persists for electrons subject to coulomb force. This is because the rotational energy, $L^2/2mr^2 = l(l+1)\hbar^2/2mr^2$, needed for approaching the centre with a given orbital momentum, $L$, outweighs the coulomb energy, $Ze^2/r$, as $r \to 0$.

As in the consideration of the coulomb distortions in § 1.4, we are here concerned with the relative chances that events localized in the nucleus can excite states with different spatial distributions. The successful assumption was that such chances are proportional to the density at the nucleus. Accordingly, the emission of orbital momentum is saved from vanishing only by the finite radius, $R$, of the nucleus; its ratio to radiation without orbital momentum is proportional to $(R/\lambda\!\!\!^{-})^{2l}$, where $\lambda\!\!\!^{-} = \hbar/q$ when the neutrino carries off $l$ units, and $\lambda\!\!\!^{-} = \hbar/p$ when the electron carries off $l$ units, of orbital momentum. This results in two expectations:

(*a*) If the energy for a given decay is released only when the nucleus can get rid of an angular momentum, $\mathbf{I}_i - \mathbf{I}_f$, at least partially in the form of $l$ units of orbital momentum, then the decay will be retarded by a factor of the order $(R/\lambda\!\!\!^{-})^{2l}$. For energies of the order released in $\beta$-decay, $\lambda\!\!\!^{-} \approx \hbar/mc \approx 3{\cdot}8(10)^{-11}$ cm. Nuclear radii vary from $5.10^{-13}$ to $10^{-12}$ cm, or so. Thus, each unit of orbital momentum which must be ejected slows the decay down by roughly a factor $(1/40)^2$ or more. This suggests an explanation for the observation (2) of the preceding section, that decays with a nuclear spin change exceeding one unit are definitely retarded.

(*b*) If a substantial fraction of the radiated energy is carried away by a neutrino with $l_\nu$ units of orbital momentum, and an electron with $l_e$ units, then the rate must have a term proportional to

$$q^{2l_\nu}p^{2l_e} \equiv [(W_0 - W)/c]^{2l_\nu} \times [(W^2 - m^2c^4)/c^2]^{l_e},$$

aside from the statistical factors. We can no longer expect the spectrum to have the statistical shape. This fits with the observation that cases of deviation from the statistical shape are associated with spin changes of more than one unit, and have retarded rates. The intrusion of factors like $(R/\lambda\!\!\!^{-})^{2l}$ is a familiar characteristic of 'multipole radiations', in electromagnetic theory. A systematic exploration of their effects is reserved for treatment in the 'Forbidden $\beta$-Decay Theory' (Chapter VII).

These considerations of the part played by orbital momenta lead us to conclude that the fastest decays, with spectra conforming to the statistical shape, are ones in which no orbital momentum needs to be ejected: $\mathbf{L} = \mathbf{l}_e + \mathbf{l}_\nu = 0$.

*The neutrino spin*

There remains the problem posed by the observation (3), of the preceding section, that one unit of total angular momentum, $\mathbf{J} = \mathbf{I}_i - \mathbf{I}_f$, may be ejected without detectable retardation, relative to cases of $\mathbf{J} = 0$.

The explanation may be sought in the fact that fundamental particles may possess intrinsic spins, independent of the spatial distribution. The electron is well known to have a half-unit of intrinsic spin, $s_e = \frac{1}{2}$, from its behaviour in a multiplicity of processes unrelated to $\beta$-decay. If the neutrino also possesses a half-unit of spin, $s_\nu = \frac{1}{2}$, then the unretarded ejection of $\mathbf{J} = \mathbf{s}_e + \mathbf{s}_\nu$ having unit magnitude could be accounted for.

The total angular momentum balance in any $\beta$-transition requires that the neutrino have a half-integral spin: $s_\nu = n + \frac{1}{2}$. This stems from the fact that orbital momenta must be whole-integral, together with the quantum theoretic rules for the addition of angular momentum vectors. For example, the vector balance $\mathbf{J} = \mathbf{I}_i - \mathbf{I}_f$ is achievable only with any of the magnitudes $J = |I_i - I_f|$, $J = I_i + I_f$ and all those in between which differ by whole-unit steps. This kind of rule has the consequence that only an even number of half-integral angular momenta can be superposed to give a whole-integral resultant. The rule is confirmed by the total spins, $\mathbf{I}$, found in nuclear states, each of which is composed of nucleons known to have half-integer intrinsic spins. Nuclei with odd numbers of nucleons are invariably found with half-integral total spins, while nuclei of even mass number always have whole-integer angular momenta. The initial and final nuclear states of $\beta$-decay have equal numbers of nucleons, hence $\mathbf{J} = \mathbf{I}_i - \mathbf{I}_f$ is always whole-integral in magnitude. When $J$ is borne away by an electron-neutrino pair, then $\mathbf{J} = \mathbf{l}_e + \mathbf{l}_\nu + \mathbf{s}_e + \mathbf{s}_\nu$; since the orbital momenta are whole-integral, $\mathbf{s}_\nu$ must be half-integral, to balance with the half-integral $\mathbf{s}_e$ in producing the whole-integral resultant, $\mathbf{J}$.

No orbital momenta, with their retarding effect, need be involved during the ejection of $\mathbf{J} = \mathbf{s}_e + \mathbf{s}_\nu$ of unit magnitude, either if $s_\nu = \frac{1}{2}$ or if $s_\nu = \frac{3}{2}$. On the other hand, $s_\nu = \frac{3}{2}$ would require the participation of orbital momentum in those cases in which $J = 0$. Since the latter cases are no more retarded than is the $J = 1$ radiation, neither must require the participation of orbital momentum, and we conclude that *the neutrino has a half-unit of spin,* just as the electron, the proton, and the neutron.

*The antineutrino*

Every type of spin-$\frac{1}{2}$ particle known, aside from the neutrino, has been found capable of existing in an 'antiparticle', as well as a 'normal', form. This was anticipated theoretically when Dirac formulated a description of fermions (spin-$\frac{1}{2}$ particles) consistent with relativistic principles. He found that at least to the charged spin-$\frac{1}{2}$ particles must be attributed the capacity to exist in any one of four 'internal states of motion'. Two of these four states correspond to the two possible orientations, $s_z = \pm\frac{1}{2}$, of the intrinsic spin. The remaining twofold multiplicity corresponds, in the case of the electron, to the negatron and positron. Antiparticles of the proton and the neutron were also anticipated, and eventually found. We may well expect that, corresponding to the spin-$\frac{1}{2}$ neutrino, $\nu$, there is also an antineutrino, $\bar{\nu}$.

Caution is called for in the last generalization, because a modification of Dirac's formalism was found, by Majorana, applicable only to neutral particles, which requires only the twofold multiplicity of internal states which corresponds to the two spin orientations. The normal and antiparticle states of Dirac's theory bear a relation to each other known as 'charge-conjugacy'. Majorana discovered that neutral particles can be restricted to 'self-charge-conjugate' states without losing independence of reference frame.

We shall, for the present, assume that antineutrinos ($\bar{\nu}$) distinct from neutrinos ($\nu$) do exist, just to maintain a symmetry of description for all the four types of fermions, e, p, n, and $\nu$, which participate in nuclear $\beta$-decay. It will be relatively simple to revert to the Majorana description of the neutrino later (Chapter X), when its consequences are explored.

A simple way of maintaining the correct relationships between antiparticles and their normal counterparts was provided by Dirac with his 'hole interpretation'. In this picture, the particle is treated as capable of having either a positive or a negative energy, $W = \pm c(p^2+m^2c^2)^{\frac{1}{2}}$, in free space. Then the negative-energy states must be treated as 'filled up' in representing the vacuum, and only deviations from this condition, either by the occupation of positive-energy states, or by *evacuations* of negative-energy states, are to be held detectable. An occupied positive-energy state is detected as a normal particle, while each vacancy, or 'hole', among the negative-energy states is detected as an antiparticle.

*Lepton conservation*

Through the use of the 'hole interpretation', we can describe all possible nuclear $\beta$-processes as implicit in the symmetrical relation,

$$\mathrm{n}+\nu \leftrightarrow \mathrm{p}+\mathrm{e}^{-}, \tag{1.21}$$

among the normal particles. Ordinary negatron emission is then a case in which the process goes rightward, a neutrino being absorbed from a negative-energy 'vacuum state'. The resulting vacancy is detected as an antineutrino, hence the relation (1.21) among the normal particles can be rewritten as $\mathrm{n} \rightarrow \mathrm{p}+\mathrm{e}^{-}+\bar{\nu}$, for that process. Positron emission is an example in which the reaction (1.21) proceeds leftward, with the absorption of an electron from a negative energy state, together with the production of a positive-energy neutrino: $\mathrm{p} \rightarrow \mathrm{n}+\nu+\mathrm{e}^{+}$. The reversal of the neutron decay, achieved in the experiment mentioned in § 1.2, becomes $\mathrm{p}+\bar{\nu} \rightarrow \mathrm{n}+\mathrm{e}^{+}$. The reactor source used in that experiment can be regarded as providing *anti*neutrinos ('holes needing filling') because it is composed of neutron-surplus, negatron-emitting nuclei.

Thus, on the basis that antiparticle production (absorption) can be viewed as the absorption (production) of the normal counterpart, we can say that every $\beta$-process involves the absorption of an electron or neutrino, and its replacement by a neutrino and electron, respectively. It becomes reasonable to speak of the electron and neutrino as alternative states of a single type of particle, the *lepton*‡ ('light particle'). The relation (1.21) then represents a conservation of leptons in nuclear $\beta$-decay.

It may seem arbitrary to choose the neutral particle emitted in negatron decay to be the antineutrino, while taking the one emitted in positron decay to be the normal neutrino, but this is merely a matter of nomenclature. Dirac's theory is completely symmetrical between the particles and antiparticles, and that fact is implied by the term charge-*conjugacy* for the relationship between them. It is customary to treat positrons, rather than negatrons, as 'holes' simply because the former are the more recently discovered and less prevalent.

*The prediction of orbital capture*

It may be noted that, in addition to the processes already considered, the lepton-conservation relation (1.21) implies the existence of negatron

‡ A term introduced by L. Rosenfeld in his early book on *Nuclear Forces* (North-Holland Publ. Co., Amsterdam, 1948).

capture by protons, producing neutron-neutrino pairs. The best chance for this to occur is provided by atoms with positron-emitting nuclei. The latter may capture one of the positive-energy, orbital atomic electrons, instead of creating a vacancy in a negative-energy state, as it does when emitting a positron. The possibility seems to have been noticed first by Sakata and Yukawa who calculated its rate on the basis of Fermi's theory; the actual occurrence of the process was first detected by Alvarez.

It is the '*s*-orbital' electrons, without orbital angular momentum about the nucleus to push them away, which have the best chance of being captured. The nucleus needs to supply less energy than for positron emission, since the mass-energy of an electron need not be created. If $M(Z)$ is the mass of the initial *nucleus*, having $Z$ protons, then the energy balance for positron emission is

$$M(Z)c^2 = M(Z-1)c^2+W+cq, \tag{1.22}$$

where $[M(Z)-M(Z-1)]c^2 \equiv W_0$ of (1.5). $W_0 > W > mc^2$ is necessary for the process to proceed. On the other hand, in orbital capture by the same nucleus,

$$M(Z)c^2+mc^2-B = M(Z-1)c^2+cq, \tag{1.23}$$

where $B \ll mc^2$ is the comparatively small binding energy of the atomic electron in its orbit. The process may proceed even when $W_0 < 0$ (negative by no more than $mc^2-B$); it can occur in cases for which positron emission is energetically impossible. Further details of the process will be treated after the theory has been more fully developed (Chapter VIII).

### Résumé

The observational facts reviewed so far are the essential ones which led to the qualitative characterization of nuclear $\beta$-processes implicit in the lepton-conservation relation (1.21). They provided the basis for the conception of the neutrino, and for assuming it to be chargeless, massless, and of spin $\frac{1}{2}$.

Additional observational details are needed to provide a sufficient basis for the complete, formal characterization of the $\beta$-interaction. So far, it has only been suggested that the interaction is localized at the transforming nucleon, and that it is essentially proportional to the electron and neutrino densities there, in the states of these particles which are to be formed.

Some basis for quantitative evaluations of the data has also been prepared, with the introduction of the statistical spectrum and its coulombic distortion, the comparative half-lives, and their qualitative relation to nuclear spin changes. The discussion of the last point brought out a fact which will have an important influence on how we now proceed. It indicated that the most directly interpretable data are to be expected from cases of allowed decay, which are uncomplicated by the necessity of ejecting orbital momentum, and conform to the simple, statistical energy dependence. The additional evidence to be relied upon as a guide to the formulation of the $\beta$-interaction will all be drawn from cases of allowed decay.

Opportunities for further observational detail are provided by the directional properties associated with the $\beta$-process. Most readily observable is the direction in which the electron is emitted, as represented by its velocity $\mathbf{v}$, or its momentum, $\mathbf{p} = (W/c^2)\mathbf{v}$. The neutrino momentum, $\mathbf{q}$, is inferrable from the much more difficult measurements of the nuclear recoil. In addition, the orientational directions of various angular momenta are involved: nuclear spins, $\mathbf{I}$, and the electron and neutrino spins, $\mathbf{s}_e$ and $\mathbf{s}_\nu$. Each of the pieces of data reviewed in the remainder of this chapter gives information about the relative disposition of some pair of the vectors $\mathbf{v}$, $\mathbf{q}$, $\mathbf{I}$, $\mathbf{s}_e$, $\mathbf{s}_\nu$, which results from the $\beta$-interaction.

## 1.7. Fermi and Gamow-Teller emissions

The allowed decays, which give no orbital momentum to the electron-neutrino pair, maintain the angular momentum balance

$$\mathbf{I}_i - \mathbf{I}_f = \mathbf{s}_e + \mathbf{s}_\nu = \mathbf{S},$$

where $\mathbf{S}$ is the resultant intrinsic spin of the leptons. The initial nuclear spins, $\mathbf{I}_i$, are randomly oriented in the types of observations reviewed so far, and no attempt is made to distinguish among radiations resulting in particular final spin orientations, $\mathbf{I}_f$. There is definition only of the *magnitudes* of $I_i$ and $I_f$, through choosing any given case of $\beta$-decay. Under such observational conditions, the only kind of orientational distinction which may still make itself felt is the relative orientation of the individual lepton spins. As will immediately be seen, some idea can be gained about the projection $\mathbf{s}_e . \mathbf{s}_\nu$, implicit in the radiation, from comparing cases with various $\Delta I = |I_f - I_i|$.

*Singlet* vs. *triplet*

The resultant, $\mathbf{S}$, of two half-units of spin can be only $\mathbf{S} = 0$, a state in which the spins are antiparallel, or '$\mathbf{S} = \mathbf{1}$', an angular momentum of one unit, describing parallel lepton spins. The latter state is called 'triplet' because one unit of angular momentum may have any of three orientations, and these are not discriminated under the observational conditions outlined above. Correspondingly, the antiparallel, $S = 0$ state is called 'singlet'.

The reason that singlet and triplet parts are distinguishable in suitable allowed decays is that they give rise to differences in selection rules. Obviously, the emission of $\mathbf{S} = 0$ radiation requires $I_f = I_i$. This selection rule, $\Delta I = 0$ (together with a requirement of no parity change, as for all allowed decays), is known as a 'Fermi selection rule'. In triplet emissions, the angular momentum balance is $\mathbf{I}_i = \mathbf{I}_f + \mathbf{1}$, a vector sum which may have any of the magnitudes $I_f - 1$, $I_f$ or $I_f + 1$. The result is the 'Gamow–Teller', or 'GT', selection rules: $\Delta I = 0$ *or* 1 (no $0 \to 0$). The additional proviso, put in the parentheses, signifies that $I_i = 0 \to I_f = 0$ is forbidden under GT selection rules, despite the admissibility of $\Delta I = 0$ when $I_i \neq 0$. It stems from the fact that an angular momentum balance among $\mathbf{S} = \mathbf{1}$ and $\mathbf{I}_i = \mathbf{I}_f = 0$ is unobtainable. The added proviso makes it possible to distinguish cases of *pure* singlet emission (the $0 \to 0$ decays), and pure triplet emission (allowed $\Delta I = 1$ decays). Cases of $\Delta I = 0$ with $I_i \neq 0$ will have superpositions of singlet and triplet radiations.

Even the latter superpositions will be non-interfering ones, with additive singlet and triplet intensities (rather than wave amplitudes). This is because the averaging over all directions, characteristic of randomly oriented nuclei, permits the orthogonality (independence) of the singlet and triplet states to have full play.

The association of Fermi's name with the selection rules appropriate to allowed singlet emission stems from Fermi's initial version of his theory, which yielded singlet radiation as the only unretarded type. Later, Gamow and Teller pointed out evidence that the triplet emissions may be equally unretarded, and that a simple supplementation of Fermi's theory makes it so. The $\beta$-interaction may be analysed as a sum of the singlet-producing 'Fermi coupling' and the triplet-producing 'GT coupling'.

### *Fermi and GT coupling strengths*

In order to express results quantitatively, Fermi and GT 'coupling constants', $C_F$ and $C_{GT}$, are introduced in such a way that the intensity with which the $\beta$-interaction produces allowed singlet and triplet emissions is proportional to $C_F^2$ and $C_{GT}^2$, respectively. These coupling strengths will be more closely defined by the uses they are put to; a final, unambiguous definition will be possible only after the formal theory is posited. $C_F$ and $C_{GT}$ can be regarded as independent magnitudes only for analyses in which the allowed singlet and triplet lepton states play independent roles, as in the emissions from randomly oriented nuclei. Other types of analysis may eventually require a completely specific interrelation between them.

Consider now the primary example of nucleonic decay, that of the free neutron into a proton, in which $I_i = \frac{1}{2} \to I_f = \frac{1}{2}$. Both singlet and triplet radiations are produced. Moreover, the $\mathbf{S} = \mathbf{1}$ of the triplet must be produced indifferently in any of its three possible orientations, by an assembly of neutrons of random orientation. This leads to the closer definition of the coupling constants as such that the decay rate of the neutron, after corrections for energy available and coulombic distortion, is proportional to

$$(ft)_n^{-1} \sim C_F^2 + 3C_{GT}^2. \tag{1.24}$$

Implicit here is a complete definition of the 'GT-to-Fermi ratio', $(C_{GT}/C_F)^2$, although this still leaves $C_F$ and $C_{GT}$ undefined individually. The most recent‡ value for the comparative half-life of the neutron is $(ft)_n = 1180 \pm 35$ sec.

We may now obtain a measurement of the GT-to-Fermi ratio by comparing the neutron decay with any other equally well understood case in which the proportions of singlet and triplet emissions must be expected to be different. We choose the $0 \to 0$ decay of $O^{14}$, already mentioned briefly in § 1.5. This decay can emit no allowed triplet radiation at all, according to the GT selection rules, hence it differs from the neutron decay sufficiently so that the comparison will be sensitive to the GT-to-Fermi ratio. Moreover, $O^{14}$ is the best measured of a series of like cases which have highly uniform comparative half-lives. As mentioned in § 1.5, $O^{14}$ is understood as having two protons extra to an inert core, either of which may transform to yield the daughter, $N^{14}$ state. Accordingly, we expect

$$(ft)_O^{-1} \sim 2C_F^2, \tag{1.25}$$

with the same constant of proportionality as in the neutron decay (1.24). We thus obtain

$$\frac{C_{GT}^2}{C_F^2} = \frac{1}{3}\left[2\frac{(ft)_O}{(ft)_n} - 1\right] = 1{\cdot}40 \pm 0{\cdot}05, \tag{1.26}$$

using the $O^{14}$ $ft$-value listed in § 1.5.

## 1.8. Electron polarization

To throw further light on the $\beta$-interaction, direct observations on the electron's spin orientation may be undertaken. Such observations must

‡ A. Sosnovskii, P. Spivak, Yu. Prokoviev, I. Kutikov, and Yu. Dobrynin, *Soviet Phys.* (*JETP*), **35**, 739 (1959).

always be made relative to some chosen axis, and then any individual electron must be found with its spin either parallel or antiparallel to that axis. Any number of decays, $d\lambda$, must be a superposition, $d\lambda = d\lambda_{\rightarrow} + d\lambda_{\leftarrow}$ of the parallel and antiparallel cases, respectively. If there is an excess of one over the other, then the fractional difference,

$$\mathscr{P} = \frac{d\lambda_{\rightarrow} - d\lambda_{\leftarrow}}{d\lambda_{\rightarrow} + d\lambda_{\leftarrow}}, \tag{1.27}$$

is called the *polarization* of the electrons, relative to the axis used.

It is, of course, simplest to work with a source of randomly oriented nuclei. Then, the only axis distinguished for the emissions is the line from source to detecting system, representable by the direction of the electron's velocity, $\mathbf{v}$. Our concern is then with the correlation symbolized by $\mathbf{s}_e . \mathbf{v}$. It is characterized by spin orientations parallel or antiparallel to the direction of motion, hence by *longitudinal* polarizations, if any. A positive longitudinal polarization, because of its predominant screw-sense, is called *right-handed*, while a negative one is *left-handed.*

*The discovery of electron polarization*

No attempt was made to look for a polarization of the emergent $\beta$-electrons for many years. It was taken for granted that none would be found in emissions from randomly oriented nuclei, on grounds of symmetry. The left half of Fig. 1.10 represents, schematically, a left-handed spinning of the electrons emitted into a random direction, from an isotropic source. It had been considered obvious that the mirror image of any experimental arrangement should produce exactly the same results as the original. Since, as the right half of Fig. 1.10 indicates, a left-handed screw-sense is mirrored as a right-handed one, it was believed inconsistent for either to exist; a vanishing net polarization was expected.

It was just such expectations based on reflectional symmetry which were called into question by Yang and Lee, as already mentioned in the introductory paragraphs of this chapter. Their ideas were immediately tested in an important experiment by Wu, Ambler, Hayward, Hoppes, and Hudson,‡ which showed that expectations from reflectional symmetry do indeed fail in $\beta$-decay. That experiment incidentally proved that a non-vanishing longitudinal polarization is necessary for the conservation of angular momentum in the case examined ($Co^{60}$) as will

‡ C. S. Wu, E. Ambler, R. Hayward, D. Hoppes, and R. Hudson, *Phys. Rev.* **107**, 641 (1957).

be explained more fully below. A direct observation of the polarization was soon carried out by Frauenfelder *et al.*‡

The outcome of a large number of observations on allowed $\beta$-emissions, whether purely singlet, purely triplet, or superpositions of both, showed

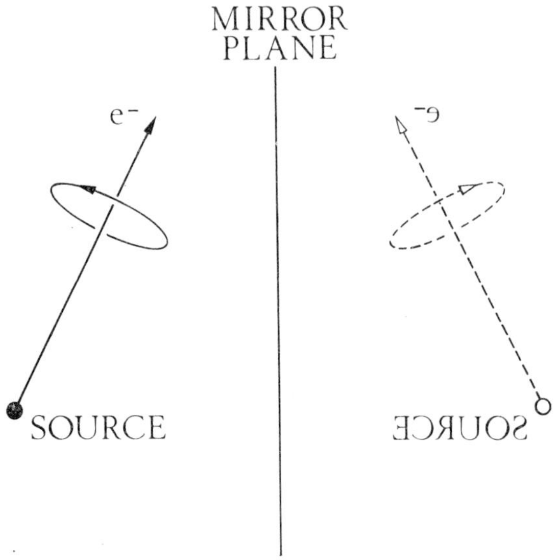


FIG. 1.10

that the negatrons are left-handedly polarized, and the positrons right-handedly. The quantitative results are:

$$\mathscr{P} = \pm v/c \quad \text{for } e^{\pm}, \tag{1.28}$$

where $v/c$ is the magnitude of the electron's velocity, in units of the light velocity.

That the screw-sense of the positron polarization is opposite to that of the negatron may be expected on the basis of the hole picture. A process which emits a left-handed negatron should require for its reversal§ a reabsorption of a left-handed negatron. If that negatron is absorbed out of a 'vacuum state', the vacancy which remains should be observed as a right-handed positron.

That result also suggests how the expectations from reflectional symmetry, discussed in connexion with Fig. 1.10, should be modified. The mirror image of a negatron should be taken to be a positron, and then the expectation would be that positrons are right-handed when negatrons

‡ H. Frauenfelder, R. Bobone, E. V. Goeler, N. Levine, H. Lewis, R. Peacock, A. Rossi, and G. DePasquali, *Phys. Rev.* **106**, 386 (1957).

§ This presupposes invariance under 'time-reversal', see § 1.10.

are left-handed. More generally, the mirror image of every particle should be taken to be its antiparticle, so that the reflection of a negatron source ($n \rightarrow p+e^-+\bar{\nu}$) becomes a positron source ($\bar{n} \rightarrow \bar{p}+e^++\nu$) in conformity with the lepton-conservation relation (1.21).

Further, there is a viewpoint from which the observed *magnitude* of the polarization, $v/c$, is the maximum to be expected. First, a longitudinal polarization might be expected to vanish in the limit $\mathbf{v} \rightarrow 0$ simply because there is then no 'quantization' axis singled out in the process. Next, we may then expect the maximum of polarization, $|\mathscr{P}| = 1$, to be reached at the maximum of velocity, $v \rightarrow c$. Finally, the reduction to $|\mathscr{P}| = v/c$ for intermediate velocities may be regarded as the result of the following behaviour, expected from relativistic quantum-mechanical principles.

It is well known that an accurate measurement of a particle's velocity, as against its momentum, can only have the results $+c$ or $-c$. This is because a precise measurement of an instantaneous velocity $u = \Delta x/\Delta t$ requires approaching the limit $\Delta t \rightarrow 0$, and then we cannot avoid disturbing the particle to such an extent that the uncertainty about its energy, $\Delta E \geqslant \hbar/\Delta t$, approaches infinity. An infinite energy corresponds to $u = \pm c$. If, instead, the particle is known to have the precise momentum $\mathbf{p} = (W/c^2).\mathbf{v}$, then the 'mean velocity', $\mathbf{v}$, so defined, must be an average of point-motions alternating between the two states $u = \pm c$. This is the well known 'zitterbewegung', a back-and-forth motion along the path, having the net drift, $\mathbf{v}$. If $a$ is the probability amplitude for the forward motion, then

$$|a|^2(+c)+(1-|a|^2)(-c) = v, \tag{1.29}$$

and

$$|a|^2 = \tfrac{1}{2}(1+v/c), \qquad 1-|a|^2 = \tfrac{1}{2}(1-v/c). \tag{1.30}$$

If, further, we deal with a negatron which is completely left-handed in every stage of the 'zitterbewegung', its spin flipping as it alternates between the opposite velocity states, then

$$\mathscr{P} = (-1)\tfrac{1}{2}(1+v/c)+(+1)\tfrac{1}{2}(1-v/c) = -v/c \tag{1.31}$$

exactly as observed.‡

‡ In the more formal description to be introduced later, the two intrinsically left-handed states being superposed here are simultaneous eigenstates of the longitudinal spin and velocity: $u_{-\frac{1}{2}}(+c)$ and $u_{+\frac{1}{2}}(-c)$. These alone cannot form a free electron state of definite energy. The latter must be described by some superposition of the two states

$$u_{\pm\frac{1}{2}}(W) = [\tfrac{1}{2}(1+v/c)]^{\frac{1}{2}}u_{\pm\frac{1}{2}}(+c)+[\tfrac{1}{2}(1-v/c)]^{\frac{1}{2}}u_{\pm\frac{1}{2}}(-c),$$

to have the definite energy $W = mc^2/[1-v^2/c^2]^{\frac{1}{2}}$. Here, the right-handed states, $u_{\pm\frac{1}{2}}(\pm c)$, are included. However, the latter yield contributions to the longitudinal spin and

The picture used here, of a spin flipping back and forth in the course of the electron's 'zitterbewegung', can be consistent with angular momentum conservation only if a compensating unit of orbital momentum (as gauged about any centre) is generated during each flip. That only their total is conserved, and not the spin and orbital momenta separately, is a well-known characteristic of the relativistic description of free electrons, quite apart from their behaviour in $\beta$-decay (Chapters III and XII).

We have the result that orbital momentum is generated even if the electron is freed from the nucleus without initial orbital momentum, as in allowed decay. This is essential to the possibility of a non-isotropic angular distribution of the electrons, to be considered next. The circumferential variations of density characteristic of non-isotropy imply the existence of wave fronts directed around the centre; there is a spatial distribution of linear momenta which have moments about the centre, hence the existence of orbital angular momentum.

*The angular distribution of the electrons*

The existence of electron polarization implies that the electrons will be emitted anisotropically under certain circumstances, as will now be seen. These circumstances will turn out to be limited, both theoretically and practically. Moreover, the observations on the angular distributions which have been feasible agree with the expectations based on the much more generally observable polarizations.

An isotropic, 'round', nucleus cannot be expected to show a preference for any particular emission direction, in a process independent of external circumstances. The nucleus must itself possess some axis, such as is provided by a non-vanishing initial spin, **I**. Thus, the search for an asymmetric angular distribution becomes a matter of seeking a correlation which can be symbolized by $\mathbf{I}.\mathbf{v}$.

For a non-isotropy to become detectable through observations on the product electrons only, the nuclei of the source must somehow be lined up into a common orientation. They must possess an initial spin axis

velocity which cancel each other, if only $u_{\mp\frac{1}{2}}(W)$ are superposed in the ratio

$$[(1+v/c)/(1-v/c)]^{\frac{1}{2}},$$

the same ratio as taken in the text for $u_{\mp\frac{1}{2}}(\pm c)$. An operator, $\gamma_5$, may be defined such that its eigenvalue is $\gamma_5 = +1$ in each of the intrinsically left-handed states $u_{\mp\frac{1}{2}}(\pm c)$, and $\gamma_5 = -1$ in each of the right-handed states $u_{\pm\frac{1}{2}}(\pm c)$. Then the superposition used in the text is a sum of

$$\tfrac{1}{2}(1+\gamma_5)u_{-\frac{1}{2}}(W) \quad \text{and} \quad \tfrac{1}{2}(1+\gamma_5)u_{+\frac{1}{2}}(W)$$

taken in equal parts of random relative phase.

just to make their 'orientation' a meaningful word, and that axis must be controllable as through the magnetic moment which is generated by spinning charge. Nuclear magnetic moments are too small to be easily controlled by an externally applied magnetic field, so advantage is taken of the much more intense fields provided by atomic electrons in sources made up of paramagnetic crystals. The atomic electrons must themselves be lined up, but that is relatively easy for an applied field, since electronic magnetic moments are more than a thousand times stronger than nucleonic ones. These circumstances limit the type of radioactive nuclei which can be employed, to such as can be incorporated into the ordered structure of very special crystals. Consequently, the cases in which the angular distribution has been observed are very few ($Co^{56,58,60}$, $Mn^{52}$,...). The $Co^{60}$ observation constituted the pioneering experiment of Wu *et al.* already mentioned. Another important case is that of a neutron itself, which required a singular method not fitting into the above category.‡ It will be reviewed later, together with the totality of the observations on the neutron (§ 1.10).

Now we consider the theoretical expectations in more detail. Clearly, pure singlet (Fermi) radiation should show no departure from isotropy. Allowed singlet emissions take no angular momentum from the nucleus and so have nothing to do with the initial nuclear orientation defined by its angular momentum. This fits with the fact that pure singlet radiation occurs only for $I_i = I_f = 0$, and no nucleus with $I_i = 0$, whatever $I_f$, can exhibit anisotropy.

Expectations for the triplet (GT) radiation follow from a consideration of the unit of total lepton spin, $\mathbf{S} = \mathbf{s}_e + \mathbf{s}_\nu$, which is emitted in these cases. Its three possible orientations, $S_z \equiv M_S = 0, \pm 1$, relative to the initial nuclear spin $\mathbf{I}_i$, will occur in ascertainable proportions, depending on the final nuclear spin magnitude, $I_f$. Corresponding proportions of the two electron spin orientations follow from the fact that $\mathbf{s}_e$ must be parallel to $\mathbf{S}$ in the triplet state. For each spin orientation of the electron, its emission direction is differently restricted, in accordance with the screw-sense found in the longitudinal polarization measurements.

The polarization results, $\mathscr{P} = \mp v/c$ for $e^\mp$, must first be transformed from reference to the emission direction, now variable, as axis, to the one steady direction now suitable as a quantization axis, the initial nuclear spin direction, $\hat{\mathbf{I}} \equiv \mathbf{I}_i/I_i$. Accordingly, let $d\lambda_{\uparrow,\downarrow}$ be rates at which negatrons emerge parallel and antiparallel to $\hat{\mathbf{I}}$. Then, the reorientation

‡ See § 5.3 for the citation of a $Ne^{19}$ measurement.

clearly‡ transforms $\mathscr{P} = -v/c$ into

$$\frac{d\lambda_\uparrow - d\lambda_\downarrow}{d\lambda_\uparrow + d\lambda_\downarrow} = -\hat{\mathbf{I}}.\mathbf{v}/c = -(v/c)\cos\theta \quad (\text{for e}^-), \tag{1.32}$$

where $\theta$ is the angle to $\mathbf{I}_\mathrm{i}$ of the negatron's emission direction. The sum $d\lambda_\uparrow + d\lambda_\downarrow$ must be isotropic, since it is the polarization which is to be held responsible for any non-isotropy, and then the 'spin up' and 'spin down' negatrons must be emitted in the angular distributions proportional to

$$d\lambda_{\uparrow,\downarrow} \sim 1 \mp (v/c)\cos\theta \quad (\text{for e}^-), \tag{1.33}$$

respectively.

The electron spin is 'up' when $M_S = +1$, and 'down' when $M_S = -1$, so that the electron's emission directions are distributed in angle according to

$$d\lambda(M_S) \sim 1 - M_S(v/c)\cos\theta \quad (\text{for e}^-), \tag{1.34}$$

in the component state with $S_z = M_S$. This expression is also correct for $M_S = 0$, which has equal populations of spin 'up' and 'down' electrons (the corresponding isotropy also fits with the conclusions about the singlet radiation, which has $M_S = 0$ only). It is now clear that the resultant angular distribution is determined by an average $\langle M_S \rangle$ of the orientations, which takes into account the proportions of $M_S = 0, \pm 1$ occurring in a given case:

$$d\lambda_{\mathrm{GT}}(\theta) \sim 1 \mp \langle M_S \rangle (v/c)\cos\theta \quad (\text{for e}^\mp). \tag{1.35}$$

This must be considered restricted to triplet radiation, $\sim C_{\mathrm{GT}}^2$. If singlet radiation is emitted together with the triplet ($I_\mathrm{f} = I_\mathrm{i}$), then by itself ($\sim C_\mathrm{F}^2$) it is merely isotropic, as argued above. However, the singlet radiation may still *interfere* ($\sim C_\mathrm{F} C_{\mathrm{GT}}$) with the triplet, now that $\mathbf{I}_\mathrm{i}$ is restricted, and so influence the anisotropy. The information essential for gauging this influence comes from observing free neutron decay, reserved for consideration in § 1.10; complete results will be given in the last section ('Conclusions') of this chapter.

Meanwhile, (1.35) is the complete angular distribution for $I_\mathrm{f} = I_\mathrm{i} \pm 1$. The case $I_\mathrm{f} = I_\mathrm{i} - 1$ is particularly simple, because then $\mathbf{S}$ and $\mathbf{s}_\mathrm{e}$ can emerge only parallel to $\mathbf{I}_\mathrm{i}$, hence $\langle M_S \rangle = M_S = +1$. The consequent ratio of forward ($\theta = 0$) to backward ($\theta = \pi$) negatrons, as given by (1.35), is $(1 - v/c)/(1 + v/c)$. This is consistent with what was actually observed in the above-mentioned experiment by Wu *et al.* for the $I_\mathrm{i} = 5 \rightarrow I_\mathrm{f} = 4$ transition of $\mathrm{Co}^{60}$.

‡ Readers having greater confidence in formal manipulations may obtain this result by subjecting the states discussed in the footnote on p. 33 to transformation by the rotation operator, $\exp(i\theta s_x)$.

The general triplet transition, in which $I_f = I_i$, $I_i+1$, or $I_i-1$, can be roughly understood with the help of the diagrams in Fig. 1.11. It is easy to see that $0 < \langle M_S \rangle < 1$ for $I_f = I_i$ and $-1 < \langle M_S \rangle < 0$ for $I_f = I_i+1$.

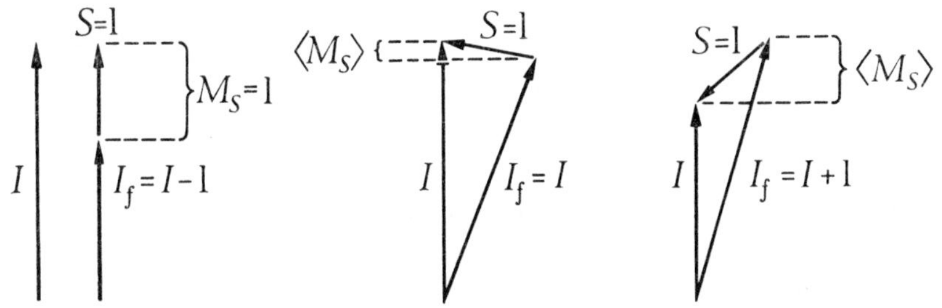


FIG. 1.11

The quantitatively correct quantum-mechanical averages $\langle M_S \rangle$ can be obtained by averaging the projection $S_z = \mathbf{S}.\hat{\mathbf{I}}$, with due recognition of the fact that it is $\langle I_z \rangle = I_i$, $\langle I_i^2 \rangle = I_i(I_i+1)$, $\langle I_f^2 \rangle = I_f(I_f+1)$ and $\langle S^2 \rangle = 2$ that are the well-defined quantities. Since

$$S_z = \mathbf{S}.\mathbf{I}_i/I_i = I_{iz}(\mathbf{S}.\mathbf{I}_i)/I_i^2 \quad \text{and} \quad I_f^2 = (\mathbf{I}_i - \mathbf{S})^2 = I_i^2 - 2\mathbf{I}_i.\mathbf{S} + S^2,$$

$$\langle M_S \rangle \equiv \langle S_z \rangle = \langle \mathbf{S}.\mathbf{I}_i \rangle I_i/I_i(I_i+1) = \tfrac{1}{2}\langle I_i^2 - I_f^2 + S^2 \rangle/(I_i+1)$$
$$= \tfrac{1}{2}[I_i(I_i+1) - I_f(I_f+1) + 2]/(I_i+1). \quad (1.36)$$

This‡ is equivalent to the table of values:

$$\left.\begin{matrix} I_f = & I_i - 1 & I_i & I_i+1 \\ \langle M_S \rangle = & 1 & 1/(I_i+1) & -I_i/(I_i+1) \end{matrix}\right\}. \quad (1.37)$$

The first of these values was anticipated above. Notice, also, that $I_i = 0$ can lead to no anisotropy, as anticipated, for $I_f = -1$ does not exist, and there is no triplet radiation when $I_f = I_i = 0$.

The same result (1.35), for the electron angular distribution in Gamow–Teller emissions, will be shown to follow from the formal theory in Chapter V. There, the successful comparison with experiments will also be presented.

## 1.9. The electron-neutrino correlation

We might next inquire about the polarization of the neutrino. This particle has barely been detected, by taking extreme measures (§ 1.2); a

‡ Those familiar with 'vector-addition coefficients' (2.11) will recognize that the polarized nuclear state can be analysed as

$$\chi_{II} = \sum_{M_S} \chi_{I_f, I-M_S}\, \chi_{1M_S} \langle I_f(I-M_S)1(M_S)|I(I)\rangle,$$

so that $$\langle M_S \rangle = \langle I_f(I-1)1(+1)|I(I)\rangle^2 - \langle I_f(I+1)1(-1)|I(I)\rangle^2,$$

and that this agrees (Table 2.1) with (1.36) and (1.37).

direct observation of its polarization, such as was done for the electron, is practically out of the question. However, deductions about the neutrino polarization can be made from studies of the directional correlation, symbolized by $\mathbf{q}.\mathbf{v}$, between the neutrino's momentum and the electron velocity. A direct observation of the neutrino momentum is also not easy, but it can be determined from the nuclear recoil, and the momentum balance (1.2). The development of this approach owes much to the work of Allen and his collaborators.‡

In order to deal directly with the neutrino, rather than its antiparticle, the discussion will be cast in terms of positron emission. The correct corresponding statements about negatron-antineutrino emissions can always be made on the basis of the 'hole picture'; they turn out to conform to the facts.

The directional correlation of the positron with the neutrino may be viewed as an angular distribution of the positrons about the neutrino momentum $\mathbf{q}$, as an axis. Our considerations can then proceed very much as for the angular distribution about the nuclear spin axis, in the preceding section, except that the angle $\theta \equiv \cos^{-1}(\mathbf{v}.\hat{\mathbf{I}}/v)$ must now be replaced by $\theta_{e\nu} \equiv \cos^{-1}(\mathbf{q}.\mathbf{v}/qv)$. In view of the positive longitudinal polarization, $\mathscr{P} = +v/c$, of the positrons, we can say that the rates of producing positron spins parallel and antiparallel to $\mathbf{q}$ are, respectively proportional to

$$d\lambda_{\uparrow,\downarrow} \sim 1 \pm (v/c)\cos\theta_{e\nu} \quad (\text{for } e^+), \tag{1.38}$$

in the same way that we come to the conclusion (1.33).

The angular distribution $d\lambda(\theta_{e\nu})$ of the electron's direction about the neutrino direction comes from adding the two polarized intensities (1.38), properly. There is first an isotropic contribution from each. The anisotropic contributions are $\pm(v/c)\cos\theta_{e\nu}$, per unit of isotropic intensity, according as the positron spin projection $s_{ez} = \pm\frac{1}{2}$ is positive or negative; hence

$$d\lambda(\theta_{e\nu}) \sim 1 + \langle 2s_{ez}\rangle(v/c)\cos\theta_{e\nu}, \tag{1.39}$$

where $\langle s_{ez}\rangle$ is the average projection of the electron spin on the neutrino momentum (in units of $\hbar$).

*In Fermi radiation*

The electron's spin is antiparallel to that of the neutrino in the singlet, Fermi radiation. *If* the neutrino were completely right-handed, so that its spin direction coincides with that of its momentum, the correlation

‡ See, for example, J. Allen, R. Burman, W. Hermannsfeldt, P. Stähelin, and T. Braid, *Phys. Rev.* **116**, 134 (1959).

distribution (1.39) would become

$$d\lambda_S(\theta_{e\nu}) \sim 1-(v/c)\cos\theta_{e\nu}. \tag{1.40}$$

The subscript '$S$' is attached to this result because, in the historical development, a $\beta$-interaction which produces allowed singlet radiation consisting of right-handed neutrinos and positrons (left-handed antineutrinos and negatrons) came to be known as 'Scalar coupling'. Because both the electron and neutrino have their polarizations reversed in

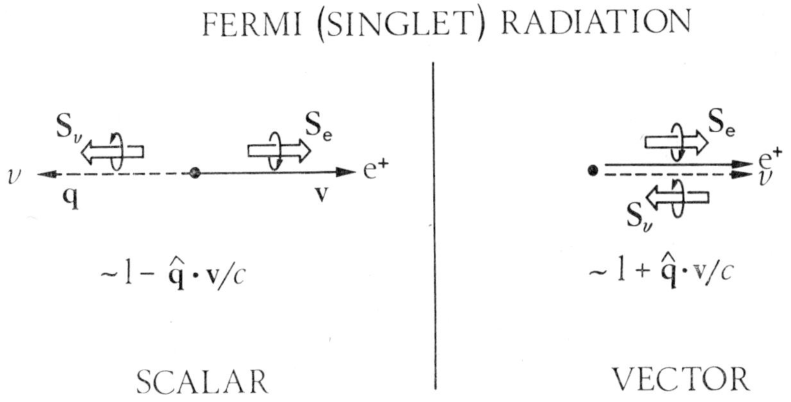


FIG. 1.12. $\hat{\mathbf{q}}.\mathbf{v}/c \equiv (v/c)\cos\theta_{e\nu}$ of equations (1.40) and (1.41).

going from positron to negatron emission, the negative correlation in (1.40) holds for both signs of the charge in 'Scalar' emissions.

A Fermi coupling which yields left-handed normal leptons with right-handed antileptons is known as 'Vector coupling'. The corresponding correlation is easily seen to have the opposite sign to that of (1.40):

$$d\lambda_V(\theta_{e\nu}) \sim 1+(v/c)\cos\theta_{e\nu}. \tag{1.41}$$

The two contrasting cases of right-handed (Scalar) and left-handed (Vector) neutrinos are schematized in Fig. 1.12, which shows the configurations of maximum occurrence.

Our considerations so far have presupposed complete longitudinal polarizations of the neutrino: $|\mathscr{P}| = 1$. The massless neutrinos never travel with less than light velocity so there is no expectation of a reduction such as that to $|\mathscr{P}| = v/c$, characteristic of the electron. On the other hand, there is no *a priori* reason for supposing that the emitted neutrinos should be polarized at all, let alone have a maximum polarization. Various amounts of polarization can be represented by various relative strengths of the Scalar and Vector couplings.

Define Scalar and Vector coupling strengths, $C_S$ and $C_V$, related to the total Fermi coupling strength already introduced by $C_F^2 = C_S^2+C_V^2$. Then the electron–neutrino correlation to be expected in singlet radiation is given in

$$d\lambda_F(\theta_{e\nu}) \sim 1+a_F\,\hat{\mathbf{q}}\,.\,\mathbf{v}/c, \tag{1.42}$$

with

$$a_F = (C_V^2-C_S^2)/(C_V^2+C_S^2). \tag{1.43}$$

This 'correlation coefficient' may have a value anywhere between $-1$ and $+1$, depending on the nature of the fundamental $\beta$-interaction.

No electron–neutrino correlation measurement on a pure Fermi emitter $(0 \to 0)$ has been found possible, so far. However, the mirror decay

$$_{18}A^{35}_{17} \to {}_{17}Cl^{35}_{18}+e^++\nu \tag{1.44}$$

seems to be a case of nearly pure Fermi radiation, despite the fact that the initial and final nuclear spins are $I_i = I_f = \frac{3}{2}$. That is concluded on the basis of the measured comparative half-life, $(ft)_A \approx 5680$ sec. Recall that our standard, pure-Fermi, emitter, $O^{14}$ (see § 1.7), has two protons contributing to its transformation rate as against the single proton of any mirror decay, such as that of $A^{35}$. We must therefore expect the fraction, $x_A$, of the total rate $\sim (ft)_A^{-1}$, devoted to the singlet radiation, to be

$$x_A = \frac{\frac{1}{2}(ft)_O^{-1}}{(ft)_A^{-1}} = \frac{(ft)_A}{2(ft)_O} = \frac{5680}{2(3060)} \approx 0{\cdot}93. \tag{1.45}$$

The remaining, GT, fraction $(1-x_A)$ seems to be much smaller than in the case of the free neutron (1.24). That it should be different for the proton of $A^{35}$ is not surprising, however. The spin $I_i = \frac{3}{2}$ of $A^{35}$ must be a resultant of orbital motion of the proton within $A^{35}$, and its intrinsic spin; the effect of this is not reliably predictable.

The correlation coefficient measured for the case of $A^{35}$ is $a = +0{\cdot}97 \pm 0{\cdot}14$ (see the reference on p. 38). On the basis that we are here dealing with pure singlet radiation, this should be identified with $a_F$ of (1.43), and then indicates that $C_S^2/C_V^2 < 0{\cdot}09$. We shall see that any GT radiation which may be present contributes negative correlation, hence lowers this upper limit still further. It appears that the Fermi radiation is generated by Vector coupling, and should henceforth be given the more specific name 'Vector radiation'.

The physical interpretation of this result is that the neutrinos, like the negatrons, are emitted with a maximal left-handed polarization—at least in Fermi radiation.

*In* GT *radiation*

To correspond to the triplet, GT radiation, in which the leptons spin in parallel, Fig. 1.12 should be modified by simply reversing the neutrino spin directions. Thus, a negative directional correlation of the leptons, in triplet radiation, signifies that the neutrino is left-handed, while it is a positive correlation which is to be interpreted as evidence for a right-handed neutrino.

The magnitude of the directional correlation is also modified in the triplet case, relative to the singlet. This is because there are three alternatives for the orientation of the triplet spin-vector, '$\mathbf{S} = \mathbf{1}$', and that will tend to wash out the correlation.

The quantum-mechanical average $\langle s_{ez} \rangle$ in (1.39) may be evaluated in the same way as $\langle M_S \rangle$ in the angular distribution (1.36). This time, the expression $s_{ez} = s_{\nu z}(\mathbf{s}_\nu . \mathbf{s}_e)/s_\nu^2$ provides the starting-point, with $s_{\nu z} = \frac{1}{2}$ and $s_\nu^2 = \frac{3}{4}$ (in units of $\hbar$). Then $S^2 = s_e^2 + 2\mathbf{s}_e . \mathbf{s}_\nu + s_\nu^2 = \frac{3}{2} + 2\mathbf{s}_e . \mathbf{s}_\nu$ yields

$$\langle s_{ez} \rangle = \tfrac{2}{3}\langle \mathbf{s}_e . \mathbf{s}_\nu \rangle = \tfrac{1}{3}\langle S^2 - \tfrac{3}{2} \rangle = \tfrac{1}{3}S(S+1) - \tfrac{1}{2}. \tag{1.46}$$

This gives the correct singlet ($S = 0$) result, $\langle 2s_{ez} \rangle = -1$, as well as the triplet ($S = 1$) result $\langle 2s_{ez} \rangle = +\frac{1}{3}$. Inserting this into (1.39) yields

$$d\lambda_{\mathrm{T}}(\theta_{e\nu}) \sim 1 + \tfrac{1}{3}(v/c)\cos\theta_{e\nu} \tag{1.47}$$

when the neutrino is right-handedly polarized, and

$$d\lambda_{\mathrm{A}}(\theta_{e\nu}) \sim 1 - \tfrac{1}{3}(v/c)\cos\theta_{e\nu} \tag{1.48}$$

for left-handed neutrinos. Both correlations retain their signs in changing from positron–neutrino to negatron–antineutrino emissions, on the basis of the 'hole picture'.

The subscript 'T' is attached to the right-handed neutrino case because a $\beta$-interaction which produces triplet radiation with right-handed normal neutrinos, and left-handed normal electrons, is called 'Tensor coupling'. A $\beta$-interaction which produces triplet radiation with left-handed normal leptons of both types (and right-handed antileptons) is called 'Pseudovector' or 'Axial Vector coupling' (denoted by the symbol 'A').

We may define Tensor and Pseudovector coupling strengths, $C_{\mathrm{T}}$ and $C_{\mathrm{A}}$, which make up the total GT coupling strength according to $C_{\mathrm{GT}}^2 = C_{\mathrm{T}}^2 + C_{\mathrm{A}}^2$. Then the triplet radiation may have the correlation in

$$d\lambda_{\mathrm{GT}}(\theta_{e\nu}) \sim 1 + a_{\mathrm{GT}}(v/c)\cos\theta_{e\nu}, \tag{1.49}$$

with

$$a_{\mathrm{GT}} = \tfrac{1}{3}(C_{\mathrm{T}}^2 - C_{\mathrm{A}}^2)/(C_{\mathrm{T}}^2 + C_{\mathrm{A}}^2) \tag{1.50}$$

restricted to the range $-\frac{1}{3}$ to $+\frac{1}{3}$.

Measurements have been made on two cases of pure GT radiation:

$He^6$ and $Ne^{23}$. Allen *et al.* (reference on p. 38) find‡

$$a(\mathrm{He}^6) = -0{\cdot}39 \pm 0{\cdot}05,$$
$$a(\mathrm{Ne}^{23}) = -0{\cdot}37 \pm 0{\cdot}04.$$

Identification with $a_{\mathrm{GT}}$ of (1.50) leaves no appreciable room for a Tensor coupling. Like the Fermi radiation, the GT radiation seems to consist exclusively of maximally left-handed normal leptons and right-handed antileptons; it seems to be generated exclusively by the Pseudovector coupling and should, henceforth, be given the more specific name 'Pseudovector radiation'.

*Further evidence*

Actually, the first definitive evidence that it is left-handed neutrinos which are generated in GT radiation was obtained in a unique experiment

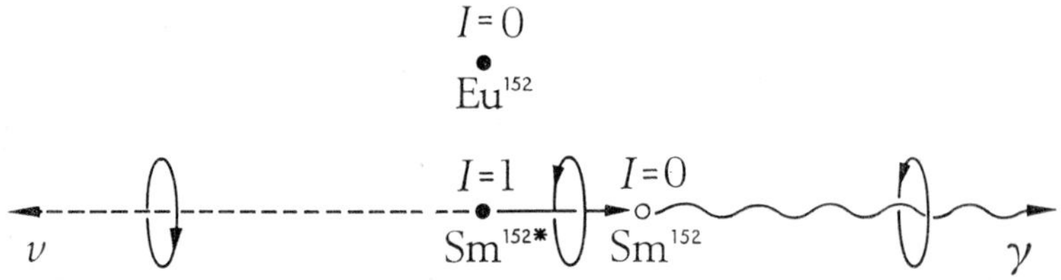


FIG. 1.13

by Goldhaber, Grodzins, and Sunyar.§ They worked with $Eu^{152}$, an isotope which decays by orbital electron capture, hence emits only a monochromatic neutrino. The initial nuclear state, for the decay in question, is spinless, and it transforms into an excited state of $Sm^{152}$ which has a unit spin. Consequently, as the daughter nucleus recoils from the neutrino, it must be spinning left- or right-handedly, according as the neutrino spins left- or right-handedly. Fig. 1.13 schematizes the case of the left-handed polarizations.

The sense of spin in the excited $Sm^{152}$ state is transferred to the $\gamma$-ray which it emits as it is de-excited into its spinless ground state. When the $\gamma$-ray is emitted in the same direction as the nuclear recoil from the neutrino, then it must have a circular polarization which is left- or right-handed according as the neutrino is left- or right-handed. The investigators were able to restrict their observations to the $\gamma$-rays codirectional with the nuclear recoil (by requiring that they resonate with normal

‡ A late measurement by C. Johnson, F. Pleasanton, and T. Carlson, *Phys. Rev.* **132**, 1149 (1963), gives $a(\mathrm{He}^6) = -0{\cdot}334 \pm 0{\cdot}003$, and $C_T^2/C_A^2 < 0{\cdot}004$.

§ M. Goldhaber, L. Grodzins, and A. Sunyar, *Phys. Rev.* **109**, 1015 (1958).

$Sm^{152}$ in a subsequent scattering) and to find the sense of their circular polarization (by differential transmission through magnetized iron). The result found was that the $\gamma$-rays, hence also the neutrinos, are left-handedly polarized.

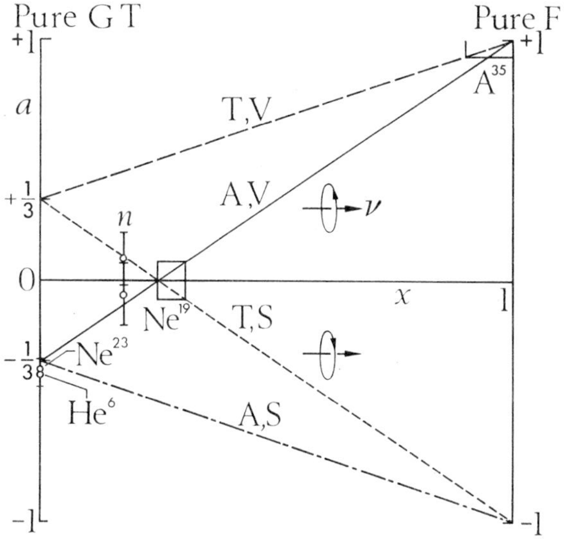


FIG. 1.14. The flagged points labelled $He^6$ and $Ne^{23}$, and the rectangles for $Ne^{19}$ and $A^{35}$, are from the reference on p. 38. The upper neutron point represents an early measurement by J. Robson, *Phys. Rev.* **100,** 933 (1955); the lower one is from the work of A. Trebukhovski *et al.*, *JETP*, **36,** 931 (1959).

The several measurements on the GT neutrinos make the case for their left-handedness stronger than for the Fermi neutrinos. However, the single case of nearly-pure Fermi radiation, $A^{35}$, receives support from cases of mixed Fermi and GT radiations, once it is granted that the GT correlation coefficient is $a_{GT} = -\frac{1}{3}$.

The correlation coefficient for an arbitrary mixture of Fermi and GT radiations can be written

$$a = xa_F + (1-x)a_{GT}, \tag{1.51}$$

where $x$ is the fraction of the decay rate devoted to Fermi emissions. How $x$ is found was exemplified by the $A^{35}$ case (1.44). Any mirror decay which has the comparative half-life $ft$ has $x = ft/2(ft)_O$, where $(ft)_O$ is the comparative half-life of our standard, pure Fermi emitter, $O^{14}$. The cases of mixed radiation in which the correlation coefficient has been measured are $Ne^{19}$ and the free neutron, both mirror decays. With the measured $ft$-values,

$$(ft)_{Ne} = 1900 \pm 200 \text{ sec} \quad \text{and} \quad (ft)_n = 1180 \pm 35 \text{ sec},$$

$x(\mathrm{Ne}^{19}) = 0{\cdot}31 \pm 0{\cdot}03$ and $x_n = 0{\cdot}192 \pm 0{\cdot}007$. The correlation coefficients which have been measured for these cases are presented in the so-called 'Scott diagram' of Fig. 1.14.

The diagram has $a(x)$ plotted against $x$. According to (1.51), all the measured $a$'s should fall on a straight line with intercepts $a_{\mathrm{GT}}$ and $a_{\mathrm{F}}$ at $x = 0$ and $x = 1$, respectively. The line corresponding to left-handed normal leptons stretches from the 'Pseudovector coupling' value, $a_{\mathrm{GT}} = -\frac{1}{3}$, for the pure GT radiation at $x = 0$, to the 'Vector coupling' value, $a_{\mathrm{F}} = +1$, at $x = 1$. The experimental points are clearly best consistent with that line. The electron–neutrino correlation coefficient (1.51) seems correctly given by

$$a = \tfrac{1}{3}(4x-1), \tag{1.52}$$

in terms of what should now be called the 'Vector radiation fraction', $x$.

## 1.10. The decay of the neutron

The free neutron is the simplest system to undergo nuclear $\beta$-decay, and it may seem more logical to have begun, rather than end, this chapter with that case. However, the elementary characteristics of the $\beta$-processes have been better exhibited in the decays of more complex nuclei, primarily because sufficiently strong sources of free neutrons are not easily available.

There is a type of information which studies of the free neutron decay are uniquely suited to give. The finding that the leptons are produced in maximally left-handed states suggests looking for a preferred screw-sense of the product nucleon, as well. This requires correlating the nucleon's spin with its momentum, and the free neutron decay is the only case in which the product nucleon is allowed to recoil freely.

Analysing the polarization of the recoil proton directly, as that was done for the electron, has been too difficult to attempt. The recoil velocity is only $v \lesssim 0{\cdot}04c$, hence, makes a poor 'quantization axis'. Some information can be gained without polarization analysis of the recoil, by starting with polarized initial nucleons, the neutrons, instead.

### *Expectations for polarized neutrons*

Neutron beams from nuclear reactors have been successfully polarized by reflecting them from magnetized cobalt mirrors. This method permits finding differences caused by reversing the polarization, simply through collecting data before and after reversing the magnetization of the cobalt reflectors.

The neutron decay events are identified by requiring coincidences between a negatron detector and a recoil proton counter. Thus, three directions are defined by the arrangements for observing polarized neutron decay: the polarization direction, representable by a unit vector, $\hat{\mathbf{I}}$, parallel to the neutron's spin; the electron's direction of motion, representable through its velocity $\mathbf{v}$; the proton recoil direction, which is most conveniently replaced by the antineutrino's momentum direction, $\hat{\mathbf{q}} = \mathbf{q}/q$, as deduced from the momentum balance.

We have already discussed the correlations of the electron's direction with that of the neutrino, and with the initial nuclear spin. These followed from the electron's polarization, hence are proportional to $v/c$. The electron–neutrino correlation (§ 1.9) added a fraction represented by $a\hat{\mathbf{q}}.\mathbf{v}/c$ to the intensity; the added term naturally averages to zero in an integration over all neutrino directions. The electron-nuclear spin correlation forms an anisotropic fraction of the electron's angular distribution, about the nuclear spin axis, which we now represent by $A\hat{\mathbf{I}}.\mathbf{v}/c$; this averages to zero for sources of randomly oriented nuclei, as well as in an integration over all electron directions. Our former discussion of the angular distribution (1.35) was restricted to pure Pseudovector (GT) radiation, in which case we found the added fraction to be $-\langle M_S\rangle(v/c)\cos\theta$, hence $A = -\langle M_S\rangle$ for pure Pseudovector emissions.

Correlations analogous to those which followed from the electron's polarization, $\sim v/c$, will also follow from the neutrino's polarization $\sim \mathbf{v}_\nu/c \equiv \hat{\mathbf{q}}$ (since the neutrino has the velocity of light). The correlation with the electron's direction has already been introduced in the form of the fraction $a\hat{\mathbf{q}}.\mathbf{v}/c$. Analogous to $A\hat{\mathbf{I}}.\mathbf{v}/c$ is the addition of a fraction $B\hat{\mathbf{I}}.\hat{\mathbf{q}}$ which provides an anisotropic term in the neutrino's angular distribution.

The preceding paragraph exhausts the pair-wise correlations of the three vectors, $\mathbf{I}$, $\mathbf{v}/c$, and $\mathbf{q}$. We may still conceive of a scalar addition to the intensity in the form of a scalar product of any one of the vectors with a vector product of the other two:

$$\hat{\mathbf{I}}.(\hat{\mathbf{q}}\times\mathbf{v}/c) = \hat{\mathbf{q}}.[(\mathbf{v}/c)\times\hat{\mathbf{I}}] = (\mathbf{v}/c).[\hat{\mathbf{I}}\times\hat{\mathbf{q}}].$$

Altogether, we may expect an observed decay intensity proportional to

$$d\lambda \sim 1+a_{\mathrm{n}}\hat{\mathbf{q}}.\mathbf{v}/c+\hat{\mathbf{I}}.[A_{\mathrm{n}}\mathbf{v}/c+B_{\mathrm{n}}\hat{\mathbf{q}}+D_{\mathrm{n}}\hat{\mathbf{q}}\times\mathbf{v}/c], \tag{1.53}$$

in its dependence on the three vectors. Experiments were designed, and carried out, to measure each of the four correlation coefficients $a_{\mathrm{n}}$, $A_{\mathrm{n}}$, $B_{\mathrm{n}}$, and $D_{\mathrm{n}}$.

*Time reversal*

The general distribution (1.53) is simplified immediately by the elimination of the last term, measured by the 'cross-correlation' coefficient $D_n$, on the basis that its existence would be inconsistent with 'invariance to time-reversal'. The latter property is a characteristic of every fundamental physical law so far discovered. Its meaning is that,

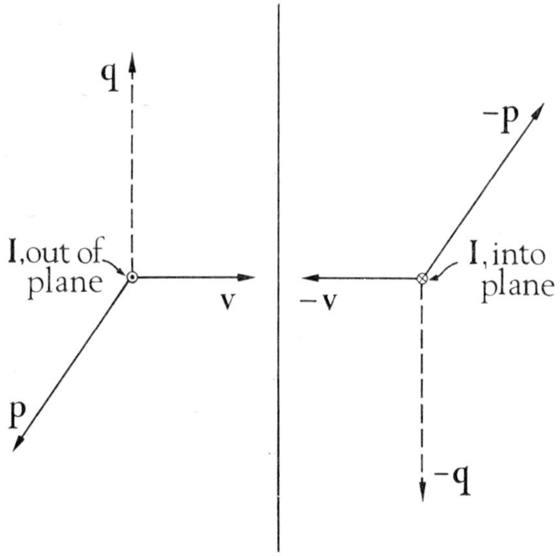


FIG. 1.15. (After M. Burgy, V. Krohn, T. Novey, G. Ringo, and V. Telegdi, *Phys. Rev. Lett.* **1**, 324 (1958).)

from any given result which depends on the relative directions of various motions, an equally valid result should follow from reversing all the motions. Thus, if there is a component of intensity given by $D_n \hat{\mathbf{I}}.(\hat{\mathbf{q}} \times \mathbf{v}/c)$, as in (1.53), then there must also exist a component $D_n(-\hat{\mathbf{I}}).[(-\hat{\mathbf{q}}) \times (-\mathbf{v}/c)]$. The two parts would cancel, and so a zero coefficient, $D_n$, is the expectation.

Requirements of invariance under the 'improper' transformations, such as the time-reversal, have become questionable since Yang and Lee's discovery, mentioned in § 1.8, that there are exceptions to the reflectional invariance. For that reason, an experimental check is desirable, and such was provided by an observation best discussed in terms of Fig. 1.15.

The left half of the figure indicates directions, **v** and **P**, in which the electron and proton recoil detectors may be set. The neutron spin is polarized normally to the plane of the detectors. A maximum effect proportional to $\hat{\mathbf{I}}.(\hat{\mathbf{q}}\times\mathbf{v}/c)$ should be obtained if the relative directions of $\mathbf{v}$ and $\mathbf{P}$ are so chosen that most neutrinos recoil at right angles to the electron. Next, consider a new arrangement, indicated in the right half of the figure, in which all the detected motions are reversed. Obviously, an equivalent of the reversed situation can be produced merely by reversing the neutron polarization in the original arrangement. Thus, an invariance to time-reversal demands that there be no change in the rate of electron–proton coincidences upon reversal of the neutron polarization. Actually, no demonstrable difference was found, the accuracy of the result being expressed as $D_n = 0{\cdot}04 \pm 0{\cdot}07$, essentially zero.

It seems that, unlike reflectional invariance, the invariance under time-reversal persists for the laws of $\beta$-interaction. We may henceforth set $D_n = 0$ in the distribution (1.53).

*The Vector and Pseudovector fractions*

The electron–neutrino directional correlation coefficient, $a_n$ of (1.53), is best measured with an unpolarized neutron beam, since then the remaining anisotropies in the distribution average out to zero. The results have already been considered in connexion with Fig. 1.14. The observed smallness of the coefficient in the case of the neutron is a direct demonstration of the near-equality (1.26) of the Vector (Fermi) and Pseudovector (GT) coupling strengths.

According to the discussion leading to (1.24), the Vector fraction in the neutron radiation is

$$x_n = C_V^2/(C_V^2+3C_A^2), \tag{1.54}$$

after the identifications $C_F = C_V$ and $C_{GT} = C_A$ which follow from our findings in § 1.9, that only left-handed normal leptons are produced in $\beta$-decay. With the evaluation $C_A^2/C_V^2 = 1{\cdot}40 \pm 0{\cdot}05$ in (1.26), the Vector fraction is $x_n = 0{\cdot}192+0{\cdot}007$ for the neutron. This is naturally the same as the value already quoted in § 1.9, since it is based on the same data. Our present interest is in the relation of $x_n$ to the coupling constants in (1.54). The electron–neutrino correlation coefficient (1.52) becomes equivalent to

$$a_n = \tfrac{1}{3}(4x_n-1) = (C_V^2-C_A^2)/(C_V^2+3C_A^2), \tag{1.55}$$

making evident the near-cancellation in it of nearly equal Vector and Pseudovector effects.

There remain to be considered the anisotropic fractions of the negatron and antineutrino angular distributions, as measured by the coefficients $A_n$ and $B_n$ in (1.53). The expectations for $A_n$ in purely Pseudovector radiation have been derived in § 1.8. According to (1.36), the correlation coefficient should be $-\langle M_S \rangle = -\frac{2}{3}$ when $I_\mathrm{i} = I_\mathrm{f} = \frac{1}{2}$, as in the neutron decay. If we let $A_\mathrm{A}$ represent just the contribution of the purely triplet part of the neutron's radiation, then

$$A_\mathrm{A} = -\tfrac{2}{3}(1-x_\mathrm{n}) = -2C_\mathrm{A}^2/(C_\mathrm{V}^2+3C_\mathrm{A}^2). \tag{1.56}$$

This cannot be taken as the full electron anisotropy coefficient, $A_\mathrm{n}$, since a possible influence of the Vector radiation remains to be considered.

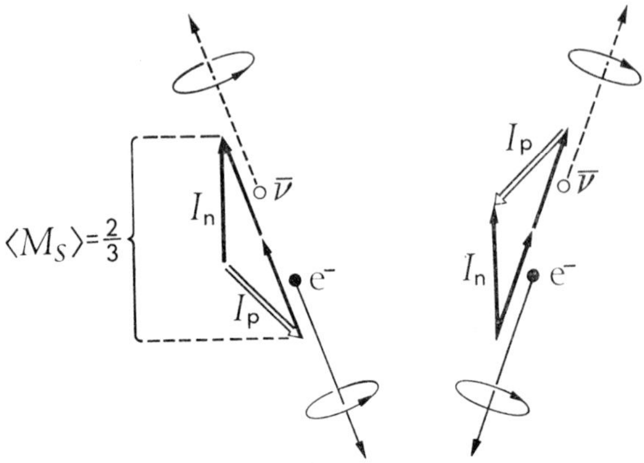


FIG. 1.16

The same arguments which led to the expectation of the electron anisotropy fraction $-\langle M_S \rangle \hat{\mathbf{I}}.\mathbf{v}/c$, in (1.35), would yield $+\langle M_S \rangle \hat{\mathbf{I}}.\hat{\mathbf{q}}$ for the antineutrino. The sign change arises because the two lepton spins are parallel in the triplet, Pseudovector radiation, but the antineutrino is right-handed while the negatron is left-handed. This means that the antineutrino will move in the direction opposite to that of the electron (just the negative electron–neutrino directional correlation characteristic of the triplet emissions). The situation is roughly represented in Fig. 1.16, which schematizes a couple of configurations between which the process may oscillate, while maintaining a total lepton spin, $\mathbf{S} = \mathbf{s}_\mathrm{e}+\mathbf{s}_\nu$, of unit magnitude.

Our conclusion is that the pure Pseudovector contribution to the antineutrino anisotropy is just

$$B_\mathrm{A} = -A_\mathrm{A} = 0{\cdot}539 \pm 0{\cdot}005. \tag{1.57}$$

The numerical value follows from the expression (1.56) after substitution of our previous evaluations of $C_\mathrm{A}^2/C_\mathrm{V}^2$, or $x_\mathrm{n}$.

Before going on to consider the expectations for the influence of the

Vector, singlet part of the radiation, we note that experimental evidence‡ for such an influence exists. The anisotropy coefficients have been measured to be

$$A_{\mathrm{n}} = -0{\cdot}11 \pm 0{\cdot}02, \qquad B_{\mathrm{n}} = +0{\cdot}88 \pm 0{\cdot}15. \tag{1.58}$$

These have the signs expected of the Pseudovector radiation by itself, but are far from the equal magnitudes expected of purely Pseudovector effects.

*The Vector–Pseudovector interference*

The singlet, allowed Vector radiation takes no angular momentum from the nucleus and is uncorrelated with the nuclear spin, so that, by itself, it yields no anisotropies. It can, however, influence the angular distributions by interfering with the triplet, allowed Pseudovector radiation. Whereas the pure Pseudovector contributions are proportional to $A_{\mathrm{A}} = -B_{\mathrm{A}} \sim C_{\mathrm{A}}^2$ in (1.56), the interference contributions should be proportional to $A_{\mathrm{AV}} \sim 2C_{\mathrm{A}}C_{\mathrm{V}}$ and $B_{\mathrm{AV}} \sim 2C_{\mathrm{A}}C_{\mathrm{V}}$. The factor 2 made explicit here is characteristic of any interference (basically, interference is represented by the cross-term in an intensity arising from the square of superposed amplitudes, e.g. $(a+b)^2 = a^2+2ab+b^2$).

In a transition yielding singlet ($S = 0$) radiation, the product proton's spin must be left in the same polarized orientation as was possessed by the initial neutron. The Vector radiation wave then produced can be coherent only with those Pseudovector transitions which also leave the nucleon's orientation unchanged, i.e. those with the zero projection, $M_S = 0$, of the total lepton spin. This is just the part of the Pseudovector radiation which does not contribute to the pure Pseudovector part of the anisotropies; we saw that $A_{\mathrm{A}} = -B_{\mathrm{A}} \sim \langle M_S \rangle$, and $M_S = 0$ naturally contributes nothing to this average. Only $M_S = +1$ actually contributes to $\langle M_S \rangle$ in the case of the polarized neutron, since $M_S = -1$ cannot be compensated by any orientation of the final proton spin so as to conserve the initial angular momentum component $I_z = +\frac{1}{2}$. The result $\langle M_S \rangle = +\frac{2}{3}$ obtained in the preceding section is to be interpreted§ as indicating that two-thirds of the Pseudovector transitions are devoted to producing the orientation $M_S = +1$ of the total lepton spin, and the remaining third has $M_S = 0$. Thus, it is just a Pseudovector fraction

‡ M. Burgy, V. Krohn, T. Novey, G. Ringo, and V. Telegdi, *Phys. Rev.* **110**, 1214 (1958).

§ Those familiar with vector-addition coefficients will recognize that we deal here with

$$\langle 1(M_S)\tfrac{1}{2}(\tfrac{1}{2}-M_S)|\tfrac{1}{2}(\tfrac{1}{2})\rangle^2 = \tfrac{2}{3}, \tfrac{1}{3}, 0 \quad \text{for } M_S = +1, 0, -1,$$

respectively. See footnote on p. 37.

$\frac{1}{3}(1-x_n)$ which interferes with the Vector fraction, $x_n$. Whereas the magnitudes of the pure Pseudovector effects were

$$B_A = -A_A = \tfrac{2}{3}(1-x_n),$$

the magnitudes of the interference supplementations of these quantities must be expected to be

$$|A_{AV}| = |B_{AV}| = 2[\tfrac{1}{3}(1-x_n)x_n]^{\frac{1}{2}} = 2|C_V C_A|/(C_V^2+3C_A^2). \quad (1.59)$$

By the word 'supplementations' here it is meant that the full anisotropy coefficients are $A_n = A_A \pm A_{AV}$ and $B_n = B_A \pm B_{AV}$, the sign to be used depending on whether the interference is actually 'constructive' or 'destructive'. The factor 2 is the one discussed in the preceding paragraph. The absolute value of the product $C_V C_A$ is inserted into the intrinsically positive expression because one of the coupling constants may happen to be defined so that it has a negative value. It was pointed out in § 1.7 that only the square $C_A^2/C_V^2$ is defined by the comparisons of the half-lives there.

We can now see that the signs of the interference effects, as determined by experimental observation, will define a fundamental property of the $\beta$-interaction—one being represented here by the relative signs of the coupling constants $C_V$, $C_A$. According to the measurements reported in (1.58),

$$\left.\begin{aligned} A_n &= A_A + A_{AV} = -0{\cdot}11 \pm 0{\cdot}02 \\ B_n &= B_A + B_{AV} = +0{\cdot}88 \pm 0{\cdot}15 \end{aligned}\right\}. \quad (1.60)$$

Thus, the interference effects suppress the pure Pseudovector anisotropy, $A_A = -0{\cdot}539 \pm 0{\cdot}005$, of the negatron and enhance $B_A = -A_A = +0{\cdot}539$ for the antineutrino. The interference contributions must be of the same sign and positive:

$$A_{AV} = B_{AV} = +2[\tfrac{1}{3}(1-x_n)x_n]^{\frac{1}{2}} \quad (1.61)$$

is the corresponding generalization of (1.59).

Once the experiments are used to determine the signs, (1.61) predicts that the interference effects should have the same magnitude for both the negatron and the antineutrino anisotropy coefficients. The predicted magnitude given by (1.61) is $A_{AV} = B_{AV} = 0{\cdot}46 \pm 0{\cdot}02$, and this yields for the full anisotropies: $A_n = -0{\cdot}54 + 0{\cdot}46 = -0{\cdot}08 \pm 0{\cdot}02$ and

$$B_n = +0{\cdot}54 + 0{\cdot}46 = +1{\cdot}00 \pm 0{\cdot}02.$$

These predictions agree with the actual measurements, (1.60), within their uncertainties.

*The screw-sense of the proton recoil*

We shall be concerned now with the physical implications of the experimental finding that the interference by the Vector radiation serves to suppress the negative correlation of the Pseudovector negatron wave with the nuclear axis, while it augments the antineutrino's anisotropy to almost a full positive correlation.

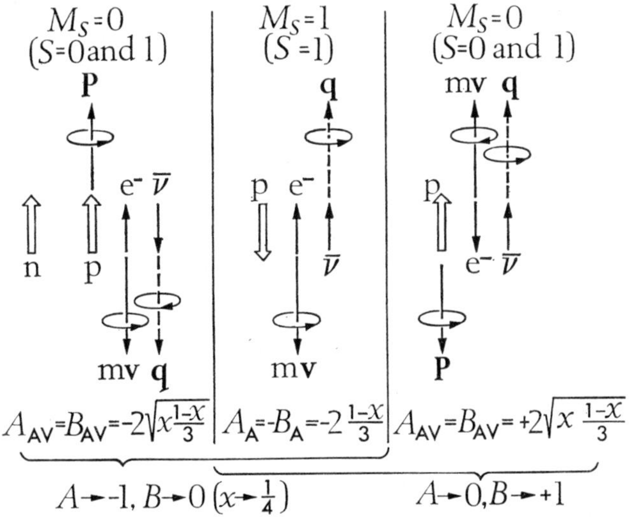


FIG. 1.17

The origin of this phenomenon in a singlet–triplet interference implies that this classification of the radiation is no longer a particularly appropriate one for dealing with the phenomenon; $S = 0$ and $S = 1$ are no longer 'good quantum numbers', describing independently acting states. It will be no less significant to deal with the individual negatron and antineutrino spin states, relative to the neutron spin as the quantization axis. The corresponding four states of the two leptons may be symbolized as $\uparrow\uparrow$, $\downarrow\downarrow$, $\uparrow\downarrow$, and $\downarrow\uparrow$, signifying orientations of each lepton, parallel or antiparallel to the neutron spin. The state $\uparrow\uparrow$ remains purely the $M_S = +1$ member of the triplet, responsible for the pure Pseudovector anisotropies, $A_A = -B_A$. The $M_S = -1$ state, $\downarrow\downarrow$, does not arise in polarized neutron decay, as seen before. The antiparallel leptons, $\uparrow\downarrow$ and $\downarrow\uparrow$, are parts of both the singlet and triplet $M_S = 0$ states; they are the only ones involved in the 'interference radiation', which leaves the nucleon spin orientation unchanged. Diagrams indicating the behaviour in all the three states radiated in the polarized neutron decay are shown in Fig. 1.17.

The middle diagram represents the state generated by the Pseudovector interaction, $\sim C_A^2 \sim (1-x_n)$, alone; it presents $\langle M_S \rangle = +\frac{2}{3}$ as the result of two-thirds of these decays being devoted to producing $M_S = +1$, rather than as a result of an equivalent 'precession' of the total lepton spin, as in Fig. 1.16. However presented, the important point to notice about the state is that it defines no particular direction for the proton recoil, since the mutually opposite lepton directions could conserve momentum by themselves.

The two $M_S = 0$ states, $(\mathrm{p}\uparrow \mathrm{e}\uparrow \bar{\nu}\downarrow)$ and $(\mathrm{p}\uparrow \mathrm{e}\downarrow \bar{\nu}\uparrow)$, which could be generated in the Vector–Pseudovector interference have the behaviours indicated on the left and right of Fig. 1.17. Because both have at least approximately co-directional lepton momenta, each requires a relatively definite proton recoil direction. Their recoil motion is right-handedly polarized in the $(\mathrm{p}\uparrow \mathrm{e}\uparrow \bar{\nu}\downarrow)$ state (on the left), and left-handedly in $(\mathrm{p}\uparrow \mathrm{e}\downarrow \bar{\nu}\uparrow)$. It is the latter state which enhances the positive correlation of the antineutrino's emission direction with the neutron spin $(\mathrm{n}\uparrow)$, as observed experimentally. Its superposition with the $M_S = 1$ state, $(\mathrm{p}\downarrow \mathrm{e}\uparrow \bar{\nu}\uparrow)$, also leads to the near-isotropy of the negatron emission, again as observed. The state with the right-handed proton recoil must be suppressed, and presumably it is its 'wrong-handedness' that is responsible for its suppression.

The conclusion is that the $\beta$-interaction is such that it preferentially produces left-handedly polarized protons. That it is principally the left-handed component states of the neutron that will participate in $\beta$-interactions can also be argued from the above findings. Since the emission of an antineutrino is equivalent to the absorption of a neutrino of opposite spin, the suppression of the state $(\mathrm{p}\uparrow \mathrm{e}\uparrow \bar{\nu}\downarrow)$ in favour of $(\mathrm{p}\uparrow \mathrm{e}\downarrow \bar{\nu}\uparrow)$ in $(\mathrm{n}\uparrow)$ decay signifies‡

$$\left.\begin{array}{ll} & \mathrm{n}\uparrow + \nu\uparrow \not\leftrightarrow \mathrm{p}\uparrow + \mathrm{e}\uparrow \\ \text{but} & \mathrm{n}\uparrow + \nu\downarrow \longleftrightarrow \mathrm{p}\uparrow + \mathrm{e}\downarrow \end{array}\right\}. \tag{1.62}$$

In the rest-frame of any one of the two-particle states here, the particles must have equal and opposite momenta. If the leptons must move left-handedly, then clearly the nucleons also move left-handedly in the unsuppressed states, whereas their motion would be right-handed in the suppressed states.

A hypothesis which these results indicate as a most promising one to make is that all fermions which participate in $\beta$-interactions do so only

‡ Because of the limited polarization ($|v|/c < 1$) of massive particles, the 'suppressed' state is not actually expected to vanish, but only to have a small intensity proportional to $(v_N/c)^2$, where $v_N$ is a nucleonic velocity.

through the 'left-handed components' of their states of motion. The precise implementation of such a hypothesis must await the introduction of more accurate mathematical modes of expression, later in this treatise.

*The coupling constants*

The conclusion reached in § 1.7, that the ratio of the Pseudovector-to-Vector couplings is given by $C_A^2/C_V^2 = 1\cdot40 \pm 0\cdot05$, relied not only on half-life measurements, but also on our understanding of the complex nucleus, $O^{14}$. It is clearly important to have an evaluation based on neutron data alone.

Independent measurements of $C_A^2/C_V^2$ are implicit in the observations on each of the three correlation coefficients $a_n$, $A_n$, and $B_n$ as (1.55), (1.56), (1.57), and (1.58) make clear. The $A_n$ measurement is easily shown to yield $x_n = 0\cdot177 \pm 0\cdot010$, which corresponds to

$$C_A^2/C_V^2 = 1\cdot55 \pm 0\cdot10. \tag{1.63}$$

The errors propagated from the $a_n$ and $B_n$ measurements are considerably larger.

Further, the measurement of

$$B_n + A_n \equiv 2B_{VA} \equiv 2A_{VA} \approx 0\cdot8 \pm 0\cdot2 \tag{1.64}$$

should, in principle, determine the relative sign of $C_A$ and $C_V$ as the relation (1.59) makes clear. However, further definition of what exactly is meant by $C_A$ and $C_V$ is necessary before a specific relative sign can be given a meaning. Our procedures for introducing $C_A$ and $C_V$, so far, have given meaning only to their absolute magnitudes. It may be mentioned at this point that the conventions adopted during the development of the formal theory are such that a *negative* ratio, $C_A/C_V$, stands for an interaction yielding a net left-handed polarization of the nucleons. We were able to conclude that the latter physical description is implied by the measurements, hence (1.59) can be written more specifically as

$$A_{AV} = B_{AV} = -2C_V C_A/(C_V^2 + 3C_A^2) > 0, \tag{1.65}$$

in terms of the stated convention.

## Conclusions

The object of this chapter has been to present the critical evidence which will serve as a guide to the more precise formulation of the nucleonic $\beta$-interaction in the succeeding chapters. Several hypotheses have been suggested by the evidence as useful ones to make; they can be stated only qualitatively, pending the introduction of an adequately precise formal language.

(*a*) The nuclear $\beta$-processes can be characterized by the lepton conservation relation, $n+\nu \leftrightarrow p+e^-$, and the transforms of it implicit in 'charge-conjugacy'.

(*b*) The reaction rates are essentially proportional to the densities at spatial points common to the four fermionic states participating.

(*c*) Only the 'left-handed' components of these states interact (with 'right-handed' components of antiparticle states implied).

(*d*) The interaction exhibits invariance to time-reversal, but shows invariance to reflections only when these are conjoined with 'charge-conjugation'.

Quantitative descriptions of all the critical observations on the unretarded, 'allowed' decays were obtained, without the necessity of introducing the formal theory. In these descriptions, the comparative half-lives, *ft*, and the 'Vector-emission fractions', $x$, serve as parameters,‡ together with the initial nuclear spins, $I$. The main results are comprisable in two expressions. The partial decay rates from sources of randomly oriented nuclei are given by

$$\frac{d\lambda}{dW\,d\Omega} = \frac{\ln 2}{4\pi ft}F\frac{q^2pW}{(mc)^5c^2}[1+\tfrac{1}{3}(4x-1)\hat{\mathbf{q}}\,.\,\mathbf{v}/c]. \tag{1.66}$$

From polarized nuclei, when no attempt to detect nuclear recoils is made (hence $\langle \mathbf{q} \rangle = 0$):

$$\frac{d\lambda}{dW\,d\Omega} = \frac{\ln 2}{4\pi ft}F\frac{q^2pW}{(mc)^5c^2}[1+A\hat{\mathbf{I}}\,.\,\mathbf{v}/c]. \tag{1.67}$$

The anisotropy coefficient in an allowed $I \rightarrow I'$ transition is

$$A = \mp\langle M_S\rangle(1-x)+\delta_{II'}\,.\,2y[xI/(I+1)]^{\frac{1}{2}} \quad (\text{for } e^{\mp}), \tag{1.68}$$

with $\langle M_S \rangle$ as tabulated in (1.37). The new symbol $y \equiv \pm(1-x)^{\frac{1}{2}}$ has been introduced to represent the Pseudovector (GT) radiation fraction, because its sign§ is actually an unknown parameter additional to $x$; a given special case may possibly have a sign opposite to the positive one (1.61) found for the neutron decay. The interference contribution as

‡ The formal theory similarly uses individual 'Fermi' and 'GT' nuclear matrix elements as parameters.

The descriptions here rest heavily on the empirical findings, like the electron polarization results, $\mathscr{P} = \pm v/c$. However, corresponding appeals to observations had to be made also in the development of the formal theory, as will be seen.

§ The sign referred to here has to do with the *a priori* unknown 'nuclear $\beta$-moments', as will be seen in Chapter V, and not with the sign of $C_A/C_V$, which has been adopted to be definitely negative. There is no sign change of the interference to be associated with going over from negatron to positron emissions, as in the pure Pseudovector term of (1.68). That can be seen, for example, from a comparison of Fig. 1.17 with a diagram obtained from it by making the replacements: $n \leftrightarrow p$, $e^- \rightarrow \nu$, $\bar{\nu} \rightarrow e^+$.

written here is easy to obtain from considerations paralleling those which led to the neutron decay result (1.61); it is only necessary to understand that $\langle M_S \rangle = 1/(I+1)$, in the general $I' = I$ case, because $M_S = 0$ in the fraction $I/(I+1)$ of the triplet emissions. There is also an anisotropy fraction, $B\hat{\mathbf{I}}.\hat{\mathbf{q}}$, in the angular distribution of neutrinos, with

$$B = \pm \langle M_S \rangle (1-x) + \delta_{II'} 2y[xI/(I+1)]^{\frac{1}{2}} \qquad (1.69)$$

for negatron and positron decays, respectively.

## II

## THE DESCRIPTION OF FERMIONS

THE $\beta$-processes consist of interactions among particles having half-units of intrinsic spin and frequently called fermions.‡ It is important here to be familiar with the general behaviour of such particles, and that is successfully described by Dirac's relativistic quantum theory. Pertinent portions of the theory will be recapitulated in this chapter, and, preliminary to that, also some useful bits of descriptive formalism from quantum mechanics in general. Long-known derivations will usually be avoided, since the object here is only to extend the application of the general disciplines to $\beta$-radio-activity. However, physical interpretations are important to applications and will be given particular attention, especially where customary treatments have been so formalistic as to obscure physical insight.

### 2.1. The formal description of angular momenta

The role of angular momenta looms large in the $\beta$-processes, and also in the general behaviour of fermions. We therefore begin with a summary of the quantum-mechanical description of angular momenta, in the forms which will prove useful in this treatise.

*A single angular momentum variable*

The prototype of angular momenta is the orbital momentum, $\mathbf{l} = \mathbf{r}\times\mathbf{p}$, of a single particle. From the basic quantum conditions, $x_i p_j - p_j x_i \equiv [x_i, p_j] = i\hbar\delta_{ij}$ (an expression of the Uncertainty Principle), there follows a non-commutation of any operators which may be used to represent the components of $\mathbf{l}$, e.g. $l_x l_y - l_y l_x \equiv (\mathbf{l}\times\mathbf{l})_z = i\hbar l_z$. Every type of angular momentum or spin, $\mathbf{j}$, has the basic commutation properties,

$$\mathbf{j}\times\mathbf{j} = i\hbar\mathbf{j}. \tag{2.1}$$

These properties permit the magnitude, $j^2 = j_x^2+j_y^2+j_z^2$, to commute with each component $j_x, j_y, j_z$, hence states of motion can exist in which $\mathbf{j}^2$ has a definite value, together with some one component, usually taken

‡ The name appropriate to particles related by a 'Universal Fermi Interaction'. Usually, the name signifies only a conformance to 'Fermi–Dirac Statistics'. The only known, fundamental particles which do conform have spin $\frac{1}{2}$.

to be $j_z$. The specific 'eigenvalues' which are permitted can be derived directly from (2.1), and have been summarized in the footnote on p. 19.

An 'eigenstate' in which $\mathbf{j}^2$ has the eigenvalue $j(j+1)\hbar^2$, and $j_z$ the eigenvalue $\mu\hbar$, will generally be symbolized by $\chi_{j\mu}$. Then, according to the meaning of 'eigenstate', operation by any operator representatives of $\mathbf{j}^2$ and $j_z$ should yield

$$\mathbf{j}^2\chi_{j\mu} = j(j+1)\hbar^2\chi_{j\mu} \quad \text{and} \quad j_z\chi_{j\mu} = \mu\hbar\chi_{j\mu}. \tag{2.2}$$

The orthonormality to be expected of the eigenstates may be symbolized by

$$\chi^\dagger_{j\mu}\chi_{j'\mu'} = \delta_{jj'}\delta_{\mu\mu'}, \tag{2.3}$$

where the dagger (†) indicates the hermitian conjugate.

In the special case of a single particle's orbital momentum, $\mathbf{j} \equiv \mathbf{l}$, the eigenstate may be given a more specific representation: $\chi_{lm} \to Y_{lm}(\theta, \phi)$. The latter is the well-known spherical harmonic function of the spatial angles, $\theta, \phi$, in which the particle density is distributed during the orbital motion. The phases adopted here are such that

$$Y_{lm} = \frac{(-)^{l+m}}{2^l l!}\left[\frac{(2l+1)(l-m)!}{4\pi(l+m)!}\right]^{\frac{1}{2}} \sin^m\theta \left[\frac{\partial}{\partial(\cos\theta)}\right]^{l+m} \sin^{2l}\theta e^{im\phi}. \tag{2.4}$$

The orthonormality property is expressed by

$$\chi^\dagger_{lm}\chi_{l'm'} \equiv \oint d\Omega\, Y^*_{lm} Y_{l'm'} = \delta_{ll'}\delta_{mm'}. \tag{2.5}$$

This is the representation in which the operator for $l_z$ takes the familiar form $-i\hbar\partial/\partial\phi$.

It is frequently useful to resolve the angular momentum into its 'spherical' components,

$$j_0 \equiv j_z \quad \text{and} \quad j_{\pm 1} = \mp 2^{-\frac{1}{2}}(j_x \pm ij_y), \tag{2.6}$$

instead of the cartesian ones $j_{x,y,z}$. Those are defined in such a way that they behave like

$$Y_{10} = (3/4\pi)^{\frac{1}{2}}z/r, \quad Y_{1,\pm 1} = \mp(3/8\pi)^{\frac{1}{2}}(x \pm iy)/r, \tag{2.7}$$

in changes of reference frame. Higher order 'spherical tensors', defined in similar analogy to $[4\pi/(2l+1)]^{\frac{1}{2}}Y_{lm}$, will be introduced where needed.

Operations by $j_{\pm 1}$, on an eigenstate of $\mathbf{j}^2$, $j_z$, yield

$$j_{\pm 1}\chi_{j\mu} = \mp[\tfrac{1}{2}(j \mp \mu)(j \pm \mu + 1)]^{\frac{1}{2}}\hbar\chi_{j\mu\pm 1}, \tag{2.8}$$

derivable from the fundamental commutators, (2.1). These operations raise or lower the projection of $\mathbf{j}$ on the quantization axis, $z$, and are consequently called 'ladder' operations. If $j_z$ has its maximum value already, $j_{+1}\chi_{jj} = 0$. Similarly, $j_{-1}\chi_{j,-j} = 0$.

*The composition of angular momenta*

A system may have different degrees of freedom with which separate, commuting angular momenta, $\mathbf{j}_1$ and $\mathbf{j}_2$, may be associated. The resultant, $\mathbf{J} = \mathbf{j}_1+\mathbf{j}_2$, of these angular momenta may then be considered. The commutators $\mathbf{J}\times\mathbf{J} = i\hbar\mathbf{J}$ follow from the corresponding commutators for $\mathbf{j}_1$ and $\mathbf{j}_2$, individually. Consequently, there exist eigenstates, $\chi_{JM}$, depending on both sets of degrees of freedom, so that operations by $\mathbf{j}_1$ and $\mathbf{j}_2$, as well as $\mathbf{J}$, have meaning. Now, $\mathbf{j}_1^2$ and $\mathbf{j}_2^2$ each commute with $\mathbf{J}^2 = \mathbf{j}_1^2+2\mathbf{j}_1\cdot\mathbf{j}_2+\mathbf{j}_2^2$, as is readily shown, so that states $\chi_{JM}(j_1,j_2)$ can exist in which $\mathbf{j}_1^2$ and $\mathbf{j}_2^2$, as well as $J^2$, $J_z$, have definite eigenvalues:

$$\left.\begin{aligned} \mathbf{J}^2\chi_{JM} = J(J+1)\hbar^2\chi_{JM}, \qquad J_z\chi_{JM} = M\hbar\chi_{JM} \\ \mathbf{j}_{1,2}^2\chi_{JM}(j_1,j_2) = j_{1,2}(j_{1,2}+1)\hbar^2\chi_{JM} \end{aligned}\right\}. \tag{2.9}$$

These simultaneous eigenstates of $\mathbf{J}^2$, $J_z$, $\mathbf{j}_1^2$, $\mathbf{j}_2^2$ exist only for the eigenvalues

$$J = |j_1-j_2|,\quad |j_1-j_2|+1,\quad \ldots,\quad j_1+j_2-1,\quad j_1+j_2. \tag{2.10}$$

The roles of $J$, $j_1$, $j_2$ may be interchanged, in this so-called 'triangle condition'. Projections of $\mathbf{j}_1$ and $\mathbf{j}_2$ cannot have definite values in these states, since $\mathbf{j}_1$ and $\mathbf{j}_2$ do not commute with $\mathbf{J}$.

As the relations (2.9) may suggest, each simultaneous eigenstate may be expressed as a superposition of products $\chi_{j_1\mu_1}\chi_{j_2\mu_2}$, the terms having the various possible individual projections $j_{1z} = \mu_1\hbar$, $j_{2z} = \mu_2\hbar$. Because $J_z = j_{1z}+j_{2z} = M\hbar$, it is necessary that $\mu_2 = M-\mu_1$ in each term. The superposition may be written

$$\chi_{JM}(j_1,j_2) = \sum_{\mu}\chi_{j_1\mu}\,\chi_{j_2,M-\mu}\langle j_1(\mu)\,j_2(M-\mu)|J(M)\rangle, \tag{2.11}$$

where the symbols $\langle j_1(\mu)\,j_2(M-\mu)|J(M)\rangle$ stand for numbers known as 'vector-addition', 'Wigner', or 'Clebsch–Gordan', coefficients.‡ Tables of them can be found in numerous places. They are defined only for $j_1$, $j_2$, $J$ values consistent with the triangle condition (2.10).

The vector-addition coefficients are defined in consistency with the appropriate orthonormalities of all the $\chi$'s. As a consequence,

$$\sum_{JM}\langle j_1(\mu_1)j_2(\mu_2)|J(M)\rangle\langle j_1(\mu_1')j_2(\mu_2')|J(M)\rangle = \delta_{\mu_1'\mu_1}\,\delta_{\mu_2'\mu_2}, \tag{2.12}$$

$$\sum_{\mu_1\mu_2}\langle j_1(\mu_1)j_2(\mu_2)|J(M)\rangle\langle j_1(\mu_1)j_2(\mu_2)|J'(M')\rangle = \delta_{J'J}\,\delta_{M'M}. \tag{2.13}$$

‡ Other notations for these, used in various published tables, are

$$(j_1\,j_2\,\mu M-\mu|\,j_1\,j_2\,JM),\quad C_{j_1j_2}(JM\,;\,\mu M-\mu),\quad \text{or}\quad C(j_1\,j_2\,J\,;\,\mu M-\mu).$$

Sometimes they are replaced by Wigner's '3-$j$ symbols':

$$\begin{pmatrix} j_1 & j_2 & J \\ \mu & M-\mu & -M \end{pmatrix} \equiv (-)^{j_2-j_1-M}(2J+1)^{-\frac{1}{2}}\langle j_1(\mu)j_2(M-\mu)|J(M)\rangle.$$

The first of these also holds without summation over $M$, the second with summation over only one of the indices $\mu_1$ or $\mu_2$, if only

$$M = M' = \mu_1+\mu_2 = \mu_1'+\mu_2'.$$

States related to each other as indicated symbolically by

$$\mathbf{j}_2+\mathbf{j}_1 = \mathbf{J}, \quad \mathbf{j}_1-\mathbf{J} = -\mathbf{j}_2, \quad \mathbf{J}-\mathbf{j}_2 = \mathbf{j}_1, \quad \text{etc.},$$

can differ at most in phase and/or normalizing factors, hence the properties:

$$\begin{aligned}
&\langle j_1(\mu)j_2(M-\mu)|J(M)\rangle \\
&\quad = \langle j_2(\mu-M)j_1(-\mu)|J(-M)\rangle \\
&\quad = (-)^{j_1+j_2-J}\langle j_2(M-\mu)j_1(\mu)|J(M)\rangle \\
&\quad = (-)^{j_1-\mu}(2J+1/2j_2+1)^{\frac{1}{2}}\langle j_1(\mu)J(-M)|j_2(\mu-M)\rangle \\
&\quad = (-)^{j_2+M-\mu}(2J+1/2j_1+1)^{\frac{1}{2}}\langle J(-M)j_2(M-\mu)|j_1(-\mu)\rangle. \qquad (2.14)
\end{aligned}$$

From the third of these, we can get

$$\langle j_1(\mu)j_1(-\mu)|0(0)\rangle = (-)^{j_1-\mu}(2j_1+1)^{-\frac{1}{2}}, \qquad (2.15)$$

by using the obvious relation:

$$\langle j_1(\mu)0(0)|J(M)\rangle = \delta_{Jj_1}\,\delta_{M\mu}. \qquad (2.16)$$

Additions of one unit of angular momentum will occur frequently enough‡ so that the table of the coefficients for that case is appended. The squares of the coefficients are listed to avoid square root signs; those numbers which are negative before squaring are designated with $(-)^2$.

TABLE 2.1

$\langle j(M-\mu)1(\mu)|J(M)\rangle^2$

| $J$ | $\mu$ | | |
|---|---|---|---|
| | $+1$ | $0$ | $-1$ |
| $j+1$ | $\dfrac{(j+M)(j+M+1)}{(2j+1)(2j+2)}$ | $\dfrac{(j-M+1)(j+M+1)}{(2j+1)(j+1)}$ | $\dfrac{(j-M)(j-M+1)}{(2j+1)(2j+2)}$ |
| $j$ | $(-)^2\,\dfrac{(j+M)(j-M+1)}{2j(j+1)}$ | $\dfrac{M^2}{j(j+1)}$ | $\dfrac{(j-M)(j+M+1)}{2j(j+1)}$ |
| $j-1$ | $\dfrac{(j-M)(j-M+1)}{2j(2j+1)}$ | $(-)^2\,\dfrac{(j-M)(j+M)}{j(2j+1)}$ | $\dfrac{(j+M+1)(j+M)}{2j(2j+1)}$ |

*The $j = l\pm\frac{1}{2}$ states*

States formed by adding a half-unit of spin, $\mathbf{s}$, to an orbital momentum, $\mathbf{l}$, will have particular importance. The resultant $\mathbf{j} = \mathbf{l}+\mathbf{s}$ can have

‡ See footnote, p. 37, for example.

either of two magnitudes $j = l \pm \frac{1}{2}$, in the eigenstates $\chi_{l\pm\frac{1}{2},\mu}(ls)$. The two groups, of $2l+2$ and $2l$ eigenstates, respectively, can be distinguished as independent (orthogonal) eigenstates of the additional dynamical variable:

$$\varkappa = -(1+2\mathbf{l}.\mathbf{s}/\hbar^2). \tag{2.17}$$

This variable has definite eigenvalues in the states $\chi_{j\mu}(ls)$, simultaneously with $j^2$, $j_z$, $l^2$, and $s^2$, since $\mathbf{l}.\mathbf{s}$ commutes with all these. Indeed, $\mathbf{l}.\mathbf{s} = \frac{1}{2}(j^2-l^2-s^2)$ has the eigenvalues $\frac{1}{2}\hbar^2[j(j+1)-l(l+1)-\frac{3}{4}]$, hence $\varkappa$ has the eigenvalue $\kappa = l$ when $j = l-\frac{1}{2}$ and $\kappa = -(l+1)$ when $j = l+\frac{1}{2}$.

It proves convenient to use, in place of $\chi_{j\mu}(ls)$ as defined by (2.11), the representation:

$$\chi_{\kappa\mu}(\theta,\phi) = \sum_{\rho=\pm\frac{1}{2}} \chi_\rho Y_{l\mu-\rho}\langle l(\mu-\rho)\tfrac{1}{2}(\rho)|j(\mu)\rangle \tag{2.18}$$

in which

$$\left.\begin{aligned} \kappa &= \pm1, \pm2, \pm3,\ldots \\ \mu &= \pm\tfrac{1}{2}, \pm\tfrac{3}{2},\ldots, \pm j \\ j &= |\kappa|-\tfrac{1}{2} \quad \text{and} \\ l &= j+\tfrac{1}{2} = \kappa \quad \text{for } \kappa > 0 \\ l &= j-\tfrac{1}{2} = -(\kappa+1) \quad \text{for } \kappa < 0 \end{aligned}\right\}. \tag{2.19}$$

The $\chi_{\pm\frac{1}{2}}$ are abbreviations for the very important spin eigenfunctions $\chi_{\frac{1}{2},\pm\frac{1}{2}}$. The eigenfunctions $\chi_{\kappa\mu}(\theta,\phi)$ may be appropriately called the 'spinor spherical harmonics'.

The vector addition coefficients which occur in (2.18) are such that

$$\chi_{\kappa\mu} = (2\kappa+1)^{-\frac{1}{2}}\{-\hat{\kappa}(\kappa-\mu+\tfrac{1}{2})^{\frac{1}{2}}\chi_{\frac{1}{2}}Y_{l\mu-\frac{1}{2}}+(\kappa+\mu+\tfrac{1}{2})^{\frac{1}{2}}\chi_{-\frac{1}{2}}Y_{l\mu+\frac{1}{2}}\}, \tag{2.20}$$

where $\hat{\kappa} \equiv \kappa/|\kappa|$ is the 'signature' of $\kappa$. The same coefficients are used in a great variety of ways, hence are given alternative forms in Table 2.2.

The orthonormality of these eigenstates,

$$\oint d\Omega\, \chi^\dagger_{\kappa\mu}\chi_{\kappa'\mu'} = \delta_{\kappa\kappa'}\delta_{\mu\mu'}, \tag{2.21}$$

is a special case of the orthonormality (2.3) for all the angular momentum eigenstates introduced here.

TABLE 2.2

$\langle l(\mu-\rho)\frac{1}{2}(\rho)|j(\mu)\rangle^2$

| | $\rho$ | |
|---|---|---|
| $j$ | $+\frac{1}{2}$ | $-\frac{1}{2}$ |
| $l+\frac{1}{2}$ | $\dfrac{l+\mu+\frac{1}{2}}{2l+1} = \dfrac{j+\mu}{2j}$ | $\dfrac{l-\mu+\frac{1}{2}}{2l+1} = \dfrac{j-\mu}{2j}$ |
| $l-\frac{1}{2}$ | $(-)^2\dfrac{l-\mu+\frac{1}{2}}{2l+1} = (-)^2\dfrac{j-\mu+1}{2(j+1)}$ | $\dfrac{l+\mu+\frac{1}{2}}{2l+1} = \dfrac{j+\mu+1}{2(j+1)}$ |

A special case of Table 2.2, evaluated for $l = \frac{1}{2}$, is useful in representing the singlet and triplet resultants, $\mathbf{S} = \mathbf{s}_1+\mathbf{s}_2$. According to (2.11), the singlet ($S = 0$) eigenfunction is the antisymmetric one:

$$\chi^s \equiv \chi_{00} = 2^{-\frac{1}{2}}(\chi_{\frac{1}{2}}\chi_{-\frac{1}{2}}-\chi_{-\frac{1}{2}}\chi_{\frac{1}{2}}). \tag{2.22}$$

The triplet ($S = 1$) of eigenstates are the symmetric ones:

$$\chi^t_M \equiv \chi_{1M} = \sum_\rho \chi_\rho \chi_{M-\rho}\langle \tfrac{1}{2}(M-\rho)\tfrac{1}{2}(\rho)|1(M)\rangle, \tag{2.23}$$

that is, $\chi^t_{\pm 1} = \chi_{\pm\frac{1}{2}}\chi_{\pm\frac{1}{2}}$ and $\chi^t_0 = 2^{-\frac{1}{2}}(\chi_{\frac{1}{2}}\chi_{-\frac{1}{2}}+\chi_{-\frac{1}{2}}\chi_{\frac{1}{2}})$.

Of course, the two spin eigenfunctions of each product refer to different spin degrees of freedom. The expressions fit the descriptions of the singlet and triplet states discussed more intuitively in § 1.10.

## 2.2. The description of spin-$\frac{1}{2}$ particles

The configuration of a spinless point-particle is, by definition, entirely determined when a vector, $\mathbf{r}$, specifying its spatial position is given, and its state of motion is adequately described by a scalar probability amplitude, $\psi(\mathbf{r})$. A spinning particle has further 'internal' degrees of freedom to be described, so that the state function must be generalized, to $\Psi(\mathbf{r},\mathbf{s})$ say. Circumstances can be assumed in which the external and internal variables 'move' independently, so that $\Psi(\mathbf{r},\mathbf{s})$ is a product of individual probability amplitudes, $\psi(\mathbf{r})\chi(\mathbf{s})$. In any other circumstances, an arbitrary state can be represented as a superposition of any complete set of independent motions: $\Psi(\mathbf{r},\mathbf{s}) = \sum_\mu \psi_\mu(\mathbf{r})\chi_\mu(\mathbf{s})$. By definition, the internal states of a spin-$\frac{1}{2}$ particle are restricted to just two, $\sim\chi_{\pm\frac{1}{2}}$, parallel and antiparallel to whatever quantization axis has been chosen as part of a reference frame. Then an arbitrary state of a fermion can be described by

$$\psi = \psi_{+\frac{1}{2}}(\mathbf{r})\chi_{\frac{1}{2}}+\psi_{-\frac{1}{2}}(\mathbf{r})\chi_{-\frac{1}{2}}. \tag{2.24}$$

In this state, $|\psi_{+\frac{1}{2}}(\mathbf{r})|^2/|\psi_{-\frac{1}{2}}(\mathbf{r})|^2$ gives the relative probability of 'up' and 'down' spin orientations, when the particle is at the position $\mathbf{r}$.

### *The Pauli spinor*

Obviously, what spatial amplitudes $\psi_{\pm\frac{1}{2}}(\mathbf{r})$ are needed to represent a given state depends on the reference system which has been chosen, since their interpretation is related to the $z$-axis of that system. They have in common with the components of any vector, say, the property of varying with changes of reference frame, even when describing an unchanging physical situation. Such two-component quantities, covariant with reference systems, are called 'half-vectors' or 'spinors'.

Once a reference frame has been chosen, the state is specified simply by giving the components $\psi_{\pm\frac{1}{2}}(\mathbf{r})$. It is convenient to display these in a 'column matrix',

$$\boldsymbol{\psi}(\mathbf{r}) = \begin{pmatrix} \psi_{+\frac{1}{2}}(\mathbf{r}) \\ \psi_{-\frac{1}{2}}(\mathbf{r}) \end{pmatrix}, \tag{2.25}$$

which will be called a 'Pauli spinor', here. The probability for finding the fermion in a spatial volume element $(d\mathbf{r})$, regardless of spin orientation, is given by the scalar

$$\boldsymbol{\psi}^\dagger\boldsymbol{\psi}(d\mathbf{r}) \equiv (|\psi_{+\frac{1}{2}}|^2+|\psi_{-\frac{1}{2}}|^2)(d\mathbf{r}) = \Big(\sum_\rho \psi_\rho^*\psi_\rho\Big)(d\mathbf{r}). \tag{2.26}$$

If $\boldsymbol{\psi}$ is normalized to represent one fermion in all space,

$$\oint (d\mathbf{r})\, \boldsymbol{\psi}^\dagger\boldsymbol{\psi} = \sum_\rho \oint (d\mathbf{r})\, \psi_\rho^*\psi_\rho = 1. \tag{2.27}$$

This indicates that dependence on the internal variables can be described by an 'index variable', $\rho$, with only two values, $\rho = \pm\frac{1}{2}$, and $\sum_\rho \oint (d\mathbf{r})...$ symbolizes the complete integration over all possible configurations of a single fermion.

By the rules of matrix multiplication, a column matrix is reduced to a scalar number when multiplied by a row matrix, thus:

$$(a_1, a_2)\begin{pmatrix} b_1 \\ b_2 \end{pmatrix} \equiv a_1 b_1 + a_2 b_2.$$

The row $(a_1, a_2)$ is regarded as a column which has been 'transposed'. If $\mathbf{a}$ is a column matrix, $\tilde{\mathbf{a}}$ is the symbol for its 'transpose':

$$a \equiv \begin{pmatrix} a_1 \\ a_2 \end{pmatrix}, \qquad \tilde{a} \equiv (a_1, a_2).$$

Thus, we may represent the scalar product of two spinors, like $\boldsymbol{\psi}^\dagger\boldsymbol{\psi}$ above, as a matrix product with

$$\boldsymbol{\psi}^\dagger \equiv \tilde{\boldsymbol{\psi}}^* = (\psi_{+\frac{1}{2}}^*, \psi_{-\frac{1}{2}}^*), \tag{2.28}$$

known as the hermitian conjugate of the spinor $\boldsymbol{\psi}$.

The spinor matrix (2.25) may be resolved as

$$\boldsymbol{\psi}(\mathbf{r}) = \psi_{+\frac{1}{2}}(\mathbf{r})\begin{pmatrix} 1 \\ 0 \end{pmatrix} + \psi_{-\frac{1}{2}}(\mathbf{r})\begin{pmatrix} 0 \\ 1 \end{pmatrix}, \tag{2.29}$$

and comparison with (2.24) yields the matrix representations

$$\boldsymbol{\chi}_{\frac{1}{2}} = \begin{pmatrix} 1 \\ 0 \end{pmatrix} \quad \text{and} \quad \boldsymbol{\chi}_{-\frac{1}{2}} = \begin{pmatrix} 0 \\ 1 \end{pmatrix} \tag{2.30}$$

for the 'eigenspinors'. These have the proper orthonormality properties,

$$\boldsymbol{\chi}_\rho^\dagger \boldsymbol{\chi}_{\rho'} = \delta_{\rho\rho'} \tag{2.31}$$

as in (2.3).

The composite states $\boldsymbol{\chi}_{\kappa\mu}$ of (2.20) can now be given the matrix representations:

$\kappa > 0 \quad (l = \kappa = j+\frac{1}{2})$:

$$\boldsymbol{\chi}_{\kappa\mu} = (2l+1)^{-\frac{1}{2}}\begin{pmatrix} -(l-\mu+\frac{1}{2})^{\frac{1}{2}}Y_{l\mu-\frac{1}{2}} \\ (l+\mu+\frac{1}{2})^{\frac{1}{2}}Y_{l\mu+\frac{1}{2}} \end{pmatrix}, \tag{2.32 a}$$

$\kappa < 0 \quad (l' = -\kappa-1 = j-\frac{1}{2})$:

$$\boldsymbol{\chi}_{\kappa\mu} = (2l'+1)^{-\frac{1}{2}}\begin{pmatrix} (l'+\mu+\frac{1}{2})^{\frac{1}{2}}Y_{l'\mu-\frac{1}{2}} \\ (l'-\mu+\frac{1}{2})^{\frac{1}{2}}Y_{l'\mu+\frac{1}{2}} \end{pmatrix}. \tag{2.32 b}$$

For a given $j$, the two kinds of states have orbital momenta differing by one unit: $l-l' = 1$.

*The Pauli matrices*

Since $\boldsymbol{\chi}_{\pm\frac{1}{2}}$ are eigenstates of the spin projection operator,

$$s_z\boldsymbol{\chi}_{\pm\frac{1}{2}} = \pm\tfrac{1}{2}\hbar\boldsymbol{\chi}_{\pm\frac{1}{2}} \tag{2.33}$$

are the suitable specializations of the eigenvalue equations (2.2). A fermion has the spin magnitude given by $s^2 = \frac{1}{2}(\frac{1}{2}+1)\hbar^2 = \frac{3}{4}\hbar^2$ whatever its state, by the definition of 'intrinsic spin', hence any state (2.24) is an eigenstate of $s^2$, and operation by $s^2$ is always equivalent to multiplication by the number $\frac{3}{4}\hbar^2$.

It is customary to measure the spin in units of $\frac{1}{2}\hbar$ by replacing $\mathbf{s}$ with $\boldsymbol{\sigma} = \mathbf{s}/(\frac{1}{2}\hbar)$. Then

$$\sigma^2 = \sigma_x^2+\sigma_y^2+\sigma_z^2 = 3 \quad \text{and} \quad \sigma_z\boldsymbol{\chi}_{\pm\frac{1}{2}} = \pm\boldsymbol{\chi}_{\pm\frac{1}{2}}. \tag{2.34}$$

Notice that operating by $\sigma_z$ twice, i.e. $\sigma_z^2$, is always equivalent to multiplication by $+1$, even in an arbitrary state (2.24). Since $\sigma_z^2 \equiv +1$ is true whatever the state, it must also be true that $\sigma_x^2 \equiv 1$ and $\sigma_y^2 \equiv 1$, since this must be independent of what axis is chosen as the quantization axis. The statements

$$\sigma_i^2 = 1 \quad \text{and} \quad \boldsymbol{\sigma}\times\boldsymbol{\sigma} = 2i\boldsymbol{\sigma}, \tag{2.35}$$

the latter of which follows from the commutation relations $\mathbf{s}\times\mathbf{s} = i\hbar\mathbf{s}$ characteristic of any angular momentum, provide an analytic definition of $\sigma_{x,y,z}$. An equivalent set of statements is

$$\tfrac{1}{2}(\sigma_i\,\sigma_j+\sigma_j\,\sigma_i) = \delta_{ij}, \qquad \sigma_x\,\sigma_y\,\sigma_z = i, \tag{2.36}$$

the latter of which merely expresses the right-handedness of the $x, y, z$-frame. Both statements (2.36) are readily proved from (2.35), and vice versa. The first of (2.36) shows that unlike components *anticommute*:

$$\sigma_j\,\sigma_i = -\sigma_i\,\sigma_j \quad \text{if } i \neq j. \tag{2.37}$$

The last of (2.36) is more frequently written

$$\sigma_{(i}\,\sigma_j = i\sigma_{k)} \tag{2.38}$$

in which the parenthesis around the indices $(i\,j\,k)$ signify that they must be taken in cyclic order, $(xyz)$ or $(yzx)$ or $(zxy)$, if the relative sign of the two sides is to be positive.

When the spinors are given matrix representations as in (2.25) and (2.30), then linear operations, as by $\sigma_z$ in (2.34), can be represented as matrix products. In general, a linear operation on a spinor generates a new spinor $\boldsymbol{\psi}'$, with components $\psi'_\rho = \sum_\tau \mathcal{O}_{\rho\tau}\psi_\tau$, where the $\mathcal{O}_{\rho\tau}$ are a set of coefficients representing the effect of the operation. The four coefficients form a square $2\times 2$ matrix, $\mathcal{O}$, and the operation can be represented as the matrix product

$$\boldsymbol{\psi}' = \mathcal{O}\boldsymbol{\psi} \equiv \begin{pmatrix} \mathcal{O}_{\frac{1}{2}\frac{1}{2}} & \mathcal{O}_{\frac{1}{2}-\frac{1}{2}} \\ \mathcal{O}_{-\frac{1}{2}\frac{1}{2}} & \mathcal{O}_{-\frac{1}{2}-\frac{1}{2}} \end{pmatrix}\begin{pmatrix} \psi_{\frac{1}{2}} \\ \psi_{-\frac{1}{2}} \end{pmatrix}$$
$$= \begin{pmatrix} \psi'_{\frac{1}{2}} = \mathcal{O}_{\frac{1}{2}\frac{1}{2}}\,\psi_{\frac{1}{2}} + \mathcal{O}_{\frac{1}{2}-\frac{1}{2}}\,\psi_{-\frac{1}{2}} \\ \psi'_{-\frac{1}{2}} = \mathcal{O}_{-\frac{1}{2}\frac{1}{2}}\,\psi_{\frac{1}{2}} + \mathcal{O}_{-\frac{1}{2}-\frac{1}{2}}\,\psi_{-\frac{1}{2}} \end{pmatrix}. \tag{2.39}$$

A general requirement must be imposed upon any matrix which is to represent a dynamical variable like $\sigma_z$: it must be 'hermitian', i.e. $\mathcal{O}^\dagger \equiv \tilde{\mathcal{O}}^* = \mathcal{O}$ or $\mathcal{O}^*_{\rho\tau} = \mathcal{O}_{\tau\rho}$, in order that the eigenvalues of the variable turn out real.

Clearly,

$$\boldsymbol{\chi}^\dagger_\rho\,\mathcal{O}\boldsymbol{\chi}_\tau = \mathcal{O}_{\rho\tau} \tag{2.40}$$

follows from (2.30), hence the matrix elements of any operator (on a given basis of eigenstates) can be found from the results of its operations on the eigenstates. We already know these results for the operator $\sigma_z$ in (2.34), and they yield

$$\sigma_z = \begin{pmatrix} 1 & 0 \\ 0 & -1 \end{pmatrix}. \tag{2.41}$$

As is always so for the matrix representation of an operator expressed on the basis of its own eigenstates, the matrix is diagonal and its diagonal elements are the possible eigenvalues.

The matrix elements of $\sigma_x$ and $\sigma_y$ follow in a similar way from the ladder operations (2.8):

if

$$\left.\begin{aligned} \sigma_\pm\boldsymbol{\chi}_{\pm\frac{1}{2}} = 0 \quad \text{and} \quad \sigma_\pm\boldsymbol{\chi}_{\mp\frac{1}{2}} = \boldsymbol{\chi}_{\pm\frac{1}{2}} \\ \sigma_\pm \equiv \tfrac{1}{2}(\sigma_x \pm i\sigma_y) \end{aligned}\right\} \tag{2.42}$$

(notice $\sigma_\pm \neq \sigma_{\pm 1} = \mp 2^{\frac{1}{2}}\sigma_\pm$). We first get the matrices

$$\sigma_+ = \begin{pmatrix} 0 & 1 \\ 0 & 0 \end{pmatrix} \quad \text{and} \quad \sigma_- = \begin{pmatrix} 0 & 0 \\ 1 & 0 \end{pmatrix} \tag{2.43}$$

and then

$$\sigma_x = \sigma_+ + \sigma_- = \begin{pmatrix} 0 & 1 \\ 1 & 0 \end{pmatrix} \quad \text{and} \quad \sigma_y = -i(\sigma_+ - \sigma_-) = \begin{pmatrix} 0 & -i \\ i & 0 \end{pmatrix}. \tag{2.44}$$

It is readily checked that these matrix representations fulfil all the requirements (2.35)–(2.38), when the rules of matrix multiplication are followed $\left[(\mathcal{O}Q)_{\mu\nu} = \sum_\rho \mathcal{O}_{\mu\rho} Q_{\rho\nu}\right]$.

The Pauli matrices $\sigma_{x,y,z}$ of (2.41) and (2.44), together with the unit matrix

$$\mathbf{1} = \begin{pmatrix} 1 & 0 \\ 0 & 1 \end{pmatrix}, \tag{2.45}$$

form a complete algebra in the sense that an arbitrary $2\times 2$ matrix can be written as a linear combination of these matrices:

$$\begin{pmatrix} f_{11} & f_{12} \\ f_{21} & f_{22} \end{pmatrix} = \tfrac{1}{2}(f_{11}+f_{22})\mathbf{1} + \tfrac{1}{2}(f_{11}-f_{22})\sigma_z + \tfrac{1}{2}(f_{12}+f_{21})\sigma_x + \tfrac{1}{2}i(f_{12}-f_{21})\sigma_y. \tag{2.46}$$

Because $\sigma_i^2 = 1$ and $\sigma_{(i}\sigma_j = i\sigma_{k)}$, an arbitrary function of the $\sigma$'s can always be reduced to a linear combination of the $\sigma$'s.

## 2.3. Relativistic description

According to Dirac's theory, the 'internal' behaviour of spin-$\frac{1}{2}$ particles at high (relativistic) velocities cannot be adequately described by just the two component states of a Pauli spinor. Instead, four possible internal states must be provided for, and, consequently, four-component 'bi-spinors', or 'Dirac spinors' are introduced.

One‡ of the ways in which the possibilities for the internal motions may be classified (i.e. the spinor resolved into components) is suggested by the 'zitterbewegung' phenomenon discussed in § 1.8. We may form a basis of eigenstates which correspond not only to the two possibilities for the spin projection on a given direction, as do the Pauli spinor components, but also to the two possible eigenvalues of the instantaneous velocity, $\pm c$, along that direction. Four eigenstates $u_{\pm\frac{1}{2}}(\pm c)$ then

‡ There is an infinite variety of ways in which any state may be analysed into component states. That is also true for the two-component spinors. The representations are related to each other by 'equivalence transformations', like $\psi'_\rho = \sum_\tau U_{\rho\tau}\psi_\tau$, where the $\psi'_\rho$ and $\psi_\tau$ stand for alternative sets of components. The matrix $U$ must be 'unitary', i.e. $U^{-1} = U^\dagger$, if probability interpretations like (2.26) are to be preserved. For example, $U$ may be so chosen that $|\psi'_{+\frac{1}{2}}/\psi'_{-\frac{1}{2}}|^2$ is the relative probability of spin orientations parallel and antiparallel to a new quantization axis, $z'$, while $\psi_{\pm\frac{1}{2}}$ refer to the initial one, $z$. In the sequel, we shall be concerned with $4\times 4$ transformation matrices $U$, and not merely with the $2\times 2$ matrices exemplified here.

replace the $\chi_{\pm\frac{1}{2}}$ of the Pauli spinor (2.24). That eigenvalues associated with motion in a given direction can be known simultaneously with the spin motion about that direction (i.e. the motions representable by commuting operators) should not be surprising in view of the general commutativity of variables associated with orthogonal degrees of freedom.

It is more surprising that velocity eigenstates should be associated with the internal variables in a system of representation in which the momentum operator, $\mathbf{p} = -i\hbar\nabla$, is still to be associated with the external variable, $\mathbf{r}$, as in non-relativistic descriptions. This situation arises because the velocity measurement hypothetically searches out even the 'intrinsic' motions of the particle, such as are associated with its spin, and because the result hypothetically has the magnitude $c$. Now, according to relativistic principles, a velocity of magnitude $c$ retains that same magnitude relative to any reference frame, whether it be a laboratory frame, or a 'rest-frame' of the particle (the disturbance by the measurement generates the velocity relative to any initial rest-frame). Any distinction between an 'internal' and 'external' velocity is lost. Further, the restrictions of the projection on a given direction to the two eigenvalues, $\pm c$, makes most convenient a formulation similar to that of the spin, which also has its projection restricted to being parallel or antiparallel to a given direction.

The 'zitterbewegung' velocities, $\pm c$, even if treated as 'intrinsic', cannot be transformed to any lesser magnitudes when referred to a laboratory frame. Consequently, the finding of a finite momentum, $\mathbf{p} = (W/c^2)\mathbf{v}$, must exclude knowledge of whether the intrinsic velocity is $+c$ or $-c$, and the resultant state must be a superposition of the two velocity states in the ratio $[(1+v/c)/(1-v/c)]^{\frac{1}{2}}$, according to (1.29). The latter ratio approaches unity for non-relativistic velocities, $v \ll c$, and this accounts for the fact that there was no need to distinguish the two 'zitterbewegung' states in the non-relativistic descriptions.

### *Dirac spinors*

The analysis of an arbitrary one-particle state is now generalized from the two-component description (2.24) to the four-component one:

$$\psi = \psi_1(\mathbf{r})u_{+\frac{1}{2}}(+c)+\psi_2\, u_{-\frac{1}{2}}(+c)+\psi_3\, u_{+\frac{1}{2}}(-c)+\psi_4\, u_{-\frac{1}{2}}(-c). \quad (2.47)$$

A special choice of representation is made here when the indices 1, 2 are assigned to the probability amplitudes for the 'forward' velocity, $+c$, while $\psi_3$, $\psi_4$ are defined as amplitudes for the 'retrograde' velocity, $-c$.

This is in addition to the specialization‡ involved in associating each of the four amplitudes with definite signs of the intrinsic velocity and of the spin projection on it. Other choices of components correspond to other 'frames of representation' in the space of 'state vectors'.

On the basis of the eigenstates put into evidence in (2.47), the column matrix representation is:

$$\psi(\mathbf{r}) = \begin{pmatrix} \psi_1(\mathbf{r}) \\ \psi_2(\mathbf{r}) \\ \psi_3(\mathbf{r}) \\ \psi_4(\mathbf{r}) \end{pmatrix} \equiv \begin{pmatrix} \boldsymbol{\varphi} = \psi_1 \boldsymbol{\chi}_{\frac{1}{2}} + \psi_2 \boldsymbol{\chi}_{-\frac{1}{2}} \\ \boldsymbol{\theta} = \psi_3 \boldsymbol{\chi}_{\frac{1}{2}} + \psi_4 \boldsymbol{\chi}_{-\frac{1}{2}} \end{pmatrix}, \tag{2.48}$$

where $\boldsymbol{\varphi}$ and $\boldsymbol{\theta}$ are 2-dimensional Pauli spinors, describing forward and retrograde motions, respectively. The resolution of 4-dimensional matrices into pairs of 2-dimensional 'sub-matrices', as in the last form, proves convenient.

The eigenspinor generalizations of $\boldsymbol{\chi}_{\pm\frac{1}{2}}$, in (2.30), are

$$\begin{aligned} u_{\frac{1}{2}}(+c) &= \begin{pmatrix} \boldsymbol{\chi}_{\frac{1}{2}} \\ 0 \end{pmatrix} \equiv \begin{pmatrix} 1 \\ 0 \\ 0 \\ 0 \end{pmatrix}, & u_{-\frac{1}{2}}(+c) &= \begin{pmatrix} 1 \\ 0 \end{pmatrix} \boldsymbol{\chi}_{-\frac{1}{2}} \equiv \begin{pmatrix} 0 \\ 1 \\ 0 \\ 0 \end{pmatrix}, \\ u_{+\frac{1}{2}}(-c) &= \begin{pmatrix} 0 \\ 1 \end{pmatrix} \boldsymbol{\chi}_{\frac{1}{2}} \equiv \begin{pmatrix} 0 \\ 0 \\ 1 \\ 0 \end{pmatrix}, & u_{-\frac{1}{2}}(-c) &= \begin{pmatrix} 0 \\ 1 \end{pmatrix} \boldsymbol{\chi}_{-\frac{1}{2}} \equiv \begin{pmatrix} 0 \\ 0 \\ 0 \\ 1 \end{pmatrix}. \end{aligned} \tag{2.49}$$

The writing of a 4-dimensional column as a so-called 'direct product' of two 2-dimensional columns, as in the last three examples in (2.49), corresponds to a factorization into states of independent motion (longitudinal and transverse). In a similar way, the arbitrary Dirac spinor (2.48) may be written

$$\psi(\mathbf{r}) = \begin{pmatrix} 1 \\ 0 \end{pmatrix} \boldsymbol{\varphi}(\mathbf{r}) + \begin{pmatrix} 0 \\ 1 \end{pmatrix} \boldsymbol{\theta}(\mathbf{r}), \tag{2.50}$$

‡ A different special choice was originally made by Dirac. In his representation, $\psi_{1,2,3,4}$ are so defined that (2.47) may be written

$$\Psi' = 2^{-\frac{1}{2}}[(\psi_1+\psi_3)u_{+\frac{1}{2}}(+c)+(\psi_2-\psi_4)u_{-\frac{1}{2}}(+c)+(\psi_1-\psi_3)u_{+\frac{1}{2}}(-c)+(\psi_2+\psi_4)u_{-\frac{1}{2}}(-c)].$$

This representation is related to (2.47) by an equivalence transformation of the type mentioned in the footnote on p. 65, with

$$U = 2^{-\frac{1}{2}} \begin{pmatrix} 1 & \sigma_z \\ 1 & -\sigma_z \end{pmatrix},$$

in a notation defined in the next pages.

where $$\boldsymbol{\varphi} = \begin{pmatrix} \psi_1 \\ \psi_2 \end{pmatrix} \quad \text{and} \quad \boldsymbol{\theta} = \begin{pmatrix} \psi_3 \\ \psi_4 \end{pmatrix} \tag{2.51}$$

are the Pauli spinors introduced in (2.48).

*Dirac matrices*

The 4-dimensional matrix of the operator, $\sigma_z$, for the spin projection on the quantization axis, can now be found in the same way as in the 2-dimensional case (2.41). We simply multiply the row matrices $u^{\dagger}_{\pm\frac{1}{2}}(\pm c)$ into the eigenvalue equations

$$\sigma_z u_{+\frac{1}{2}}(\pm c) = +u_{+\frac{1}{2}}(\pm c), \quad \sigma_z u_{-\frac{1}{2}}(\pm c) = -u_{-\frac{1}{2}}(\pm c), \tag{2.52}$$

with the result

$$\sigma_z = \begin{pmatrix} 1 & 0 & 0 & 0 \\ 0 & -1 & 0 & 0 \\ 0 & 0 & 1 & 0 \\ 0 & 0 & 0 & -1 \end{pmatrix} \equiv \begin{pmatrix} \sigma_z & 0 \\ 0 & \sigma_z \end{pmatrix}, \tag{2.53}$$

where the last form contains $2 \times 2$ Pauli matrices, and furnishes a convenient abbreviation of the $4 \times 4$ display. No difficulty should arise from using the same symbol, $\sigma_z$, for both the 2- and 4-dimensional matrices.

The operator for intrinsic velocity is conventionally denoted by $c\boldsymbol{\alpha}$. (Early works, following Dirac himself, use $-c\boldsymbol{\alpha}$ instead.) The eigenstates (2.49) have the eigenvalues $\pm c$ for the intrinsic velocity component, $c\alpha_z$, along the axis of quantization, hence

$$\alpha_z = \begin{pmatrix} 1 & 0 & 0 & 0 \\ 0 & 1 & 0 & 0 \\ 0 & 0 & -1 & 0 \\ 0 & 0 & 0 & -1 \end{pmatrix} \equiv \begin{pmatrix} \mathbf{1} & 0 \\ 0 & -\mathbf{1} \end{pmatrix}. \tag{2.54}$$

The last form contains the $2 \times 2$ unit and null matrices.

Our four basic eigenspinors (2.49) can be classified into pairs in three ways. In (2.52), two pairs are distinguished according to spin projection, as eigenstates of $\sigma_z$. The second way, according to velocity projection, led to the matrix for $\alpha_z$. The remaining classification separates the states into an 'intrinsically' left-handed pair and a right-handed pair. We may define‡ a 'chirality operator' in such a way that it has the eigenvalue $+1$ in left-handed states, and $-1$ in right-handed ones. We adopt the symbol $\gamma_5$ for this operator, in order to conform to conventions which grew up during the development of the Dirac theory:

$$\gamma_5 u_{\mp\frac{1}{2}}(\pm c) = +u_{\mp\frac{1}{2}}(\pm c); \qquad \gamma_5 u_{\pm\frac{1}{2}}(\pm c) = -u_{\pm\frac{1}{2}}(\pm c). \tag{2.55}$$

‡ An elegant synonym for 'handedness' apparently coined by Eddington, and introduced into contexts like the present one by Watanabe.

Projections on each of $u^{\dagger}_{\pm\frac{1}{2}}(\pm c)$, in turn, yield the matrix

$$\gamma_5 = \begin{pmatrix} -1 & 0 & 0 & 0 \\ 0 & 1 & 0 & 0 \\ 0 & 0 & 1 & 0 \\ 0 & 0 & 0 & -1 \end{pmatrix} \equiv \begin{pmatrix} -\sigma_z & 0 \\ 0 & \sigma_z \end{pmatrix} = -\sigma_z \alpha_z. \tag{2.56}$$

The last equality follows readily from forming the matrix product indicated.

*Dirac algebra*

Just as there are four 'independent' 2-dimensional matrices, in the sense demonstrated in (2.46), so there are just sixteen independent 4-dimensional matrices. The basic sixteen can be chosen in various ways, so that any other is a linear combination of the chosen ones; we adopt ones which are conveniently resolvable into 2-dimensional matrices. We have first the unit matrix, to be denoted $\rho_0$, and having the elements $(\rho_0)_{\mu\nu} = \delta_{\mu\nu}$. We introduce next

$$\rho_1 = \begin{pmatrix} 0 & \mathbf{1} \\ \mathbf{1} & 0 \end{pmatrix}, \qquad \rho_2 = \begin{pmatrix} 0 & -i.\mathbf{1} \\ i.\mathbf{1} & 0 \end{pmatrix}, \qquad \rho_3 = \begin{pmatrix} \mathbf{1} & 0 \\ 0 & -\mathbf{1} \end{pmatrix}, \tag{2.57}$$

constructed on the plan of the Pauli $\sigma$'s. As a consequence, these 4-dimensional matrices have the same properties (2.36) as the $\sigma$'s:

$$\tfrac{1}{2}(\rho_i \rho_j + \rho_j \rho_i) = \delta_{ij} \quad \text{and} \quad \rho_{(i}\rho_j = i\rho_{k)}. \tag{2.58}$$

We introduce three more constructed like $\sigma_z$ of (2.53):

$$\mathbf{\Sigma} = \begin{pmatrix} \boldsymbol{\sigma} & 0 \\ 0 & \boldsymbol{\sigma} \end{pmatrix}; \tag{2.59}$$

the three components will be denoted by $\Sigma_{1,2,3}$ to emphasize their abstract character. After all, we may choose $\sigma_x = \Sigma_3$, rather than $\sigma_z = \Sigma_3$, when we wish to adopt the $x$- rather than $z$-axis as the axis of quantization. The $\Sigma$'s have the same properties (2.36) as the 2-dimensional $\sigma$'s. We round out the basic sixteen by adding the nine matrices:

$$\rho_1 \mathbf{\Sigma}, \quad \rho_2 \mathbf{\Sigma}, \quad \text{and} \quad \rho_3 \mathbf{\Sigma}. \tag{2.60}$$

All these matrices form a basis for representing any arbitrary matrix $f$ as a linear combination,

$$f = \sum_{i=0}^{3} (f_i \rho_i) + \sum_{i=0}^{3} \sum_{j=1}^{3} (f_{ij} \rho_i \Sigma_j), \tag{2.61}$$

with arbitrary coefficients $f_i, f_{ij}$. This is the four-dimensional generalization of (2.46).

The matrices $\rho_0$, $\boldsymbol{\rho}$ ($\rho_{1,2,3}$) and $\boldsymbol{\Sigma}$ have the advantage as a basis that each is both hermitian and unitary (and therefore the squares are unity):

$$\boldsymbol{\rho}^\dagger = \boldsymbol{\rho} = \boldsymbol{\rho}^{-1} \quad \text{and} \quad \boldsymbol{\Sigma}^\dagger = \boldsymbol{\Sigma} = \boldsymbol{\Sigma}^{-1}, \tag{2.62}$$

where $(\rho^\dagger)_{\mu\nu} = \rho^*_{\nu\mu}$ and $\rho_i^{-1}\rho_i = \rho_0$. The commutation properties following from (2.36) and (2.58) are simple to handle by noticing that all the $\rho$'s commute with all the $\Sigma$'s:

$$[\rho_i, \Sigma_j] \equiv \rho_i \Sigma_j - \Sigma_j \rho_i = 0. \tag{2.63}$$

A final, very important property possessed by all the matrices $\boldsymbol{\rho}$, $\boldsymbol{\Sigma}$, and $\rho_i\, \Sigma_j$ is that each has a vanishing 'trace', i.e. the sum of the diagonal elements is zero. Only the unit matrix has a non-zero trace:

$$\operatorname{tr} \rho_0 \equiv \Sigma_\mu (\rho_0)_{\mu\mu} = 4.$$

It is of critical interest for the Dirac formalism that sets of as many as five of the sixteen matrices may be chosen so that they mutually anticommute, e.g.

$$\rho_1 \boldsymbol{\Sigma}, \quad \rho_2, \quad \rho_3. \tag{2.64}$$

There are two other such sets of five, formed by interchanging the $\rho$'s.

This subsection has been concerned merely with outlining the algebra available for describing the internal mechanics of a Dirac particle. The preceding subsection presented a special choice of matrix representatives for actual dynamical variables:

$$\sigma_z = \Sigma_3, \quad \alpha_z = \rho_3, \quad \text{and} \quad \gamma_5 = -\rho_3\, \Sigma_3. \tag{2.65}$$

Aside from the unit matrix, these are the only diagonal matrices of the sixteen. Diagonal matrices commute with each other and can be used to represent only commuting observables, in a given system of representation. That $\sigma_z$, $\alpha_z$, and $\gamma_5$ commute was presumed when the basis (2.47) was constructed.

Dirac's original choice of representation differs from (2.65), being

$$\boldsymbol{\sigma} = \boldsymbol{\Sigma}, \quad \boldsymbol{\alpha} = \rho_1 \boldsymbol{\Sigma}, \quad \gamma_5 = -\sigma_i\, \alpha_i = -\rho_1. \tag{2.66}$$

He chose to diagonalize another dynamical variable, denoted $\beta$ ($= \rho_3$), in place of $\alpha_z$. The physical significance of $\beta$ is not briefly explainable; it will be introduced in the next section.

## 2.4. The Dirac equation

The preceding section was primarily concerned with means for describing internal motions of a Dirac particle. To be considered next is the behaviour of the external variables, like the position $\mathbf{r}$ and its conjugate momentum $\mathbf{p}$, and, further, the possible interactions among the internal and external variables. Since both types of motion have to do with the same particle, energy-momentum exchanges between them are not inconceivable even for a free (isolated) particle, since only a total energy-momentum is necessarily conserved.

A free particle of definite momentum $\mathbf{p}$ and energy $W$ must be representable as a plane wave, so that a spinor describing it can be written

$$\psi = \begin{pmatrix} \boldsymbol{\varphi} \\ \boldsymbol{\theta} \end{pmatrix} e^{i(\mathbf{p}.\mathbf{r}-Wt)/\hbar}, \tag{2.67}$$

where $\boldsymbol{\varphi}$ and $\boldsymbol{\theta}$ are Pauli spinors for the forward and retrograde motions, as in (2.48), but redefined to be independent of the space-time variables $\mathbf{r}$, $t$. They could be chosen arbitrarily in representing the energy-momentum eigenstate if the internal motions they describe were independent of the external motion, but previous considerations already show they cannot be. To yield the velocity $v = c^2p/W$ that a particle of definite momentum $\mathbf{p}$ must possess, the amplitudes of the forward and retrograde motions must have the ratio implicit in (1.30):

$$\boldsymbol{\theta} = \left(\frac{1-v/c}{1+v/c}\right)^{\frac{1}{2}} \boldsymbol{\varphi} = \left(\frac{W-cp}{W+cp}\right)^{\frac{1}{2}} \boldsymbol{\varphi} = \frac{W-cp}{mc^2}\boldsymbol{\varphi}, \tag{2.68 a}$$

the last form following from the relation $W^2-c^2p^2 = m^2c^4$. Conversely,

$$\boldsymbol{\varphi} = \{(W+cp)/mc^2\}\boldsymbol{\theta}. \tag{2.68 b}$$

It is obviously being presumed here that the resolution of the Dirac spinor into Pauli spinors, used in (2.67), is on a basis of eigenstates of a velocity component collinear with the momentum $\mathbf{p}$. We are implicitly using $\mathbf{p}$ as the quantization axis, so that $\alpha_z \equiv \boldsymbol{\alpha}.\mathbf{p}/p$.

The relations (2.68) can be written

$$\left.\begin{aligned} W\boldsymbol{\varphi} &= cp\boldsymbol{\varphi}+mc^2\boldsymbol{\theta} \\ W\boldsymbol{\theta} &= -cp\boldsymbol{\theta}+mc^2\boldsymbol{\varphi} \end{aligned}\right\}. \tag{2.69}$$

According to the representation $\alpha_z = \rho_3$ (2.54) being used here,

$$p\alpha_z\psi \equiv \boldsymbol{\alpha}.\mathbf{p}\psi = \begin{pmatrix} p\boldsymbol{\varphi} \\ -p\boldsymbol{\theta} \end{pmatrix} e^{(i\mathbf{p}.\mathbf{r}-Wt)/\hbar}.$$

We may also define a new internal dynamical variable, $\beta$, with the representation $\beta = \rho_1$ (2.57) on the present basis, so that

$$mc^2\beta\psi \equiv mc^2\begin{pmatrix} 0 & 1 \\ 1 & 0 \end{pmatrix}\psi = \begin{pmatrix} mc^2 & \boldsymbol{\theta} \\ mc^2 & \boldsymbol{\varphi} \end{pmatrix} e^{i(\mathbf{p}.\mathbf{r}-Wt)/\hbar}.$$

Thus, with the help of $\boldsymbol{\alpha}$, $\beta$, the two Pauli spinor equations (2.69) can be written as a single Dirac spinor equation:

$$W\psi = (c\boldsymbol{\alpha}.\mathbf{p}+\beta mc^2)\psi. \tag{2.70}$$

The operator here is expressed in terms of 3-dimensional scalars, so that the equation should hold for any relatively rotated reference frames, hence for an arbitrary choice of quantization axis, and not only the one, coinciding with $\mathbf{p}$, used so far.

*The Dirac hamiltonian*

The interactions among variables are usually represented by forming a 'hamiltonian' operator function of the variables, $H$, such that its eigenvalues are the possible values of the energy, $W$. The result (2.70) indicates that the internal and external motions of a Dirac particle exchange energy in a way representable by

$$H = c\boldsymbol{\alpha}.\mathbf{p}+\beta mc^2. \tag{2.71}$$

Here, $\mathbf{p}$ is the operator for the momentum; $\mathbf{p} = -i\hbar\boldsymbol{\nabla}$ if the probability amplitudes are to be represented by continuous functions of position, $\mathbf{r}$. This hamiltonian was the one found by Dirac to yield a properly relativistic description of free, spin-$\frac{1}{2}$ particles. Considered apart from its relation to the other variables, the energy operator gets the representation $i\hbar\partial/\partial t$ from its conjugacy to the time in the basic quantum conditions. The equation of the hamiltonian operation to the time-displacement operation yields the fundamental equation of motion,

$$i\hbar\partial\psi/\partial t = H\psi = (-i\hbar c\boldsymbol{\alpha}.\boldsymbol{\nabla}+\beta mc^2)\psi, \tag{2.72}$$

the Dirac equation for a free particle.

The relation $W^2 = c^2p^2+m^2c^4$, between the external variables $W$, $p$ alone, must also be maintained. Thus, for any state $\psi$ of a free particle,

$$-\hbar^2\partial^2\psi/\partial t^2 = [-c^2\hbar^2\nabla^2+m^2c^4]\psi. \tag{2.73}$$

Being free of the internal variables, this 'Klein–Gordon' equation is expected to hold for any free particle having mass $m$, whether a fermion or not. To be maintained under the more restrictive condition (2.72), which is specialized for Dirac particles, it is necessary that applying the operation $H$ twice have the result:

$$H^2 \equiv (c\boldsymbol{\alpha}.\mathbf{p}+\beta mc^2)^2 = c^2p^2+m^2c^4.$$

This implies that

$$\Sigma_{ij}p_ip_j(\alpha_i\alpha_j+\alpha_j\alpha_i)+\Sigma_i p_i(\alpha_i\beta+\beta\alpha_i)mc+\beta^2m^2c^2 = p^2+m^2c^2$$

holds for arbitrary $p_x$, $p_y$, $p_z$. For the two sides to match, the internal variables $\boldsymbol{\alpha}$, $\beta$ must obey the conditions

$$\left.\begin{aligned} \tfrac{1}{2}(\alpha_i\alpha_j+\alpha_j\alpha_i) &= \delta_{ij} \\ \alpha_i\beta+\beta\alpha_i = 0, \quad \beta^2 &= 1 \end{aligned}\right\}. \tag{2.74}$$

The particular matrix representations used in the preceding sections, $\alpha_z = \rho_3$ and $\beta = \rho_1$, are consistent with these conditions, in view of (2.58). Dirac's original representation, $\beta = \rho_3$ and $\boldsymbol{\alpha} = \rho_1 \boldsymbol{\Sigma}$ (2.66), is equally consistent. Formal manipulations may be carried on without adopting specific representations at all, deductions being made directly from such relationships as (2.74).

*The Dirac current*

The solutions of Dirac's equation which are useful for describing a fermion in various actual physical situations are such as permit interpreting

$$\psi^\dagger\psi(d\mathbf{r}) \equiv \sum_{\mu=1}^{4} |\psi_\mu(\mathbf{r})|^2\,(d\mathbf{r}) \tag{2.75}$$

as a scalar probability of finding the particle in the volume element $(d\mathbf{r})$, regardless of internal configuration. Now, volumes are subject to Lorentz contraction when viewed relative to moving reference frames, hence the density $\psi^\dagger\psi$ cannot itself be an invariant scalar. Rather $\psi^\dagger\psi$ must undergo dilatation, as do time periods; its behaviour is like that of the time-coordinate, the fourth component of the 4-vector $x_\mu(\mathbf{r}, ict)$. A probability current density, $\mathbf{w}$, must be definable, such that $w_4 = ic\psi^\dagger\psi$ is the fourth component of a 4-vector, $w_\mu(\mathbf{w}, ic\psi^\dagger\psi)$. The 'conservation of particles' then demands that a continuity equation be obeyed:

$$\boldsymbol{\nabla}.\mathbf{w}+\partial(\psi^\dagger\psi)/\partial t \equiv \Sigma_\mu\, \partial w_\mu/\partial x_\mu = 0. \tag{2.76}$$

What $\mathbf{w}$ must be is readily found by investigating the consequences of the Dirac equation for $\partial(\psi^\dagger\psi)/\partial t$. It thus turns out that

$$\mathbf{w} = c\psi^\dagger\boldsymbol{\alpha}\psi, \tag{2.77}$$

which is not unexpected when it is remembered that $\rho\mathbf{v}$ is the current density of any density $\rho$ with velocity $\mathbf{v}$. Since $w_\mu(c\psi^\dagger\boldsymbol{\alpha}\psi,\ ic\psi^\dagger\psi)$ is a 4-vector, $\psi^\dagger\psi$ is not a scalar, and $\psi^\dagger\boldsymbol{\alpha}\psi$, rather than $\boldsymbol{\alpha}$ itself, has the properties characteristic of the three spatial components of a 4-vector.

Now, for a state $\psi$ with a given momentum and energy,

$$\psi^\dagger H\psi = c(\psi^\dagger\boldsymbol{\alpha}\psi).\mathbf{p}+(\psi^\dagger\beta\psi)mc^2 = W\psi^\dagger\psi \tag{2.78}$$

is a scalar expression, as is particularly evident from the scalar product $\mathbf{w}.\mathbf{p}+w_4(iW/c)$ in it. We see that it is the multiplication of

$$\bar{\psi} \equiv \psi^\dagger\beta \tag{2.79}$$

into $\psi$, rather than $\psi^\dagger\psi$, which produces an invariant, scalar product. Since $\beta^2 = 1$, $\psi^\dagger \equiv \bar{\psi}\beta$, and the current-density 4-vector may be denoted $w_\mu(c\bar{\psi}\beta\boldsymbol{\alpha}\psi,\ ic\bar{\psi}\beta\psi)$. It is now clear that the internal dynamical variable components defined by

$$\gamma_\mu(-i\beta\boldsymbol{\alpha}, \beta) \tag{2.80}$$

must themselves have the transformation properties of a 4-vector. This was actually proved years ago.‡

The current 4-vector may now be written

$$w_\mu = ic\bar{\psi}\gamma_\mu\psi, \tag{2.81}$$

and the Dirac equation is easily shown to become (after multiplication into (2.72) of $\beta/\hbar c$):

$$(\gamma_\mu\,\partial/\partial x_\mu + mc/\hbar)\psi = 0. \tag{2.82}$$

These expressions make the relativistic covariances explicit.

*The five internal covariants*

It is convenient to continue the discussion in terms of the 4-vector $\gamma_\mu$, as a replacement for $\boldsymbol{\alpha}$, $\beta$, because of its clear behaviour in changes of reference frame. The entire dependence on inner variables in Dirac's equation of motion (2.82) is expressed in terms of $\gamma_\mu$. We shall now see that it also provides a complete description of all possible internal motions in the sense that any other inner dynamical variable can be expressed as some function of $\gamma_\mu$.

The variety of possible internal motions is limited to a 'space of states' which can be spanned by just four spinor components. Then, any inner variable must be representable by a $4\times 4$ matrix. There are just sixteen 'independent' 4-dimensional matrices which can be constructed, as discussed in § 2.3. All sixteen of the dynamical variables thus possible can be expressed as functions of $\gamma_\mu$.

The possible functions of $\gamma_\mu$ are as much restricted as their possible $4\times 4$ representatives. That stems from the defining property

$$\tfrac{1}{2}(\gamma_\mu\gamma_\nu + \gamma_\nu\gamma_\mu) = \delta_{\mu\nu}, \tag{2.83}$$

which is equivalent to the anticommutation relations (2.74) among the $\alpha$'s and $\beta$. If we begin forming functions of the $\gamma$-components by constructing products of them, then every product can be reduced to one in which no one component of the four occurs more than once; for example, $\gamma_x\gamma_y\gamma_x = -\gamma_x^2\gamma_y = -\gamma_y$ because different $\gamma$-components anticommute, while the square of any one is unity. Consequently, an arbitrary function of them can be written as a sum of sixteen terms like

$$f = f_0 + \sum f_\mu\gamma_\mu + \sum f_{\mu\nu}\gamma_\mu\gamma_\nu + \sum f_{\mu\nu\rho}\gamma_\mu\gamma_\nu\gamma_\rho + f_5\gamma_x\gamma_y\gamma_z\gamma_4. \tag{2.84}$$

These are only sixteen terms if the summations are appropriately restricted. With a choice of 4-dimensional matrix representations for the $\gamma$'s, $f$ can be made to coincide with the arbitrary matrix (2.61), which also has sixteen (possibly complex) parameters.

‡ W. Pauli, *Handb. d. Phys.*, vol. xxiv/1 (1931).

Each type of $\gamma$-product distinguished in (2.84) transforms differently in changes of reference frame. The products $\gamma_\mu \gamma_\nu = -\gamma_\nu \gamma_\mu$ behave like components of a second rank tensor since they are formed as products of 4-vector components. To represent them, we define the antisymmetric tensor of six distinct components

$$\sigma_{\mu\nu} = (\gamma_\mu \gamma_\nu - \gamma_\nu \gamma_\mu)/2i = -i\gamma_\mu \gamma_\nu \quad (\mu \neq \nu). \tag{2.85}$$

The insertion of the factor $i$ makes each component hermitian:

$$\sigma_{\mu\nu}^\dagger = i\gamma_\nu^\dagger \gamma_\mu^\dagger = i\gamma_\nu \gamma_\mu = -i\gamma_\mu \gamma_\nu = \sigma_{\mu\nu},$$

if the $\gamma$'s themselves are hermitian (as they must be to have real eigenvalues). Further, each component has a unit square. A sample 'space-space' component is

$$\sigma_{xy} = (\gamma_x \gamma_y - \gamma_y \gamma_x)/2i = (\boldsymbol{\gamma} \times \boldsymbol{\gamma})_z/2i \equiv (\boldsymbol{\alpha} \times \boldsymbol{\alpha})_z/2i.$$

We adopt the symbol

$$\boldsymbol{\sigma} = (\boldsymbol{\alpha} \times \boldsymbol{\alpha})/2i = (\boldsymbol{\gamma} \times \boldsymbol{\gamma})/2i \tag{2.86}$$

for the three distinct components of this type because, as we shall see in the next subsection, they are to be identified with the spin-vector components. A sample 'space-time' component is $\sigma_{x4} = -i\gamma_x \gamma_4 = \alpha_x$, so that the total array of the tensor components is

$$(\sigma_{\mu\nu}) = \begin{pmatrix} 0 & \sigma_z & -\sigma_y & \alpha_x \\ -\sigma_z & 0 & \sigma_x & \alpha_y \\ \sigma_y & -\sigma_x & 0 & \alpha_z \\ -\alpha_x & -\alpha_y & -\alpha_z & 0 \end{pmatrix}, \tag{2.87}$$

and we may symbolize them more briefly by $\sigma_{\mu\nu}(\boldsymbol{\sigma}, \boldsymbol{\alpha})$. We learned in the preceding subsection that the $\alpha$'s do not transform like the first three components of a 4-vector, rather that $\boldsymbol{\gamma} = -i\beta\boldsymbol{\alpha}$ does. Now we learn that the $\alpha$'s are components of an antisymmetric tensor, together with the $\sigma$'s.

We take up next the dynamical variable formed from the product of four $\gamma$-components [last term of (2.84)]:

$$\gamma_5 = \gamma_x \gamma_y \gamma_z \gamma_4 = i\alpha_x \alpha_y \alpha_z = -\sigma_z \alpha_z. \tag{2.88}$$

The last equality follows from (2.86) and this, together with the presumption that $\sigma_z$ represents our spin operator, accounts for the notational identification with the chirality operator of (2.56). It is now obvious that $\gamma_5 = -\sigma_z \alpha_z = -\alpha_z \sigma_z = -\sigma_x \alpha_x = -\sigma_y \alpha_y$.

The notation $\gamma_5$ is used for the chirality operator because it is the fifth member of the mutually anticommuting set [see (2.64)] formed together with $\gamma_x$, $\gamma_y$, $\gamma_z$, and $\gamma_4$. For example,

$$\gamma_5\gamma_x \equiv \gamma_x\gamma_y\gamma_z\gamma_4\gamma_x = -\gamma_x\gamma_y\gamma_z\gamma_x\gamma_4 = -\gamma_x\gamma_x\gamma_y\gamma_z\gamma_4 = -\gamma_x\gamma_5.$$

The relations (2.83) can be extended to $\mu$ or $\nu = 5$.

From its construction, $\gamma_5$ must have a behaviour distinct from any other of the terms in (2.84), in changes of reference frame, and it consists of just one component. It must therefore be invariant, like a scalar, in proper space (-time) rotations of the frame. It does undergo change, however, when the transformation is from a right- to a left-handed frame, as in 'space-inversions', $\mathbf{r} \to -\mathbf{r}$. Any proper 4-vector must behave like $x_\mu$ $(\mathbf{r}, ict)$, hence $\gamma_\mu(\boldsymbol{\gamma}, \gamma_4) \to \gamma'_\mu(-\boldsymbol{\gamma}, \gamma_4)$ in space-inversions. Then

$$\gamma_5 \to \gamma'_5 = (-\gamma_x)(-\gamma_y)(-\gamma_z)\gamma_4 = -\gamma_5. \tag{2.89}$$

Quantities which only change sign, in transformations of reference frame which include inversions, are called *pseudoscalars*.

The investigation of the $\gamma$-products in (2.84) is now completed by considering the four distinct components: $\gamma_\rho\gamma_\sigma\gamma_\nu$ (with no two $\gamma$-components alike). These four quantities are more economically labelled by the one $\gamma$-component missing from each triple product, and they may be represented by

$$\omega_\mu = i\gamma_5\gamma_\mu, \tag{2.90}$$

defined so that it is hermitian and unitary. This will obviously behave like a 4-vector in proper rotations, considering the properties of $\gamma_\mu$ and $\gamma_5$, but $\boldsymbol{\omega} = i\gamma_5\boldsymbol{\gamma}$ does not change sign, as a polar vector does, in space-inversions. For this reason, $\omega_\mu$ is called a *pseudovector* (or 'axial 4-vector').

The general inner dynamical variable (2.84) can now be written

$$f = f_0 + \sum f_\mu\gamma_\mu + i\sum f_{\mu\nu}\sigma_{\mu\nu} + \sum f'_\mu\omega_\mu + f_5\gamma_5, \tag{2.91}$$

in terms of the 'five covariants':

$$\left.\begin{array}{ll} \text{the } \textit{scalar}, & 1 = \gamma_\mu^2 = \sigma_{\mu\nu}^2 = \omega_\mu^2 = \gamma_5^2 \\ \text{the } \textit{vector}, & \gamma_\mu(-i\beta\boldsymbol{\alpha}, \beta) \\ \text{the } \textit{tensor}, & \sigma_{\mu\nu}(\boldsymbol{\sigma}, \boldsymbol{\alpha}) \\ \text{the } \textit{pseudovector}, & \omega_\mu(\beta\boldsymbol{\sigma}, -i\beta\gamma_5) \\ \text{the } \textit{pseudoscalar}, & \gamma_5 = i\alpha_x\alpha_y\alpha_z \end{array}\right\}. \tag{2.92}$$

Each has the covariance named only when its operations on states $\psi$ are evaluated by projections on $\bar{\psi} = \psi^\dagger\beta$, rather than $\psi^\dagger$.

*Relativistic angular momentum*

Another way in which the interaction between the internal and external motions shows itself is in a continual exchange of angular momentum, between the intrinsic spin and the orbital momentum about whatever centre is chosen for gauging it. If that centre is made the origin of the coordinates, then the orbital momentum can be written simply as $\mathbf{l} = \mathbf{r}\times\mathbf{p}$. As will now be discussed, $\mathbf{l}$ is not conserved, at any constant value, even during a free particle's motion, when no external torques are being applied.

Any time rate of change of a dynamical variable is representable by the operator resultant of its commutator with the hamiltonian; thus, $[\mathbf{l}, H] = i\hbar\dot{\mathbf{l}}$. To be conserved ($\dot{\mathbf{l}} = 0$), the variable must commute with the hamiltonian, and that is also the condition for the dynamical variable and the conserved energy to have definite eigenvalues simultaneously, in some state.

The evaluation of the commutator of $\mathbf{l}$ with the Dirac hamiltonian (2.71) yields

$$[H,\mathbf{l}] = -i\hbar c(\boldsymbol{\alpha}\times\mathbf{p}). \tag{2.93}$$

Thus, $\dot{\mathbf{l}} = c(\boldsymbol{\alpha}\times\mathbf{p})$, and the orbital momentum is not conserved by itself, as already asserted.

Next, the identification of $(\boldsymbol{\alpha}\times\boldsymbol{\alpha})/2i \equiv (\boldsymbol{\gamma}\times\boldsymbol{\gamma})/2i$, in (2.86), as the spin angular momentum must be justified. For this purpose, it should be recognized that the proper characterization of the orbital momentum, in space-time, is as the three 'space-space' components of the antisymmetrical tensor

$$l_{\mu\nu} \equiv x_\mu p_\nu - x_\nu p_\mu \quad (\mu,\nu = 1,2,3,4). \tag{2.94}$$

It is each of the six distinct components of this tensor which becomes a conserved constant, when the variables $\mathbf{r}, \mathbf{p}$ are isolated, as for a spinless particle. That follows from the necessary invariance of the description of an isolated system to rotations of the space-time reference frame (which include Lorentz transformations), more general than rotations in space only. The constancy of any 'space-time' component, like

$$l_{x4} = xp_4 - x_4 p_x = i(W/c)(x - tc^2p_x/W) = i(W/c)(x - v_x t), \tag{2.95}$$

for a spinless isolated particle, describes the uniform net translation which such a particle must have.

A properly identified spin angular momentum must be additive to $l_{\mu\nu}$, hence must have the same transformation properties. The only inner dynamical variable with the requisite properties is the antisymmetrical tensor $\sigma_{\mu\nu}$, defined in (2.85). We therefore supplement the evaluation (2.93) with that of

$$[H,\boldsymbol{\sigma}] \equiv (1/2i)[H,\boldsymbol{\alpha}\times\boldsymbol{\alpha}] = 2ic(\boldsymbol{\alpha}\times\mathbf{p}). \tag{2.96}$$

Together, the evaluations show that

$$[H, \mathbf{l}+\tfrac{1}{2}\hbar\boldsymbol{\sigma}] \equiv [H,\mathbf{j}] = 0, \tag{2.97}$$

so that a total angular momentum defined by $\mathbf{j} = \mathbf{l}+\frac{1}{2}\hbar\boldsymbol{\sigma}$ is conserved, as to be expected for an isolated spinning particle.

One point may still need clarification. According to the presentation of the states (2.67), (2.68), a choice like $\boldsymbol{\varphi} = \boldsymbol{\chi}_{+\frac{1}{2}}$ is perfectly legitimate, and yet this implies simultaneous knowledge of a definite energy, $W$, and a definite spin projection. This is not actually in contradiction to the general non-commutativity of the energy and spin variables, however. It must be remembered that the state (2.67) is presented on a special basis, for which the quantization axis is along the momentum direction, $\hat{\mathbf{p}} = \mathbf{p}/p$. In that case, $\sigma_z \equiv \boldsymbol{\sigma}.\hat{\mathbf{p}} = -\gamma_5(\boldsymbol{\alpha}.\hat{\mathbf{p}})$, and this does commute with $H = c\boldsymbol{\alpha}.\hat{\mathbf{p}}p+\beta mc^2$, since $\gamma_5$ and $\boldsymbol{\alpha}$ commute, and so do $\boldsymbol{\sigma}$ and $\beta$. Angular momenta about $\mathbf{p}$ are being considered, and there is no orbital momentum about that direction.

# III

# DIRAC WAVE FIELDS

## 3.1. Plane waves

PLANE Dirac waves have already been introduced (2.67), (2.68), but in a special representation based on the momentum direction as quantization axis. That choice was made in order that the component Pauli spinors, $\boldsymbol{\varphi}$ and $\boldsymbol{\theta}$, have interpretations as forward and retrograde components of the 'zitterbewegung'. It will generally be more convenient to have available, instead, representations of the plane waves in which the momentum may have an arbitrary direction relative to the $z$-axis of quantization.

*In Dirac representation*

The most widely used representation is the one introduced initially by Dirac, and characterized by $\beta = \rho_3$, $\boldsymbol{\alpha} = \rho_1\boldsymbol{\sigma}$, and $\boldsymbol{\sigma} = \boldsymbol{\Sigma}$ (2.66). The plane wave, momentum eigenstate may again be resolved into Pauli spinors, $\boldsymbol{\varphi}$ and $\boldsymbol{\theta}$, as in (2.67), but, in the Dirac representation, these will no longer have simple physical meanings. They are determined by substituting the form (2.67) into the Dirac equation (2.72), which can then be resolved into

$$\left.\begin{aligned} W\boldsymbol{\varphi} &= c\boldsymbol{\sigma}.\mathbf{p}\boldsymbol{\theta}+mc^2\boldsymbol{\varphi} \\ W\boldsymbol{\theta} &= c\boldsymbol{\sigma}.\mathbf{p}\boldsymbol{\varphi}-mc^2\boldsymbol{\theta} \end{aligned}\right\}, \tag{3.1}$$

replacing (2.69). The second equation gives $\boldsymbol{\theta}$ as the result of an operation on $\boldsymbol{\varphi}$:

$$\boldsymbol{\theta} = (W+mc^2)^{-1}c\boldsymbol{\sigma}.\mathbf{p}\boldsymbol{\varphi}. \tag{3.2}$$

With $W = (c^2p^2+m^2c^4)^{\frac{1}{2}}$, $\boldsymbol{\theta}$ must have a smaller amplitude than $\boldsymbol{\varphi}$ and, for that reason, the Dirac representation is said to yield a resolution into 'large' and 'small' Pauli spinor components. The smaller component tends to vanish in the non-relativistic limit, $p \ll mc$, leaving a description by the single Pauli spinor, $\boldsymbol{\varphi}$.

For consistency of the two equations (3.1),

$$\boldsymbol{\varphi} = (W-mc^2)^{-1}c\boldsymbol{\sigma}.\mathbf{p}\boldsymbol{\theta} = (W^2-m^2c^4)^{-1}(c\boldsymbol{\sigma}.\mathbf{p})^2\boldsymbol{\varphi}. \tag{3.3}$$

Since $(\boldsymbol{\sigma}.\mathbf{p})^2 = p^2$, as is easily verified, this requirement is fulfilled if $W = +(c^2p^2+m^2c^4)^{\frac{1}{2}}$, or if $W = -(c^2p^2+m^2c^4)^{\frac{1}{2}}$. The energy may have either a positive or a negative eigenvalue for a given momentum $\mathbf{p}$.

Notice that, for the negative eigenvalue, it is $\boldsymbol{\theta}$ rather than $\boldsymbol{\varphi}$ that is the 'large component'.

Hereafter we shall use $W$ to denote the positive energy, and write the negative eigenvalue as $-W$. The further discussion of the latter we leave to the next subsection. Even for a given one of the energy eigenvalues, the Dirac equation leaves open the choice of one Pauli spinor, say $\boldsymbol{\varphi}$, which may then be an arbitrary linear combination of the Pauli spin eigenstates, $\boldsymbol{\chi}_{\pm\frac{1}{2}}$. We get two orthogonal plane waves, which can serve as a basis, by choosing $\boldsymbol{\varphi} \sim \boldsymbol{\chi}_{+\frac{1}{2}}$ and $\boldsymbol{\varphi} \sim \boldsymbol{\chi}_{-\frac{1}{2}}$, in turn:

$$\psi_{\pm\frac{1}{2}} = \left(\frac{W+mc^2}{2WV}\right)^{\frac{1}{2}} \begin{pmatrix} 1 \\ c\boldsymbol{\sigma}.\mathbf{p}/(W+mc^2) \end{pmatrix} \boldsymbol{\chi}_{\pm\frac{1}{2}}\, e^{i(\mathbf{p}.\mathbf{r}-Wt)/\hbar}. \tag{3.4}$$

Normalizing factors have been inserted here such that

$$\oint (d\mathbf{r})\psi_{\mu}^{\dagger}\psi_{\mu'} = \delta_{\mu\mu'}, \tag{3.5}$$

when the integration is extended over an indefinitely large volume, $V$.

Neither of the states $\psi_{\pm\frac{1}{2}}$ has a definite eigenvalue for the spin projection on the quantization axis, $\sigma_z$. That is to be expected from the failure of the energy and spin operators to commute (2.96). On the other hand, these do commute in the limit $\mathbf{p} = 0$, and $\psi_{\pm\frac{1}{2}}$ describe 'up' and 'down' spins in that limit (the rest-frame of the particle).

*The antiparticle states*

The states with the negative energy eigenvalue, $-W$, are more conveniently classified into a basic pair for which $\boldsymbol{\theta} \sim \boldsymbol{\chi}_{+\frac{1}{2}}$ and $\boldsymbol{\chi}_{-\frac{1}{2}}$, rather than $\boldsymbol{\varphi}$. This is because $\boldsymbol{\theta}$ is now the 'large component'. We shall present these states for the momentum $-\mathbf{p}$, rather than $+\mathbf{p}$, and when $\boldsymbol{\theta} \sim \boldsymbol{\chi}_{\mu}$, the state will be denoted by $\psi_{-\mu}^{C}$. Accordingly,

$$\psi_{\pm\frac{1}{2}}^{C} = \mp\left(\frac{W+mc^2}{2WV}\right)^{\frac{1}{2}} \begin{pmatrix} c\boldsymbol{\sigma}.\mathbf{p}/(W+mc^2) \\ 1 \end{pmatrix} \boldsymbol{\chi}_{\mp\frac{1}{2}}\, e^{-i(\mathbf{p}.\mathbf{r}-Wt)/\hbar}. \tag{3.6}$$

The signs before the expression are introduced merely so that this definition of $\psi_{\mu}^{C}$ will coincide, even in phase, with another one to be given just below.

From its construction, $\psi_{\mu}^{C}$ describes a normal particle of 'energy' $-W$, momentum $-\mathbf{p}$, and a spin projection $-\mu\hbar$. We shall henceforth interpret it as describing an *anti*particle, of energy $+W$, momentum $+\mathbf{p}$, and spin-projection $+\mu\hbar$. This is as expected from the 'hole picture' mentioned in § 1.6.

The antiparticle states $\psi_{\mu}^{C}$ can be obtained by what is known as a 'charge-conjugation' operation, $\psi_{\mu}^{C} = C\psi_{\mu}^{*}$, directly from the normal particle states $\psi_\mu$ with the same dynamical properties (i.e. $+W$, $+p$, $+\mu\hbar$). As indicated, part of the operation consists of taking the complex conjugate, which has different effects in different representations. For that reason, the remainder of the operation, by $C$, is different in different representations. In the Dirac representation, used for (3.4) and (3.6), it turns out that

$$C = \rho_2 \Sigma_2, \qquad C^2 = 1, \tag{3.7}$$

as can be verified quite readily by applying it to (3.4) or (3.6) and so confirming either $\psi_\mu^C = C\psi_\mu^*$ or $\psi_\mu = C\psi_\mu^{C*}$. It happens that $C = -i\beta\alpha_2 = \gamma_2$ in the Dirac representation, but the coincidence with that dynamical variable holds only in that special representation.

The four states $\psi_\mu$ and $\psi_\mu^C$, of (3.4) and (3.6), correspond to the multiplicity of four independent states, with distinct 'internal configurations', to be expected in a description by spinors with four components as parameters. It is significant that they become classifiable into two pairs, interpretable as normal and antiparticle states, respectively. Thus, the doubling of internal degrees of freedom, in going from the Pauli to the Dirac spinor, can be regarded as arising from the necessity for accommodating descriptions of antiparticles.

*Left- and right-handed states*

The findings in Chapter I concerning the longitudinal polarizations of fermions produced in $\beta$-processes make it important to become familiar with formal descriptions of left- and right-handedly moving particles.

The detection of longitudinal polarizations starts with a sorting out of particles having a definite momentum direction, $\hat{\mathbf{p}} = \mathbf{p}/p$, and then the relative numbers having spins parallel, $\boldsymbol{\sigma}.\hat{\mathbf{p}} = +1$, and antiparallel, $\boldsymbol{\sigma}.\hat{\mathbf{p}} = -1$, to $\mathbf{p}$ are counted. It is $\boldsymbol{\sigma}.\hat{\mathbf{p}}$ that is usually called the 'helicity' operator.‡ Its eigenstates, describing normal particles, may be represented by $\psi_{\pm\frac{1}{2}}$ of (3.4), if the Pauli eigenspinors $\boldsymbol{\chi}_{\pm\frac{1}{2}}$ are now defined relative to $\hat{\mathbf{p}}$ as quantization axis.

A distinction should now be emphasized, between the two helicity eigenstates arising from polarization analyses, and the four 'chirality eigenstates' of (2.55). For example, the left-handed helicity state $\psi_{-\frac{1}{2}}$ is a simultaneous eigenstate of the momentum $\mathbf{p}$ and of the longitudinal polarization $\boldsymbol{\sigma}.\hat{\mathbf{p}} = -1$. On the other hand, the 'intrinsically' left-handed chirality states $u_{\mp\frac{1}{2}}(\pm c)$ are simultaneous eigenstates of the intrinsic *velocity* $c(\boldsymbol{\alpha}.\hat{\mathbf{p}}) = \pm c$ and the chirality

$$\gamma_5 = -(\boldsymbol{\sigma}.\hat{\mathbf{p}})(\boldsymbol{\alpha}.\hat{\mathbf{p}}) = +1,$$

‡ For an example of its formal usage, see G. Wick, *Ann. Phys.* **18**, 65 (1962).

as referred to the quantization axis $\hat{\mathbf{p}}$; there are two of these, with polarizations $\boldsymbol{\sigma}.\hat{\mathbf{p}} = \mp 1$, as respectively denoted by the subscripts on them. Whereas it is the helicity eigenstates which are sorted out by the polarization detection procedures, it is the chirality eigenstates which determine strengths of $\beta$-interaction, as already indicated by the discussion of the result (1.31) and to be more precisely stated now.

The $\beta$-interactions are such that a certain definite intensity ratio, $d\lambda_{\rightarrow}/d\lambda_{\leftarrow}$ of the two helicity eigenstates, $\psi_{\pm\frac{1}{2}}$, is formed, leading to an observed net polarization, $-v/c$, for normal particles. That ratio can be understood as determined by the density ratio with which the positive chirality ($\gamma_5 = +1$) components $u_{\pm\frac{1}{2}}(\mp c)$ are contained in $\psi_{\pm\frac{1}{2}}$, respectively. A general way to project the components of each chirality out of any spinor state $\psi$ can be seen from the identity

$$\psi \equiv \tfrac{1}{2}(1+\gamma_5)\psi + \tfrac{1}{2}(1-\gamma_5)\psi. \tag{3.8}$$

It follows from $\gamma_5^2 = +1$ that the two parts are orthogonal eigenstates of $\gamma_5$, with eigenvalues $+1$ and $-1$ respectively. The important, intrinsically left-handed, projection will be given the special denotation

$$\phi = \tfrac{1}{2}(1+\gamma_5)\psi \; (= +\gamma_5 \phi). \tag{3.9}$$

Notice that $\frac{1}{2}(1+\gamma_5)\phi = \phi$, as befits a projection.

The projections by $\frac{1}{2}(1+\gamma_5)$ of the normal particle eigenstates (3.4) can be given the forms

$$\phi_{\pm\frac{1}{2}} = \begin{pmatrix} 1 \\ -1 \end{pmatrix} \mathbf{u}_{\pm\frac{1}{2}} . (2V)^{-\frac{1}{2}} e^{i(\mathbf{p}.\mathbf{r}-Wt)/\hbar}, \tag{3.10}$$

containing the Pauli spinors‡

$$\mathbf{u}_{\pm\frac{1}{2}} = \frac{1}{2}\left(\frac{W+mc^2}{W}\right)^{\frac{1}{2}} \left(1 - \frac{c\boldsymbol{\sigma}.\mathbf{p}}{W+mc^2}\right) \boldsymbol{\chi}_{\pm\frac{1}{2}}. \tag{3.11}$$

In normalizations to unit density ($V = 1$),

$$\phi^{\dagger}_{\pm\frac{1}{2}} \phi_{\pm\frac{1}{2}} = \mathbf{u}^{\dagger}_{\pm\frac{1}{2}} \mathbf{u}_{\pm\frac{1}{2}} = \tfrac{1}{2}(1 \mp cp_z/W). \tag{3.12}$$

‡ In a representation in which $\gamma_5 \rightarrow \rho_3$ is diagonal, and $\beta \rightarrow \rho_1$ is not, obtainable from the Dirac representation by the unitary transformation

$$U = 2^{-\frac{1}{2}} \begin{pmatrix} \mathbf{1} & -\mathbf{1} \\ \mathbf{1} & \mathbf{1} \end{pmatrix}$$

(it corresponds to (2.47) with the definitions of $\psi_1$ and $\psi_3$ interchanged),

$$\psi_\mu = \begin{pmatrix} \mathbf{u}_\mu \\ \bar{\mathbf{u}}_\mu \end{pmatrix} (2V)^{-\frac{1}{2}} e^{i(\mathbf{p}\cdot\mathbf{r}-Wt)/\hbar},$$

where $\bar{\mathbf{u}}_\mu$ differs from $\mathbf{u}_\mu$ by having the sign of $\boldsymbol{\sigma} . \mathbf{p}$ reversed. Then $\phi_\mu = \frac{1}{2}(1+\gamma_5)\psi_\mu$ is obtained merely by putting $\bar{\mathbf{u}}_\mu \rightarrow 0$, while the intrinsic right-handed projection has $\mathbf{u}_\mu \rightarrow 0$.

The assertion above was that

$$d\lambda_{\rightarrow}/d\lambda_{\leftarrow} = |\phi_{\frac{1}{2}}|^2/|\phi_{-\frac{1}{2}}|^2, \tag{3.13}$$

when $\hat{\mathbf{p}}$ is used as the quantization axis; this ratio is then just

$$(1-v/c)/(1+v/c), \tag{3.14}$$

which plainly yields the observed polarization, $-v/c$. The conclusion may be stated that $\beta$-interactions generate a given state $\psi$ with an amplitude proportional to its positive chirality projection, $\frac{1}{2}(1+\gamma_5)\psi$.

The projection by $\frac{1}{2}(1+\gamma_5)$ of an antiparticle state $\psi_\mu^C = C\psi_\mu^*$ is‡

$$\phi_\mu^C = \tfrac{1}{2}(1+\gamma_5)C\psi_\mu^* = C[\tfrac{1}{2}(1-\gamma_5)\psi_\mu]^*. \tag{3.15}$$

As indicated, $\gamma_5$ anticommutes with the charge-conjugation operator, $C$. This can be proved independently of representation, but it will suffice to check it in the Dirac representation. Since $\gamma_5 = -\rho_1$ is real, $\gamma_5^* = \gamma_5$. Moreover, $C = \rho_2\Sigma_2 = \gamma_2$ according to (3.7) and the statements following it. Thus, the anticommutation property follows from (2.83) with $\mu = 2$ and $\nu = 5$. The consequence is that antiparticle states generated in proportion to their $\frac{1}{2}(1+\gamma_5)$ projections will have net *right-handed* polarizations. In place of (3.10),

$$\phi_{\pm\frac{1}{2}}^C = \tfrac{1}{2}(1+\gamma_5)\psi_{\pm\frac{1}{2}}^C = \pm\begin{pmatrix}1\\-1\end{pmatrix}\mathbf{u}_{\mp\frac{1}{2}}(2V)^{-\frac{1}{2}}e^{-i(\mathbf{p}.\mathbf{r}-Wt)/\hbar} \tag{3.16}$$

follows§ from (3.6), and then

$$\phi_{\pm\frac{1}{2}}^{C\dagger}\phi_{\pm\frac{1}{2}}^C = \mathbf{u}_{\mp\frac{1}{2}}^\dagger\mathbf{u}_{\mp\frac{1}{2}} = \tfrac{1}{2}(1\pm cp_z/W) \tag{3.17}$$

replace (3.12). The sign reversals here correspond to a change from left-handedly polarized normal particles to right-handed antiparticles, as in (1.38).

## 3.2. Spherical waves

To describe the wave field being generated by a highly localized source, it may seem most appropriate to use spherical waves diverging from it, rather than the plane waves. Actually, the choice between the two types of analysis is a matter of convenience, since any‖ wave field can be equivalently represented as a superposition of plane wave, or spherical wave, components. Formally, a spherical wave may be fourier-analysed into plane waves; conversely, a plane wave may be expanded into a

‡ Notice that $\phi_\mu^C$ is *not* the charge-conjugate of $\phi_\mu$, in the sense that $\phi_\mu^C \neq C\phi_\mu^*$.

§ The signs in front of (3.16) may be chosen arbitrarily, except for comparisons against formal charge conjugation operations, and will be disregarded in applications to avoid distraction by inessentials.

‖ Sometimes special measures are needed to take care of singularities. See the last sentence of this section.

series of spherical harmonics, or, better, the spinor spherical harmonics, $\chi_{\kappa\mu}(\theta, \phi)$ of (2.18), to form a superposition of spherical waves. Physically, it is legitimate to ask about the generation of any specific linear momentum $\mathbf{p}$, hence for the amplitude of a specific plane wave component in the radiated field. Conversely, the query may be about the angular momentum being carried away, hence about the spherical wave constitution of the radiated field.

As in the plane wave case, the Dirac spinor will again be resolved into 'large' and 'small' Pauli spinors, but now with different functions of position $\boldsymbol{\varphi}(\mathbf{r})$, $\boldsymbol{\theta}(\mathbf{r})$ replacing the $\boldsymbol{\varphi}$, $\boldsymbol{\theta} \exp i\mathbf{p}.\mathbf{r}/\hbar$ of the plane wave case. The new Pauli spinors must again satisfy the Dirac equations (3.1), but now the specific momentum $\mathbf{p}$ must be replaced by its operator representative, $\mathbf{p} = -i\hbar\boldsymbol{\nabla}$.

*Dirac eigenstates of angular momentum*

Eigenstates of the total angular momentum, $\mathbf{j}$, are obtained by choosing $\boldsymbol{\varphi}(\mathbf{r}) \sim \chi_{\kappa\mu}(\hat{\mathbf{r}})$, in place of the choices $\boldsymbol{\varphi} \sim \chi_{\pm\frac{1}{2}}$ which yielded the plane wave basis $\psi_\mu$ of (3.4). The eigenstates $\chi_{\kappa\mu}$, as constructed in (2.18), are functions of the position vector's direction, $\hat{\mathbf{r}} = \mathbf{r}/|\mathbf{r}|$, which may be used to represent the angles $\theta$, $\phi$.

More specifically, we put $\boldsymbol{\varphi}(\mathbf{r}) = g_\kappa(r)\chi_{\kappa\mu}(\hat{\mathbf{r}})$, with $g_\kappa(r)$ representing whatever radial dependence will follow from the Dirac equation. Then

$$\boldsymbol{\theta}(\mathbf{r}) = (W+1)^{-1}(-i\boldsymbol{\sigma}.\boldsymbol{\nabla})g_\kappa(r)\chi_{\kappa\mu}(\hat{\mathbf{r}}) \tag{3.18}$$

replaces (3.2). At this point the common practice of using units in which $\hbar = c = m = 1$ has been introduced, to simplify the expressions.‡ The purely formal work of applying the operations in (3.18) need not be repeated here.§ The result is

$$\boldsymbol{\theta} = i(W+1)^{-1}\left(\frac{d}{dr}+\frac{1+\kappa}{r}\right)g_\kappa \chi_{-\kappa\mu}. \tag{3.19}$$

As a consequence, the Dirac spinor takes the form

$$\psi_{\kappa\mu}(\mathbf{r}) = \begin{pmatrix} g_\kappa(r)\chi_{\kappa\mu}(\hat{\mathbf{r}}) \\ if_{-\kappa}(r)\chi_{-\kappa\mu}(\hat{\mathbf{r}}) \end{pmatrix} e^{-iWt}, \tag{3.20}$$

with

$$f_{-\kappa}(r) = (W+1)^{-1}\left(\frac{d}{dr}+\frac{1+\kappa}{r}\right)g_\kappa(r). \tag{3.21}$$

The spinor $\psi_{\kappa\mu}$ is plainly an eigenstate of $j^2$ and $j_z$, since $\chi_{\pm\kappa\mu}$ both are

‡ Reversions to ordinary units will be made without notice, since the presence of $\hbar$, $m$, $c$ in equations will signalize such reversions adequately.

§ See, for example, M. E. Rose, *Elementary Theory of Angular Momentum* (Wiley, 1953).

and with the same eigenvalues $j$, $\mu$. Indeed, we have here two eigenstates for a given $j$, $\mu$, corresponding to the choices $\kappa = \pm(j+\frac{1}{2})$ which are possible according to (2.19). The two eigenstates may be distinguished from each other as independent (orthogonal) eigenfunctions of the operator $\beta\varkappa$ which is a relativistic generalization of (2.17):

$$\beta\varkappa\psi_{\kappa\mu} = \kappa\psi_{\kappa\mu}.$$

It is a more common practice to make the distinction between the two eigenstates with $\kappa = \pm(j+\frac{1}{2})$ on the basis of the orbital momentum, or of the 'parity', of their large components: $g_{\pm(j+\frac{1}{2})}$, $\boldsymbol{\chi}_{\pm(j+\frac{1}{2})\mu}$. The corresponding orbital momenta, $l = j+\frac{1}{2}$ and $l = j-\frac{1}{2}$, differ by one unit. Since the spatial dependence $\sim\boldsymbol{\chi}_{\kappa\mu}(\hat{\mathbf{r}}) \sim Y_{l\mu\pm\frac{1}{2}}(\hat{\mathbf{r}})$ is even or odd, relative to reflections $\mathbf{r}\to-\mathbf{r}$ through the origin, according as $l$ is even or odd, the parities of the two states are opposite. The small components, $\sim\boldsymbol{\chi}_{\mp(j+\frac{1}{2})\mu}$, represent the orbital momenta differing by one unit from those of the large components, and the parities opposite to those of the large components, which are generated even during a free motion of the particle.

*The radial waves*

So far, the radial dependence $g_\kappa(r)$ has been left arbitrary; it becomes restricted when the state is required to have a definite energy, $W$. The Dirac equation not only imposes the condition (3.18) on the relation of the small to the large component, but also a reciprocal one, generalized from (3.3) of the plane wave case:

$$\boldsymbol{\varphi} = g_\kappa\boldsymbol{\chi}_{\kappa\mu} = (W-1)^{-1}(-i\boldsymbol{\sigma}.\boldsymbol{\nabla})if_{-\kappa}\boldsymbol{\chi}_{-\kappa\mu}. \tag{3.22}$$

The same operation which yielded (3.19) from (3.18) here leads to

$$g_\kappa = -(W-1)^{-1}\left(\frac{d}{dr}+\frac{1-\kappa}{r}\right)f_{-\kappa}, \tag{3.23}$$

supplementing (3.21).

The general solution of the coupled equations (3.21), (3.23), for $g_\kappa$, $f_\kappa$, can be expressed as an arbitrary linear combination of an outgoing wave, $h_l(pr)$, and an incoming wave, $h_l^*(pr)$, of types known‡ as 'spherical Hankel functions'. The argument $\rho = pr$ is the radial distance in units of the de Broglie wavelength (divided by $2\pi$): $\lambda\!\!\!^{-} = \hbar/p \equiv 1/p = (W^2-1)^{-\frac{1}{2}}$, here. The spherical Hankel functions are adequately defined by

$$h_0(\rho) = \frac{e^{i\rho}}{i\rho} \quad \text{and} \quad h_l(\rho) = (-\rho)^l\left(\frac{d}{\rho\, d\rho}\right)^l h_0(\rho). \tag{3.24}$$

‡ See, e.g. L. I. Schiff, *Quantum Mechanics* (McGraw-Hill, 1949), p. 79.

Clearly, each $h_l$ will have the factor $\exp i\rho$, multiplied by a polynomial in $\rho^{-1}$. That behaviour, coupled with the time factor, $\exp(-iWt)$, yields results proportional to an outgoing wave $\exp i(pr-Wt)$, with a radially modulated amplitude. Similarly, $h_l^*(pr)$ will yield an incoming wave, $\exp\{-i(pr+Wt)\}$. These behaviours persist to infinity,

$$h_l(\rho \to \infty) \approx \rho^{-1} \exp i[\rho - \tfrac{1}{2}(l+1)\pi] \tag{3.25}$$

being the asymptotic expression.

If $g_\kappa(r)$ is chosen to be proportional to $h_l(pr)$, then (3.21) determines $f_{-\kappa}$:

$$g_\kappa = N_W h_{l(\kappa)} \to f_{-\kappa} = \hat{\kappa} N_W [(W-1)/(W+1)]^{\frac{1}{2}} h_{l(-\kappa)}, \tag{3.26}$$

with $N_W$ a constant to be determined by the choice of normalization. Whereas $l(\kappa > 0) = \kappa$ and $l(\kappa < 0) = -\kappa-1$, according to (2.19), $l(-\kappa) = \kappa-1$ for positive $\kappa$, and $l(-\kappa) = -\kappa$ for negative $\kappa$. Thus, $l(-\kappa) = l(\kappa)-\hat{\kappa}$, where $\hat{\kappa} = \kappa/|\kappa|$.

The radial waves (3.26) are irregular at the origin, $r = 0$, since

$$h_l(\rho \to 0) \approx -i.1.1.3.5\ldots(2l-1)/\rho^{l+1} \tag{3.27}$$

approaches infinity there. A regular solution, called the 'spherical Bessel function', $j_l(\rho)$, can be formed by superposing the outgoing and incoming waves in equal parts:

$$j_l(\rho) = \tfrac{1}{2}[h_l(\rho)+h_l^*(\rho)]. \tag{3.28}$$

This has the behaviour near the origin:

$$j_l(\rho \to 0) \approx \rho^l/1.3.5\ldots(2l+1). \tag{3.29}$$

The proportionality to $(pr)^l = (r/\lambda\!\!\!^{-})^l$ is a reflection of the centrifugal effects illustrated in Fig. 1.9. The spherical Bessel functions are appropriately referred to as 'standing spherical waves', as their behaviour at remote distances,

$$j_l(\rho \to \infty) \approx \rho^{-1} \cos[\rho - \tfrac{1}{2}(l+1)\pi], \tag{3.30}$$

demonstrates.

*Normalization per unit energy*

Particles with a continuous spectrum of energies must be described by superpositions of energy eigenstates, like

$$\Psi(\mathbf{r}, t) = \int dW \sum_{\kappa\mu} a_{W\kappa\mu} \psi_{\kappa\mu}(\mathbf{r}, t). \tag{3.31}$$

The coefficients $a_{W\kappa\mu}$ have definition only relative to the normalization adopted for the $\psi_{\kappa\mu}$, i.e. the choice made for the constants $N_W$ in (3.26). 'Normalization per unit energy' is so defined that $\sum_{\kappa\mu} |a_{W\kappa\mu}|^2 \, dW$ becomes interpretable as the probability of finding a particle with its energy in the range $dW$, relative to

$$\oint (d\mathbf{r})|\Psi|^2 = \int dW \sum_{\kappa\mu} |a_{W\kappa\mu}|^2 \quad (=1). \tag{3.32}$$

For the interpretation to be a valid one, the space integral here must be reducible to the energy integral, by substituting (3.31) for $\Psi^\dagger$ and $\Psi$. The result of the substitutions into the space integral is

$$\oint (d\mathbf{r}) \int dW \int dW' \sum_{\kappa\mu\kappa'\mu'} a^*_{W\kappa\mu} a_{W'\kappa'\mu'} \psi^\dagger_{\kappa\mu} \psi'_{\kappa'\mu'}$$

with $\psi'_{\kappa'\mu'}$ to be evaluated at the energies $W'$. When the $\psi$'s are resolved into the Pauli spinors of (3.20), the angular part of the space integration, $\oint (d\mathbf{r}) \equiv \int\limits_0^\infty dr\, r^2 \oint d\Omega$, is easily disposed of, by making use of the orthonormality (2.21), of the $\chi_{\kappa\mu}$. The last expression is thereby reduced to

$$\int dW \int dW' \sum_{\kappa\mu} a^*_{W\kappa\mu} a_{W'\kappa\mu} \int\limits_0^\infty dr\, r^2 [g^*_\kappa g'_\kappa + f^*_{-\kappa} f'_{-\kappa}] e^{i(W-W')t}.$$

This reduces further, to just the requisite energy integral of (3.32), if the radial functions are so normalized that

$$\int\limits_0^\infty dr\, r^2 [g^*_\kappa g'_\kappa + f^*_{-\kappa} f'_{-\kappa}] = \delta(W'-W), \tag{3.33}$$

the 'Dirac delta-function' which vanishes for every energy $W'$ except $W' = W$, and has the unit integral

$$\int dW'\, \delta(W'-W) = \int\limits_{W-\Delta W}^{W+\Delta W} dW' \int\limits_0^\infty dr\, r^2 [g^*_\kappa g'_\kappa + f^*_{-\kappa} f'_{-\kappa}] = 1 \tag{3.34}$$

over any interval enclosing $W$, even as $\Delta W \to 0$.

Now, the radial oscillations $g_\kappa \sim h_{l(\kappa)}$ and $f_{-\kappa} \sim h_{l(-\kappa)}$, of (3.26), die out with $r \to \infty$ only as $1/r$, according to the asymptotic form,

$$h_l(r \to \infty) \approx (pr)^{-1} \exp i[pr - \tfrac{1}{2}(l+1)\pi],$$

of (3.25). Consequently, for a given energy $W' = W$, $\int\limits_0^\infty dr\, r^2 |h_l|^2 \to \infty$!

On the other hand, only a vanishingly small fraction of the superposition (3.31) is allowed to have $W' = W$, and $W' \neq W$ produces oscillations of zero radial average in the integrand of (3.34); the consequence is that the integral is finite, and normalizable to unity, as required. That is actually demonstrated by evaluating the normalization constant $N_W$ needed to give the unit result in (3.34). No error is introduced in the integration by using only the asymptotic form of $h_l$, since all regions except $r \to \infty$ give comparatively vanishing contributions, and their substitutions from (3.26) transform (3.34) into

$$1 = \int_{W-\Delta W}^{W+\Delta W} dW' N_W N_{W'}(pp')^{-1}\left[1+\left(\frac{W-1}{W+1}\cdot\frac{W'-1}{W'+1}\right)^{\frac{1}{2}}\right] \int_0^\infty dr\, e^{i(p'-p)r}.$$

In this, $W' = W$ may be put everywhere except in the exponential, since the latter gives a zero radial average except for $p' = p$. An interchange of the radial and energy integrations then gives

$$\begin{aligned} 1 &= [2N_W^2/p(W+1)] \int_0^\infty dr \int_{p-\Delta p}^{p+\Delta p} dp' e^{i(p'-p)r} \\ &= 2\pi N_W^2/p(W+1), \end{aligned}$$

whatever $\Delta W$ or $\Delta p = W\Delta W/p$ is chosen. This shows that the outgoing waves (3.26), as also the ingoing waves obtained by taking the complex conjugate, will be normalized per unit energy if $N_W = [p(W+1)/2\pi]^{\frac{1}{2}}$ is adopted.

The same normalization is retained for the regular, 'standing' waves when these are formed by adding the ingoing to the outgoing waves, and dividing by $2^{\frac{1}{2}}$. Since $j_l$ is defined, in (3.28), as half the sum of $h_l$ and $h_l^*$,

$$\left.\begin{aligned} g_\kappa &= [p(W+1)/\pi]^{\frac{1}{2}} j_{l(\kappa)}(pr) \\ f_{-\kappa} &= \hat{\kappa}[p(W-1)/\pi]^{\frac{1}{2}} j_{l(-\kappa)}(pr) \end{aligned}\right\} \tag{3.35}$$

are the regular radial functions, normalized per unit energy. The resultant orthonormality properties of the spherical waves $\psi_{\kappa\mu}$ may be summarized by

$$\oint (d\mathbf{r})\psi^\dagger_{\kappa\mu}(W)\psi_{\kappa'\mu'}(W') = \delta_{\kappa\kappa'}\delta_{\mu\mu'}\delta(W-W'). \tag{3.36}$$

The arguments $(W)$ and $(W')$ are inserted in order to specify the energies used in each spherical wave.

When the same wave field $\Psi(\mathbf{r}, t)$ as (3.31) is instead analysed into the plane wave components, $\psi_\mu$ of (3.4), then it is appropriate to introduce probability coefficients $a_\mu$ such that

$$\Psi(\mathbf{r}, t) = \oint [(d\mathbf{p})V/(2\pi)^3] \sum_\mu a_\mu(\mathbf{p})\psi_\mu(\mathbf{r}, t). \tag{3.37}$$

The factor $(d\mathbf{p})V/(2\pi\hbar)^3$ is the well-known count of the number of plane wave states which can be accommodated in an indefinitely large volume $V$, having momenta in the range $(d\mathbf{p})$ [see § 1.3]. It will be recalled that the $\psi_\mu$'s are normalized to unity in the volume $V$. Since $\psi_\mu \sim \exp(i\mathbf{p}.\mathbf{r})$, there is implicit here a fourier-integral analysis of the form

$$\Psi = \oint (d\mathbf{p}')A(\mathbf{p}')e^{i\mathbf{p}'.\mathbf{r}} \quad \text{with } A(\mathbf{p}) = \oint (d\mathbf{r})\Psi e^{-i\mathbf{p}.\mathbf{r}}/(2\pi)^3. \quad (3.38)$$

The last integral is the standard way to evaluate the fourier coefficients needed to make the preceding integral represent the given $\Psi$. Inserting one integral into the other yields

$$A(\mathbf{p}) = \oint (d\mathbf{p}')A(\mathbf{p}') \oint (d\mathbf{r})e^{i(\mathbf{p}'-\mathbf{p}).\mathbf{r}}/(2\pi)^3.$$

The two sides can be identical only if

$$\oint (d\mathbf{r})e^{i(\mathbf{p}'-\mathbf{p}).\mathbf{r}}/(2\pi)^3 = \delta(\mathbf{p}'-\mathbf{p}), \quad (3.39)$$

a delta-function which vanishes except for $\mathbf{p}' = \mathbf{p}$, and has the unit integral

$$\oint (d\mathbf{p}')\delta(\mathbf{p}'-\mathbf{p}) = 1. \quad (3.40)$$

The expression (3.39) is a well-known fourier-integral representation of a delta-function.

The precise significance of the coefficients $a_\mu(\mathbf{p})$ in the wave field (3.37) is found by substituting the latter into

$$\oint (d\mathbf{r})|\Psi|^2 = \sum_{\mu\mu'} [V/(2\pi)^3]^2 \oint (d\mathbf{p}) \oint (d\mathbf{p}')a_\mu^*(\mathbf{p})a_{\mu'}(\mathbf{p}') \oint (d\mathbf{r})\psi_\mu^\dagger \psi_{\mu'}'.$$

The space integral here is readily reduced to the form (3.39). Since, further, $\psi_\mu$ is so normalized that

$$\psi_\mu^\dagger \psi_{\mu'} = \delta_{\mu\mu'}/V, \quad (3.41)$$

the result is

$$\oint (d\mathbf{r})|\Psi|^2 = \oint [(d\mathbf{p})V/(2\pi)^3] \sum_\mu |a_\mu(\mathbf{p})|^2 \quad (=1). \quad (3.42)$$

Thus, $\sum_\mu |a_\mu(\mathbf{p})|^2$ should be interpreted as the fraction of the states in the range $(d\mathbf{p})$ which are occupied by the wave field $\Psi$.

Comparison of (3.37) and (3.31) makes clear that the normalization of $\psi_\mu$ can be changed, from unity in $V$, to the normalization per unit energy, simply by multiplying it by the factor

$$[pWV/(2\pi)^3]^{\frac{1}{2}}. \quad (3.43)$$

With this, it is implied that the integration over all directions of $\mathbf{p}$ must supplement integrations over energy, in evaluating results. In other words, the factor (3.43) on $\psi_\mu$ produces a normalization per unit energy *and* per unit solid angle of momentum directions. Its square, after it is multiplied by the total solid angle $4\pi$ becomes recognizable as just the number of plane wave states in the volume $V$, per unit of energy range $dW$.

*Plane and spherical wave intertransformations*

A given plane wave field, $\psi_\rho$ of (3.4), can be expressed as a superposition of spherical waves like (3.31), by generalizing the well-known expansion of the plane wave into Legendre polynomials,

$$e^{i\mathbf{p}.\mathbf{r}} = \sum_l (2l+1)i^l j_l(pr)P_l(\hat{\mathbf{p}}.\hat{\mathbf{r}}). \tag{3.44}$$

Only the regular radial waves, $j_l$, can appear here because, whatever the centre $r = 0$ about which the analysis is made, the plane wave is obviously regular there, as everywhere. The dependences on the directions of the momentum $\mathbf{p}$, and position vector $\mathbf{r}$, can be separated by making use of the well-known spherical harmonic 'addition theorem':

$$P_l(\hat{\mathbf{p}}.\hat{\mathbf{r}}) = 4\pi(2l+1)^{-1} \sum_m Y_{lm}^*(\hat{\mathbf{p}})Y_{lm}(\hat{\mathbf{r}}). \tag{3.45}$$

Now, a Pauli spinor plane wave, $\chi_\rho \exp(i\mathbf{p}.\mathbf{r})$ is easily expanded into the eigenstates $\chi_{\kappa\mu}(\hat{\mathbf{r}})$, by making use of

$$\chi_\rho Y_{lm}(\hat{\mathbf{r}}) = \sum_{\kappa\mu} \chi_{\kappa\mu} \oint d\Omega(\chi_{\kappa\mu}^\dagger \chi_\rho)Y_{lm} = \sum_{\kappa(l)} \langle l(m)\tfrac{1}{2}(\rho)|j(m+\rho)\rangle \chi_{\kappa,m+\rho}(\hat{\mathbf{r}}), \tag{3.46}$$

which follows easily from the definition of $\chi_{\kappa\mu}$ (2.18). The Pauli plane wave spinor, thus represented, is just the large component of the Dirac plane wave spinor, $\psi_\rho$ of (3.4), and the representation superposes just the large components of the regular spherical wave spinors (3.20), (3.35). The small components of both the plane and spherical spinors are derivable from the large components by the same operation (3.2), (3.18). Consequently, the large component analysis is sufficient to give the desired result:

$$\psi_\rho(\mathbf{r}) = [(2\pi)^3/pWV]^{\frac{1}{2}} \sum_{\kappa\mu} i^l[\chi_{\kappa\mu}^\dagger(\hat{\mathbf{p}}).\chi_\rho]\psi_{\kappa\mu}(\mathbf{r}), \tag{3.47 a}$$

where
$$\chi_{\kappa\mu}^\dagger.\chi_\rho \equiv \langle l(\mu-\rho)\tfrac{1}{2}(\rho)|j(\mu)\rangle Y_{l,\mu-\rho}^*(\hat{\mathbf{p}}). \tag{3.47 b}$$

It should be emphasized that the $\psi_{\kappa\mu}$ are the regular spherical waves, with the radial behaviour (3.35).

An inversion of the relationship (3.47) is quite straightforward, giving any regular free spherical wave as a superposition of plane waves:

$$\psi_{\kappa\mu}(\mathbf{r}) = [pWV/(2\pi)^3]^{\frac{1}{2}} \oint (d\hat{\mathbf{p}}) \sum_\rho i^{-l(\kappa)}[\chi_\rho^\dagger.\chi_{\kappa\mu}(\hat{\mathbf{p}})]\psi_\rho(\mathbf{r}), \tag{3.48}$$

where the last square bracket is just the complex conjugate of (3.47 b). The differential $(d\hat{\mathbf{p}})$ stands for an element of solid angle into which the momentum of a plane wave component is directed. The irregular, outgoing or incoming, spherical waves can be completely (i.e. everywhere) represented as superpositions of plane waves only if the latter are generalized to include imaginary angles between $\mathbf{p}$ and $\mathbf{r}$ (so-called 'integral representations' of Hankel functions).

## 3.3. Coulomb-distorted waves

The analysis into spherical waves is particularly suited for taking into account forces centred on the origin, such as the coulomb force due to the nuclear charge, $+Ze$. This electrostatic effect is representable by a central potential, $V(r)$, and it influences the spherical waves only in their radial modulation. They continue to have the form (3.20), but now the radial functions, $g_\kappa$ and $f_{-\kappa}$, are solutions of equations (3.21) and (3.23) in which the constant kinetic energy $W$ is replaced by the radially-modulated kinetic energy, $W-V(r)$.

*Distortion by a point charge*

Even the most energetic electrons characteristic of $\beta$-decay have wave lengths which are long compared to nuclear dimensions, hence it is usually sufficient to treat the nucleus as a point-charge in gauging its electrostatic effect. We confine ourselves for the present to the effect on negatrons, hence take $V(r) = -Ze^2/r \equiv -\alpha Z/r$ (since $\alpha \equiv e^2/\hbar c = e^2$ when $\hbar = c = 1$). As is appropriate for a point-charge field extending down to $r = 0$, only the 'regular' solutions, yielding integrable densities at the origin, will be presented. When normalized per unit energy, they can be written as the real combinations

$$\begin{aligned} g_\kappa &= [p(W+1)/4\pi]^{\frac{1}{2}}(Q+Q^*), \\ f_{-\kappa} &= i[p(W-1)/4\pi]^{\frac{1}{2}}(Q-Q^*), \end{aligned} \tag{3.49}$$

where

$$Q = D(|\kappa|)(\gamma+i\nu)(2pr)^{\gamma-1}e^{-ipr+i\eta}F(\gamma+1+i\nu, 2\gamma+1;\, 2ipr). \tag{3.50}$$

The last factor is the 'confluent hypergeometric function', which has the series representation

$$F(a,b;\, z) = \frac{\Gamma(b)}{\Gamma(a)}\sum_{n=0}^{\infty}\frac{\Gamma(a+n)}{\Gamma(b+n)}\frac{z^n}{n!}. \tag{3.51}$$

The real constant factor

$$D(|\kappa|) = 2e^{\frac{1}{2}\pi\nu}|\Gamma(\gamma+i\nu)|/\Gamma(2\gamma+1) \tag{3.52}$$

depends only on the absolute value of $\kappa$, through

$$\gamma = +(\kappa^2-\alpha^2Z^2)^{\frac{1}{2}} \tag{3.53}$$

which coincides with (1.15) for $\kappa = \pm 1$ $(j = \frac{1}{2})$. The quantity $\nu = +\alpha ZW/p$ is the same as (1.13), for negatrons. $Q$ depends on the sign of $\kappa$ only through the phase factor

$$e^{2i\eta} = -(\kappa - i\alpha Z/p)/(\gamma + i\nu). \tag{3.54}$$

It is easy to check that this expression has an absolute value of unity.

The combinations $\frac{1}{2}(Q+Q^*)$ and $\frac{1}{2}i(Q-Q^*)$ properly reduce to the regular $V = 0$ functions, $j_{l(\kappa)}$ and $\hat{\kappa} j_{l(-\kappa)}$, respectively, in the limit $Z \to 0$. However, $Q$ itself does not then reduce to the purely outgoing wave,‡ $h_l$, despite the relation $j_l = \frac{1}{2}(h_l + h_l^*)$; such a simple correspondence is prevented by the fact that any wave passing through a varying force field suffers continual reflections. On the other hand, as $r \to \infty$, $Q$ does reduce to an outgoing wave alone (standing wave components in it die out relatively faster with $r$):

$$Q(r \to \infty) \approx (pr)^{-1} \exp i(pr + \delta), \tag{3.55}$$

where
$$\delta(\kappa) = \nu \ln(2pr) - \arg \Gamma(\gamma + i\nu) + \eta - \tfrac{1}{2}\pi\gamma. \tag{3.56}$$

For $Z = 0$, $\delta(\kappa) \to -\frac{1}{2}[l(\kappa)+1]\pi$ exactly as in the asymptotic form (3.25) of $h_l$. The consequent asymptotic forms of $g_\kappa$ and $f_{-\kappa}$ are

$$\left.\begin{aligned} g_\kappa(\infty) &\approx [p(W+1)/\pi]^{\frac{1}{2}}(pr)^{-1}\cos[pr+\delta(\kappa)] \\ f_{-\kappa}(\infty) &\approx \hat{\kappa}[p(W-1)/\pi]^{\frac{1}{2}}(pr)^{-1}\cos[pr+\delta(\kappa)+\tfrac{1}{2}\hat{\kappa}\pi] \end{aligned}\right\}. \tag{3.57}$$

Comparison with (3.30) and (3.35) shows these to be the same as the asymptotic forms of the regular $V = 0$ waves, except for the additional phase shift

$$\delta'(\kappa) = \delta(\kappa) + \tfrac{1}{2}[l(\kappa)+1]\pi, \tag{3.58}$$

common to both $g_\kappa$ and $f_{-\kappa}$. The relation $l(-\kappa) = l(\kappa) - \hat{\kappa}$ is useful in establishing this.

*Plane waves emerging from a coulomb field*

To answer questions about the emergence at infinity of a particle with a specific momentum, $\mathbf{p}$, it is necessary to construct superpositions of the spherical waves, like (3.47) ,which will represent a plane wave at least at infinity. Mere substitution of the coulomb-distorted spherical waves, in place of the $V = 0$ spherical waves used in (3.47), is not sufficient. Even at infinity, the coulomb-distorted waves are phase-shifted relative to the free ones, by $\delta'$ of (3.58), and since this phase shift varies with $\kappa$, the various terms of the superposition would not be in the correct relative phase to yield a plane wave resultant. On the other hand, if we cancel

‡ Irregular solutions in the coulomb field are needed to construct functions which reduce to $h_l$ for $Z = 0$; the irregular solutions are obtainable from the regular ones (3.49) essentially by reversing the sign of $\gamma$.

the phase shift in the outgoing parts, $\sim Q(r)$, of the distorted spherical waves, by introducing the factors $\exp\{-i\delta'(\kappa)\}$ into the terms of the superposition (3.47), then at least the emergent (outgoing) part of the field will form the required plane wave.

Actually, the situation is not quite as straightforward as the last statement may suggest. $\delta'(\kappa)$ varies slowly with position because of the term $\nu \ln(2pr)$ in (3.56), and only constant coefficients can be used in the superposition, if it is to continue to be a possible Dirac field of definite energy, as is each individual spherical wave, $\psi_{\kappa\mu}$. The remedy is simple because $\nu \ln(2pr)$ is independent of $\kappa$; we merely modify the factors to be introduced to the constant ones $\exp\{-i\delta''(\kappa)\}$, with

$$\delta''(\kappa) = \tfrac{1}{2}[l(\kappa)+1]\pi - \arg\Gamma(\gamma+i\nu)+\eta-\tfrac{1}{2}\pi\gamma, \tag{3.59}$$

in place of $\delta'$ of (3.58). Thus, we construct a superposition on the model of (3.47),

$$\Psi_\rho(\mathbf{r}) = [(2\pi)^3/pWV]^{\frac{1}{2}} \sum_{\kappa\mu} i^l \langle l(\mu-\rho)\tfrac{1}{2}(\rho)|j(\mu)\rangle Y^*_{l,\mu-\rho}(\hat{\mathbf{p}})e^{-i\delta''}\psi_{\kappa\mu}(\mathbf{r}), \tag{3.60}$$

with coulomb-distorted spherical waves $\psi_{\kappa\mu}$, replacing the free spherical waves of (3.47). The asymptotic behaviour of this field is easy to derive from comparing the behaviour of the distorted waves (3.57) with the undistorted ones as given by (3.30) and (3.35):

$$\Psi_\rho(r\to\infty) \approx e^{i\nu\ln 2pr}\psi_\rho+(A/r)e^{-i(pr+Wt)}. \tag{3.61}$$

Here, $\psi_\rho$ is the same plane wave as in (3.47), and $A$ is well-defined by the procedure, but, for the purposes here, it need only be known that it is independent of $r$ except through the occurrence of the phase factors, $\exp(\pm i\nu \ln 2pr)$, in it. Only an *ingoing* wave, the last term of (3.61), has been 'left over', after the close as possible matching of the outgoing parts to those characteristic of the plane wave.

The slowly varying phase factor, $\exp(i\nu\ln 2pr)$, is needed to make (3.61) strictly a state of definite energy, in an ideal point-charge field which extends uninterruptedly to infinity. There are then slight variations of the outgoing momentum even in regions remote from the charge, but these variations are of the completely negligible order $\nu\lambda\!\!\!^{-}/r$ with $r\to\infty$. The phenomenon is plainly an effect of over-idealization, and the phase factor which represents it can be regarded as a constant over any finite region used for momentum detection 'at infinity'. The phase factor could be dropped without making the state effectively different.

A result of greater interest‡ is the fact that an *ingoing* spherical wave

‡ See G. Breit and H. A. Bethe, *Phys. Rev.* **93**, 888 (1954), for a more detailed description of the phenomenon discussed here.

is needed to maintain outgoing waves which combine to form a plane wave of definite momentum. This necessity is complementary to the case of the standard 'scattering' state, in which an *outgoing* spherical scattered wave is a necessary result of maintaining ingoing waves which combine to form a plane wave incident on the force centre. The state (3.60), (3.61) is the solution of a problem in which a spherical wave is 'sent in', to converge on a point charge, just such that a scattered wave of definite momentum emerges. This does not mean, of course, that such a spherical wave must actually be 'sent in' in order to have a $\beta$-interaction generate a particle emerging with a definite momentum at infinity. It does mean that, when we wish to pick out of any wave field $\Psi$ which may be generated, the component corresponding to a specific emerging momentum, in the presence of nuclear charge, then it is a component $\Psi_p$, of the form (3.60), that must be picked out.

*The electron density at the nucleus*‡

The experience reviewed in Chapter I leads to the expectation that the wave fields arising in $\beta$-decay are generated in proportion to their densities at the nucleus. We therefore investigate the values of $|\Psi_p(0)|^2$, with the $\Psi_p(r)$ of (3.60) normalized to unity in $V$.

The coulomb-distorted spherical waves, $\psi_{\kappa\mu}$, which are combined to form $\Psi_p$, are proportional to $(2pr)^{\gamma-1}$, according to (3.50). They all, therefore, vanish at $r = 0$, except those with the minimum total angular momentum $j = \frac{1}{2}$, for which $\kappa = \pm 1$ and so

$$\gamma = (\kappa^2-\alpha^2Z^2)^{\frac{1}{2}} \to \gamma_0 = (1-\alpha^2Z^2)^{\frac{1}{2}} < 1.$$

As discussed in § 1.6, this is because orbital momentum is necessarily generated when $j > \frac{1}{2}$, and that introduces centrifugal force which repels the electron from $r = 0$. The waves $\psi_{\pm 1,\mu}$ which survive at the origin are actually weakly singular there, $\sim (2pr)^{-(1-\gamma_0)}$. As discussed in § 1.4, we may evaluate them at some finite 'nuclear radius', $R$, instead. Notice that the constant $D$, of (3.52), is closely related to the electron density ratio, $F(Z, W)$ of (1.14):

$$D(1) = [2F(Z, W)/(1+\gamma_0)]^{\frac{1}{2}}(2pR)^{1-\gamma_0}, \tag{3.62}$$

for the special cases of $\kappa = \pm(j+\frac{1}{2}) = \pm 1$.

The evaluation of $\Psi_p(R)$ is much simplified when the purely formal relations following from the definition (2.18) of $\chi_{\kappa\mu}$,

$$\boldsymbol{\sigma}\cdot\hat{\mathbf{r}}\chi_{\kappa\mu}(\hat{\mathbf{r}}) = -\chi_{-\kappa\mu}(\hat{\mathbf{r}}), \qquad \boldsymbol{\sigma}.\hat{\mathbf{p}}\chi_{\kappa\mu}(\hat{\mathbf{p}}) = -\chi_{-\kappa\mu}(\hat{\mathbf{p}}), \tag{3.63}$$

‡ J. D. Jackson, S. Treiman and H. Wyld, *Nucl. Phys.* **4**, 206 (1957).

are used. These, together with $\boldsymbol{\chi}_{-1,\mu} = (4\pi)^{-\frac{1}{2}}\boldsymbol{\chi}_{\mu}$ (the Pauli eigenspinor), make it quite simple to show that

$$\Psi_{p}(R) = [(W+\gamma_0)F/2WV]^{\frac{1}{2}}\begin{pmatrix} 1 \\ B\boldsymbol{\sigma}.\mathbf{p}/(W+\gamma_0)\end{pmatrix}\boldsymbol{\chi}_{\rho}\, e^{-iWt} \tag{3.64}$$

after noting the following. First, a constant phase factor has been dropped; such phase factors are immaterial, since the field may be generated in arbitrary phase. More serious has been the replacement by unity of the operator factor,

$$1+i\boldsymbol{\alpha}.\hat{\mathbf{r}}\alpha Z/(1+\gamma_0). \tag{3.65}$$

The justification for this is that the form (3.64) will be useful only for allowed transitions, and the term $\sim \hat{\mathbf{r}}$ can contribute only in forbidden transitions as will eventually be seen.

The symbol $B$ in (3.64) is an abbreviation for

$$B \equiv 1+i\alpha Z/p. \tag{3.66}$$

The identity of $\Psi_{p}(R)$ in the limit $Z \to 0$, with the plane wave $\psi_{p}(0)$, of (3.4), is evident, since $F(0, W) = 1$. Thus $\Psi_{p}(R)$ is a coulomb modification of the plane wave which is adequate for treating the allowed transitions. The density at the nucleus is given by

$$|\Psi_{p}(R)|^2 \equiv \Psi_{p}^{\dagger}\Psi_{p} = F(Z, W)/V.$$

Its ratio to the free plane wave density (3.41) is

$$|\Psi_{p}(R)/\psi_{p}|^2 = F(Z, W), \tag{3.67}$$

just as described in § 1.4.

In § 3.1 the conclusion was reached that the intensities generated in $\beta$-decay are proportional to the densities of only the intrinsically left-handed components (3.9) of any state. Thus,

$$\Phi_{p}(R) = \tfrac{1}{2}(1+\gamma_5)\Psi_{p}(R) = 2^{-\frac{1}{2}}\begin{pmatrix} \mathbf{U}_{p}(R) \\ -\mathbf{U}_{p}(R)\end{pmatrix}e^{-iWt}, \tag{3.68 a}$$

with

$$\mathbf{U}_{p}(R) = \tfrac{1}{2}[(W+\gamma_0)F(Z, W)/WV]^{\frac{1}{2}}[1-B\boldsymbol{\sigma}.\mathbf{p}/(W+\gamma_0)]\boldsymbol{\chi}_{\rho}. \tag{3.68 b}$$

The consequent coulomb effect on the result (3.12) is

$$\begin{aligned}\Phi_{p}^{\dagger}\Phi_{p} &= (F/2V)[1-\tfrac{1}{2}(B+B^*)(\mathbf{p}/W).(\boldsymbol{\chi}_{\rho}^{\dagger}\boldsymbol{\sigma}\boldsymbol{\chi}_{\rho})] \\ &= (F/2V)[1\mp p_z/W] \quad \text{for } \rho = \pm\tfrac{1}{2}.\end{aligned} \tag{3.69}$$

There is only a modification of the total intensity, and no change in the polarization

$$\begin{aligned}\mathscr{P} &= (|\Phi_{\frac{1}{2}}|^2-|\Phi_{-\frac{1}{2}}|^2)/(|\Phi_{\frac{1}{2}}|^2+|\Phi_{-\frac{1}{2}}|^2) \\ &= -(v/c)\cos\theta_{ez}.\end{aligned} \tag{3.70}$$

This expression applies specifically to negatrons, of course, hence the negative sign. The positron case is given in (3.89).

## 3.4. Charge-conjugation in an electromagnetic field

The spherical waves presented so far are those suited for describing normal, rather than antiparticle, states, under the conventions adopted. States $\psi^C$, which describe antiparticles, can always be derived from normal particle states $\psi$, by the charge-conjugation operation, $\psi^C = C\psi^*$, of (3.7). That has already been demonstrated for free particle states (3.6), but becomes a more substantial problem in the presence of an electromagnetic field, which leads to a discrimination between negative and positive charge on the particle.

*A Dirac particle in an electromagnetic field*

It is well known that an arbitrary electromagnetic field can be described by a four-vector potential, $A_\alpha(\mathbf{A}, i\phi)$, which is generally expressible as a function $A_\alpha(x_\alpha)$ of the space-time four-vector, $x_\alpha(\mathbf{r}, ict)$. It is also well known that a charged particle moving in such a field exchanges momentum and energy with it in such a way that the particle's kinetic momentum-energy four-vector, $(m'\mathbf{v}, im'c)$ with $m' = m/(1-v^2/c^2)^{\frac{1}{2}}$, is no longer the variable 'conjugate' to $x_\alpha$, either in the classical hamiltonian description, or in the sense of the uncertainty principle. We continue with the symbol $p_\alpha$ for the new conjugate momentum, the one that gets the representation $p_\alpha = -i\hbar\partial/\partial x_\alpha$ from the fundamental commutation relations, when operating on $\psi(x_\alpha)$. The modification by the electromagnetic field is such that, in the relationships in which the kinetic momentum-energy appears, it is replaced by

$$p_\alpha + (e/c)A_\alpha = -i\hbar[\partial/\partial x_\alpha + (ie/\hbar c)A_\alpha], \tag{3.71}$$

for a negatron with charge $-e$. Thus, the Dirac equation (2.82) becomes

$$[\gamma_\alpha(\partial/\partial x_\alpha + ieA_\alpha/\hbar c) + mc/\hbar]\psi = 0, \tag{3.72}$$

and the Dirac hamiltonian $H \equiv -icp_4$ becomes

$$H = c\boldsymbol{\alpha}.(\mathbf{p} + e\mathbf{A}/c) + \beta mc^2 - e\phi, \tag{3.73}$$

in place of (2.71). The result here is consistent with the treatment of the static nuclear charge field in the preceding section, in which $\mathbf{A} = 0$ and $-e\phi = V(r) = -Ze^2/r$.

When the Dirac equation is given the standard form, $i\hbar\partial\psi/\partial t = H\psi$, for the equation of motion, instead of the explicitly covariant form (3.72), then

$$i\hbar\partial\psi/\partial t = [-i\hbar c\boldsymbol{\alpha}.(\boldsymbol{\nabla} + ie\mathbf{A}/\hbar c) + \beta mc^2 - e\phi]\psi. \tag{3.74}$$

This form has some advantages for investigating charge-conjugacy.

*Charge-conjugation*

We first seek the equation which must be satisfied by $\psi^C = C\psi^*$, with $C$ as defined by (3.7) in the Dirac representation, and when $\psi$ is a solution of (3.74). Applying $C$ to the complex conjugate of (3.74) yields

$$-i\hbar\partial\psi^C/\partial t = C[i\hbar c\boldsymbol{\alpha}^*.(\boldsymbol{\nabla}-ie\mathbf{A}/\hbar c)+\beta^* mc^2-e\phi]\psi^*.$$

In the Dirac representation, $\alpha^*_{x,z} = \rho_1^*\,\Sigma^*_{1,3} = \rho_1\,\Sigma_{1,3} = \alpha_{x,z}$ and $\beta^* = \rho_3 = \beta$ are real, while $\alpha_y^* = \rho_1\,\Sigma_2^* = -\alpha_y$ is imaginary. The operator $C = \rho_2\,\Sigma_2$ commutes with $\alpha_x$ and $\alpha_z$, but anticommutes with $\alpha_y$ and $\beta$. Consequently,

$$i\hbar\partial\psi^C/\partial t = [-i\hbar c\boldsymbol{\alpha}.(\boldsymbol{\nabla}-ie\mathbf{A}/\hbar c)+\beta mc^2+e\phi]\psi^C, \tag{3.75}$$

which is the same as the equation (3.74) for $\psi$, except for the sign of the charge. In the limit $A = 0$, $\phi = 0$, we interpreted $\psi^C = C\psi^*$ as the state of an antiparticle having the same dynamical properties as the normal particle described by $\psi = C\psi^{C*}$. We now see that when an electromagnetic field is 'turned on', it affects the antiparticle as if it had a charge opposite to that of the normal particle. The antiparticle of a negatron is a positron.

Defining properties of $C$ which hold in any representation can be obtained by starting with a comparison of the equation for $\psi^*$, with an equation for $C\psi^*$ which differs from (3.74) only in the sign of the charge $e$. The equations agree if

$$\boldsymbol{\alpha}C = C\boldsymbol{\alpha}^* \quad\text{and}\quad \beta C = -C\beta^*. \tag{3.76 a}$$

Equivalent relations can be expressed in terms of $\boldsymbol{\gamma} = -i\beta\boldsymbol{\alpha}$ and $\gamma_4 = \beta$:

$$\boldsymbol{\gamma}C = C\boldsymbol{\gamma}^* \quad\text{and}\quad \gamma_4 C = -C\gamma_4^*, \tag{3.76 b}$$

also obtainable directly by working with the explicitly covariant equations (3.72) instead of (3.74). These relations are sufficient to determine $C$ within an arbitrary constant factor, which is determined within a phase by the unitarity condition, $C^\dagger C = 1$, imposed to preserve the probability interpretation: $\psi^{C\dagger}\psi^C = \psi^\dagger\psi$. By subjecting the defining equations (3.76) to matrix transposing operations, it can be seen that $\tilde{C}$ obeys the same equation as $C$, hence is the same within a constant factor. If that factor is chosen to be unity, the 'reflexivity' property

$$\psi^C = C\psi^* \quad\text{and}\quad \psi = C\psi^{C*} \tag{3.77}$$

follows. Thus

$$C^\dagger C = 1 \quad\text{and}\quad \tilde{C} = C \tag{3.78}$$

are requirements imposed on $C$ besides the equations (3.76). It is easy to see that $C = \rho_2 \Sigma_2$ of the Dirac representation (3.7), possesses all these properties and is real besides ($C^2 = 1$).

The investigation so far has shown how a positron state $\psi^C$ may be derived from a negatron state $\psi$, but not yet what the dynamical properties of the positron in $\psi^C$ will be, relative to those of the negatron in $\psi$. This can perhaps be seen most clearly by noticing first that $\psi^C$ of (3.75) can also be used to describe a negatron, but in an electromagnetic field $-\mathbf{A}$, $-\phi$ instead of $\mathbf{A}$, $\phi$, as for $\psi$ of (3.74). The negatron in $\psi^C$ will have the energy density

$$\psi^{C\dagger} H \psi^C = \tilde{\psi} C^\dagger (i\hbar\partial/\partial t) C\psi^* = -(\psi^\dagger H\psi)^*, \tag{3.79}$$

just the negative (since the energy in an actual state is real) of the negatron's energy in $\psi$. It is similarly easy to see that the linear and orbital momentum densities, as represented by the operators $-i\hbar\boldsymbol{\nabla}$ and $-i\hbar\mathbf{r}\times\boldsymbol{\nabla}$, have opposite signs for negatrons in $\psi$ and $\psi^C$. The relations (3.76) are needed to show a similar property for the spin density, as represented by $\boldsymbol{\sigma} = \boldsymbol{\alpha}\times\boldsymbol{\alpha}/2i$:

$$\psi^{C\dagger}\boldsymbol{\sigma}\psi^C = \tilde{\psi} C^\dagger \boldsymbol{\alpha} C \times C^{-1}\boldsymbol{\alpha} C\psi^*/2i = -(\psi^\dagger\boldsymbol{\sigma}\psi)^*. \tag{3.80}$$

What is specifically shown by these considerations can be most briefly expressed by using the symbol $\psi(\mathrm{e}^-, +W, +\mathbf{p}, +\mu, +Z)$ to denote a negatron state in the presence of the electromagnetic field $\mathbf{A}$, $\phi$; the latter is represented by $+Z$ in the symbol, since a specific example may be the presence of a nuclear charge which is attractive to the negatron. The symbol $+\mu$ refers to the angular momentum orientation. It is not implied that $\psi$ is necessarily a simultaneous eigenstate of the variables symbolized, but only that certain density distributions of those quantities are implicit in the specifications of any state. The above findings can now be summarized in the expression

$$\psi^C(\mathrm{e}^-, -W, -\mathbf{p}, -\mu, -Z) = C\psi^*(\mathrm{e}^-, +W, +\mathbf{p}, +\mu, +Z). \tag{3.81}$$

As indicated, $\psi^C$ describes a negative energy negatron in the presence of a field $-\mathbf{A}$, $-\phi$ (e.g. due to a charge repulsive to negatrons). Notice that the spatial density $\psi^{C\dagger}\psi^C = \tilde{\psi} C^\dagger C\psi^* = (\widetilde{\psi^\dagger\psi}) \equiv \psi^\dagger\psi$ is the same for a negative energy negatron in a repulsive field, as for a positive energy negatron in an attractive field.

Now, the behaviour exhibited by the negative energy negatron is interpreted as that of a positive energy positron:

$$\psi^C(\mathrm{e}^-, -W, -\mathbf{p}, -\mu, -Z) \equiv \psi^C(\mathrm{e}^+, +W, +\mathbf{p}, +\mu, -Z). \tag{3.82}$$

The retention of the sign on $Z$ corresponds to the fact that a mere reinterpretation of behaviour in a given situation cannot alter the electromagnetic field which is present. Comparison with (3.81) yields the reasonable interpretation that the behaviour of a positron in a field repulsive to negatrons (therefore attractive to positrons) is the same as that of a negatron in a field attractive to negatrons, e.g. the spatial distributions are the same. This means that the state of a positron in a given field $\mathbf{A}, \phi$ must be obtained, by charge-conjugation, from the state of a negatron in the field $-\mathbf{A}, -\phi$:

$$\psi^C(\mathrm{e}^+, +W, +\mathbf{p}, +\mu, +Z) = C\psi^*(\mathrm{e}^-, +W, +\mathbf{p}, +\mu, -Z). \quad (3.83)$$

In general, the charge-conjugate of a state is one in which *all* charges are reversed, including the sources of any electromagnetic fields which are present.

*Spherical positron waves*

The findings in the preceding subsection make it simple to derive states describing positrons from the negatron states already presented.

The positron state $\psi^C_{\kappa\mu}$, which has energy $+W$, angular momentum $j = |\kappa| - \frac{1}{2}$ and the projection of it, $\mu$, is obtained by applying the charge conjugation operation to $\psi_{\kappa\mu}$ of (3.20). Since this requires applying $C = \rho_2\,\Sigma_2$ to $\psi^*_{\kappa\mu}$, the relation

$$\sigma_2 \boldsymbol{\chi}^*_{\kappa\mu} = \hat{\kappa}(-)^{\mu+1}\boldsymbol{\chi}_{\kappa,-\mu} \quad (3.84)$$

becomes useful; it follows readily from the definition (2.18) of $\boldsymbol{\chi}_{\kappa\mu}$. Then

$$\psi^C_{\kappa\mu} = \hat{\kappa}(-)^{\mu+1}\begin{pmatrix} f_{-\kappa}(-Z)\boldsymbol{\chi}_{-\kappa,-\mu} \\ ig_{\kappa}(-Z)\boldsymbol{\chi}_{\kappa,-\mu} \end{pmatrix} e^{iWt}, \quad (3.85)$$

if the radial waves are chosen to be the real ones (3.49). The arguments $(-Z)$ are inserted as a reminder that negatron solutions, $f_{-\kappa}$, $g_{\kappa}$, in the negative of the actual electromagnetic field are to be used here, according to (3.83).

When complex radial waves are treated, like the free outgoing waves (3.26), then $g^*_{\kappa}$ and $f^*_{-\kappa}$ replace $g_{\kappa}$, $f_{-\kappa}$ in (3.85). (Notice that the charge-conjugate of an outgoing wave remains an outgoing wave, since

$$[\exp i(pr - Wt)]^* = \exp\{-i(pr - Wt)\}.)$$

There is a corresponding complication for superpositions like (3.60), which have running wave resultants

$$\Psi^C_{\rho} = [(2\pi)^3/pWV]^{\frac{1}{2}} \sum_{\kappa\mu} i^{-l}\langle l(\mu-\rho)\tfrac{1}{2}(\rho)|j(\mu)\rangle Y_{l,\mu-\rho}(\hat{\mathbf{p}})e^{i\delta''(-Z)}\psi^C_{\kappa\mu}. \quad (3.86)$$

Here occur differences from (3.60), in the relative phases of the waves being superposed. In particular, the amplitude at the nucleus, as obtained from the charge-conjugation of (3.64), becomes

$$\Psi_\rho^C(R) = (-)^{\rho+\frac{1}{2}}\left[\frac{(W+\gamma_0)F(-Z,W)}{2WV}\right]^{\frac{1}{2}}\begin{pmatrix} B\boldsymbol{\sigma}.\mathbf{p}/(W+\gamma_0) \\ 1 \end{pmatrix}\boldsymbol{\chi}_{-\rho}\, e^{iWt}, \quad (3.87)$$

because $B^*(-Z) = 1-i(-\alpha Z)/p = B(+Z)$. Despite such non-uniformities in changes of sign, the positron density ratio at the nucleus is simply $F(-Z, W)$, replacing (3.67), exactly as discussed in § 1.4.

The projection by $\frac{1}{2}(1+\gamma_5)$ of $\Psi_\rho^C(R)$ is

$$\Phi_\rho^C(R) = 2^{-\frac{1}{2}}(-)^{\rho-\frac{1}{2}}\begin{pmatrix} \overline{\mathbf{U}}_\rho(R) \\ -\overline{\mathbf{U}}_\rho(R) \end{pmatrix} e^{iWt} \quad (3.88\,\text{a})$$

with

$$\overline{\mathbf{U}}_\rho(R) = \tfrac{1}{2}[(W+\gamma_0)F(-Z,W)/WV]^{\frac{1}{2}}[1-B\boldsymbol{\sigma}.\mathbf{p}/(W+\gamma_0)]\boldsymbol{\chi}_{-\rho}. \quad (3.88\,\text{b})$$

When this replaces $\Phi$ of (3.70), the consequent polarization of the positrons comes out to be

$$\mathscr{P} = +v_z/c, \quad (3.89)$$

with the positive sign observed in positron emissions. The sign change relative to (3.70) can be traced to the occurrence of $\boldsymbol{\chi}_{-\rho}$, instead of $\boldsymbol{\chi}_\rho$, in (3.88).

# IV

# THE LAW OF $\beta$-INTERACTION

FERMI formulated the theory of $\beta$-radiation on the model of the theory of electromagnetic radiation. The latter underwent various stages of development and it is one of the earlier stages to which corresponds the version of the $\beta$-theory to be discussed in this chapter. It makes no explicit use of 'field quantization', which will be postponed to Chapter IX. Some theoretical questions will consequently become inconvenient to answer immediately, but the correct physical expectations will emerge. The approach will permit obtaining all the observable results of the most complete theory, yet will avoid a lengthy discursion into highly formal considerations, having a relatively small residue of physics.

## 4.1. The $\gamma$-interaction

A complete description of an electromagnetic radiation process requires subjecting to quantum conditions not only the degrees of freedom of the radiating mechanical system, but also the variables describing the electromagnetic field. However, an older and still valued procedure uses field variables only as given parameters specifying a 'perturbation' of the mechanical system. The state is treated as a function of the mechanical variables only, like $\psi$ of (3.74) for the case of a radiating negatron. In the latter case, the part

$$H_\gamma = -e(\phi - \boldsymbol{\alpha}.\mathbf{A}) \tag{4.1}$$

of the hamiltonian operator (3.73) is the 'perturbation'. To have a given photon radiated, an electromagnetic potential describing the field which represents the photon must be chosen for (4.1). In the case of spontaneous radiation, the electron can be regarded as 'perturbing' the field, and exciting an oscillation in it through the mutual coupling, $H_\gamma$.

In the state $\psi$, the purely mechanical energy density $\psi^\dagger(c\boldsymbol{\alpha}.\mathbf{p}+\beta mc^2)\psi$ can be said to be supplemented by an 'interaction-energy density',

$$h_\gamma \equiv \psi^\dagger H_\gamma \psi = -e\psi^\dagger\psi\phi + e\psi^\dagger\boldsymbol{\alpha}\psi.\mathbf{A}. \tag{4.2}$$

The expressions

$$\rho \equiv -e\psi^\dagger\psi \quad \text{and} \quad \mathbf{i} \equiv -ec\psi^\dagger\boldsymbol{\alpha}\psi \tag{4.3}$$

should be recognized as the electric charge and current densities of the negatron in $\psi$, considering (2.75) and (2.77). Consequently, the total interaction energy can be written

$$\oint (d\mathbf{r})h_\gamma = \oint (d\mathbf{r})(\rho\phi - \mathbf{i}\,.\,\mathbf{A}/c). \tag{4.4}$$

The last integral may be recognized as a classical expression for the interaction energy between a field and a charge-current $\rho$, $\mathbf{i}$.

The coupling-energy density (4.2) can be given an explicitly covariant form by defining the charge-current density four-vector

$$i_\alpha(\mathbf{i}, ic\rho) = -iec\bar{\psi}\gamma_\alpha\psi; \tag{4.5}$$

this is just $w_\alpha$ of (2.81) multiplied by $-e$. Now,

$$h_\gamma = -\sum_\alpha i_\alpha A_\alpha/c = ie\sum_\alpha (\bar{\psi}\gamma_\alpha\psi)A_\alpha, \tag{4.6}$$

which is patently a scalar. These expressions are seen most frequently without the summation sign, because of a 'summation convention' by which any product of two factors having identical indices is to be understood as demanding summation over the common index. The corresponding form for the interaction (hamiltonian) operator is

$$H_\gamma = ie\beta\gamma_\alpha A_\alpha \tag{4.7}$$

(summation over $\alpha = 1, 2, 3, 4$ understood).

## 4.2. The β-interaction

Electromagnetic radiation is generated through a coupling (4.6) proportional to the current density $\sim \bar{\psi}\gamma_\alpha\psi$, in the state $\psi$ of the particle. Fermi assumed that a neutron $\beta$-radiates, and transforms into a proton, through a coupling proportional to a 'transition current'

$$\bar{\psi}_\mathrm{p}\gamma_\alpha\psi_\mathrm{n} \equiv \psi_\mathrm{p}^\dagger\beta\gamma_\alpha\psi_\mathrm{n},$$

associated with the neutron-to-proton transformation. Here, $\psi_\mathrm{n}$ and $\psi_\mathrm{p}$ are Dirac spinors describing a nucleon which is to be interpreted as a neutron when in $\psi_\mathrm{n}$, a proton in $\psi_\mathrm{p}$.

An immediate modification of Fermi's initial assumption will be made in view of the more recent experimental findings.‡ According to the summary at the end of Chapter I, fermions appear to participate in $\beta$-interaction only through the 'left-handed components' of their states of motion. The proper formal description of such components, according to the results obtained at the end of § 3.1, and of § 3.3, is embodied in

‡ The modification about to be made was explicitly introduced in 1957–8, even before the evidence which suggests it became entirely clear. The modified theory, called the 'V–A Law', was advanced independently by E. Sudarshan and R. E. Marshak, and by R. P. Feynman and M. Gell-Mann. The background of the development will be discussed in Chapter X.

projections $\frac{1}{2}(1+\gamma_5)\psi \equiv \phi$. We shall therefore assume to begin with that the $\beta$-coupling is proportional to the nucleonic transition current

$$J_\alpha(\mathrm{pn}) = \phi_\mathrm{p}^\dagger \beta\gamma_\alpha \phi_\mathrm{n}. \tag{4.8}$$

There is, naturally, a 'jumping to conclusions' here; some such jump is inevitable, since no experimental finding can have infinite accuracy, and possible generalizations are limited only by the imagination of theorists. We shall eventually see that the modification of Fermi's initial assumption adopted here also has the effect of widening the scope of allowed transitions to include triplet, as well as singlet, emissions.

Assumptions about the role of the leptons must be made next, in analogy to the role of the photons represented by the vector potential in the $\gamma$-coupling (4.6). Guidance may be sought in a contemplation of the symmetry with which the fermions enter the $\beta$-interaction as represented by the 'lepton conservation relation', $\mathrm{n}+\nu \leftrightarrow \mathrm{p}+\mathrm{e}^-$, of (1.21). The processes evidently may involve a 'leptonic transition current', $J_\alpha(\mathrm{e}\nu) = \phi_\mathrm{e}^\dagger \beta\gamma_\alpha \phi_\nu$, on the same footing as the nucleonic current $J_\alpha(\mathrm{pn})$.

*The interaction energy density*

The preceding discussion makes it seem promising to assume that the $\beta$-interaction energy density will have the symmetrical form

$$h_\beta = 8^{\frac{1}{2}} g J_\alpha(\mathrm{pn}) J_\alpha(\mathrm{e}\nu) + \mathrm{c.c.} \tag{4.9}$$

A 'Fermi coupling constant', $g$, has been introduced here, to play a role analogous to that of the electronic charge, $e$, in the electromagnetic coupling (4.6). It will measure the strength of the $\beta$-interaction, and can in principle be determined from any one well-measured decay rate. The basis for its currently accepted value will be discussed in the last section of Chapter V. The factor $8^{\frac{1}{2}}$ separated off in the expression (4.9) is a result of 'historical accidents' during the development of the definition of $g$.

The proper reality of the interaction energy density is ensured by the addition of the complex conjugate term indicated in (4.9). Since $\mathbf{J}^*(\mathrm{pn}) = \phi_\mathrm{n}^\dagger \boldsymbol{\gamma}\beta\phi_\mathrm{p} = -\phi_\mathrm{n}^\dagger \beta\boldsymbol{\gamma}\phi_\mathrm{p} = -\mathbf{J}(\mathrm{np})$, and $J_4^*(\mathrm{pn}) = J_4(\mathrm{np})$, the energy density can be written more explicitly as

$$h_\beta = 8^{\frac{1}{2}} g[(\phi_\mathrm{p}^\dagger \beta\gamma_\alpha \phi_\mathrm{n})(\phi_\mathrm{e}^\dagger \beta\gamma_\alpha \phi_\nu) + (\phi_\mathrm{n}^\dagger \beta\gamma_\alpha \phi_\mathrm{p})(\phi_\nu^\dagger \beta\gamma_\alpha \phi_\mathrm{e})]. \tag{4.10}$$

This form came to be known as the 'V-A Law', in the jargon of the $\beta$-theorists. It must be understood that each $\phi = \frac{1}{2}(1+\gamma_5)\psi$, the intrinsically left-handed projection from the actual state of the fermion.

The second term in $h_\beta$ gives the interaction of proton-to-neutron and electron-to-neutrino transition currents. This indicates that only the first term is to be held responsible for neutron-to-proton transitions, and only the second for proton-to-neutron processes. Actually, such a restriction is automatic in the language of 'quantized fields', when the amplitudes $\phi$ serve as operators. It is still possible to restrict the formalism equivalently to '$c$-number' amplitudes $\phi$, simply by adopting the restriction as a convention. It may also be enforced by supplementing the formalism with the useful concept of 'isospin'.

*The isospin*

The fact that neutrons and protons can be transformed into each other has led to regarding them as alternative states of a single type of particle, the nucleon. This particle then requires a further 'internal variable' for its description, one which gives the particle the possibility of being found either in a 'proton' or a 'neutron' state. The new variable is analogous to the spin in that it leads to just two alternative states. Indeed, the needs of the entire description are admirably fitted by a complete analogue of the Pauli spin formalism (§ 2.2).

Eigenstates in which the nucleon is definitely a proton or a neutron will be represented as proportional to $\xi_p$ or $\xi_n$, respectively, these having exactly the same column matrix representatives as $\boldsymbol{\chi}_{\pm\frac{1}{2}}$ (2.30). The general nucleon state is then the 'isospinor'

$$\Psi = \begin{pmatrix} \psi_p \\ \psi_n \end{pmatrix} = \psi_p\,\xi_p + \psi_n\,\xi_n, \tag{4.11}$$

analogous to (2.24), except that $\psi_p$ and $\psi_n$ are Dirac spinors.

The variable analogous to the actual spin, $\mathbf{s} = \frac{1}{2}\hbar\boldsymbol{\sigma}$, is denoted $\mathbf{t} = \frac{1}{2}\boldsymbol{\tau}$, and is called‡ the 'isobaric spin' or, for brevity, 'isospin'. The components $\tau_{1,2,3}$ are given exactly the same Pauli matrix representations as $\sigma_{x,y,z}$ in (2.41) and (2.44). Of course, the resolution of $\mathbf{t}$ or $\boldsymbol{\tau}$ into components has nothing to do with reference frames in ordinary space; the latter do not affect the neutron vs. proton character of the nucleon. A new, three-dimensional space may be conceived, to accommodate the isospin vectors. It is generally called the 'charge space'.

The proton state is an eigenstate of $\tau_3$ for eigenvalue $+1$, while the neutron state has $\tau_3 = -1$:

$$\tau_3\,\xi_p = +1.\xi_p \quad \text{and} \quad \tau_3\,\xi_n = -1.\xi_n. \tag{4.12}$$

‡ Earlier, the less appropriate name 'isotopic spin' was used. Moreover, $t_3 = +\frac{1}{2}$ was assigned to the neutron, rather than proton, for a time.

The variable $\tau_3$ is closely associated with the charge on the nucleon; the latter is given by the expectation value of

$$Q = \tfrac{1}{2}e(1+\tau_3) = e(t_3+\tfrac{1}{2}) \tag{4.13}$$

in any nucleon state. The other components of $\boldsymbol{\tau}$ become most useful in the combinations $\tau_\pm = \frac{1}{2}(\tau_1 \pm i\tau_2)$, which have the matrix representations (2.43). Because

$$\tau_+ \xi_a = \delta_{an}\xi_p \quad \text{and} \quad \tau_- \xi_a = \delta_{ap}\xi_n, \tag{4.14}$$

$\tau_+$ serves as an operator for neutron-to-proton, and $\tau_-$ for proton-to-neutron, transformations.

*The $\beta$-coupling operator*

In terms of the projection by $\frac{1}{2}(1+\gamma_5)$ of $\Psi$ (4.11),

$$\Phi \equiv \tfrac{1}{2}(1+\gamma_5)\Psi = \begin{pmatrix}\Phi_p\\ \Phi_n\end{pmatrix}, \tag{4.15}$$

the nucleonic transformation currents can be written

$$J_\alpha(\text{pn}) = \Phi^\dagger\beta\gamma_\alpha\tau_+\Phi \quad \text{and} \quad J_\alpha(\text{np}) = \Phi^\dagger\beta\gamma_\alpha\tau_-\Phi. \tag{4.16}$$

Then

$$h_\beta = 8^{\frac{1}{2}}g(\Phi^\dagger\beta\gamma_\alpha\tau_+\Phi)J_\alpha(e\nu)+\text{c.c.} \tag{4.17}$$

is identical with (4.9) and (4.10). In terms of the nucleonic state $\Psi$ itself,

$$J_\alpha(\text{pn}) = \Psi^\dagger\tfrac{1}{2}(1+\gamma_5)\beta\gamma_\alpha\tau_+\Psi, \tag{4.18}$$

since $\gamma_5$ commutes with $\beta\gamma_\alpha\tau_+$, and $\frac{1}{4}(1+\gamma_5)^2 = \frac{1}{2}(1+\gamma_5)$. This result makes it obvious how to represent the $\beta$-interaction operator, $H_\beta$, in the hamiltonian for the nucleon. The operator must be such that $\Psi^\dagger H_\beta\Psi \equiv h_\beta$ for any $\Psi$, hence

$$H_\beta = 2^{\frac{1}{2}}g(1+\gamma_5)\beta\gamma_\alpha\tau_+J_\alpha(e\nu)+\text{h.c.}, \tag{4.19}$$

where 'h.c.' stands for the hermitian conjugate of the first term.

When dealing with an entire nucleus of $A$ nucleons, the coupling of each to the 'electron-neutrino field' must be allowed for:

$$H_\beta(A) = 8^{\frac{1}{2}}g\sum_{a=1}^{A}\tfrac{1}{2}(1+\gamma_5^a)\beta^a\gamma_\alpha^a\tau_+^a[J_\alpha(e\nu)]_{\mathbf{r}^a}+\text{h.c.} \tag{4.20}$$

As indicated, the electron-neutrino current should properly be evaluated at the position of the transforming nucleon i.e. at $\mathbf{r}^a$ for the $a$th nucleon. Even when the initial and final nuclear states, in a given case, differ only as regards the individual state of a single nucleon all the terms of (4.20) come into play. A structure of $A$ indistinguishable fermions must be described by a state function antisymmetrized in all the particles, so that each one may be said to contribute fractionally to the transformation. This does not mean that the transition rate is multiplied $A$-fold by the effect; the order of magnitude of a single nucleon transition is retained in a properly normalized description.

## 4.3. Transition rates

Suppose that the variables of the nuclear system, when isolated from interaction with any extra-nuclear variables, are capable of moving in any of the complete set of energy eigenstates symbolized‡ by $|k\rangle\exp(-iE_k t/\hbar)$. These are presumed orthonormalized, $\langle l|k\rangle = \delta_{lk}$, where $\langle l|$ is the symbol for the hermitian conjugate of $|l\rangle$. If $H_A$ is the hamiltonian operator for the isolated nucleus, then $H_A|k\rangle = E_k|k\rangle$.

When the isolation of the nucleus is now disturbed, as through its coupling $H_\beta$ to the 'electron-neutrino field', then, whatever the state $|(t)\rangle$ of the entire system, its dependence on the nuclear variables may still be represented by

$$|(t)\rangle = \sum_k |k\rangle a_k(t)e^{-iE_k t/\hbar}, \tag{4.21}$$

with some coefficients $a_k(t)$. The notation $|(t)\rangle$ is meant to indicate that this is not one of the set $|k\rangle$, but a more general, time-dependent state. $|a_k(t)|^2$ is to be interpreted as the probability that the nucleus will be found in state $k$, at time $t$.

If the results of the $\beta$-coupling are to be sought in the form (4.21), then this should be subjected to the equation of motion

$$(i\hbar\partial/\partial t)|(t)\rangle = (H_A+H_\beta)|(t)\rangle. \tag{4.22}$$

Substituting the form (4.21) into this yields

$$i\hbar\dot{a}_{\mathrm{f}}(t) = \sum_k \langle \mathrm{f}|H_\beta|k\rangle a_k(t)e^{i(E_{\mathrm{f}}-E_k)t/\hbar}, \tag{4.23}$$

after projection on some one state $\langle \mathrm{f}|\exp iE_{\mathrm{f}}\,t/\hbar$. These coupled equations for the various $a_{\mathrm{f}}(t)$, determine the transitions among the various nuclear states superposed in (4.21), as generated by the $\beta$-interaction matrix elements $\langle \mathrm{f}|H_\beta|k\rangle$. They constitute a modification of the so-called 'interaction representation'. The modification is known as 'Dirac's variation of constants method'.

*The restriction to first-order processes*

The transition equations (4.23) can be used to find the growth in time of various nuclear states from a specific initial state, so that $a_k(t=-\infty) = \delta_{ki}$. As indicated, an infinite time of development will be allowed for, so that a maximum definition of the energy will be

‡ The 'ket', $|\,\rangle$, and 'bra', $\langle\,|$, notation is that of P. A. M. Dirac, *Principles of Quantum Mechanics* (Clarendon Press, Oxford, 1935).

permitted by the uncertainty principle. Before any new states have grown appreciably, their rate of growth is determined by

$$i\hbar\dot{a}_f = \langle f|H_\beta|i\rangle e^{-iW_0t/\hbar}, \tag{4.24}$$

where $W_0 = E_i - E_f$ is the nuclear energy released in the transition $i \to f$. It is the transition rates which follow from this initial time development, treated as valid for all times, which are customarily identified with the observed rates.

The relations (4.24) take into account only 'first-order processes', i.e. transitions $i \to f$, direct from the initial to the final states. They show that at least the initial magnitudes of every $a_k \neq a_i$ will be proportional to the corresponding $\langle k|H_\beta|i\rangle$. Accordingly, corrections from terms $k \neq i$ in (4.23) are initially proportional to products like $\langle f|H_\beta|k\rangle\langle k|H_\beta|i\rangle$, which measure indirect, 'second-order' transitions $i \to k \to f$. The corrections arising from the diminution of $a_i(t)$, from the value $a_i = 1$ presumed in (4.24), are likewise of 'second order'.

The 'second-order' corrections to the probability amplitudes, since they require the $\beta$-coupling to operate twice, are smaller than the first-order effects by a ratio proportional to the $\beta$-coupling strength, $g$. After the latter are found it will be easy to appreciate that effects proportional to such higher powers of $g$ are undetectably small; the $\beta$-coupling strength is far smaller than the electromagnetic interaction, and even in the latter case the second-order effects become detectable only in rare instances, where the precision of observation has been pushed to an extreme.

Further deductions about transition rates from (4.24) require knowledge of the time-dependence of the $\beta$-coupling. Whatever this is, the matrix elements may be fourier-analysed according to

$$\langle f|H_\beta|i\rangle = \int_{-\infty}^{\infty} d\omega \langle f|H_\beta|i\rangle_\omega e^{i\omega t}, \tag{4.25}$$

where

$$\langle f|H_\beta|i\rangle_\omega = \int_{-\infty}^{\infty} (dt/2\pi)\langle f|H_\beta|i\rangle e^{-i\omega t} \tag{4.26}$$

must be so defined to comply with the fourier integral theorem. Comparison of these relations yields the fourier representation of a one-dimensional $\delta$-function,

$$\delta(\omega) = \int_{-\infty}^{\infty} (dt/2\pi)e^{i\omega t}, \qquad \int_{-\infty}^{\infty} d\omega\, \delta(\omega) = 1, \tag{4.27}$$

in the same way as in the three-dimensional case (3.39). Now, the time integration of (4.24) gives

$$i\hbar a_{\mathrm{f}}(\infty) = 2\pi \int_{-\infty}^{\infty} d\omega \langle \mathrm{f}|H_\beta|\mathrm{i}\rangle_\omega \,\delta(\omega - W_0/\hbar)$$

$$= 2\pi\langle \mathrm{f}|H_\beta|\mathrm{i}\rangle_{W_0/\hbar}, \tag{4.28}$$

since $a_{\mathrm{f}}(-\infty) = 0$ is supposed. The lesson to be derived from this is that the overall time-development of a given final state comes from a monochromatic frequency in the coupling. Of course, the relations (4.28) and (4.26) are consistent with

$$|a_{\mathrm{f}}(\infty)|^2 = \hbar^{-2}\left|\int_{-\infty}^{\infty} dt \langle \mathrm{f}|H_\beta|\mathrm{i}\rangle e^{-iW_0t/\hbar}\right|^2 \tag{4.29}$$

for the final probability fraction, a result which is already implied more directly by (4.24).

*Spontaneous and induced processes*

The oscillations in the $\beta$-coupling, which have the important role just reviewed, come from the neutrino-electron current in the $\beta$-interaction operator (4.20),

$$J_\alpha(\mathrm{e}\nu) = \phi_{\mathrm{e}}^\dagger \beta\gamma_\alpha \phi_\nu = \psi_{\mathrm{e}}^\dagger \tfrac{1}{2}(1+\gamma_5)\beta\gamma_\alpha \psi_\nu, \tag{4.30}$$

and from $J_\alpha(\nu\mathrm{e})$. We must therefore consider the possible forms of $\psi_{\mathrm{e}}$ and $\psi_\nu$.

General forms which a Dirac state may have were given in (3.31) and (3.37), where alternative analyses, into free spherical and plane waves, were presented. Similar forms can be constructed which superpose electron waves distorted by the nuclear coulomb field, either spherical ones with the radial modulations (3.49), or the distorted plane waves, (3.60). In all these cases, the wave field is presented as a superposition of energy eigenstates, which, to be quite general, should include the 'negative energy' eigenstates. The latter may be equivalently replaced by charge conjugates of positive energy states. Thus, a general field $\psi_{\mathrm{e}}$ or $\psi_\nu$ can be given a form like

$$\psi = \int_{W>0} dW \sum_k \,[u_k\, e^{-iWt/\hbar} + u_k^C\, e^{+iWt/\hbar}], \tag{4.31}$$

where $u_k$ (and $u_k^C$) are time-independent Dirac spinors, with arbitrary normalizations and phases. The indices $k$ represent sets of eigenvalues, of momentum or angular momentum, for instance, which can be known simultaneously with the energy. Clearly, the substitution of forms like this, for the $\psi_{\mathrm{e}}$ and $\psi_\nu$ of (4.30), will automatically provide a fourier analysis of the $\beta$-coupling matrix elements, of the type (4.25); the frequencies will have the various relations $\omega = (\pm W \pm cq)/\hbar$ to the electron energies $W$, and neutrino energies, $cq$. (Preference is sometimes shown for avoiding reference to 'negative energies' by referring to 'negative frequencies', instead. That makes it unnecessary to conceive filled 'negative energy states' of the vacuum.)

Displays like (4.31) provide an economical way for showing all the possibilities for the states, e.g. the fact that charge conjugate states must be considered. However, they may be misleading in another respect. Using any specific superposition of the type (4.31) implies settling upon some set of specific, hence 'coherent', phase differences among the eigenstates. Actually, we are usually interested in the chances of producing or absorbing lepton waves in any phase whatever, since such phases can rarely be controlled in the experimental observations. If, then, the waves are represented by superpositions like (4.31), their squares giving observed intensities, as in (4.29), will contain cross-terms indicating interferences among coherent waves. Arbitrariness of the relative phases, 'incoherence', can still be allowed for by averaging over all possible phases, and that causes the interference cross-terms to vanish. It is more economical to ask for the production or absorption of a single, independent eigenstate in the first place; then totals are properly obtained by superposing the squared amplitudes, instead of squaring superposed amplitudes, of all the eigenstates to be counted in the final result.

Now, in forming the neutrino-to-electron current $J_\alpha(\mathrm{e}\nu)$ of (4.21) from electron and neutrino eigenstates, four possibilities may be distinguished, depending on whether a normal or charge conjugate state is chosen for each lepton:

$$J_\alpha(\mathrm{e}^-\bar{\nu}) = (\phi_\mathrm{e}^\dagger \beta\gamma_\alpha \phi_\nu^C)_{t=0}\, e^{+i(W+cq)t/\hbar}, \tag{4.32 a}$$

$$J_\alpha(\mathrm{e}^+\nu) = (\phi_\mathrm{e}^{C\dagger} \beta\gamma_\alpha \phi_\nu)_0\, e^{-i(W+cq)t/\hbar}, \tag{4.32 b}$$

$$J_\alpha(\mathrm{e}^-\nu) = (\phi_\mathrm{e}^\dagger \beta\gamma_\alpha \phi_\nu)_0\, e^{+i(W-cq)t/\hbar}, \tag{4.32 c}$$

$$J_\alpha(\mathrm{e}^+\bar{\nu}) = (\phi_\mathrm{e}^{C\dagger} \beta\gamma_\alpha \phi_\nu^C)_0\, e^{-i(W-cq)t/\hbar}. \tag{4.32 d}$$

Corresponding expressions for the electron-to-neutrino current $J_\alpha(\nu\mathrm{e})$, which accompanies the proton-to-neutron transformations $\sim \tau_-$ of (4.20), can be written merely by exchanging $\phi_\nu \leftrightarrow \phi_\mathrm{e}$. As the discussion leading to (4.10) shows $\mathbf{J} \leftrightarrow -\mathbf{J}^*$ and $J_4 \leftrightarrow J_4^*$ in this exchange.

The four currents (4.32) correspond to four independent types of processes which may accompany a neutron-to-proton transformation, given suitable conditions. Their interpretation follows from the energy relations which develop because only the frequency $\omega = (E_\mathrm{i} - E_\mathrm{f})/\hbar$

leads to a permanent transition, as (4.28) shows. Accordingly, $J_\alpha(\text{e}^-\bar{\nu})$ is generated only when $W+cq = W_0 = E_\text{i}-E_\text{f}$, i.e. when the nuclear energy release is shared by a negatron and an antineutrino, as in a spontaneous emission of these particles. For $J_\alpha(\text{e}^+\nu)$,

$$W+cq = -W_0 = E_\text{f}-E_\text{i};$$

the nucleus must now gain energy from a positron and a neutrino, as when these are simultaneously incident on the nucleus and are absorbed by it. For $J_\alpha(\text{e}^-\nu)$, $W = W_0+cq$ and an emitted negatron is gaining energy from a positive energy neutrino absorbed by the nucleus; the nucleus may contribute to this energy or may be simultaneously excited by it ($W_0 \gtrless 0$). $J_\alpha(\text{e}^+\bar{\nu})$ represents antineutrino emission following upon the nuclear absorption of a positron incident on the nucleus. All the four processes are of the type $\text{n}+\nu \rightarrow \text{p}+\text{e}^-$, discussed in connexion with the 'lepton-conservation relation', (1.21).

A corresponding set of interpretations apply to the electron-to-neutrino currents, $J_\alpha(\nu\text{e})$, which accompany processes of the type $\text{p}+\text{e}^- \rightarrow \text{n}+\nu$. Altogether, then, eight types of processes can be distinguished, six of which require the external incidence of leptons on the nucleus, so-called 'induced' transitions. Two of the latter types, orbital electron capture and the capture of antineutrinos by protons, have been observed, as mentioned in Chapter I. However, these require evaluations of different types than do the spontaneous emissions of primary interest, hence will be left to later chapters. We concentrate now on the spontaneous negatron-antineutrino emissions (4.32 a), and on the positron-neutrino emissions represented by

$$J_\alpha(\nu\text{e}^+) = (\phi_\nu^\dagger \beta\gamma_\alpha \phi_\text{e}^C)_0 e^{+i(W+cq)t/\hbar}. \tag{4.33}$$

In either case, the time factor has the same form.

*The formal relation of* $\text{e}^+$ *to* $\text{e}^-$ *emissions*

Consider the complex ($\equiv$ hermitian) conjugate of the positron-neutrino current (4.33):

$$J_\alpha^*(\nu\text{e}^+) = [\psi_\nu^\dagger \beta\gamma_\alpha.\tfrac{1}{2}(1+\gamma_5)C\psi_\text{e}^*]^\dagger = \tilde{\psi}_\text{e}\, C^\dagger.\tfrac{1}{2}(1+\gamma_5)\gamma_\alpha \beta\psi_\nu.$$

It shows that the current itself may be written:

$$J_\alpha(\nu\text{e}^+) = \psi_\text{e}^\dagger \tilde{C}\tfrac{1}{2}(1+\gamma_5)^*\gamma_\alpha^*\beta^*\psi_\nu^*.$$

Now $\tilde{C} = C$ according to (3.78), and the properties $C\gamma^* = \gamma C$, $C\gamma_4^* \equiv C\beta^* = -\beta C$ of (3.76) can be used to transfer $C$ to a position preceding all the other operations. Since $\gamma_5 = \gamma_1\gamma_2\gamma_3\gamma_4$,

$$C\gamma_5^* = -\gamma_5 C, \tag{4.34}$$

and it is also clear that $C\gamma_\alpha^* \beta^* = \beta\gamma_\alpha C$. Accordingly, after the transfer is completed,

$$J_\alpha(\nu e^+) = \psi_e^\dagger \beta\gamma_\alpha \cdot \tfrac{1}{2}(1-\gamma_5)\psi_\nu^C. \tag{4.35}$$

This is exactly the same as the negatron-antineutrino current of (4.32 a), except that the intrinsically right-hand projections by $\frac{1}{2}(1-\gamma_5)$ have replaced the left-handed ones $\phi \equiv \frac{1}{2}(1+\gamma_5)\psi$.

The formal relation developed here accords with the qualitative discussion in § 1.8, where it was pointed out that the antiparticles can consistently be regarded as mirror images (right- vs. left-handed) of their normal counterparts, as they engage in $\beta$-processes.

*The decay constant*

With the time-dependence of the $\beta$-coupling settled in (4.32 a), (4.33) as $\langle f|H_\beta|i\rangle \sim \exp i(W+cq)t/\hbar$, the probability (4.29), for reaching a final nuclear state $|f\rangle$, can be written

$$|a_f(\infty)|^2 = \hbar^{-2}|\langle f|H_\beta|i\rangle|^2 \left| \int_{-\infty}^{\infty} dt\, e^{i(W+cq-W_0)t/\hbar} \right|^2.$$

One of the two conjugate time-integrals multiplied together here may be replaced by $2\pi\hbar\delta(W+cq-W_0)$, according to (4.27). Thus, the transition cannot develop into a permanent one except for energies consistent with the conservation principle. The expression exists only for $W+cq = W_0$, hence the second of the two time-integrals becomes simply $T = \int_{-\infty}^{\infty} dt \to \infty$. This signifies merely that if a long enough time, $T$, is allowed for the transitions, then their number will be proportional to $T$. This is not unexpected if it is remembered that a steady supply of initial states ready to decay is implied when $a_i = 1$ is presumed, as in (4.24). $|a_f(\infty)|^2/T$ should then be interpreted as an effective decay rate per nucleus, and identified with a 'decay constant' such as was introduced in § 1.1.

As discussed so far, $\langle f|H_\beta|i\rangle$ is supposed evaluated for only one set of possibilities for the final nuclear and lepton states, e.g. a specific pair of lepton energies, $W$ and $cq$, is presumed. The result obtained is therefore only some 'partial' decay constant, which will be denoted $d\lambda$:

$$d\lambda = (2\pi/\hbar)|\langle f|H_\beta|i\rangle|^2\delta(W+cq-W_0). \tag{4.36}$$

In general, many such must be added together, one for each set of possibilities that a given nuclear population will have, before its total decay constant, $\lambda$, is obtained.

## 4.4. The theory of neutron decay

A basic qualification in the application of the theory to 'physical' nucleons will be found necessary. We may learn of it by considering the decay of a free neutron.

*The nucleonic transformation currents*

To begin with, the free neutron and the product proton will be described by plane wave Dirac spinors (3.4). We start with a neutron at rest so that

$$\psi_{\mathrm{n}} = \begin{pmatrix} \chi_M \\ 0 \end{pmatrix} V^{-\frac{1}{2}} e^{-iM_{\mathrm{n}}c^2t/\hbar}, \tag{4.37 a}$$

if $M$ is the projection of the neutron spin on the quantization axis. The proton has a recoil but the recoil *energy* is negligible (§ 1.3) compared to the energy release $W_0 = (M_{\mathrm{n}} - M_{\mathrm{p}})c^2$, and even more so compared to the proton rest mass, so that

$$\psi_{\mathrm{p}} = \begin{pmatrix} \chi_{M'} \\ 0 \end{pmatrix} V^{-\frac{1}{2}} e^{i(\mathbf{P}.\mathbf{r} - M_{\mathrm{p}}c^2t)/\hbar} \tag{4.37 b}$$

may be assumed.

With the nuclear states as described here,

$$\langle \mathrm{f}|H_\beta|\mathrm{i}\rangle = 8^{\frac{1}{2}}g \oint (d\mathbf{r})[\psi_{\mathrm{p}}^\dagger \tfrac{1}{2}(1+\gamma_5)\beta\gamma_\alpha \psi_{\mathrm{n}}]J_\alpha(e^-\bar{\nu}) \tag{4.38}$$

is the matrix element of the coupling (4.19). The quantity in the square bracket is just the neutron transformation current, $J_\alpha(\mathrm{pn})$ of (4.8). It will be most instructive to treat it in two covariant parts,

$$J_\alpha(\mathrm{pn}) = \tfrac{1}{2}(J_\alpha^{\mathrm{V}} + J_\alpha^{\mathrm{A}}), \tag{4.39 a}$$

where

$$J_\alpha^{\mathrm{V}} = \bar{\psi}_{\mathrm{p}}\gamma_\alpha\psi_{\mathrm{n}} \quad \text{and} \quad J_\alpha^{\mathrm{A}} = \bar{\psi}_{\mathrm{p}}\gamma_\alpha\gamma_5\psi_{\mathrm{n}} \tag{4.39 b}$$

are a vector and pseudovector, respectively, according to (2.80) and (2.90). With the resolutions of $\gamma_\alpha(-i\beta\boldsymbol{\alpha}, \beta)$, it is easy to show that

$$\mathbf{J}^{\mathrm{V}} = 0, \qquad J_4^{\mathrm{V}} = \delta_{M'M} V^{-1} e^{-i(\mathbf{P}.\mathbf{r}+W_0t)/\hbar},$$
$$\mathbf{J}^{\mathrm{A}} = i(\chi_{M'}^\dagger \boldsymbol{\sigma} \chi_M) V^{-1} e^{-i(\mathbf{P}.\mathbf{r}+W_0t)/\hbar}, \qquad J_4^{\mathrm{A}} = 0. \tag{4.40}$$

The fact that $\gamma_5 \boldsymbol{\alpha} = -\boldsymbol{\sigma}$ has been employed here. Clearly, the vector current permits no angular momentum to be radiated. It may also be clear that the pseudovector current involves the radiation of one unit of angular momentum; that this is so will be left to later discussion (§ 5.1). Granting the last assertion, it becomes evident that the classification into the vector and pseudovector nucleonic transformation currents corresponds to the classification into 'Fermi' and 'GT' emissions, in Chapter I. Indeed, the latter classification was specialized to parts called 'Vector' and 'Pseudovector' radiations in § 1.9. Recall also that Fermi's initial assumption, as reported in the first paragraph of § 4.2, was that only the Vector current generates $\beta$-radiation; thus, the modification adopted here introduces Pseudovector $\equiv$ GT $\equiv$ triplet emissions.

*The leptonic transformation current*

The plane wave (3.10) may be used to describe the negatron, since the coulomb distortion by the single proton charge is quite negligible (its effect will be seen in (5.36) of the next chapter). The charge conjugate plane wave (3.16) will be used for the antineutrino, after setting the mass in it equal to zero; moreover, $q$ and $cq$ will denote the antineutrino's momentum and energy. To avoid a multiplicity of indices, the letters e and $\nu$ will serve double duty by standing for the spin projection quantum numbers of the electron and neutral lepton, respectively. After these choices, the leptonic current (4.32 a) can be resolved into

$$\left.\begin{aligned} \mathbf{J} &= -i\phi_{\mathrm{e}}^{\dagger}\boldsymbol{\alpha}\phi_{\nu}^{C} = i(\mathbf{u}_{\mathrm{e}}^{\dagger}\boldsymbol{\sigma}\mathbf{u}_{\nu})V^{-1}e^{-i[(\mathbf{p}+\mathbf{q}).\mathbf{r}-(W+cq)t]/\hbar} \\ J_4 &= \phi_{\mathrm{e}}^{\dagger}\phi_{\nu}^{C} = (\mathbf{u}_{\mathrm{e}}^{\dagger}\mathbf{u}_{\nu})V^{-1}e^{-i[(\mathbf{p}+\mathbf{q}).\mathbf{r}-(W+cq)t]/\hbar} \end{aligned}\right\}, \tag{4.41}$$

where $\mathbf{u}_{\mathrm{e}}$, $\mathbf{u}_{\nu}$ are Pauli spinors of the type (3.11) and (3.16). This, together with the nucleonic currents (4.40), transforms the transition matrix element (4.38) into

$$\langle \mathrm{f}|H_{\beta}|\mathrm{i}\rangle = (2^{\frac{1}{2}}g/V^2)(Q_{\mathrm{V}}+Q_{\mathrm{A}}) \oint (d\mathbf{r})e^{-i(\mathbf{P}+\mathbf{p}+\mathbf{q}).\mathbf{r}/\hbar}, \tag{4.42}$$

when evaluated 'on the energy shell', $W_0 = W+cq$, as required for the decay constant (4.36). Here, the temporary symbols

$$\begin{aligned} Q_{\mathrm{V}} &\equiv \delta_{M'M}(\mathbf{u}_{\mathrm{e}}^{\dagger}\,\mathbf{u}_{\nu}), \\ Q_{\mathrm{A}} &\equiv -(\boldsymbol{\chi}_{M'}^{\dagger}\boldsymbol{\sigma}\boldsymbol{\chi}_{M}).(\mathbf{u}_{\mathrm{e}}^{\dagger}\boldsymbol{\sigma}\mathbf{u}_{\nu}) \end{aligned} \tag{4.43}$$

have been introduced, mainly to preserve the distinction between the Vector and Pseudovector nucleon current contributions.

The product of the matrix element (4.42) with its complex conjugate is needed for the decay rate. In one factor of this product, the spatial integral in (4.42) may be set equal to $(2\pi\hbar)^3\delta(\mathbf{P}+\mathbf{p}+\mathbf{q})$, according to (3.40). Momentum conservation is enforced in this way. The consequence for the complex conjugate of the same integral is to allow survival of only the unit value of the exponential, so that the integral becomes $\oint (d\mathbf{r}) \equiv V$. Then

$$|\langle \mathrm{f}|H_{\beta}|\mathrm{i}\rangle|^2 = (2g^2/V^3)(2\pi\hbar)^3\delta(\mathbf{P}+\mathbf{p}+\mathbf{q})|Q_{\mathrm{V}}+Q_{\mathrm{A}}|^2. \tag{4.44}$$

This alone accounts for only a highly restricted fraction of the neutron decays. We may add together such contributions to all the decays in which the three resultant momenta end anywhere in the ranges $(d\mathbf{P})$,

$(d\mathbf{p})$, and $(d\mathbf{q})$, respectively, by multiplying (4.44) with the number of states in these ranges:

$$\frac{(d\mathbf{P})V}{(2\pi\hbar)^3}\frac{(d\mathbf{p})V}{(2\pi\hbar)^3}\frac{(d\mathbf{q})V}{(2\pi\hbar)^3}. \tag{4.45}$$

Actually, for a given lepton momentum $\mathbf{p}+\mathbf{q}$, the proton momentum is restricted to $\mathbf{P} = -(\mathbf{p}+\mathbf{q})$ by the δ-function in (4.44); this can be eliminated by the integration $\oint (d\mathbf{P})\delta(\mathbf{P}+\mathbf{p}+\mathbf{q}) = 1$. Similarly, the energy conserving δ-function in the decay rate (4.36) restricts the antineutrino energy to $cq = W-W_0$; the integral $\int c\,dq\,\delta(W+cq-W_0) = 1$ will eliminate the δ-function and the differential $c\,dq = c(d\mathbf{q})/q^2(d\hat{\mathbf{q}})$ as well. The result will be a partial decay constant,

$$d\lambda = [2g^2/(2\pi)^5\hbar^7c]q^2(d\hat{\mathbf{q}})(d\mathbf{p})|Q_\mathrm{V}+Q_\mathrm{A}|^2, \tag{4.46}$$

counting decays in which the negatron momentum ends in the range $(d\mathbf{p})$ and the neutrino's direction in the solid angle $(d\hat{\mathbf{q}})$. Moreover, a specific set of spin projections $M$, $M'$, e, $\nu$ are implicit in $Q_{\mathrm{V,A}}$ as defined in (4.43).

*The singlet emissions*

The observations on neutron decay reported in § 1.10 attempt no detection of polarizations, although polarized initial neutrons were used in some measurements. Consequently, the decay rate (4.46) will be summed over the spin projections, $M'$, e, $\nu$, of the proton and the leptons. We consider the purely Vector part of the radiation first, as measured by

$$\sum_{\mathrm{e}\nu} |Q_\mathrm{V}|^2 = \delta_{M'M}(\mathbf{u}_\mathrm{e}^\dagger\,\mathbf{u}_\nu)(\mathbf{u}_\nu^\dagger\,\mathbf{u}_\mathrm{e}). \tag{4.47}$$

The two parentheses in the last expression should be recognized as each others' complex conjugates, and the summation convention is employed.

The spin sum in (4.47) is most elegantly performed by the use of trace techniques according to which amplitude products like

$$\begin{aligned}(\mathbf{u}^\dagger A\mathbf{v})(\mathbf{u}^\dagger B\mathbf{v})^* &\equiv A_{\alpha\beta}(v_\beta\, v_\gamma^*)B_{\delta\gamma}^*(u_\delta\, u_\alpha^*)\\ &= \mathrm{tr}[A(\mathbf{v}\mathbf{v}^\dagger)B^\dagger(\mathbf{u}\mathbf{u}^\dagger)],\end{aligned} \tag{4.48}$$

containing arbitrary operators $A$, $B$ and spinors $\mathbf{u}$, $\mathbf{v}$, are reduced to diagonal sums ('traces') of matrix products. The products of spinor components like $(\mathbf{u}\mathbf{u}^\dagger)_{\delta\alpha} = u_\delta\, u_\alpha^*$ form square arrays which are called 'density matrices'. Such are particularly easy to find after summations over spin, with the help of the fundamental density matrix,

$$\Big(\sum_\mu\Big)\boldsymbol{\chi}_\mu\boldsymbol{\chi}_\mu^\dagger = \begin{pmatrix}1\\0\end{pmatrix}(1\ \ 0)+\begin{pmatrix}0\\1\end{pmatrix}(0\ \ 1) = \begin{pmatrix}1 & 0\\0 & 1\end{pmatrix} \equiv \mathbf{1}, \tag{4.49}$$

which is made up of Pauli eigenspinors. The density matrix for spinors $\mathbf{u}_\mu$ of the type (3.11), summed over spins, is

$$\mathbf{u}_\mu\,\mathbf{u}_\mu^\dagger = \frac{W+mc^2}{4W}\left(1-\frac{c\boldsymbol{\sigma}\,.\,\mathbf{p}}{W+mc^2}\right)(\boldsymbol{\chi}_\mu\,\boldsymbol{\chi}_\mu^\dagger)\left(1-\frac{c\boldsymbol{\sigma}\,.\,\mathbf{p}}{W+mc^2}\right).$$

Since the middle factor is merely a unit matrix and

$$c^2(\boldsymbol{\sigma}\,.\,\mathbf{p})^2 = c^2p^2 = W^2-m^2c^4,$$

$$\mathbf{u}_\mathrm{e}\,\mathbf{u}_\mathrm{e}^\dagger = \tfrac{1}{2}(\mathbf{1}-\boldsymbol{\sigma}\,.\,\mathbf{v}/c) \tag{4.50}$$

for an electron of velocity $\mathbf{v} = c^2\mathbf{p}/W$. For the antineutrinos,

$$\mathbf{u}_{-\nu}\,\mathbf{u}_{-\nu}^\dagger \equiv \mathbf{u}_\nu\,\mathbf{u}_\nu^\dagger = \tfrac{1}{2}(\mathbf{1}-\boldsymbol{\sigma}\,.\,\hat{\mathbf{q}}). \tag{4.51}$$

Thus

$$\sum_{\mathrm{e}\nu} |Q_\mathrm{V}|^2 = \delta_{M'M}\,\mathrm{tr}[(\mathbf{u}_\nu\,\mathbf{u}_\nu^\dagger)(\mathbf{u}_\mathrm{e}\,\mathbf{u}_\mathrm{e}^\dagger)]$$
$$= \tfrac{1}{4}\delta_{M'M}\,\mathrm{tr}(\mathbf{1}-\boldsymbol{\sigma}\,.\,\hat{\mathbf{q}})(\mathbf{1}-\boldsymbol{\sigma}\,.\,\mathbf{v}/c).$$

Any function of $\boldsymbol{\sigma}$ can be reduced to an expression linear in $\boldsymbol{\sigma}$ (2.46), and for this purpose it is helpful to use the theorem

$$(\boldsymbol{\sigma}\,.\,\mathbf{p})(\boldsymbol{\sigma}\,.\,\mathbf{q}) = \mathbf{p}\,.\,\mathbf{q}+i\boldsymbol{\sigma}\,.\,(\mathbf{p}\times\mathbf{q}), \tag{4.52}$$

which follows easily from the properties (2.37), (2.38) of the Pauli matrices, and is a generalization of $(\boldsymbol{\sigma}\,.\,\mathbf{p})^2 = p^2$. Then advantage can be taken of the simple fact that $\mathrm{tr}\,\boldsymbol{\sigma} = 0$ for any component of $\boldsymbol{\sigma}$, while $\mathrm{tr}\,\mathbf{1} = 2$. The final result for the intensity expression is

$$\sum_{\mathrm{e}\nu} |Q_\mathrm{V}|^2 = \delta_{M'M}\cdot\tfrac{1}{2}(1+\hat{\mathbf{q}}\,.\,\mathbf{v}/c), \tag{4.53}$$

describing just the positive electron-neutrino correlation already anticipated for Vector radiation (see Fig. 1.12, for example).

It is worth while to make a discursion at this point, to show that the Vector intensity (4.53) is just the square of an emitted wave amplitude consisting of projections of appropriate handedness out of a *singlet* lepton wave, as befits Fermi emissions. In terms of matrix elements resolved on a Pauli eigenspinor basis, like $A_{\mu\mu'} \equiv \boldsymbol{\chi}_\mu^\dagger A\boldsymbol{\chi}_{\mu'}$, the Vector intensity expression (4.47) may be written as

$$\sum_{\mathrm{e}\nu} |Q_\mathrm{V}|^2 = [(W+mc^2)/16W][(\mathbf{1}-\boldsymbol{\sigma}\,.\,\boldsymbol{\pi})(1-\boldsymbol{\sigma}\,.\,\hat{\mathbf{q}})]_{\mathrm{e}\nu}[(\mathbf{1}-\boldsymbol{\sigma}\,.\,\hat{\mathbf{q}})(\mathbf{1}-\boldsymbol{\sigma}\,.\,\boldsymbol{\pi})]_{\nu\mathrm{e}},$$

if $\boldsymbol{\pi} \equiv c\mathbf{p}/(W+mc^2)$. Now, any diagonal sum of matrix products like $[AB]_{\mathrm{e}\nu}[CD]_{\nu\mathrm{e}} \equiv A_{\mathrm{e}\mu}\,B_{\mu\nu}\,C_{\nu\mu'}\,D_{\mu'\mathrm{e}}$ is obviously equivalent to $[DA]_{\mu'\mu}[BC]_{\mu\mu'}$, hence the four matrix factors in the intensity expression may be rearranged to

$$[\boldsymbol{\chi}_{\mu'}^\dagger(\mathbf{1}-\boldsymbol{\sigma}\,.\,\boldsymbol{\pi})^2\boldsymbol{\chi}_\mu][\boldsymbol{\chi}_\mu^\dagger(\mathbf{1}-\boldsymbol{\sigma}\,.\,\hat{\mathbf{q}})^2\boldsymbol{\chi}_{\mu'}]$$
$$= \boldsymbol{\chi}_{\mu'}^\dagger(\mathrm{e})\boldsymbol{\chi}_\mu^\dagger(\nu)(\mathbf{1}-\boldsymbol{\sigma}_\mathrm{e}\,.\,\boldsymbol{\pi})^2(\mathbf{1}-\boldsymbol{\sigma}_\nu\,.\,\hat{\mathbf{q}})^2\boldsymbol{\chi}_\mu(\mathrm{e})\boldsymbol{\chi}_{\mu'}(\nu),$$

in which electron spin variables, subject to operation by $\boldsymbol{\sigma}_e$, and antineutrino spin operations, $\boldsymbol{\sigma}_\nu$, must be distinguished. The direct products $\boldsymbol{\chi}_\mu(e)\boldsymbol{\chi}_{\mu'}(\nu)$ may now be replaced by projections out of the singlet eigenfunction (2.22), $\boldsymbol{\chi}^s(e,\nu) \equiv 2^{-\frac{1}{2}}(\boldsymbol{\chi}_{\frac{1}{2}}\boldsymbol{\chi}_{-\frac{1}{2}} - \boldsymbol{\chi}_{-\frac{1}{2}}\boldsymbol{\chi}_{\frac{1}{2}})$, with the help of operations by $\sigma_\pm \equiv \frac{1}{2}(\sigma_x \pm i\sigma_y)$ on the neutrino spin variables only:

$$\boldsymbol{\chi}_{\pm\frac{1}{2}}(e)\boldsymbol{\chi}_{\pm\frac{1}{2}}(\nu) = \pm 2^{\frac{1}{2}}\sigma_\pm(\nu)\boldsymbol{\chi}^s(e,\nu),$$

$$\boldsymbol{\chi}_{\pm\frac{1}{2}}(e)\boldsymbol{\chi}_{\mp\frac{1}{2}}(\nu) = \pm 2^{\frac{1}{2}}\sigma_\mp(\nu)\sigma_\pm(\nu)\boldsymbol{\chi}^s,$$

according to the properties (2.42) of $\sigma_\pm$. That enables giving the Vector intensity expression the form

$$\sum_{e\nu} |Q_V|^2 = [(W+mc^2)/8W](\boldsymbol{\chi}^s)^\dagger(\mathbf{1}-\boldsymbol{\sigma}_e\,.\,\boldsymbol{\pi})^2\mathcal{O}_\nu\boldsymbol{\chi}^s,$$

where $\mathcal{O}_\nu$ is an operator on neutrino spin variables only; $\mathcal{O}_\nu = \mathcal{O}_{+-}+\mathcal{O}_{-+}$ if

$$\mathcal{O}_{\pm\mp} \equiv \sigma_\mp(\mathbf{1}-\boldsymbol{\sigma}\,.\,\hat{\mathbf{q}})^2\sigma_\pm - \sigma_\mp\,\sigma_\pm(\mathbf{1}-\boldsymbol{\sigma}\,.\,\hat{\mathbf{q}})^2\sigma_\pm\,\sigma_\mp.$$

After simplifications enabled by $(\mathbf{1}-\boldsymbol{\sigma}\,.\,\hat{\mathbf{q}})^2 = 2(\mathbf{1}-\boldsymbol{\sigma}\,.\,\hat{\mathbf{q}})$ and the anticommutation relations $\sigma_\pm^2 = \sigma_\mp^2 = 0$, $\sigma_+\sigma_- + \sigma_-\sigma_+ = \mathbf{1}$, $\sigma_\pm\sigma_z + \sigma_z\sigma_\pm = 0$:

$$\mathcal{O}_\nu = 2[1+\sigma_z\hat{q}_z + \sigma_+(\hat{q}_x - i\hat{q}_y) + \sigma_-(\hat{q}_x + i\hat{q}_y)],$$

which is just $\mathcal{O}_\nu = 2(\mathbf{1}+\boldsymbol{\sigma}\,.\,\hat{\mathbf{q}}) = (\mathbf{1}+\boldsymbol{\sigma}\,.\,\hat{\mathbf{q}})^2$. The result is a Vector intensity expression,

$$\sum_{e\nu} |Q_V|^2 = \frac{W+mc^2}{8W}\left|\left(\mathbf{1} - \frac{c\boldsymbol{\sigma}_e\,.\,\mathbf{p}}{W+mc^2}\right)(\mathbf{1}+\boldsymbol{\sigma}_\nu\,.\,\hat{\mathbf{q}})\boldsymbol{\chi}^s\right|^2, \tag{4.54}$$

of just the form promised. Quite appropriately, the amplitude embodies a left-handed projection (having the square $\frac{1}{2}(\mathbf{1}-\boldsymbol{\sigma}_e\,.\,\mathbf{v}/c)$) of the negatron description, and a *right*-handed one for the antineutrino. It is simple to check directly that this yields the correct final result (4.53). Findings of this type may acquire great importance since they yield descriptions of the processes in fairly exhaustive detail, yet embody such a minimum of assumptions that they can survive quite drastic reformulations of the fundamental theory.

*The triplet emission*

Unlike the Vector radiation just reviewed, the Pseudovector contributions depend on the nuclear orientations, as already asserted in § 1.8 and § 1.10. There is no real loss of generality when the initial neutron's spin direction is taken as the quantization axis, so that $M = +\frac{1}{2}$.

It is convenient to analyse the scalar product in (4.43) as

$$Q_A = \sum_m Q_A^m = -(\boldsymbol{\chi}_{M'}^\dagger\,\sigma_m^\dagger\,\boldsymbol{\chi}_M)(\mathbf{u}_e^\dagger\,\sigma_m\,\mathbf{u}_\nu), \tag{4.55}$$

where $m = 0, \pm 1$ specify the three spherical components (2.6) of the Pauli spin vector: $\sigma_0 \equiv \sigma_z$, $\sigma_{\pm 1} \equiv \mp 2^{-\frac{1}{2}}(\sigma_x \pm i\sigma_y)$. It is then obvious that

$$\left.\begin{aligned} \chi^{\dagger}_{M'}\sigma_0\chi_M &= \pm\delta_{M'M} && \text{for } M = \pm\tfrac{1}{2} \\ \chi^{\dagger}_{M'}\sigma^{\dagger}_{\pm 1}\chi_M &= \mp 2^{\frac{1}{2}}\delta_{M',M\mp 1} && \text{for } M = \pm\tfrac{1}{2} \\ &= 0 && \text{for } M = \mp\tfrac{1}{2} \end{aligned}\right\}, \tag{4.56}$$

for which the help of (2.8) may be invoked. This result shows that $m$ is the loss by the nucleon, hence gain by the leptons, of $z$-component of angular momentum. It also shows that the three contributions $Q_{\mathrm{A}}^{0,\pm 1}$ cannot interfere with each other, in producing the intensity in (4.46), since they require different and incoherent nucleonic orientations. A neutron with an initial 'up' spin produces two independent, purely Pseudovector intensities:

$$\sum_{e\nu} |Q_{\mathrm{A}}^0|^2 = \delta_{M',+\frac{1}{2}}(\mathbf{u}_{\mathrm{e}}^{\dagger}\sigma_z\mathbf{u}_{\nu})(\mathbf{u}_{\nu}^{\dagger}\sigma_z\mathbf{u}_{\mathrm{e}}), \tag{4.57 a}$$

$$\sum_{e\nu} |Q_{\mathrm{A}}^1|^2 = 2\delta_{M',-\frac{1}{2}}(\mathbf{u}_{\mathrm{e}}^{\dagger}\sigma_1\mathbf{u}_{\nu})(\mathbf{u}_{\nu}^{\dagger}\sigma_1^{\dagger}\mathbf{u}_{\mathrm{e}}). \tag{4.57 b}$$

Each of these can be expressed as the square of a 'triplet' lepton amplitude, i.e. in the form (4.54) with the triplet spin function $\chi^t_m$, of (2.23), replacing $\chi^s$. These forms can be obtained in the same way as (4.54), and can be verified by showing that they lead to exactly the same results as do (4.57 a, b). Details are not given because the only advantage gained is a more complete justification for regarding the allowed Pseudovector radiation as 'triplet'.

The intensities are most directly obtained by the trace technique used in (4.48):

$$\begin{aligned} \sum_{e\nu} |Q_{\mathrm{A}}^0|^2 &= \delta_{M'M}\,\mathrm{tr}\,\sigma_z(\mathbf{u}_{\nu}\mathbf{u}_{\nu}^{\dagger})\sigma_z(\mathbf{u}_{\mathrm{e}}\mathbf{u}_{\mathrm{e}}^{\dagger}) \\ &= \delta_{M',+\frac{1}{2}}\tfrac{1}{2}(1-\hat{\mathbf{q}}\,.\,\mathbf{v}/c+2\hat{q}_z v_z/c), \end{aligned} \tag{4.58 a}$$

$$\begin{aligned} \sum_{e\nu} |Q_{\mathrm{A}}^1|^2 &= \delta_{M',-\frac{1}{2}}\tfrac{1}{4}\,\mathrm{tr}(\sigma_x+i\sigma_y)(1-\boldsymbol{\sigma}\,.\,\hat{\mathbf{q}})(\sigma_x-i\sigma_y)(1-\boldsymbol{\sigma}\,.\,\mathbf{v}/c) \\ &= \delta_{M',-\frac{1}{2}}(1-\hat{q}_z v_z/c+\hat{q}_z-v_z/c). \end{aligned} \tag{4.58 b}$$

The sum of these intensities is

$$\sum_{e\nu M'} [|Q_{\mathrm{A}}^0|^2+|Q_{\mathrm{A}}^1|^2] = \tfrac{3}{2}[1-\tfrac{1}{3}\hat{\mathbf{q}}\,.\,\mathbf{v}/c+\tfrac{2}{3}\hat{\mathbf{I}}\,.\,(\hat{\mathbf{q}}-\mathbf{v}/c)]. \tag{4.59}$$

Here $\hat{q}_z$ and $v_z$ have been represented as projections of the vectors $\hat{\mathbf{q}}$ and $\mathbf{v}$ on the unit vector $\hat{\mathbf{I}}$, which points out the direction of the initial neutron spin. These terms would disappear in an average over randomly oriented neutrons, leaving a net Pseudovector intensity $\frac{3}{2}(1-\frac{1}{3}\hat{\mathbf{q}}\,.\,\mathbf{v}/c)$. The factor 3 relative to the Vector intensity (4.53) is the one expected as early as in (1.24). The electron-antineutrino correlation is the one expected on grounds discussed in § 1.9.

*The Vector-Pseudovector interference*

The Pseudovector amplitude $Q_A^0$ is generated without any change of nuclear orientation, as (4.58 a) indicates. It is therefore coherent with the Vector amplitude $Q_V$, for any given spin-orientations e, $\nu$ of the leptons. There may then be an interference of the two amplitudes in producing the contribution $\sum |Q_V+Q_A^0|^2$ to the decay rate (4.46). The pure radiation terms, $\sum |Q_V|^2$ and $\sum |Q_A^0|^2$, have already been evaluated, in (4.53) and (4.58 a). There remains the interference cross-term,

$$\sum_{e\nu} Q_V^* Q_A^0 = -(\mathbf{u}_\nu^\dagger \mathbf{u}_e)(\mathbf{u}_e^\dagger \sigma_z \mathbf{u}_\nu), \tag{4.60}$$

and its complex-conjugate, as these follow from (4.43) and (4.55). Application of the trace technique to the spin sums here yields:

$$\begin{aligned}\sum_{e\nu} Q_V^* Q_A^0 &= -\tfrac{1}{4}\,\mathrm{tr}\,\sigma_z(1-\boldsymbol{\sigma}.\hat{\mathbf{q}})(1-\boldsymbol{\sigma}.\mathbf{v}/c)\\ &= \tfrac{1}{2}\hat{\mathbf{I}}.(\mathbf{v}/c+\hat{\mathbf{q}}-i[\hat{\mathbf{q}}\times\mathbf{v}/c]).\end{aligned} \tag{4.61}$$

Exactly the same result can be obtained by projecting

$$-\frac{1}{2}\left(\frac{W+mc^2}{2W}\right)^{\frac{1}{2}}\left(1-\frac{c\boldsymbol{\sigma}_e.\mathbf{p}}{W+mc^2}\right)(1+\boldsymbol{\sigma}_\nu.\hat{\mathbf{q}})\chi_0^t$$

onto the singlet amplitude which appears, squared, in (4.54). This is as to be expected from a 'singlet-triplet interference'.

*Renormalization of the nucleonic currents*

The resultant decay rate of the neutron is obtained by adding together, and inserting into (4.46), the various contributions to

$$\sum_{e\nu}\{|Q_V+Q_A^0|^2+|Q_A^1|^2\},$$

as evaluated in (4.53), (4.59), and (4.61). The result is

$$\frac{d\lambda}{dp} = \frac{g^2p^2q^2(d\hat{\mathbf{p}})(d\hat{\mathbf{q}})}{8\pi^5\hbar^7c}(1+\hat{\mathbf{I}}.\hat{\mathbf{q}}). \tag{4.62}$$

This is the prediction from the 'V-A Law' (4.10) for the decay of a polarized neutron; for randomly oriented neutrons, the last term averages to zero. Comparison with the most general correlations to be expected, as embodied in (1.53), shows that the negatron is predicted to emerge isotropically, both relative to the neutron's orientation $\hat{\mathbf{I}}$, and the nuclear recoil direction, i.e. both the electron anisotropy fraction $A\hat{\mathbf{I}}.\mathbf{v}/c = 0$ and the electron-neutrino correlation $a\hat{\mathbf{q}}.\mathbf{v}/c = 0$. Further, the Law appears to be 'time-reversal invariant' since the correlation fraction $D\hat{\mathbf{I}}.(\hat{\mathbf{q}}\times\mathbf{v}/c) = 0$ (see 'Time Reversal' in § 1.10). Finally, there is a maximal positive correlation of the antineutrino's direction with the neutron spin, as measured by the neutrino anisotropy coefficient $B = +1$.

The actual experimental observations, as reviewed in § 1.10, deviate from those predictions. Particularly definite is the existence of an anisotropic negatron fraction $A\hat{\mathbf{I}}.\mathbf{v}/c$ with $A = -0{\cdot}11 \pm 0{\cdot}02$. A way of formulating this deviation from the above-predicted isotropy, $A = 0$, is offered by the discussion in § 1.10, as arising from an inequality of Vector and Pseudovector 'coupling constants', $|C_V| \neq |C_A|$. In the present context, this corresponds to modifying the nucleonic transformation current (4.39) to

$$J_\alpha(\text{pn}) = \tfrac{1}{2}(C_V\, J_\alpha^V - C_A\, J_\alpha^A). \tag{4.63}$$

Whereas the 'V-A Law' (4.10) admits only left-handed nucleonic components, $\phi = \frac{1}{2}(1+\gamma_5)\psi$, the modification now proposed in effect admits right-handed components also, since the current may now be written

$$J_\alpha = \tfrac{1}{4}\psi_p^\dagger \beta\gamma_\alpha[(C_V - C_A)(1+\gamma_5) + (C_V + C_A)(1-\gamma_5)]\psi_n. \tag{4.64}$$

The 'V-A Law' corresponds to the special case of this with $C_A = -C_V$; it was already stated in leading up to (1.65), that a negative relative sign of these coupling constants corresponds to a net left-handed nucleonic polarization.

There is a basis on which such modifications as represented by the factors $C_V$ and $C_A$ in (4.63) may be expected. It is well known that the description of nucleons by the simple Dirac spinors (4.37 a, b) may be grossly inadequate. Nucleons interact strongly with the pion field, so that a neutron *in vacuo* for example, is expected to spend a substantial fraction of its time as a proton surrounded by a cloud of transiently emitted pions. Certainly, this might be expected to affect the negatron-emitting proclivities of the neutron, and may well affect its Vector and Pseudovector currents differently. Unfortunately, convergent calculations of such effects are beyond the powers of present-day physical theory. This is so even in an analogous electromagnetic effect, by which every charge is surrounded by a transient cloud of negatron-positron pairs. However, the situation is much better understood in the electromagnetic case, and proves representable by what is known as a 're-normalization' of charge: this modifies the charge on any particle by a factor which cannot be convergently calculated, but the result is simply assumed to be the experimentally observed charge. Uncalculable factors $C_V$, $-C_A$, modifying the $\beta$-coupling strength, are assumed to exist, and will simply be evaluated by comparisons with experimental observations.

Separate evaluations of the Vector and Pseudovector effects were made available in deriving the 'V-A Law' result (4.62). Consequently, obtaining the effects of the renormalized nucleonic current (4.63) merely requires a new combination of the same calculations. This can be written:

$$\frac{d\lambda}{dp} = \frac{g^2p^2q^2(d\hat{\mathbf{p}})(d\hat{\mathbf{q}})}{32\pi^5\hbar^7c}\xi_{\mathrm{n}}(1+a_{\mathrm{n}}\,\hat{\mathbf{q}}\,.\,\mathbf{v}/c+\hat{\mathbf{I}}\,.\,[A_{\mathrm{n}}\,\mathbf{v}/c+B_{\mathrm{n}}\,\hat{\mathbf{q}}]), \tag{4.65}$$

with

$$\left.\begin{aligned} \xi_{\mathrm{n}} &= C_{\mathrm{V}}^2+3C_{\mathrm{A}}^2 \\ \xi_{\mathrm{n}}\,a_{\mathrm{n}} &= C_{\mathrm{V}}^2-C_{\mathrm{A}}^2 \\ \xi_{\mathrm{n}}\,A_{\mathrm{n}} &= -2C_{\mathrm{A}}^2-2C_{\mathrm{V}}\,C_{\mathrm{A}} \\ \xi_{\mathrm{n}}\,B_{\mathrm{n}} &= +2C_{\mathrm{A}}^2-2C_{\mathrm{V}}\,C_{\mathrm{A}} \end{aligned}\right\}. \tag{4.66}$$

These results check exactly with those already obtained in § 1.10.

Because of the findings here, the $\beta$-theory will henceforth be carried on with the generalization of the coupling form (4.20) given by

$$H_\beta = 2^{\frac{1}{2}}g\sum_a (C_{\mathrm{V}}-C_{\mathrm{A}}\,\gamma_5^a)\beta^a\gamma_\alpha^a\,\tau_+^a\,[J_\alpha(\mathrm{e}\nu)]_{\mathbf{r}^a}+\mathrm{h.c.} \tag{4.67}$$

It is not at all certain that the renormalization should be the same in complex nuclei as it is for the free neutron, although the near-agreement of $C_{\mathrm{A}}^2/C_{\mathrm{V}}^2$, as determined from neutron data alone (1.63), and the value obtained with the help of data from the complex nucleus $\mathrm{O}^{14}$ (1.26), indicates that the renormalization effects within complex nuclei may not be radically different from those for the free neutron.

# V

## ALLOWED $\beta$-EMISSIONS

THE character of nuclei invites two immediate approximations in the treatment of their $\beta$-decay. That can best be seen after decomposing the internal nucleon variables $\gamma_\alpha^a$ into $\gamma_4^a \equiv \beta^a$ and $\boldsymbol{\gamma}^a = -i\beta^a\boldsymbol{\alpha}^a$, in the interaction hamiltonian $H_\beta(A)$ of (4.67):

$$H_\beta = 2^{\frac{1}{2}}g \sum_a \tau_+^a\{J_4^a(C_V - C_A\gamma_5^a) - i\mathbf{J}^a.(C_V\boldsymbol{\alpha}^a + C_A\boldsymbol{\sigma}^a)\} + \text{h.c.}, \quad (5.1)$$

since $-\gamma_5\boldsymbol{\alpha} = \boldsymbol{\sigma}$.

(1) Nuclei are much smaller than the lepton wavelengths characteristic of their $\beta$-decay, the nuclear radius $R$ never being larger than about $\frac{1}{40}(\hbar/mc)$, as already noted in § 1.6. Since the lepton current $J_\alpha$, as it enters the transition amplitude $\langle f|H_\beta|i\rangle$ of (4.36), needs only be known within the spatial limits of the nuclear states, and is practically constant within those limits, it may as well be evaluated at the nuclear centre. Putting $J_\alpha^a(\mathbf{r}_a = 0) \equiv J_\alpha^0$:

$$\langle f|H_\beta|i\rangle \approx 2^{\frac{1}{2}}g\Big\{J_4^0\Big[C_V \int 1 - C_A \int \gamma_5\Big] - i\mathbf{J}^0.\Big[C_A \int \boldsymbol{\sigma} + C_V \int \boldsymbol{\alpha}\Big]\Big\}, \quad (5.2)$$

into which customary abbreviations like

$$\int 1 \equiv \Big\langle f\Big|\sum_a \tau_\pm^a\Big|i\Big\rangle \quad \text{and} \quad \int \boldsymbol{\sigma} \equiv \Big\langle f\Big|\sum_a \tau_\pm^a\,\boldsymbol{\sigma}^a\Big|i\Big\rangle \quad (5.3)$$

have been introduced.

(2) The constituents of nuclei are adequately described in non-relativistic approximation, nuclear energies being much smaller than nucleon rest-masses (MeV vs. GeV). That makes magnitudes of order $v^a/c$, like that of the velocity operator $\boldsymbol{\alpha}^a$ or of $\gamma_5^a = -\sigma_i^a\,\alpha_i^a$, negligible. Confirmation is obtainable from the non-relativistic descriptions of nuclear states, which, according to the discussion of (3.2), depend on the inner variables of any one nucleon as indicated by

$$\psi_{i,f} \approx \begin{pmatrix} \boldsymbol{\varphi}_{i,f} \\ 0 \end{pmatrix},$$

i.e. the 'small' Pauli spinor components are to be neglected. It follows that, whereas $\int 1$ and $\int \boldsymbol{\sigma}$ will be proportional to $\psi_f^\dagger\psi_i \approx \boldsymbol{\varphi}_f^\dagger\boldsymbol{\varphi}_i$ and $\psi_f^\dagger\boldsymbol{\sigma}\psi_i \approx \boldsymbol{\varphi}_f^\dagger\boldsymbol{\sigma}\boldsymbol{\varphi}_i$, respectively, $\int \gamma_5$ will be proportional to $\psi_f^\dagger\gamma_5\psi_i \approx 0$ and $\int \alpha$ to $\psi_f^\dagger\boldsymbol{\alpha}\psi_i \approx 0$. The same effect has already been met in connexion with the neutron transformation current (4.40), where it was an obvious consequence of the negligibility of the proton recoil.

The effect of the two approximations is to reduce the $\beta$-transition amplitude to

$$\langle \mathrm{f}|H_\beta|\mathrm{i}\rangle \approx 2^{\frac{1}{2}}g\Big\{C_{\mathrm{V}}\,J_4^0 \int 1 - iC_{\mathrm{A}}\,\mathbf{J}^0 . \int \boldsymbol{\sigma}\Big\}. \tag{5.4}$$

The reduction will next be seen to yield just the allowed transitions as discussed in § 1.5.

## 5.1. Selection rules

The characteristics of the individual nuclear states enter into the determination of allowed $\beta$-decay only through the nuclear matrix elements, $\int 1$ and $\int \boldsymbol{\sigma}$. These serve as parameters in the $\beta$-processes and observations on the latter can be used to help determine their values, just as observations on certain electromagnetic effects are used to determine the magnetic moments of nuclei. Theoretical calculations of the $\beta$-moments are no more reliable than are calculations of nuclear magnetic moments, in the present state of nuclear structure theory.

There is, however, one type of theoretical conclusion that can be drawn reliably about each nuclear matrix element: the selection rules on total angular momenta, and parities, which must be observed for the element not to vanish. It is characteristic selection rules by which the allowed transitions were first distinguished, in § 1.5.

*Allowed selection rules*

Selection rules reflect the conservation of angular momentum and of parity. The part of the formalism which enforces such conservation principles is the orthogonality of states which differ in angular momentum and/or parity. Thus, if the nuclear states $|\mathrm{i}\rangle$ and $|\mathrm{f}\rangle$ have angular momenta $IM$ and $I'M'$, respectively, then they can be represented as proportional to the angular momentum eigenstates, $\boldsymbol{\chi}_{IM}$ and $\boldsymbol{\chi}_{I'M'}$, of § 2.1, and

$$\langle \mathrm{f}|\mathrm{i}\rangle \sim \boldsymbol{\chi}^\dagger_{I'M'}\boldsymbol{\chi}_{IM} = \delta_{I'I}\,\delta_{M'M}. \tag{5.5}$$

This orthogonality is not interfered with in matrix elements like

$$\int 1 \equiv \langle \mathrm{f}|\sum \tau^a_{\pm}|\mathrm{i}\rangle \sim \delta_{I'I}\,\delta_{M'M}, \tag{5.6}$$

where the operation is independent of spins, and of directions. We have the immediate selection rule: $\int 1 \neq 0$ only if $\Delta I \equiv |I'-I| = 0$.

The parity refers to the evenness or oddness of the dependence on spatial positions. Suppose that the nuclear state $|\mathrm{i}\rangle$ is proportional to $\Psi_{\mathrm{i}}(\mathbf{r}_1, \mathbf{r}_2,..., \mathbf{r}_A)$ in its dependence on the position vectors $\mathbf{r}_1,..., \mathbf{r}_A$ of the $A$ nucleons. Its parity is then called even or odd according as $\Psi_i$ does not or does change sign under the 'parity operation',

$$P\Psi_i(\mathbf{r}_1,..., \mathbf{r}_A) \equiv \Psi_i(-\mathbf{r}_1,..., -\mathbf{r}_A). \tag{5.7}$$

Obviously, $P^2 = 1$ and the eigenstates of $P$ can only have eigenvalues $\pi_i \equiv \pm 1$. That nuclear states are indeed parity eigenstates, i.e. are always either even or odd, is supported by a vast body of evidence pertaining to nuclear structure theory. The projection of two nuclear states on each other can be written equivalently in two ways:

$$\begin{aligned}\langle \mathrm{f}|\mathrm{i}\rangle &= \oint ... \oint (d\mathbf{r}_1)...(d\mathbf{r}_A)\Psi_f^\dagger(\mathbf{r}_1,..., \mathbf{r}_A)\Psi_i(\mathbf{r}_1,..., \mathbf{r}_A) \\ &= \oint ... \oint (d\mathbf{r}_1) ... (d\mathbf{r}_A)\Psi_f^\dagger(-\mathbf{r}_1,..., -\mathbf{r}_A)\Psi_i(-\mathbf{r}_1,..., -\mathbf{r}_A).\end{aligned}$$

The two lines should become each other's negatives if the parity of $\Psi_f$ is opposite to that of $\Psi_i$, hence each must then be zero. This orthogonality is not interfered with in either of the two matrix elements $\int 1$ or $\int \boldsymbol{\sigma}$, since the operators introduce no dependence on $\mathbf{r}_1,..., \mathbf{r}_A$. We have the selection rule that $\int 1 \neq 0$, $\int \boldsymbol{\sigma} \neq 0$ only if the nuclear parity does not change in the transition.

The angular momentum selection rule for $\int \boldsymbol{\sigma}$ requires somewhat more elaborate discussion, which is left to the next subsection. We anticipate the result in order to sum up the *allowed selection rules*:

$$\left.\begin{aligned}\int 1 &= 0 \quad \text{unless } \Delta I = 0,\ \pi_i \pi_f = +1 \\ \int \boldsymbol{\sigma} &= 0 \quad \text{unless } \Delta I = 0 \text{ or } 1,\ \pi_i \pi_f = +1 \\ &= 0 \quad \text{also for } I = 0 \rightarrow I' = 0\end{aligned}\right\}. \tag{5.8}$$

The notation $\pi_i \pi_f = +1$ indicates that parity operations on the initial and final nuclear states each result in multiplication by a unit of the same sign. These rules coincide with the ones already indicated in § 1.5, hence the justification of the assertion that the approximations yielding the form (5.4) for the transition matrix element, i.e. as a combination of $\int 1$ and $\int \boldsymbol{\sigma}$, correspond to a restriction to allowed transitions. The approximations are expected to be good ones, so that any transitions which occur in violation of the allowed selection rules must arise from effects which were judged negligibly small. Thus, what were called 'forbidden transitions' in § 1.5 must have very slow rates as compared to the allowed transitions.

The selection rules characteristic of the element, $\int 1$, were associated with singlet leptonic radiation and called 'Fermi selection rules', in

§ 1.7. Similarly, $\int \boldsymbol{\sigma}$ is associated with triplet radiation and 'GT rules'. The justification for the nomenclature 'singlet' and 'triplet', for the leptonic currents $J_4$ and $\mathbf{J}$, respectively, of (5.4), has already been discussed in connexion with (4.54), (4.57), and (4.61).

*The Wigner–Eckart theorem*

The angular momentum selection rules for $\int \boldsymbol{\sigma}$ follow from just the vector character of $\boldsymbol{\sigma}$ (thus, they are the same as for $\int \mathbf{r}$, a transition matrix for electric dipole radiation, familiar from atomic spectroscopy). Such a fact may not be surprising, in view of the basic definitions of angular momenta as quantities the conservation of which follows from invariances in rotations of the reference frame. The general conclusions about matrix elements are embodied in a powerful theorem due to Wigner and Eckart. The substance of the theorem can be stated, without a preliminary excursion into group theory, by supposing that the matrix elements are already analysed into matrix elements of 'spherical tensor operators'. This turns out to be not too much to ask, since it is a natural outcome of usual approaches.

Any vector is a 'spherical tensor of first order' when it is resolved into components as in (2.6) for the angular momentum operator, $\mathbf{j}$, and in (2.7) for the unit vector $\hat{\mathbf{r}}$. The spherical tensor components $\sigma_0 \equiv \sigma_z$ and $\sigma_{\pm 1} = \pm 2^{-\frac{1}{2}}(\sigma_x \pm i\sigma_y)$ have already been put to use in (4.56). A spherical tensor of order $l$ is any quantity with $(2l+1)$ components which vary in spatial rotations of the reference frame in the same way as do the $(2l+1)$ spherical harmonics, $Y_{lm}$ (i.e. with the same matrix of coefficients forming the linear relations between the components in one frame and those in a relatively rotated frame). The general spherical tensor, $S_{Jm}$, has the same rotational transformation properties as the angular momentum eigenfunction, $\chi_{Jm}$ (although there is no need for spherical tensors of half-integer order).

The last statement makes it clear that any two spherical tensor operations on independent degrees of freedom can be combined, like the eigenfunctions in (2.11), into composite spherical tensors defined as

$$S_{j\mu} = \sum_{\mu_1 \mu_2} S_{j_1 \mu_1} S_{j_2 \mu_2} \langle j_1(\mu_1) j_2(\mu_2) | j(\mu) \rangle. \tag{5.9}$$

Such combinations are often denoted $(S_{j_2} . S_{j_2})_{j\mu}$. Of course, only the terms with $\mu_1 + \mu_2 = \mu$ survive in this expression because of the properties of the vector-addition coefficients. The way it is written makes clearer the outcome of operation by $\sum_{j\mu} \langle j_1(\mu_1') j_2(\mu_2') | j(\mu) \rangle \ldots$. The latter inverts the relationship to

$$\sum_{j\mu} \langle j_1(\mu_1')j_2(\mu_2')|j(\mu)\rangle S_{j\mu} = S_{j_1\mu_1'}S_{j_2\mu_2'}, \tag{5.10}$$

as a consequence of the orthonormality (2.12).

The result (5.10) makes it unsurprising that operation by a spherical tensor on an angular momentum eigenfunction yields

$$S_{Jm}\chi_{IM} = \sum_{I'} \langle I(M)J(m)|I'(M+m)\rangle K_{JII'}\chi_{I',M+m}, \tag{5.11}$$

where the $K_{JII'}$ are factors depending on the nature of the operation, but independent of orientations because the physical significance should not depend on the frame chosen. In other words, the effects of the choice of frame orientation should not be different in (5.10) and (5.11). An example of a relation like (5.11) is the particularly useful one

$$Y_{l_1m_1}(\hat{\mathbf{r}})Y_{l_2m_2}(\hat{\mathbf{r}}) = \sum_L [(2l_1+1)(2l_2+1)/4\pi(2L+1)]^{\frac{1}{2}}\times$$
$$\times\langle l_1(0)l_2(0)|L(0)\rangle\langle l_1(m_1)l_2(m_2)|L(m_1+m_2)\rangle Y_{L,m_1+m_2}(\hat{\mathbf{r}}), \tag{5.12}$$

which amounts to an expansion in spherical harmonics, of the product of two spherical harmonics.

The burden of the Wigner–Eckart theorem is that the matrix element of any spherical tensor $S_{Jm}$, combining states of angular momenta $IM$ and $I'M'$, is proportional to a vector-addition coefficient,

$$\langle \delta' I'M'|S_{Jm}|\delta IM\rangle \sim \langle I(M)J(m)|I'(M')\rangle, \tag{5.13}$$

and that this constitutes the entire dependence on the orientations $M$, $M'$ and $m$. The symbols $\delta$, $\delta'$ stand for whatever further specifications the states may have besides the indicated angular momenta. The result is as to be expected from projecting (5.11) onto $\chi_{I'M'}$. These considerations are perhaps plausible enough to make a lengthy excursion into the formal proof‡ unnecessary.

The vector addition coefficient vanishes unless the angular momenta are related by the 'triangle condition' (2.10) and this constitutes the selection rules. The angular momentum conservation relation $\mathbf{I}+\mathbf{J} = \mathbf{I}'$ is thus embodied. Accordingly, $S_{Jm}$ represents an interaction in which the angular momentum $\mathbf{J}$ is added to the system (or $-\mathbf{J}$ 'radiated' from it), in a transition $\mathbf{I} \rightarrow \mathbf{I}'$.

In the special case of any vector matrix element like $\int \boldsymbol{\sigma}$, the selection rules follow from the proportionality

$$\langle \sigma_m\rangle \sim \langle I(M)1(m)|I'(M')\rangle. \tag{5.14}$$

‡ To be found in many places, e.g. E. P. Wigner, *Group Theory* (Academic Press, 1959); M. E. Rose, *Angular Momentum* (Wiley, 1957); A. R. Edmonds, *Angular Momentum in Quantum Mechanics* (Princeton, 1957).

This survives only for $M' = M+m$ and $I' = I$ or $I\pm1$. Moreover, the vector-addition coefficient here vanishes for $I = I' = 0$, all as recorded in the selection rules (5.8).

*The nuclear β-moments*

The proportionality constant in the Wigner–Eckart relation will be so denoted that

$$\langle\delta' I' M'|S^{\dagger}_{Jm}|\delta I M\rangle = \langle I'(M')J(m)|I(M)\rangle\langle S_J\rangle, \tag{5.15}$$

where the hermitian conjugate operator has the property of being proportional to

$$S^{\dagger}_{Jm} \sim (-)^m S_{J,-m}, \tag{5.16}$$

quite analogously to the well-known property of the spherical harmonics, $Y^*_{lm} = (-)^m Y_{l,-m}$ (to be discussed further in § 6.3). Now it is the angular momentum $+\mathbf{J}$ that is ejected by the system, rather than $-\mathbf{J}$ as in (5.13). The schematized symbol $\langle S_J\rangle$ defined by (5.15), stands for what is known as a 'reduced matrix element'. Its characteristic property is its independence of the angular momentum orientations, which follows from the Wigner–Eckart theorem (5.13) and the properties (2.14) of the vector-addition coefficients. The definition of the reduced element here differs by a factor from the several in the literature. The definition here has been so chosen that its absolute square is just equal to the sum of the absolute squares of the unreduced elements (5.15), with the various $m$ for a given initial orientation $M$. That follows easily from (2.13).

A specific example of a reduced element can be obtained from (5.12), for the matrix element

$$\oint (d\hat{\mathbf{r}})Y^*_{l'm'}\,Y_{LM}\,Y_{lm} = (-)^M\langle l'(m')L(-M)|l(m)\rangle\langle Y_L\rangle. \tag{5.17 a}$$

It then follows that

$$\langle Y_L\rangle = (-)^L(2L+1/4\pi)^{\frac{1}{2}}\langle l(0)L(0)|l'(0)\rangle, \tag{5.17 b}$$

for the specific, simple states given in (5.17 a). The vector-addition coefficient here has the property that it vanishes unless $l+l'+L$ is even, thus embodying the parity conservation in the transition element (5.17 a). The latter represents an 'emission' of the parity $(-)^L$, since

$$Y_{LM}(-\hat{\mathbf{r}}) = (-)^L Y_{LM}(\hat{\mathbf{r}}), \tag{5.18}$$

which is obvious from the definition (2.4).

Equally useful is the reduced matrix element of $\boldsymbol{\sigma}$ for a given spin degree of freedom,

$$\chi^{\dagger}_{\mu'}\,\sigma_m\,\chi_{\mu} = (-)^m\langle\tfrac{1}{2}(\mu')1(-m)|\tfrac{1}{2}(\mu)\rangle\langle\sigma\rangle, \tag{5.19 a}$$

where, according to the Tables 2.1 or 2.2,

$$\langle\sigma\rangle = 3^{\frac{1}{2}}. \tag{5.19 b}$$

This simple result holds only relative to states describing one spin degree of freedom, which provides the only angular momentum. Such a description applies to the neutron as discussed in § 4.4, and so

$$\int \sigma_m^\dagger = 3^{\frac{1}{2}}\langle \tfrac{1}{2}(M')1(m)|\tfrac{1}{2}(M)\rangle$$

for the neutron. This agrees with the results already obtained in (4.56).

Any reduced matrix element of the type $\langle S_J\rangle$, evaluated as in (5.15) for the parent and daughter states of a $\beta$-process, will be called a 'nuclear $\beta$-moment'. The $\beta$-moments of allowed decay for $I \to I'$ are defined by

$$\left.\begin{aligned} \int 1 &= \langle I'(M')0(0)|I(M)\rangle\langle 1\rangle = \delta_{I'I}\,\delta_{M'M}\langle 1\rangle \\ \int \sigma_m^\dagger &= \langle I'(M')1(m)|I(M)\rangle\langle\sigma\rangle \end{aligned}\right\}. \tag{5.20}$$

In particular, $\langle 1\rangle = \int 1$ is called the 'singlet', or 'Fermi' moment, while $\langle\sigma\rangle$ is called the 'triplet' or 'Gamow–Teller' moment. Notice that

$$\langle\sigma\rangle^2 = \sum_m \left|\int \sigma_m\right|^2 = \left|\int \sigma_x\right|^2 + \left|\int \sigma_y\right|^2 + \left|\int \sigma_z\right|^2 \tag{5.21}$$

because the definition adopted for the moments was arranged to yield just such results. It will eventually be seen (§ 6.3) that the phases of the nuclear states can be adopted in such a way that $\langle\sigma\rangle$ is real simultaneously with $\langle 1\rangle$.

## 5.2. The allowed emission phenomena

To obtain suitable detail about the $\beta$-emissions, rates will be sought for decays in which the electron and neutrino momenta end in specific ranges, $(d\mathbf{p})$ and $(d\mathbf{q})$. It is the 'distorted plane waves', $\Psi_e$ of (3.60), which must be used for the electron, because of the presence of nuclear charge; thus, the electron momentum $\mathbf{p}$ is that attained at infinity. Both the lepton waves will be supposed normalized to unity in $V$, so that the desired rate is obtained by multiplying (4.36) by

$$(d\mathbf{p})(d\mathbf{q})V^2/(2\pi\hbar)^6. \tag{5.22}$$

The energy-conserving $\delta$-function of (4.36) is eliminated by integration over the infinitesimal range of neutrino energy permitted for a given electron momentum, just as in deriving the neutron decay rate (4.46). With the 'allowed approximation' (5.4) for the transition matrix,

$$\frac{d\lambda}{dp} = \frac{2g^2p^2q^2(d\hat{\mathbf{p}})(d\hat{\mathbf{q}})}{(2\pi)^5\hbar^7c}V^2\left|C_V J_4 \int 1 - iC_A\,\mathbf{J}.\int \boldsymbol{\sigma}\right|^2 \tag{5.23}$$

is the partial decay rate indicated by the differential elements.

*The role of nuclear orientations*

The scalar product in the transition matrix element can be written

$$\mathbf{J}.\int \boldsymbol{\sigma} \equiv \sum_m J_m \int \sigma_m^\dagger = \langle\sigma\rangle \sum_m J_m \langle I'(M')1(m)|I(M)\rangle, \qquad (5.24)$$

according to the definition of the β-moment (5.20). The three electron-neutrino current components, $J_{0,\pm 1}$ in (5.24), accompany the formation of three independent (incoherent) final nuclear orientations, $M' = M$, $M \mp 1$, starting from any initial one, $M$. Accordingly, the squared transition amplitude (5.4) as it enters (5.23), becomes

$$|\langle \mathrm{f}|H_\beta|\mathrm{i}\rangle|^2 = 2g^2\Big\{\Big|C_\mathrm{V} J_4 \int 1 - iC_\mathrm{A} J_0 \int \sigma_z\Big|^2 + \\ + C_\mathrm{A}^2\Big[|J_{+1}|^2\Big|\int \sigma_{-1}\Big|^2 + |J_{-1}|^2\Big|\int \sigma_{+1}\Big|^2\Big]\Big\}. \qquad (5.25)$$

This indicates that a Vector-Pseudovector interference is still to be allowed for, when the $M' = M$ state is produced. A summation over all possible final nuclear orientations, $M'$, can now be considered completed.

The total intensity (5.25) can be expressed as a sum of three contributions. The pure Vector contribution is, with $\int 1 \equiv \langle 1\rangle$,

$$|\langle \mathrm{f}|H_\beta|\mathrm{i}\rangle|^2_\mathrm{V} = \delta_{I'I}.2g^2C_\mathrm{V}^2\langle 1\rangle^2|J_4|^2, \qquad (5.26\,\mathrm{a})$$

independent of nuclear orientations, as expected. The pure Pseudovector contribution is

$$|\langle \mathrm{f}|H_\beta|\mathrm{i}\rangle|^2_\mathrm{A} = 2g^2C_\mathrm{A}^2\langle\sigma\rangle^2 \sum_m |J_m|^2\langle I'(M-m)1(m)|I(M)\rangle^2, \qquad (5.26\,\mathrm{b})$$

as follows from (5.24). The Vector-Pseudovector interference becomes

$$|\langle \mathrm{f}|H_\beta|\mathrm{i}\rangle|^2_\mathrm{VA} = \delta_{I'I}\, 2g^2C_\mathrm{V}\, C_\mathrm{A}\langle 1\rangle\langle\sigma\rangle[I/(I+1)]^{\frac{1}{2}}(M/I)(iJ_0^* J_4 + \mathrm{c.c.}), \qquad (5.26\,\mathrm{c})$$

after a substitution from Table 2.1 for the specific vector-addition coefficient, $\langle I(M)1(0)|I(M)\rangle$, which enters here (5.24).

To obtain the decay rates *for randomly oriented nuclei*, the contributions (5.26) should be averaged over the initial nuclear orientations, $-I \leqslant M \leqslant I$, by applying the operation $(2I+1)^{-1}\sum_M \dots$. This averaging plainly does not affect the Vector contribution (5.26 a) at all, and the Vector-Pseudovector interference (5.26 c), being proportional to $M$, averages to zero. In the Pseudovector contribution (5.26 b), each squared vector-addition coefficient is replaced by the average

$$(2I+1)^{-1}\sum_M [(2I+1)/3]\langle I'(m-M)I(M)|1(m)\rangle^2 \equiv \tfrac{1}{3},$$

after use of the symmetry relations (2.14). This has now been put in a form to which the summation theorem (2.13) applies directly, and the result is simply $\frac{1}{3}$, for each $I'$. Thus,

$$(2I+1)^{-1}\sum_M |\langle \mathrm{f}|H_\beta|\mathrm{i}\rangle|^2_{\mathrm{A}} = 2g^2C_{\mathrm{A}}^2\langle\sigma\rangle^2.\tfrac{1}{3}\sum_m |J_m|^2, \tag{5.27 a}$$

together with just the Vector contribution (5.26 a), will yield the total intensity from randomly oriented nuclei.

*For polarized initial nuclei*, the total intensity has an isotropic part (i.e. independent of nuclear orientation) which is the same as for the randomly oriented nuclei, (5.26 a) plus (5.27 a). Added to that are certain 'anisotropies' which average to zero for the randomly oriented nuclei. One of these is the Vector-Pseudovector interference contribution (5.26 c), characterized by its proportionality to $(M/I)$. There is also a term proportional to $(M/I)$ in the Pseudovector contribution (5.26 b). That is found when Table 2.1 is consulted for the vector-addition coefficients occurring in (5.26 b):

$$(M/I)\langle M_{\mathrm{S}}\rangle 2g^2C_{\mathrm{A}}^2\langle\sigma\rangle^2.\tfrac{1}{2}(|J_{+1}|^2-|J_{-1}|^2), \tag{5.27 b}$$

where $\langle M_{\mathrm{S}}\rangle$ is exactly the coefficient (1.37) already found in Chapter I. The substitutions from Table 2.1 into (5.26 b) also reveal terms proportional to $M^2$; when the total expression has (5.27 a, b) subtracted from it, the remainder is a 'second-order anisotropy' which can be written

$$2g^2C_{\mathrm{A}}^2\langle\sigma\rangle^2\{[M^2-\tfrac{1}{3}I(I+1)]/I(2I-1)\}\tfrac{1}{2}\Lambda[|J_{+1}|^2+|J_{-1}|^2-2|J_0|^2]. \tag{5.27 c}$$

Here, the coefficients‡ $\Lambda$ can be tabulated as

$$\left.\begin{array}{llll} & \Lambda = 1, & -(2I-1)/(I+1), & I(2I-1)/(I+1)(2I+3) \\ \text{for} & I' = I-1, & I, & I+1 \end{array}\right\}. \tag{5.28}$$

The second-order anisotropy disappears for randomly oriented nuclei because

$$(2I+1)^{-1}\sum_M M^2 = \tfrac{1}{3}\langle I_x^2+I_y^2+I_z^2\rangle = \tfrac{1}{3}I(I+1). \tag{5.29}$$

It also vanishes for $I \leqslant \frac{1}{2}$ since $M^2-\frac{1}{3}I(I+1) = 0$ in both the cases $I = M = 0$ and $I = \frac{1}{2}$, $M = \pm\frac{1}{2}$. (For a like reason, nuclei with $I \leqslant \frac{1}{2}$ possess no quadrupole moments.)

It should be emphasized that the sum of the expressions (5.27 a, b, c) is exactly equivalent to the total Pseudovector contribution (5.26 b), regardless of the state of the nuclear orientations.

*The lepton intensities*

The electron-neutrino current can be written

$$J_\alpha = \Phi_{\mathrm{e}}^\dagger \beta\gamma_\alpha \phi_\nu^C. \tag{5.30}$$

‡ Results complete enough to contain these terms seem to have been published first by J. D. Jackson, S. B. Treiman, and H. W. Wyld, *Nucl. Phys.* **4**, 206 (1957).

This applies to negatron emission if, as usual, the projections

$$\Phi_e = \tfrac{1}{2}(1+\gamma_5)\Psi_e \quad \text{and} \quad \phi_\nu^C = \tfrac{1}{2}(1+\gamma_5)\psi_\nu^C$$

are employed. The positron emissions can be economically treated at the same time if, for the remainder of this subsection, it is agreed that

$$\Phi_e(Z) = \tfrac{1}{2}(1\pm\gamma_5)\Psi_e(\pm Z), \qquad \phi_\nu^C = \tfrac{1}{2}(1\pm\gamma_5)\psi_\nu^C \quad (\text{for } e^\mp). \tag{5.31}$$

This accords with the result (4.35) for the relation between the negatron- and positron-emission currents.

The lepton currents can be resolved into

$$J_4 = \Phi_e^\dagger \phi_\nu^C, \qquad \mathbf{J} = \pm i\Phi_e^\dagger \boldsymbol{\sigma}\phi_\nu^C \quad (\text{for } e^\mp), \tag{5.32}$$

since $\beta\boldsymbol{\gamma} = -i\boldsymbol{\alpha} = i\boldsymbol{\sigma}\gamma_5$ and $\gamma_5(1\pm\gamma_5) = \pm(1\pm\gamma_5)$. As in (4.41), e and $\nu$ will serve as spin-projection quantum numbers.

For the intensities (5.25), products of the type

$$J_\alpha J_\beta^* = \Phi_e^\dagger \beta\gamma_\alpha \phi_\nu^C \phi_\nu^{C\dagger} \gamma_\beta \beta\Phi_e$$

are needed. Now, there is little point in finding separate intensities for the two neutrino orientations $\nu = \pm\frac{1}{2}$, since the chances of detecting neutrino polarizations directly seem very remote. Accordingly, we sum over neutrino spins with the help of the density matrix

$$\sum_\nu \phi_\nu^C \phi_\nu^{C\dagger} = (4V)^{-1}(1+\gamma_5)(1-\boldsymbol{\sigma}.\hat{\mathbf{q}}) = \sum_\nu \phi_\nu \phi_\nu^\dagger. \tag{5.33}$$

This is derivable in several ways; direct calculation from (3.10) and (3.16), or by using $\phi^C = \frac{1}{2}(1+\gamma_5)\psi^C$ and $\psi^C = C\psi^*$, are no more onerous than other ways. Of course, each of the spinors (3.10), (3.16), or (3.4) must be adapted to neutrinos ($m \to 0$, $W \to cq$, $\mathbf{p} \to \mathbf{q}$). When $\phi_\nu^C$ is given the meaning (5.31), in order to include positron emission, then the signs of $\gamma_5$ and of $\boldsymbol{\sigma}$ must both be reversed in (5.33), to change from the negatron to the positron case.

The intensities needed for (5.25) then become (the upper signs referring to negatron, the lower to positron, emissions):

$$\sum_\nu |J_4|^2 = (2V)^{-1}\Phi_e^\dagger(1\mp\boldsymbol{\sigma}.\hat{\mathbf{q}})\Phi_e, \tag{5.34 a}$$

$$\sum_\nu |J_0|^2 = (2V)^{-1}\Phi_e^\dagger(1\pm\boldsymbol{\sigma}.\hat{\mathbf{q}}\mp 2\sigma_z\hat{q}_z)\Phi_e, \tag{5.34 b}$$

$$\sum_\nu |J_{+1}|^2 = (2V)^{-1}(1\pm\hat{q}_z)\Phi_e^\dagger(1+\sigma_z)\Phi_e, \tag{5.34 c}$$

$$\sum_\nu |J_{-1}|^2 = (2V)^{-1}(1\mp\hat{q}_z)\Phi_e^\dagger(1-\sigma_z)\Phi_e, \tag{5.34 d}$$

$$\sum_\nu iJ_0^* J_4 = (2V)^{-1}\Phi_e^\dagger[\pm\sigma_z-\hat{q}_z-i(\boldsymbol{\sigma}\times\hat{\mathbf{q}})_z]\Phi_e, \tag{5.34 e}$$

where the $z$-components are projections on whatever quantization axis may be chosen.

For the isotropic part (5.27 a) of the Pseudovector radiation,

$$\tfrac{1}{3}\sum_{m\nu}|J_m|^2 = (2V)^{-1}\Phi_e^\dagger(1\pm\tfrac{1}{3}\boldsymbol{\sigma}.\hat{\mathbf{q}})\Phi_e \quad (\text{for } e^\mp), \tag{5.35 a}$$

is needed. The 'first-order anisotropy' (5.27 b) requires:

$$\sum_\nu \tfrac{1}{2}(|J_{+1}|^2-|J_{-1}|^2) = (2V)^{-1}\Phi_e^\dagger(\sigma_z\pm\hat{q}_z)\Phi_e \quad (\text{for } e^\mp). \tag{5.35 b}$$

In the 'second-order anisotropy' there is (5.27 c):

$$\sum_\nu \tfrac{1}{2}(|J_{+1}|^2+|J_{-1}|^2-2|J_0|^2) = \pm(2V)^{-1}\Phi_e^\dagger(3\sigma_z\hat{q}_z-\boldsymbol{\sigma}.\hat{\mathbf{q}})\Phi_e \quad (\text{for } e^\mp). \tag{5.35 c}$$

It is already clear from this that the second-order anisotropy cannot be detected without requiring coincidences with definite nuclear recoil directions.

All the intensities (5.34) and (5.35) are linear combinations of $(\Phi_e^\dagger\Phi_e)$ and components of $(\Phi_e^\dagger\boldsymbol{\sigma}\Phi_e)$. Since these need to be evaluated only at the nucleus, in the allowed approximation, projections by $\tfrac{1}{2}(1\pm\gamma_5)$ of the spinor $\Psi_e(\pm Z)$ of (3.64) may be used. The product $\Phi_e^\dagger\Phi_e$ has already been presented in (3.69) for the case of negatrons. Here, it will be written:

$$\Phi_e^\dagger\Phi_e = [F(\pm Z, W)/2V](1\mp\boldsymbol{\sigma}_e.\mathbf{v}/c) \quad (\text{for } e^\mp), \tag{5.36}$$

where $\boldsymbol{\sigma}_e$ stands for the expectation value, $\boldsymbol{\chi}_e^\dagger\boldsymbol{\sigma}\boldsymbol{\chi}_e$, in whatever state $\boldsymbol{\chi}_e$ the electron spin may be sought. Note that $e = +\tfrac{1}{2}$ is to be used when either the negatron or positron spin is to be parallel to the quantization axis. Similar evaluation yields ($m = c = 1$)

$$\Phi_e^\dagger\boldsymbol{\sigma}\Phi_e = [F(\pm Z, W)/2V]\times \\ \times\{\mp\mathbf{v}+\hat{\mathbf{p}}(\boldsymbol{\sigma}_e.\hat{\mathbf{p}})+(\gamma_0/W)\hat{\mathbf{p}}\times(\boldsymbol{\sigma}_e\times\hat{\mathbf{p}})-(\alpha Z/W)\boldsymbol{\sigma}_e\times\hat{\mathbf{p}}\}, \tag{5.37}$$

with the upper signs referring to negatron, the lower to positron, emissions. The vector $\hat{\mathbf{p}} = \mathbf{p}/p$ is the unit vector in the direction of the electron's emission.

*The correlation distribution*

The complete result for the allowed decay rate, detailed in every respect except that the neutrino orientations are summed together, is obtained when the expressions (5.36), (5.37) are substituted into (5.34), (5.35), and the results collected into (5.23):

$$\frac{d\lambda}{dp} = \frac{g^2F(\pm Z, W)p^2q^2\,d\Omega_e d\Omega_\nu}{2(2\pi)^5\hbar^7c}\xi\{(1+\bar{B}\hat{\mathbf{I}}.\mathbf{q})(1\mp\boldsymbol{\sigma}_e.\mathbf{v}/c)+ \\ +[\mathbf{v}/c\mp(\boldsymbol{\sigma}_e.\hat{\mathbf{p}})\hat{\mathbf{p}}\mp(\gamma_0\,mc^2/W)\hat{\mathbf{p}}\times(\boldsymbol{\sigma}_e\times\hat{\mathbf{p}})\pm(\alpha Zmc^2/W)(\boldsymbol{\sigma}_e\times\hat{\mathbf{p}})]\,\boldsymbol{.} \\ \boldsymbol{.}\,[a\hat{\mathbf{q}}+\bar{A}\hat{\mathbf{I}}+(1-x)\bar{\Lambda}(\tfrac{1}{3}\hat{\mathbf{q}}-(\hat{\mathbf{q}}.\hat{\mathbf{I}})\hat{\mathbf{I}})]\} \quad (\text{for } e^\mp). \tag{5.38}$$

This rate is proportional to a strength factor

$$\xi = C_V^2\langle 1\rangle^2+C_A^2\langle\sigma\rangle^2, \tag{5.39 a}$$

which is the sum of Vector and Pseudovector contributions. The 'Vector (Fermi) Fraction',

$$x = C_V^2\langle 1\rangle^2/\xi, \tag{5.39 b}$$

is to be identified with the parameter $x$ used in Chapter I, before the Fermi theory was introduced. A comparably definite expression for $x$ was possible in Chapter I only for the case of the neutron (1.54); the expressions agree in this case, since $\langle 1\rangle = 1$ and $\langle\sigma\rangle = 3^{\frac{1}{2}}$, according to (5.19 b), for the neutron decay. The quantity $a$ in (5.38) is an abbreviation for $a = \frac{1}{3}(4x-1)$, and is identical with the electron-neutrino correlation coefficient of (1.52).

The unit vector $\hat{\mathbf{I}}$ is the direction of the nuclear spin vector $\mathbf{I}$ whenever the latter is definite, as for a completely polarized source ($M = I$). Otherwise, it is the 'nuclear polarization' axis relative to which the orientation numbers $M$ are defined; its presence is not needed for an unpolarized source as will immediately be clear. It was introduced into (5.38) as the $z$-axis to which the various $z$-components in the lepton intensities (5.34), (5.35) refer.

The nuclear orientation numbers $M$ are implicit in the definitions of the coefficients $\bar{A}$, $\bar{B}$, and $\bar{\Lambda}$,

$$\frac{\bar{A}}{A} = \frac{\bar{B}}{B} = \frac{\langle M\rangle}{I} \quad \text{and} \quad \frac{\bar{\Lambda}}{\Lambda} = \frac{3\langle M^2\rangle - I(I+1)}{I(2I-1)}, \tag{5.40}$$

where $A$, $B$, and $\Lambda$ are just the anisotropy coefficients (1.68), (1.69), and (5.28) introduced earlier. All the quantities $\bar{A}$, $\bar{B}$, and $\bar{\Lambda}$ vanish for unpolarized nuclei, and, with them, all reference to the vector $\hat{\mathbf{I}}$ in (5.38). For a completely polarized source, $\bar{A} = A$, $\bar{B} = B$, and $\bar{\Lambda} = \Lambda$. Otherwise, $M$ and $M^2$ must be averaged (incoherently) over the populations of the states $M = \pm I, \pm(I-1),...$ which characterize the source actually used; the results of such averaging are denoted $\langle M\rangle$ and $\langle M^2\rangle$ in (5.40).

The expressions for the electron and neutrino anisotropies, $A$ and $B$, as given in (1.68) and (1.69), are written in terms of the Vector fraction $x$ and the square root $y = \pm(1-x)^{\frac{1}{2}}$ of the Pseudovector fraction. The sign of this square root had to be treated as an unknown parameter additional to $x$ in Chapter I, except for the special case of the neutron ($y_n > 0$). Now the identification

$$\xi x^{\frac{1}{2}}y = -C_V C_A\langle 1\rangle\langle\sigma\rangle \tag{5.41}$$

can be made, so that prediction of the sign in question becomes a matter of knowing the nuclear states sufficiently well to determine the relative sign of $\langle 1\rangle$ and $\langle\sigma\rangle$. It becomes more appropriate now to write all the correlation coefficients directly in terms of the nuclear β-moments, since it is these which now parametrize the results:

$$\left.\begin{aligned} \xi a &= C_V^2\langle 1\rangle^2 - \tfrac{1}{3}C_A^2\langle\sigma\rangle^2 \\ \xi(A-B) &= \mp 2\langle M_S\rangle C_A^2\langle\sigma\rangle^2 \quad \text{for e}^{\mp} \\ \xi(A+B) &= -4C_V C_A\langle 1\rangle\langle\sigma\rangle[I/(I+1)]^{\frac{1}{2}} \end{aligned}\right\}. \tag{5.42}$$

The triplet lepton spin orientation average $\langle M_S\rangle$ was given in (1.37). These expressions agree with (4.66) for the case of the neutron, when $I = I' = \frac{1}{2}$, $\langle M_S\rangle = \frac{2}{3}$, $\langle 1\rangle = 1$ and $\langle\sigma\rangle = 3^{\frac{1}{2}}$ (5.19 b).

The complete expression (5.38) is needed only for coincidental observations on the electron polarization and the nuclear recoil, from a source of polarized nuclei. Experiments so detailed have not been feasible up to now, hence (5.38) will next be summed and averaged over various properties, in order to find expectations for observations of types which have been more practical.

*Observations on randomly oriented nuclei*

When no measures are taken to orient the nuclei, there are no anisotropies of the kind (5.27 b, c) or (5.26 c) which led to the terms measured by $\bar{A}$, $\bar{B}$, and $\bar{\Lambda}$ in (5.38). The latter expression should be averaged by applying the operation $(2I+1)^{-1}\sum_M \ldots$, and then the terms with $\bar{A}$, $\bar{B}$, and $\bar{\Lambda}$ disappear. If, moreover, no attempt is made to discriminate between polarizations of the emitted electrons, then $\sum_{\text{e}} \boldsymbol{\sigma}_{\text{e}} \equiv \sum_{\text{e}} \boldsymbol{\chi}_{\text{e}}^{\dagger}\boldsymbol{\sigma}\boldsymbol{\chi}_{\text{e}}$ vanishes everywhere in (5.38). All the other terms are multiplied by two, since $\sum_{\text{e}} \boldsymbol{\chi}_{\text{e}}^{\dagger}\boldsymbol{\chi}_{\text{e}} = 2$, i.e. both polarizations are observed indiscriminately. The surviving terms are those arising in pure Vector radiation (5.26 a), added to the isotropic Pseudovector contribution (5.27 a), proportional, respectively, to the lepton intensities:

$$\left.\begin{aligned} \sum_{\text{e}\nu} |J_4|^2 &= (F/2V^2)(1+\hat{\mathbf{q}}\,.\,\mathbf{v}/c) \\ \tfrac{1}{3}\sum_{\text{e}\nu m} |J_m|^2 &= (F/2V^2)(1-\tfrac{1}{3}\hat{\mathbf{q}}\,.\,\mathbf{v}/c) \end{aligned}\right\}. \tag{5.43}$$

These are just the individual Vector ≡ singlet, and Pseudovector ≡ triplet, electron-neutrino correlation distributions discussed in § 1.9. The resultant decay rate is

$$\frac{d\lambda}{dp} = \frac{g^2F(\pm Z, W)}{(2\pi)^5\hbar^7 c}\,p^2q^2\,d\Omega_{\text{e}}\,d\Omega_\nu\,\xi(1+a\hat{\mathbf{q}}\,.\,\mathbf{v}/c), \tag{5.44}$$

under the observational conditions as delimited in this paragraph. The general electron-neutrino correlations, with $a = \frac{1}{3}(4x-1)$, have already been adequately discussed in connexion with the 'Scott diagram' of Fig. 1.14.

Integration over the electron and neutrino directions yields

$$d\lambda/dp = [g^2/2\pi^3\hbar^7c]\xi F(\pm Z, W)p^2q^2, \tag{5.45}$$

just the statistical spectrum foretold in (1.10). This makes clear that introduction of the Fermi theory does not change the basis for our conclusion in § 1.3 that the neutrino mass is negligibly small, and probably zero. The conclusion was based on a statistical spectrum shape, and this is now seen to follow from the Fermi theory of allowed decay.

A final integration, over the spectrum, yields the comparative half-life as defined by (1.11) and (1.17):

$$ft = f(Z, W_0)[\ln 2/\lambda] = (\ln 2)(g^2/2\pi^3\hbar^7c)^{-1}(mc)^{-5}\xi^{-1}. \tag{5.46}$$

It is now clear how this may vary even among the allowed transitions, being dependent on the nuclear $\beta$-moments through the proportionality to $\xi^{-1}$. Some discussion of the variations to be expected, based on current knowledge concerning nuclear states, will be undertaken in § 5.3.

*Polarizations* of the electrons have so far been observed only in decays of randomly oriented nuclei, and with no attempt to correlate them with the nuclear recoils. Consequently, the intensities (5.43) are replaced by

$$\oint (d\hat{\mathbf{q}}) \sum_{\nu} |J_4|^2 = \oint (d\hat{\mathbf{q}}) \tfrac{1}{3} \sum_{\nu m} |J_m|^2 = 2\pi\Phi_e^\dagger\Phi_e/V, \tag{5.47}$$

as follows from (5.34 a), (5.35 a). The proportionality to (5.47) was already anticipated in (3.69). When the decay rate (5.38) is integrated over neutrino directions, as well as averaged over the random nuclear orientations, it yields:

$$d\lambda/(d\mathbf{p}) = [g^2/(2\pi)^4\hbar^7c]Fq^2\xi(1\mp\boldsymbol{\sigma}_e.\mathbf{v}/c), \tag{5.48}$$

for negatron and positron emissions, respectively. The left-handed negatron, and right-handed positron, longitudinal polarizations, $\mathscr{P} = \mp v/c$, follow directly. This is the final check that the observed polarizations have been properly incorporated into the theory.

*Angular distributions from polarized nuclei*

The observations on polarized nuclei have so far been made without attempting to discriminate between any lepton polarizations. To correspond to this, the decay rate (5.38) should be multiplied by two, and terms proportional to $\boldsymbol{\sigma}_e$ should be set equal to zero:

$$\frac{d\lambda}{dp} = \frac{g^2Fp^2q^2\,d\Omega_e\,d\Omega_\nu}{(2\pi)^5\hbar^7c}\xi\{1+a\hat{\mathbf{q}}.\mathbf{v}/c+\hat{\mathbf{I}}.[\bar{A}\mathbf{v}/c+\bar{B}\hat{\mathbf{q}}]+$$
$$+(1-x)\bar{\Lambda}[\tfrac{1}{3}\hat{\mathbf{q}}.\mathbf{v}/c-(\hat{\mathbf{I}}.\hat{\mathbf{q}})(\hat{\mathbf{I}}.\mathbf{v}/c)]\}. \tag{5.49}$$

Compare this with the neutron case (1.53) and (4.65), where $I = \frac{1}{2}$ hence $\bar{\Lambda} = 0$.

The fraction $\sim \bar{\Lambda}$ exists only for nuclei with $I > \frac{1}{2}$, as pointed out below (5.29). On the other hand, it does not require polarization, but only alignment, of the nuclei; this refers to techniques in which states $\pm M$ are equally populated, so that the anisotropies $\bar{A}$ and $\bar{B}$ vanish, but the anisotropy proportional to $\bar{\Lambda}$ need not. Of course, the detection requires observations on nuclear recoils. Detection of the recoils from oriented nuclei has been achieved only for the neutron (§ 1.10), and in this case $\bar{\Lambda} = 0$ because $I = \frac{1}{2}$.

Aside from the neutron case, observations on polarized nuclei have only been carried out without recoil detection ($\langle \hat{\mathbf{q}} \rangle = 0$), so that the distribution (5.49) simplifies to $\sim 1+\bar{A}\hat{\mathbf{I}}.\mathbf{v}/c$, an electron *angular distribution* as in (1.67). As stated in connexion with (1.35), this has been checked for the $I \to I-1$ (Pseudovector $\equiv$ GT $\equiv$ triplet) decay of $Co^{60}$ when $A = -1$, simply. Results have also been reported‡ for three positron angular distributions; these came from the $I = 2 \to 2$ transition of $Co^{58}$, the $4 \to 4$ transition of $Co^{56}$ and the $6 \to 6$ transition of $Mn^{52}$. The theoretical expectations, (1.68) or (5.42), for such cases are

$$A = (1-x)/(I+1) \pm 2[x(1-x)I/(I+1)]^{\frac{1}{2}}, \tag{5.50}$$

according as $\langle\sigma\rangle/\langle 1\rangle$ is positive or negative. If there were no Vector contribution§ ($x = 0$), the expectations would be $A = \frac{1}{3}, \frac{1}{5}$, and $\frac{1}{7}$, respectively. The measurements gave $A(Co^{58}) = 0{\cdot}325 \pm 0{\cdot}047$, $A(Co^{56}) = 0{\cdot}22 \pm 0{\cdot}02$, and $A(Mn^{52}) = 0{\cdot}23 \pm 0{\cdot}01$. Only in the last case is there a definite indication of some Vector contribution:

$$\langle 1\rangle/\langle\sigma\rangle \approx 0{\cdot}046 \pm 0{\cdot}005$$

when the experiments are interpreted in this way.

The last clause refers to the fact that, on the basis of the angular distribution measurements alone, a second interpretation is possible, in which the interference term gives the major contribution (and then $y(Co^{58}) = (1-x)^{\frac{1}{2}} = 0{\cdot}19 \pm 0{\cdot}03$, $y(Co^{56}) = 0{\cdot}11 \pm 0{\cdot}01$ and $y(Mn^{52}) = 0{\cdot}12 \pm 0{\cdot}06$). However, complementary measurements, on correlations of the positrons with $\gamma$-radiation following their emission, indicate that the first interpretations ($x \ll y$) are the correct ones. Accounting for the apparent smallness of the Fermi (Vector) β-moments

‡ E. Ambler, K. Hayward, D. Hoppes, R. Hudson, and C. S. Wu, *Phys. Rev.* **106**, 1361 (1957); **108,** 503 (1957); **110,** 787 (1958).

§ See § 5.3 for the result that, in so far as nuclear forces are charge-independent, $\langle 1\rangle \approx 0$ is to be expected in these cases.

$\langle 1\rangle$, versus the GT (Pseudovector) ones $\langle\sigma\rangle$, is a problem in nuclear structure theory (§ 5.3).

*Polarizations of electrons from oriented nuclei*

That the β-electrons from oriented nuclei should exhibit polarization was pointed out by Tolhoek and DeGroot‡ long before the electron polarizations from randomly oriented nuclei were discovered (§ 1.8).

It is difficult enough to detect electron polarizations without requiring coincidences with specific nuclear recoil directions. For that reason, the discussion here will be confined to expectations for emission rates which include all possible neutrino directions, $\hat{\mathbf{q}}$. Upon the integration over neutrino directions, all the terms of (5.38) which are proportional to $\hat{\mathbf{q}}$ will vanish. The result may be written:

$$d\lambda/(d\mathbf{p}) = [2g^2Fq^2/(2\pi)^4\hbar^7c]\xi(1+\bar{A}\hat{\mathbf{I}}.\mathbf{v}/c).\tfrac{1}{2}(1+\boldsymbol{\sigma}_e.\mathscr{P}), \quad (5.51\,\text{a})$$

if the vector $\mathscr{P}$ is so defined that the term containing it includes all surviving terms of (5.38) which are proportional to $\boldsymbol{\sigma}_e \equiv \chi_e^\dagger\boldsymbol{\sigma}\chi_e$. The consequent definition can be seen to be

$$\mathscr{P} = \mp\frac{\mathbf{v}/c+\bar{A}[\hat{\mathbf{p}}(\hat{\mathbf{p}}.\hat{\mathbf{I}})(1-\gamma_0 mc^2/W)+(mc^2/W)(\gamma_0\hat{\mathbf{I}}-\alpha Z\hat{\mathbf{p}}\times\hat{\mathbf{I}})]}{1+\bar{A}\hat{\mathbf{I}}.\mathbf{v}/c}, \quad (5.51\,\text{b})$$

for $e^\mp$, respectively.

An apt name for $\mathscr{P}$ is 'polarization vector', since its projection on any chosen axis is just the expected polarization relative to that axis. Originally (§ 1.8) the polarization was defined as the fractional difference between emission rates of electrons spinning parallel and antiparallel to the chosen axis. By definition, these two states of opposite spin, $\chi_\pm$, are just such that only the component of $\chi_\pm\boldsymbol{\sigma}\chi_\pm$ parallel to the axis survives, and this component has the values $\pm 1$ in these states.§ Accordingly,

‡ H. A. Tolhoek and S. R. DeGroot, *Physica*, **17**, 1 (1951).

§ It is really adequate to adopt the chosen axis as the quantization ($z$-) axis for $e = \pm\frac{1}{2}$ of $\boldsymbol{\sigma}_e = \chi_e^\dagger\boldsymbol{\sigma}\chi_e$, so that the only surviving component is $\sigma_{ez} = \pm 1$. A more cautious statement is made in the text to allay the distrust of readers who remember that (5.38) was derived using $\hat{\mathbf{I}}$ as the quantization axis, and is still so to be used in whatever entirely separate measurements are made to determine the degree of nuclear polarization. If $\hat{\mathbf{I}}$ is retained as the quantization axis here, then $e = \pm\frac{1}{2}$ in $\boldsymbol{\sigma}_e = \chi_e^\dagger\boldsymbol{\sigma}\chi_e$ denote spins parallel and antiparallel to $\hat{\mathbf{I}}$. The states of spin parallel and antiparallel to another axis on which $\boldsymbol{\sigma}$ has the component $\sigma_3$ will be some linear combinations, $\chi_\pm = \sum_e a_e^\pm\chi_e$, with the properties $\sigma_3\chi_\pm = \pm\chi_\pm$ and $\sum_e |a_e^\pm|^2 = 1$. To get rates of electron emissions into $\chi_\pm$ requires summing (5.38) with each term weighted by $|a_e^\pm|^2$. Then $\boldsymbol{\sigma}_e$ is replaced by $\sum_e |a_e^\pm|^2\boldsymbol{\sigma}_e = \chi_\pm\boldsymbol{\sigma}\chi_\pm$, which has $\sigma_3 = \pm 1$ as its only non-vanishing component. This elaboration is not really necessary because the rotationally invariant appearance of (5.38) can be trusted, and axes can be chosen to suit one's convenience at any stage.

the last factor of (5.51 a) becomes $\frac{1}{2}(1\pm\mathscr{P}_3)$ if $\mathscr{P}_3$ denotes the projection of $\mathscr{P}$ on the chosen axis. Now

$$\frac{(1+\mathscr{P}_3)-(1-\mathscr{P}_3)}{(1+\mathscr{P}_3)+(1-\mathscr{P}_3)} = \mathscr{P}_3$$

is the polarization, in agreement with the assertion above.

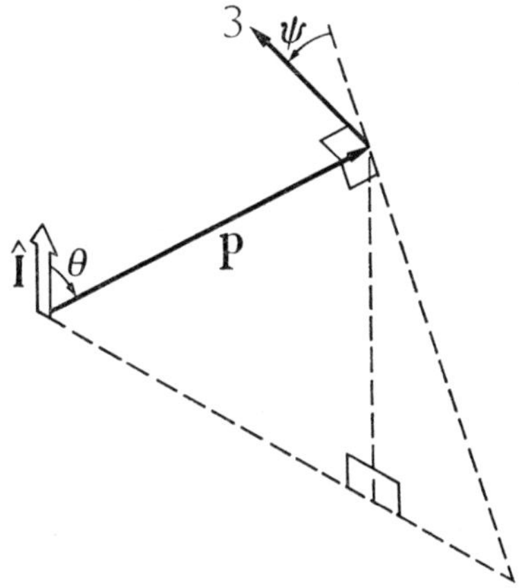


FIG. 5.1

Longitudinal electron polarizations (i.e. along **v** or $\hat{\mathbf{p}}$) from randomly oriented nuclei were discussed earlier. It can now be seen how the expectations are modified when measurements are made only on electrons coming off at an angle $\theta$ to a nuclear polarization axis $\hat{\mathbf{I}}$. It is only necessary to project $\mathscr{P}$ onto $\hat{\mathbf{p}}$ to obtain:

$$\mathscr{P}_{\text{long}} = \mp[v/c+\bar{A}\cos\theta]/[1+\bar{A}(v/c)\cos\theta] \quad \text{for } e^{\mp}. \tag{5.52}$$

This properly reduces to $\mp v/c$ for randomly oriented nuclei, when $\bar{A} = A\langle M\rangle/I = 0$. Suppose that the $Co^{60}$ nuclei in the Wu *et al.* experiment (§ 1.8) were perfectly polarized, so that $\bar{A} = A = -1$. Then (5.52) gives $\mathscr{P} = +1$, so that the few negatrons, $\sim(1-v/c)$, emitted in the direction $\hat{\mathbf{I}}$ of the nuclear spin have a right-handed polarization. This is just what is to be expected when the leptons must carry off the unit of angular momentum lost by the nucleus, in its $5\rightarrow 4$ transition.

Transverse electron polarizations may also be detected. Suppose the chosen plane of polarization, which must pass through the line of **p**, is rotated (in a right-handed sense about **p**) by an angle $\psi$ out of the plane containing **p** and $\hat{\mathbf{I}}$ (see Fig. 5.1). The appropriate projection of $\mathscr{P}$ then yields:

$$\mathscr{P}_{\text{trans}} = \mp\bar{A}(mc^2/W)\sin\theta[\gamma_0\cos\psi-\alpha Z\sin\psi]/[1+\bar{A}(v/c)\cos\theta], \tag{5.53}$$

for $e^{\mp}$, respectively. This naturally vanishes for unpolarized nuclei. For electrons coming off into the equatorial plane normal to the nuclear polarization axis ($\theta = \frac{1}{2}\pi$), the polarization parallel to the nuclear spin is $\mp A\gamma_0(mc^2/W)$, while it is smaller by the factor $-\alpha Z/\gamma_0$ relative to any axis in the equatorial plane.

Especially the transverse polarizations raise questions of interpretation. The longitudinal spin component, $\boldsymbol{\sigma}.\hat{\mathbf{p}}$, commutes with the free particle energy operator, $H = c\boldsymbol{\alpha}.\mathbf{p}+\beta mc^2$, but other Dirac spin components do not, as already discussed in §§ 2.4 and 3.1. That precludes knowing that the polarization is exactly transverse to the momentum. However, it can now be pointed out that our procedures for evaluating the polarizations tacitly dealt with spin orientations relative to the electron's rest-frame. The orientations were taken to be described by the Pauli spinor $\boldsymbol{\chi}_e$, which forms only the large component of the Dirac plane wave, and gives the entire angular momentum only at the limit $\mathbf{p} = 0$, as seen in § 3.1. It is legitimate to define the polarizations as that implies if only it corresponds to what the experiments measure. Tolhoek and DeGroot‡ clarified the whole question, and showed that indeed the polarization as defined for spin orientations relative to the particle rest-frame is obtainable in the laboratory.

A typical procedure is to compare scattering to the right and left by a central field, like that of a nuclear charge. The scattered electron wave can be constructed analogously to the incoming part of the coulomb-distorted wave (3.61). It is only necessary to reverse the sign of the phase $\delta''$ in (3.60) in order to have a distorted wave with all *ingoing* parts such as are characteristic of an incident plane wave having a definite momentum $\mathbf{p}$. The remainder will be an *outgoing* scattered wave, $(A_e/r)\exp\{+i(pr-Wt)\}$ with the amplitude

$$A_e = \frac{1}{2ip}\left[\frac{(2\pi)^3(W+1)}{\pi WV}\right]^{\frac{1}{2}} \sum_{\kappa\mu} [e^{2i\eta(\kappa)}-1]\langle l(\mu-e)\tfrac{1}{2}(e)|j(\mu)\rangle \times$$
$$\times Y^*_{l,\mu-e}(\hat{\mathbf{p}})\begin{pmatrix} 1 \\ p\boldsymbol{\sigma}.\hat{\mathbf{r}}/W+1\end{pmatrix}\boldsymbol{\chi}_{\kappa\mu}(\hat{\mathbf{r}}). \quad (5.54)$$

Units with $m = c = \hbar = 1$ are being used, and $\eta(\kappa)$ is a phase shift which need not be specified aside from the fact that it is independent of orientations (a suitable phase shift can describe the scattering by any central field). The plane incident wave, $\psi_e$, from which the scattered amplitude (5.54) arises was normalized to unity in $V$, hence carries a current density $v/V = p/WV$. Consequently, the total scattering cross-section (total

‡ H. A. Tolhoek and S. R. DeGroot, *Physica*, **17**, 1 (1951).

outward scattered current per unit incident current density) is

$$\sigma = \oint (d\hat{\mathbf{r}}) A_{\mathrm{e}}^{\dagger} \boldsymbol{\alpha}.\hat{\mathbf{r}} A_{\mathrm{e}}/(p/WV).$$

It will be most convenient to use the electron's momentum, $\mathbf{p}$, as the polar axis, so that $Y^*_{l,\mu-\mathrm{e}}(\hat{\mathbf{p}}) = \delta_{\mu\mathrm{e}}[(2l+1)/4\pi]^{\frac{1}{2}}$. This automatically restricts the spin projections $\mathrm{e} = \pm\frac{1}{2}$ to being parallel vs. antiparallel to the electron's momentum; in order to have a more generally polarized plane wave incident it must be taken to be some coherent superposition, $\psi = \sum_{\mathrm{e}} a_{\mathrm{e}} \psi_{\mathrm{e}}$, with the scattered amplitude $A = \sum_{\mathrm{e}} a_{\mathrm{e}} A_{\mathrm{e}}$. Now, the differential cross-section for scattering into $d\Omega \equiv (d\hat{\mathbf{r}})$ becomes

$$d\sigma/d\Omega = (WV/p)(A^{\dagger}\boldsymbol{\alpha}.\hat{\mathbf{r}}A) = \Big|\sum_{\mathrm{e}} a_{\mathrm{e}} F_{\mathrm{e}}(\theta,\phi)\Big|^2 \tag{5.55 a}$$

if $\sum_{\mathrm{e}} |a_{\mathrm{e}}|^2 = 1$, and

$$F_{\mathrm{e}}(\theta,\phi) = (ip)^{-1} \sum_{\kappa} [\pi(2l+1)]^{\frac{1}{2}} (e^{2i\eta(\kappa)}-1)\langle l(0)\tfrac{1}{2}(e)|j(e)\rangle \boldsymbol{\chi}_{\kappa\mathrm{e}}. \tag{5.55 b}$$

The definition (2.18) of $\boldsymbol{\chi}_{\kappa,\pm\frac{1}{2}}$ leads to

$$\left.\begin{aligned} F_{+\frac{1}{2}} &= f(\theta)\boldsymbol{\chi}_{+\frac{1}{2}} + g(\theta)e^{+i\phi}\boldsymbol{\chi}_{-\frac{1}{2}} \\ F_{-\frac{1}{2}} &= f(\theta)\boldsymbol{\chi}_{-\frac{1}{2}} - g(\theta)e^{-i\phi}\boldsymbol{\chi}_{+\frac{1}{2}} \end{aligned}\right\}, \tag{5.55 c}$$

where

$$\left.\begin{aligned} f(\theta) &= (2ip)^{-1} \sum_{l} [(l+1)(e^{i\eta(l)}-1) + l(e^{i\eta(-l-1)}-1)]P_l(\cos\theta) \\ g(\theta) &= (2ip)^{-1} \sum_{l} [e^{i\eta(-l-1)} - e^{i\eta(l)}]P_l^1(\theta) \end{aligned}\right\}. \tag{5.55 d}$$

Here, $P_l^1(\theta)$ is the well-known associated Legendre polynomial related to

$$Y_{l1} = -[(2l+1)/4\pi l(l+1)]^{\frac{1}{2}} P_l^1(\theta) \exp i\phi.$$

These expressions enable separation of the $\phi$-dependence in the differential cross-section:

$$d\sigma/d\Omega = |f(\theta)|^2 + |g(\theta)|^2 + (f^*g - fg^*)(a_{\frac{1}{2}} a^*_{-\frac{1}{2}} e^{i\phi} - \text{c.c.}). \tag{5.55 e}$$

This is now sufficiently specific for the purposes here.

Consider the situation schematized in Fig. 5.2. It is a special case of an arrangement for comparing scattering to 'right' and 'left' (at $\phi = \pm\frac{1}{2}\pi$):

$$\frac{d\sigma_R - d\sigma_L}{d\sigma_R + d\sigma_L} = \frac{i(f^*g - fg^*)(a_{\frac{1}{2}} a^*_{-\frac{1}{2}} + a^*_{\frac{1}{2}} a_{-\frac{1}{2}})}{|f|^2 + |g|^2}. \tag{5.56}$$

It is now evident that such a comparison is a direct measurement of the initial polarization as described by the coefficients $a_{\pm\frac{1}{2}}$. The particular values $a_{+\frac{1}{2}} = a_{-\frac{1}{2}} = 2^{-\frac{1}{2}}$ correspond to an incident plane wave having $(\boldsymbol{\chi}_{+\frac{1}{2}} + \boldsymbol{\chi}_{-\frac{1}{2}})/2^{\frac{1}{2}}$ for the spin state of its *large component*. The resultant

Pauli spinor here is just the eigenfunction of the *Pauli* $\sigma_x = +1$, hence describes transverse polarization 'relative to the electron's rest-frame', in the same sense as the polarizations defined by the above-adopted usage.

It is also relatively easy to see that more negatrons should be scattered to the right than to the left, in the situation depicted in Fig. 5.2, when the

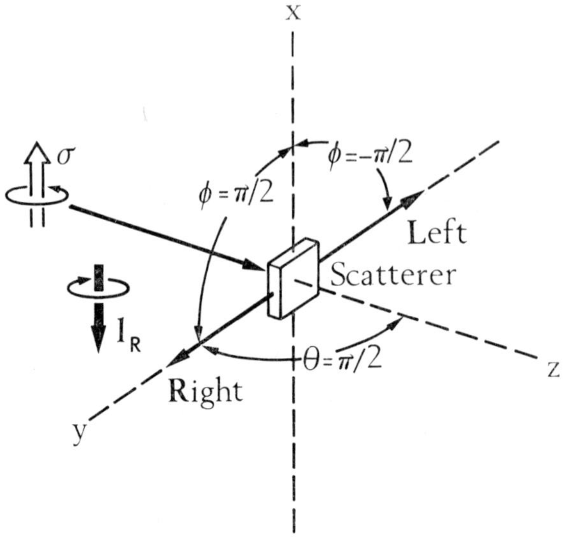


FIG. 5.2

incident spin is 'up' ($\sigma_x = +1$). The right-left difference can be traced to the effect of a 'spin-orbit coupling' which is automatically generated by the relativistic behaviour of an electron in any central field, $V(r)$. When the kinetic energy is reduced to $W-V(r)$, the small component wave-function (3.2) becomes

$$\boldsymbol{\theta} = f\boldsymbol{\sigma}.\mathbf{p}\boldsymbol{\varphi} \quad \text{with } f(r) = 1/[W-V(r)+1]. \tag{5.57}$$

Here $\mathbf{p} \equiv -i\boldsymbol{\nabla}$ and units $m = c = \hbar = 1$ are being used. Substitution into the Dirac equation (3.1) with $W \to W-V(r)$ shows that the large component $\boldsymbol{\varphi}$ becomes an eigenfunction of the energy operator

$$W-1 = \boldsymbol{\sigma}.\mathbf{p}(f\boldsymbol{\sigma}.\mathbf{p})+V(r) = fp^2-i\boldsymbol{\nabla}f.\mathbf{p}+\boldsymbol{\sigma}.[\boldsymbol{\nabla}f\times\mathbf{p}]+V. \tag{5.58}$$

Since $f(r)$ is central, $\boldsymbol{\nabla}f = (f'/r)\mathbf{r}$ and the spin-dependent term can be written

$$E_s = f^2V'(r)\boldsymbol{\sigma}.\mathbf{l}, \tag{5.59}$$

where $\mathbf{l} = \mathbf{r}\times\mathbf{p}$ is the orbital momentum. $E_s$ is additive to $V(r)$ of (5.58) and effectively represents a spin-orbit force supplementing the scattering force. Now $V'$ and $V$ have opposite signs for any potential $V$ which falls off to zero with distance from its centre, so the scattering effect is enhanced when $\boldsymbol{\sigma}.\mathbf{l}$ is negative. Negatrons are attracted by nuclear scattering centres, hence swing around the 'far side' of the nucleus as they are scattered. Their orbital momenta are directed oppositely to the spins for scattering to the 'right', in the situation of Fig. 5.2. Thus, it is the rightward deflections which are enhanced by the spin-orbit coupling.

The scattering analysis here does not work for longitudinal polarizations [either $a_{+\frac{1}{2}} = 0$ or $a_{-\frac{1}{2}} = 0$ in (5.56)]. However, the longitudinal polarizations can be converted into transverse ones by first passing the electrons through a suitable electromagnetic field. It is simplest to use an electric field which bends the electron beam through a right angle [more precisely $(W/mc^2)\frac{1}{2}\pi$, according to Tolhoek and DeGroot]. A purely electric field does not affect the spin, hence the electron's direction of motion will have been turned relative to the spin direction. Some experimenters use crossed electric and magnetic fields to 'twist the spin' without deflecting the beam direction.

## 5.3. The allowed β-moments

All the allowed emission phenomena are described with the help of coefficients (5.39), (5.42), which are parametrized by the singlet and triplet $\beta$-moments, $\langle 1 \rangle$ and $\langle \sigma \rangle$. Accurate theoretical expectations for the moments can only be derived from sufficiently accurate and complete descriptions of the nuclear states, yet constructing these presents many-body problems which are far too complex for reliable solution. The best that can be done is to assume much simplified state descriptions which may at least help with the interpretation of the observed facts. A full exploitation of this approach requires using a vast number of observational details about the nuclei, taking the considerations far afield from the theory of the $\beta$-processes. The account here will be confined to just the simplest and most generally applicable ideas, ones which need to be familiar before more particularized attempts can be fairly understood.

*Favoured and unfavoured transitions*

An idea of the observed facts about allowed decay rates which call for explanation can be gained from examining Tables 5.1–5.5. All these tables list comparative half-lives, $(ft)_{\text{exp}}$, as *measured* for cases known to conform to the allowed selection rules (5.8) on various evidences about the nuclear spins and parities. The *theoretical* expectations, as they follow from (5.46), may be presented in ratio to $(ft)_{\text{n}} = (1180 \pm 35)$ sec for the decay of a free neutron. Using $C_A^2/C_V^2 = 1{\cdot}4$ for the GT-to-Fermi ratio (1.26),

$$(ft)_{\text{theo}} \approx 5{\cdot}2(ft)_{\text{n}}/(\langle 1\rangle^2+1{\cdot}4\langle\sigma\rangle^2) \approx (6140\text{ sec})/(\langle 1\rangle^2+1{\cdot}4\langle\sigma\rangle^2), \tag{5.60}$$

since $\langle 1\rangle^2 = 1$ and $\langle\sigma\rangle^2 = 3$ for the free neutron.

The nuclei listed in the tables are denoted $_Z X_N^A$, to make explicit the numbers of protons and neutrons in each. It can then be seen that the Tables 5.1 and 5.4 contain special families of nuclei, having $A = 4n\pm 1$ and $A = 4n\pm 2$, respectively ($n$ an integer). The first family consists of the 'mirrors' already met in § 1.5, where also some of the $A = 4n\pm 2$ cases ('$0 \to 0$ decays among isobaric triads') were introduced. It is only within those special families that comparative half-lives of less than about $10^4$ sec are found, fluctuating around $10^{3\cdot 5}$ sec or so. The other tables contain samplings from the general run of allowed transitions. These can be seen to have substantially slower decay rates, with *ft*-values fluctuating around $10^5$ sec, and higher. Relative to this general run of cases, the mirrors and some of the $A = 4n\pm 2$ nuclei are said to undergo 'favoured transitions'.

The prevalence of $ft \approx 10^5$ sec implies that it is usual for the β-moments to have magnitudes substantially less than unity. This is not surprising when a whole structure of $A$ nucleons plays a role in making the energy available for the β-transformation of a single nucleon. Moments of order unity, such as characterize the decay of a free neutron, can be expected only if the structure as a whole needs undergo very little readjustment to form the daughter configuration. This should be unusual, in view of the many degrees of freedom possessed by $A$ particles, even for states selected by the criteria on angular momenta and parities. Some degree of 'mismatch' between the parent and daughter nuclear states is only too likely.

This view brings up a first specific problem: how to account for the near absence of mismatch in the favoured transitions and for the fact that these are largely‡ confined to the mirrors and the light $A = 4n+2$ nuclei. The main ideas which help in the explanation were introduced by Wigner§ during the development of his 'supermultiplet' theory, and this is responsible for frequent references to the favoured transitions as 'super-allowed'. Those ideas will be discussed next.

‡ M. Bolsterli and E. Feenberg, *Phys. Rev.* **97**, 736 (1955), and **99**, 7 (1955), offer evidence for a few favoured transitions to *excited* states of nuclei outside the special families, but accountable for in about the same way.

§ E. P. Wigner, *Phys. Rev.* **51**, 106 (1937), and **56**, 519 (1938).

*Effects of 'charge-independence'*

Accurate nuclear state descriptions are difficult to construct not only because of the inherent complexity of any problem of more than two particles, but also because the internucleon forces turn out to be functions of practically every conceivable degree of freedom. There is one simplifying principle which has been discovered: the specifically nuclear binding forces seem to be quite accurately 'charge-independent'. In particular, the interaction between any two nucleons in a given state of relative motion is the same whether they are two neutrons, two protons, or a neutron-proton pair. Only the relatively minor electromagnetic interactions, and the neutron-proton mass difference, disturb this type of neutron-proton equivalence at all appreciably.

In a $\beta$-transformation, there is merely a substitution of a proton for a neutron, or vice versa, and, with charge-independent forces, it would seem that a final configuration identical with the initial one, except in the transformed nucleon, should always be available. However, the Pauli exclusion principle intervenes. It will generally prevent the transformed nucleon from assuming exactly the same motions with respect to every other nucleon as it had before the transformation, and this makes a great difference in the effect of the nuclear forces. Considerable readjustment of the structure is practically unavoidable when unequal numbers of neutrons and protons, as in the general run of $\beta$-decays, are met by the transforming nucleon.

The last statement immediately suggests that favoured transitions can generally be expected only among nuclei with equal numbers of neutrons and protons aside from the transforming nucleon. That defines the mirrors. The initial and final states in the mirror decays can be said to differ only by the interchange of the neutrons with the protons, and structures which are identical except in the nature of the transforming nucleon are to be expected. The energies will differ only by the electrostatic repulsion of $Z$ proton pairs, minus one neutron-proton mass difference, and this is what makes energy available for the $\beta$-transformation.

The picture is in accord with the details of the mirror decays. The lightest nucleus of the family, ${}_1H_2^3$, is unstable relative to ${}_2He_1^3$ because it is heavier by a neutron-proton mass difference minus the electrostatic repulsion of just one proton pair. The six pairs of electrostatic repulsions among the four protons of ${}_4Be_3^7$ are already sufficient to make it unstable relative to its daughter ${}_3Li_4^7$, despite the latter having one more neutron. ($Be^7$ actually undergoes electron capture rather than positron emission, but a comparable *ft*-value is definable for it, as will be seen in Chapter VIII.) The electrostatic repulsion continues to accumulate in the remainder of the mirror family, and can be shown to account quantitatively for the energy releases, $W_0$. For $A > 43$, no mirrors seem to exist, presumably because the electrostatic repulsion has made the structures too unstable to keep together long enough for a $\beta$-process to occur. The heavier nuclei which do exist all have more neutrons than protons and undergo unfavoured decays.

Because the exclusion principle allows two like nucleons, if antiparallel in spin, to have exactly the same spatial distributions, the possibility of favoured transitions is extended to $A = 4n+2$ nuclei having two nucleons extra to a 'core' of equal and even numbers of neutrons and protons. The addition to such a core of two neutrons, or two protons, or an *anti-parallel* neutron-proton pair, should be able to result in nearly identical structures. It is members of such 'isobaric triads' of states which serve as parents and daughters in the favoured $0 \rightarrow 0$ decays. There also occur favoured transitions between the like-nucleon isobars and a state of the middle one in which the neutron-proton pair has parallel rather than antiparallel spins. These are triplet emissions which may even be helped by the nucleon spin flip.

These qualitative statements in explanation of the favoured decays need support by quantitative calculations, but such can be done in adequate consistency with all else that is known about nuclei only by drawing upon more particularized information, some of which will be made available in the succeeding subsections. Wigner was able to carry his supermultiplet theory to quantitative conclusions without such particulars by neglecting the spin dependence of the nuclear forces. The later discovery of strong spin-orbit couplings in the motions of nucleons through nuclear matter has reduced the usefulness of such an approximation.

*The isospin selection rule*

Quantitative treatment of the effects of the charge-independence is helped by using the isospin description introduced in § 4.2. In so far as the forces can be treated as completely charge-independent, the nuclear states may be taken to be simultaneous eigenstates not only of energy and the total angular momentum, **I**, but also of the total isospin,

$$\mathbf{T} = \sum_{a=1}^{A} \tfrac{1}{2}\boldsymbol{\tau}^a; \tag{5.61}$$

this follows from the obvious commutability of **T** with charge-independent interactions. States with different $T$-values are not expected to be degenerate, but to have distinct energies, primarily because each description must be antisymmetric in indistinguishable nucleons (the isospin variable is now relied on to generate any appropriate distinctions of protons from neutrons). An eigenstate of definite $T$ has a characteristic symmetry in its isospin dependence, and the space-spin dependence must have the complementary symmetry character. Each distribution of different symmetry leads to different effects from the internucleon forces, hence the expectation of a distinctive $T$-value for each nuclear energy state. This $T$-value must be assigned in accordance with any evidence about the nuclei which may be available. The chief finding is that the states with the lowest energies tend‡ to have the lowest $T$-values (the simplest symmetries). Of course, all this is predicated upon the relative negligibility of the isospin-symmetry destroying electromagnetic effects. Heavier nuclei, with their accumulations of electrostatic repulsion, must be expected to have a mixing of various $T$-values into a given energy state.

It follows from the definition of isospin that its eigenstates have properties analogous (isomorphic) to those discussed for the angular momentum eigenstates, $\chi_{IM}$ of § 2.1. The isospin eigenstates will be denoted $\xi_{TT_3}$, and a nuclear state with a given $T$ will be representable by

$$|I(M)T(T_3)\alpha\rangle \to \sum_{\beta} R_{\alpha\beta}\,\chi_{IM}^{(\beta)}\,\xi_{TT_3}^{(\beta)}, \tag{5.62}$$

where the $R_{\alpha\beta}$ are rotationally invariant (radial) functions of space variables. The summation over $\beta$ acknowledges the possibility that eigenstates of various 'intermediate symmetries' may still have the same eigenvalues $T, T_3$; $R_{\alpha\beta}\chi^{(\beta)}$ is then a space-spin eigenstate of a symmetry complementary to that of $\xi^{(\beta)}$, in such a way that the final result is antisymmetric in any pair of nucleons. Correspondingly, the total state may not be unique for a given $I, M, T, T_3$, hence the supplementary label $\alpha$. For a nucleus of $Z$ protons and $N = A-Z$ neutrons, $T_3 = \frac{1}{2}(Z-N)$. Since $T_3 = \pm T, \pm(T-1),\ldots$, the lowest energy state is usually expected to have $T = \frac{1}{2}|Z-N|$, the lowest $T$-value possible to it.

Of greatest interest for the $\beta$-moments is the analogue of the 'ladder'

‡ All the substates $T_3 = \pm T, \pm(T-1),\ldots$ of a given $T$-multiplet should be equally well bound by the charge-independent specifically nuclear forces. Then the addition of the electrostatic repulsions should make $T_3 \equiv \frac{1}{2}(Z-N) = -T$, the substate with the fewest protons, most stable. It is well known that the existing stable nuclei tend to have $N = Z$, i.e. $T_3 = -T \to 0$. Only for $Z > 20$ does a slowly increasing surplus of neutrons begin to set in, presumably together with a gradual destruction of the isospin symmetries, because of accumulating electrostatic repulsions.

property (2.8),

$$T_{\pm}\,\xi_{TT_3} = [(T\mp T_3)(T\pm T_3+1)]^{\frac{1}{2}}\xi_{T,T_3\pm 1}, \tag{5.63}$$

where

$$T_{\pm} = T_1 \pm iT_2 = \sum_a \tau_{\pm}^a \tag{5.64}$$

since $\tau_{\pm} = \frac{1}{2}(\tau_1 \pm i\tau_2)$. This is a generalization of (4.14) to many-nucleon states. Now the singlet moment $\langle 1\rangle \equiv \int 1$ of (5.3) is simply a matrix element of the operator $\sum \tau_{\pm}^a = T_{\pm}$. It then follows for state descriptions like (5.62) that

$$\langle 1\rangle = \Bigl(\int R_{\alpha'\beta}^{*}\,R_{\alpha\beta}\Bigr)\delta_{I'I}\,\delta_{M'M}\,\delta_{T'T}\,\delta_{T_3',T_3\pm 1}[T(T+1)-T_3'\,T_3]^{\frac{1}{2}}, \tag{5.65}$$

with all primed symbols referring to the final state. The important outcome here is a new selection rule for the existence of singlet (Fermi, $\Delta I = 0$) emissions:

$$\langle 1\rangle = 0 \quad \text{unless } \Delta T = 0 \quad (\Delta T_3 = \pm 1), \tag{5.66}$$

in so far as charge-dependent (electromagnetic) forces can be neglected, so that $T$ is a 'good quantum number'.

For the mirror transitions, and the $0\to 0$ decays among the triads, it can be assumed that, to good approximation, the description of the daughter differs in no way from that of the parent (5.62) except for the replacement of one neutron by a proton (or vice versa) as represented by $\xi_{TT_3}^{(\beta)} \to \xi_{T,T_3\pm 1}^{(\beta)}$. The normalized operation $[T(T+1)-T_3(T_3\pm 1)]^{-\frac{1}{2}}T_{\pm}$ which effects this is symmetrized among all the nucleons, as the descriptions themselves must be, but $T_3 \to T_3 \pm 1$ indicates that only one nucleon is finally transformed. Thus, (5.65) is expected to reduce to

$$\langle 1\rangle = [T(T+1)-T_3(T_3\pm 1)]^{\frac{1}{2}} \tag{5.67}$$

for the favoured Fermi (singlet) emissions. Estimates‡ of corrections to this, such as arise from the electrostatic repulsion and other effects which can be conceived, indicate that (5.67) should not be wrong by more than a very few per cent, for the favoured transitions.

Each mirror nucleus has $T_3 = +\frac{1}{2}$ or $T_3 = -\frac{1}{2}$, hence all the ground states should have $T = \frac{1}{2}$, Then $\langle 1\rangle \to 1$ and (5.60) becomes better defined:

$$(ft)_{\text{mirrors}} \approx (6140\ \text{sec})/(1+1{\cdot}4\langle\sigma\rangle^2), \tag{5.68}$$

for their $\Delta T = 0$ transitions.

The members of a triad have $T_3 = 0, \pm 1$, forming a $T = 1$ 'iso-multiplet' of states. Their pure Fermi $0\to 0$ decays have $\langle\sigma\rangle = 0$ and $\langle 1\rangle = 2^{\frac{1}{2}}$, hence (5.60) becomes

$$(ft)_{0\to 0} \approx 3070\ \text{sec}, \tag{5.69}$$

‡ W. M. MacDonald, *Phys. Rev.* **110**, 1420 (1958).

in good accord with the observed values listed in § 1.5. (Of course the $O^{14}$ case played a role in determining the theoretical prediction.) It may at once be objected that the $T_3 = 0$ $(Z = N)$ member of the triad should have $T = 0$ in its ground state, and not be a member of the $T = 1$ isomultiplet. However, the $T_3 = 0$, $T = 1$ state may then be expected to be a low-lying excited state, identifiable at least through the fact that it should differ in energy from its $T_3 = \pm 1$ fellows by just the electrostatic repulsion of $Z$ proton pairs (minus a neutron-proton mass difference). This is exactly what is found for the $0 \to 0$ decays of ${}_6C_4^{10}$ and ${}_8O_6^{14}$, which respectively end in second and first excited states of their daughters, ${}_5B_5^{**}$ and ${}_7N_7^{*}$. The (presumably $T = 0$) ground states have spins $I = 3$ and $I = 1$, respectively. When $Z > 8$, the electrostatic repulsions have accumulated sufficiently for the middle $(T_3 = 0)$ isobar to become unstable (relative to $T_3 = -1$). Since ${}_9F_9^{18}$ and ${}_{15}P_{15}^{30}$ have non-vanishing spins in their ground states, they undergo no $0 \to 0$ decay; moreover, the $\beta$-transitions they do undergo $(1 \to 0)$ release less energy than is expected between members of an isotriplet, in consistency with a $T = 1$ state above ground in the $T_3 = 0$ parent. On the other hand, for reasons not clearly understood, the spinless $T = 1$ $(T_3 = 0)$ states of $Cl^{34}$ and $Sc^{42}$ fall lower than the $T = 0$ states, thus becoming ground states able to exhibit $0 \to 0$ decays. Their energy releases are found consistent with membership in an isotriplet, and $\langle 1 \rangle^2 = 2$ can be validly expected for them. A few $0 \to 0$ decays are also known among heavier nuclei, e.g. ${}_{32}Ge_{34}^{66} \to {}_{31}Ga_{35}^{66} \to {}_{30}Zn_{36}^{66}$. The states in this chain are presumably to be assigned values $T = \frac{1}{2}(N-Z) = 1$, 2, and 3 respectively, hence the transitions are expected to be forbidden by the isospin selection rule. They are indeed found to have very prolonged lifetimes, the experimental $ft$-values being $10^{\geqslant 6 \cdot 8}$ sec and $10^{7 \cdot 88}$ sec in the two steps of the chain. If these finite values are viewed‡ as arising from admixtures of $T = 2$ state into the $T = 1$ $(T_3 = -1)$, and of $T = 3$ into the $T = 2$ $(T_3 = -2)$, state caused by a partial breakdown of the charge-independence, then the upper limits on the admixtures set by the slow rates are only 0·03 per cent and 0·014 per cent, respectively. This persistence of the isospin symmetries to surprisingly large $Z$ seems to be supported by the measurements on the electron anisotropy quoted in connexion with (5.50). Except for a small amount in one of the three cases, no singlet-triplet interference is detected, presumably because the singlet moment $\langle 1 \rangle \approx 0$, as required by the isospin selection rule.

‡ W. P. Alford and J. B. French, *Phys. Rev. Letters*, **6**, 119 (1961).

As simple a result as the isospin selection rule seems not to be derivable for the triplet moments, $\langle\sigma\rangle$, without making questionable approximations. To make quantitative estimates for $\langle\sigma\rangle$, it seems necessary to draw on more detailed facts about nuclei, such as will be discussed in the following subsections.

*The 'shell model' for the mirrors*

Advantage may be taken of the fact that only one nucleon is transformed in a first-order $\beta$-process, to treat it as moving in some average field arising from its interactions with all the other nucleons. If this average field were taken to be a static potential which is spherically symmetric about the mass centre of the whole nucleus, then the single, transforming nucleon's angular momentum $\mathbf{j} = \mathbf{l}+\mathbf{s}$ would be conserved (as well as $\mathbf{l}$ and $\mathbf{s}$ individually). The simplest model is obtained when all the angular momentum $\mathbf{I}$ exhibited by the nucleus can be identified with $\mathbf{j}$. The contributions of the 'core' nucleons, i.e. all those exclusive of the transforming particle,‡ must then be presumed to cancel each other, and this is possible only if they are even in number. Thus, a single-nucleon model for the whole nucleus is *ab initio* restricted to odd-$A$ nuclei.

The assumption of the separate conservation of $\mathbf{l}$ and $\mathbf{s}$, in magnitude and direction, is valid in a central scalar average field, but this assumption will be dropped at once. The general evidence about nuclei indicates that there is a strong spin-orbit (i.e. proportional to $\mathbf{l}.\mathbf{s}$) coupling at least for motion in a sufficiently large accumulation of nuclear matter. The orbital momentum magnitude may still be definite in such motion, and the two alternatives in the single-particle model, $l = I-\frac{1}{2}$ and $l = I+\frac{1}{2}$, are expected to occur with different energies if the spin-orbit coupling is substantial. Accordingly, one of the eigenfunctions (2.18), of definite $l$, $j = I$, $\mu = M$, will be used to describe the transforming nucleon's motion:

$$|I(M)l\rangle \rightarrow \xi R_l(r)\boldsymbol{\chi}_{\kappa M}(\hat{\mathbf{r}}), \tag{5.70}$$

where $\kappa = I+\frac{1}{2} = l$ *or* $\kappa = -(I+\frac{1}{2}) = -l-1$. The isospin state $\xi$ may be either the neutron or the proton eigenstate of (4.12), and $R_l(r)$ is to describe the radial motion. The form (5.70) does not have definite values for the projections of $\mathbf{l}$ and $\mathbf{s}$, and is consistent with a supplementation of the assumed central field by a spin-orbit coupling (like $\varkappa$ of (2.17), $\mathbf{l}.\mathbf{s}$ commutes with $l^2$, $j^2$, and $j_z$). The description here conforms

‡ Of course, all nucleons are capable of transformation and proper descriptions are antisymmetrized among them. The important consideration is: the equivalents of how many nucleons are such that the transformation of any one will form the daughter state (make energy available).

with a primitive application of Mayer and Jensen's 'shell model' to odd-$A$ nuclei.‡

The one-particle description (5.70) cannot be used for $T \neq \frac{1}{2}$ states, unless isospin symmetries play no essential role in determining the character of the state. It yields for the singlet moment:

$$\langle 1 \rangle = \delta_{I'I}\,\delta_{M'M}\,\delta_{l'l}\int\limits_0^\infty dr\, r^2 (R'_l)^* R_l. \tag{5.71}$$

Departures from the value $\langle 1 \rangle = 1$ expected for the mirrors are here formulated as 'mismatches' of the initial and final radial distributions of the transforming nucleon. However, if any substantial departures were found in actual cases, it is doubtful that they should be understood in this way. The model (5.70) has also been used for evaluating expectations for magnetic moments, properties of single states having $R'_l \equiv R_l$, yet substantial departures from the measured moments have been found. It is preferable to ascribe at least the substantial deviations to the over-simplification obviously inherent in a single-nucleon model. Hereafter, such radial integrals will be set equal to unity, and the results for moments treated as their 'maximal' possible values.

The model does have the virtue that it can yield specific expectations for the triplet moments, $\langle \sigma \rangle$. These may be calculated for nuclear states like (5.70) with the help of (5.20):

$$\begin{aligned}\langle I'(M)1(0)|I(M)\rangle\langle\sigma\rangle &= \langle I'(M)l'|\sigma_z\,\tau_\pm|I(M)l\rangle \\ &= \oint (d\hat{\mathbf{r}})\boldsymbol{\chi}^\dagger_{\kappa' M}\,\sigma_z\,\boldsymbol{\chi}_{\kappa M}(\hat{\mathbf{r}}).\end{aligned} \tag{5.72 a}$$

With the definition (2.18) of $\boldsymbol{\chi}_{\kappa M}$ and the orthogonality properties (2.5) (2.21), this integral becomes

$$\delta_{l'l}\sum_\mu (-)^{\mu-\frac{1}{2}}\langle l(M-\mu)\tfrac{1}{2}(\mu)|I'(M)\rangle\langle l(M-\mu)\tfrac{1}{2}(\mu)|I(M)\rangle. \tag{5.72 b}$$

Here, $l = I-\frac{1}{2} = I'+\frac{1}{2}$ in $I \to I' = I-1$ cases and $l = I+\frac{1}{2} = I'-\frac{1}{2}$ when $I' = I+1$; in the $\Delta I = 0$ cases, either $l = I\pm\frac{1}{2}$ may occur. Evaluations of the vector-addition coefficients as given in Table 2.2 lead to

$$\left.\begin{aligned}\langle\sigma\rangle &= [(I+1)/I]^{\frac{1}{2}} && \text{for } I' = I = l+\tfrac{1}{2} \\ &= -[I/(I+1)]^{\frac{1}{2}} && \text{for } I' = I = l-\tfrac{1}{2} \\ &= (-)^{I+\frac{1}{2}-l}[(2I'+1)/(l+\tfrac{1}{2})]^{\frac{1}{2}} && \text{for } I' = I\pm 1\end{aligned}\right\} \tag{5.73}$$

as 'maximal' values. These results comprise variations between the

‡ M. G. Mayer and J. H. D. Jensen, *Elementary Theory of Nuclear Shell Structure* (Chapman & Hall, London, 1955).

limits given by $\frac{1}{3} \leqslant \langle\sigma\rangle^2 \leqslant 3$. They were first obtained by Wigner‡ without special reference to the shell model.

The specific assignments of $l$ and $j = I$ which are needed for applications of (5.73) are guided by studies of the 'systematics' of nuclei, i.e. the dependence of various observed nuclear properties on the number and kinds of the nucleons composing them. The conclusions from such studies (ref., p. 149) are most economically presentable as an order in which successive 'orbitals' are filled, as neutrons and protons are added to a nuclear structure. Each orbital is given a designation like $s_{1/2}$, $p_{3/2}$, $p_{1/2}$, $d_{5/2,3/2}$, $f_{7/2,5/2,...}$ with $s, p, d, f, g, h, i,...$ corresponding to $l = 0, 1, 2, 3, 4, 5, 6,...$ and the subscripts denoting $j = l \pm \frac{1}{2}$. The most consistent order of assignment (with occasional exceptions to be expected) is found to be that indicated by

$$s_{1/2}^2 | p_{3/2}^4 | p_{1/2}^2 | d_{5/2}^6 \, s_{1/2}^2 \, d_{3/2}^4 | f_{7/2}^8 | p_{3/2}^4 \, f_{5/2}^6 \, p_{1/2}^2 \, g_{9/2}^{10} | \cdot$$
$$\cdot | g_{7/2}^8 \, d_{5/2}^6 \, d_{3/2}^4 \, s_{1/2}^2 \, h_{11/2}^{12} | h_{9/2}^{10} \, f_{7/2}^8 \, f_{5/2}^6 \, p_{3/2}^4 \, p_{1/2}^2 \, i_{13/2}^{14} | i_{11/2}^{12} \cdots \quad (5.74)$$

The superscripts give the numbers, $2j+1$, of like nucleons which can fill the corresponding orbitals. The orbitals which are repeated in the sequence presumably arise with additional nodes in their radial waves. The vertical bars indicate junctures at which 'shells' of exceptional stability seem to be completed. Most of the assignments used in the ensuing tabulations conform to the order (5.74), but the evidence has sometimes required modifications, especially within partially closed shells (i.e. between successive vertical bars).

The maximal $\langle\sigma\rangle$ values (5.73) should apply best to the mirror decays. The pertinent information about these transitions is listed in Table 5.1. All but the $Be^7$ transition to the excited state $Li^{7*}$ ($\frac{3}{2} \rightarrow \frac{1}{2}$, hence $\langle 1 \rangle = 0$) are expected to have $\langle 1 \rangle^2 = 1$, as in the expression (5.68) for the $ft$-value. It is from this expression that the column of $(ft)_{\text{theo}}$ values was computed, using the listed $\langle\sigma\rangle^2_{\text{theo.}}$ values. The latter were calculated from (5.73) and the assignments recorded in the column headed 'transition'. The results show some correlation with the measured $ft$-values, e.g. the sharp dips in magnitude which occur in the passages across the shell boundaries at the 'magic number' $N$ or $Z = 8$ and $N$ or $Z = 20$. The overall agreement is about as good as is usual in nuclear structure theory for moments of any kind (including electromagnetic ones) unless additional adjustable parameters are introduced (like 'intermediate-coupling' strengths, or adjustable 'core-deformation' parameters).

‡ Reference p. 142. G. Breit and J. Knipp, *Phys. Rev.* **54**, 652 (1938), worked out the application to the two transitions of $Be^7$.

TABLE 5.1

*The mirror transitions*

| *Parent* | *Daughter* | $(ft)_{\text{exp}}$ *(sec)* | *Transition* | $\langle\sigma\rangle^2_{\text{theo}}$ | $(ft)_{\text{theo}}$ | *From* $\mu_{\text{exp}}$ |
|---|---|---|---|---|---|---|
| ${}_0\text{n}^1_1$ | ${}_1\text{H}^1_0$ | $1180 \pm 35$ | $s_{1/2} \to s_{1/2}$ | 3 | 1180 | 1180 |
| ${}_1\text{H}^3_2$ | ${}_2\text{He}^3_1$ | $1137 \pm 20$ | $s_{1/2} \to s_{1/2}$ | 3 | 1180 | 1030 |
| ${}_4\text{Be}^7_3$ | ${}_3\text{Li}^7_4$ | $2300 \pm 78$ | $p_{3/2} \to p_{3/2}$ | $\frac{5}{3}$ | 1840 | 2410 |
| ${}_4\text{Be}^7_3$ | $\text{Li}^{7*}$ | $3600 \pm 122$ | $p_{3/2} \to p_{1/2}$ | $\frac{4}{3}$ | 3290 | .. |
| ${}_6\text{C}^{11}_5$ | ${}_5\text{B}^{11}_6$ | $3840 \pm 70$ | $p_{3/2} \to p_{3/2}$ | $\frac{5}{3}$ | 1840 | 3270 |
| ${}_7\text{N}^{13}_6$ | ${}_6\text{C}^{13}_7$ | $4700 \pm 80$ | $p_{1/2} \to p_{1/2}$ | $\frac{1}{3}$ | 4190 | 3800 |
| ${}_8\text{O}^{15}_7$ | ${}_7\text{N}^{15}_8$ | $4475 \pm 30$ | $p_{1/2} \to p_{1/2}$ | $\frac{1}{3}$ | 4190 | 4070 |
| ${}_9\text{F}^{17}_8$ | ${}_8\text{O}^{17}_9$ | $2330 \pm 80$ | $d_{5/2} \to d_{5/2}$ | $\frac{7}{5}$ | 2070 | 2080 |
| ${}_{10}\text{Ne}^{19}_9$ | ${}_9\text{F}^{19}_{10}$ | $1900 \pm 100$ | $s_{1/2} \to s_{1/2}$ | 3 | 1180 | 1330 |
| ${}_{11}\text{Na}^{21}_{10}$ | ${}_{10}\text{Ne}^{21}_{11}$ | $3500 \pm 200$ | $(d^3_{5/2})_{3/2} \to (d^3_{5/2})_{3/2}$ | 0·19 | 4850 | .. |
| ${}_{12}\text{Mg}^{23}_{11}$ | ${}_{11}\text{Na}^{23}_{12}$ | $4780 \pm 150$ | ,, ,, | ,, | 4850 | 4450 |
| ${}_{13}\text{Al}^{25}_{12}$ | ${}_{12}\text{Mg}^{25}_{13}$ | $4280 \pm 350$ | $d_{5/2} \to d_{5/2}$ | $\frac{7}{5}$ | 2070 | 3200 |
| ${}_{14}\text{Si}^{27}_{13}$ | ${}_{13}\text{Al}^{27}_{14}$ | $4500 \pm 100$ | ,, ,, | $\frac{7}{5}$ | 2070 | 3330 |
| ${}_{15}\text{P}^{29}_{14}$ | ${}_{14}\text{Si}^{29}_{15}$ | $4750 \pm 200$ | $s_{1/2} \to s_{1/2}$ | 3 | 1180 | 3510 |
| ${}_{16}\text{S}^{31}_{15}$ | ${}_{15}\text{P}^{31}_{16}$ | $4820 \pm 250$ | $s_{1/2} \to s_{1/2}$ | 3 | 1180 | 4500 |
| ${}_{17}\text{Cl}^{33}_{16}$ | ${}_{16}\text{S}^{33}_{17}$ | $6000 \pm 500$ | $d_{3/2} \to d_{3/2}$ | $\frac{3}{5}$ | 3340 | 6100 |
| ${}_{18}\text{A}^{35}_{17}$ | ${}_{17}\text{Cl}^{35}_{18}$ | $5680 \pm 400$ | ,, ,, | $\frac{3}{5}$ | 3340 | 5500 |
| ${}_{19}\text{K}^{37}_{18}$ | ${}_{18}\text{A}^{37}_{19}$ | $4250 \pm 500$ | ,, ,, | $\frac{3}{5}$ | 3340 | .. |
| ${}_{20}\text{Ca}^{39}_{19}$ | ${}_{19}\text{K}^{39}_{20}$ | $4150 \pm 300$ | ,, ,, | $\frac{3}{5}$ | 3340 | 5150 |
| ${}_{21}\text{Sc}^{41}_{20}$ | ${}_{20}\text{Ca}^{41}_{21}$ | $2560 \pm 160$ | $f_{7/2} \to f_{7/2}$ | $\frac{9}{7}$ | 2190 | .. |
| ${}_{22}\text{Ti}^{43}_{21}$ | ${}_{21}\text{Sc}^{43}_{22}$ | 2500 | $f_{7/2} \to f_{7/2}$ | $\frac{9}{7}$ | 2190 | .. |

It can be held that treating all but one nucleon as inert in the $\beta$-transformation amounts to supposing that the underlying core of nucleons forms a 'saturated', i.e. 'filled-up', configuration. This does not always accord with the shell model (5.74), which provides orbitals that can in general be saturated only by more than two nucleons of each kind. For example, ${}_{10}\text{Ne}^{21}_{11}$ may be viewed as having three $d_{5/2}$ neutrons, plus two $d_{5/2}$ protons, extra to a saturated ${}_8\text{O}^{16}_8$ core, rather than just the odd $d_{5/2}$ neutron extra to an inert ${}_{10}\text{Ne}^{20}_{10}$; indeed, the construction of some many-particle description seems to be needed to account for the observed $I = \frac{3}{2} \neq \frac{5}{2}$. On the basis that only saturated shell model configurations should be treated as inert, many-particle states‡ would have to be constructed to describe most of the mirrors. That cannot be done uniquely, in general, without additional assumptions; the treatment

‡ A. Winther and O. Kofoed-Hansen, *K. Danske Vidensk. Selsk. Skr.* **27**, No. 14 (1953), made an early investigation of such, with improved results for a few cases but leaving most of the discrepancies in Table 5.1 untouched.

of any equal number of neutrons and protons as an inert configuration may be as plausible as others.

Perhaps the most defensible assumption about the mirror states is that they can be transformed into each other by the isospin ladder operation used to get the singlet moment (5.67). Unfortunately, this assumption is not by itself sufficient to yield a definite result for $\langle\sigma\rangle$; it does help reduce the evaluation of $\langle\sigma\rangle$ to that of the expectation value $\left\langle\sum_a \sigma_3^a \tau_3^a\right\rangle$ in either the initial or final state (next subsection). The last evaluation is also the essential one for deriving the magnetic moment for the state, as might be expected from the fact that the individual neutron and proton magnetic moments, $\mu_n$ and $\mu_p$, contribute terms $\mu_{n,p}\boldsymbol{\sigma}$ to the magnetic moment operator (5.84). Thus, a relation between the $\beta$-moment $\langle\sigma\rangle$ and the magnetic moment $\mu$, in either of the states $T_3 = \pm\frac{1}{2}$, can be derived:

$$\langle\sigma\rangle = (-)^{T_3-\frac{1}{2}}\left(\frac{I+1}{I}\right)^{\frac{1}{2}} \frac{2\mu - I[l+\frac{1}{2}\pm(\mu_p+\mu_n-\frac{1}{2})]/(l+\frac{1}{2})}{\mu_p-\mu_n-\frac{1}{2}\pm(l+\frac{1}{2})}, \qquad (5.75)$$

with $l$ the orbital momentum of any one of the (presumed equivalent) extra-core nucleons. All the magnetic moments here are to be expressed in units of the 'nuclear magneton', $e\hbar/2M_p c$, making $\mu_p = +2{\cdot}793$ and $\mu_n = -1{\cdot}913$. When experimental magnetic moments, $\mu_{exp}$, measured for the various stable daughter states in Table 5.1, are substituted for $\mu$ in (5.75), they lead to the $ft$-values shown in the last column of the table. The corrections to $(ft)_{theo}$ thus obtained are all in the right direction except for the two $p_{\frac{1}{2}}$ transitions. In almost all cases there is marked improvement, e.g. in the case of $Cl^{33}$. This outcome at least tends to confirm the validity of treating the mirror states as transforms of each other by the isospin ladder operation.

*The signs of the moments*

The effects of singlet-triplet interference, which occurs in emissions from oriented nuclei, depend on the relative sign of the moments, being proportional to the product $\langle 1\rangle.\langle\sigma\rangle$, as in the lepton anisotropy coefficients $A$, $B$ of (5.42). Signs of $\langle\sigma\rangle$, relative to $\langle 1\rangle = +1$, have already been derived in (5.73), but their validity depends on how far the single-particle model of the nuclear states can be trusted. That the question has importance is shown by the example of $Ne^{19}$; (5.73) gives $\langle 1\rangle\langle\sigma\rangle = +3^{\frac{1}{2}}$ for $\frac{1}{2}\to\frac{1}{2}$ transitions, yet a measurement‡ of the electron anisotropy coefficient $A$ indicates $\langle 1\rangle\langle\sigma\rangle \approx -3^{\frac{1}{2}}$ in that case.

‡ E. Commins and D. Dobson, *Phys. Rev. Letters*, **10**, 347 (1963).

The single-particle state (5.70) was discussed as describing the motion of the transforming nucleon in the field of all the untransformed nucleons. This may have validity for the $A = 4n+1$ mirrors, in which the transforming nucleon is an odd one which also determines the characteristics of the state (e.g. its magnetic moment as well as its spin). However, in the $A = 4n-1$ mirror decays it is one of the *even* number of nucleons which transforms. This does not necessarily invalidate the use of the single-particle model for obtaining the *magnitudes* of the $\beta$-moments. These are determined by the space-spin distribution characteristic of the state and that may still be well represented. However, it is too much to expect that even the phases generated in the $\beta$-transformation will be correctly represented.

Proper treatment will be least ambiguous for cases in which no orbital momenta need be considered, i.e. when only $s_{1/2}$ nucleons are involved in any essential way. This is clearly a good assumption for ${}_1H_2^3 \rightarrow {}_2He_1^3$, and seems to be nearly valid also for ${}_{10}Ne_9^{19} \rightarrow {}_9F_{10}^{19}$. The latter nuclei each have 3 nucleons extra to a saturated, 'doubly magic', ${}_8O_8^{16}$ core. Occupying the same, $l = 0$, space configuration, the two of the 3 nucleons which are alike must have antiparallel spins, and there should be a resultant magnetic moment characteristic of a free nucleon of the 'unlike' kind. Measurements confirm this: $\mu(Ne^{19}) \approx -1{\cdot}89$ is observed, vs. the free neutron magnetic moment $\mu_n = -1{\cdot}91$, and $\mu(F^{19}) \approx +2{\cdot}63$ vs. $\mu_p = +2{\cdot}79$. However, it is not this odd nucleon which participates in the $\beta$-transformation, which generates *positrons*. Clearly, a description of at least three extra-core particles must be constructed to settle questions about the effect of the nuclear state.

With only nucleonic spins to be described, the 3-particle angular momentum eigenstates may be constructed out of Pauli eigenspinors, $\chi_{\pm\frac{1}{2}}$, which will here be denoted $\uparrow$ and $\downarrow$ simply. The total of $2^3$ independent states which can be formed from three half-spins are classifiable into a quartet ($I = \frac{3}{2}$) and *two* doublets ($I = \frac{1}{2}$). The two $I = \frac{1}{2}$, $M = +\frac{1}{2}$ eigenstates of interest here are well known‡ to be

$$\left.\begin{aligned} \chi^{A}(1,2,3) &= 2^{-\frac{1}{2}}(\uparrow\downarrow-\downarrow\uparrow)\uparrow \\ \chi^{S}(1,2,3) &= 6^{-\frac{1}{2}}[(\uparrow\downarrow+\downarrow\uparrow)\uparrow-2\uparrow\uparrow\downarrow] \end{aligned}\right\} \tag{5.76}$$

when respectively antisymmetrized and symmetrized in the first two degrees of freedom. The possible $T = \frac{1}{2}$, $T_3 = +\frac{1}{2}$ isospin eigenstates

‡ See, for example, L. Schiff, *Quantum Mechanics* (McGraw-Hill, New York, 1949), formula (33.9). The state $\chi^{S}$ may also be constructed by combining $\chi_{1m}^{t}$ of (2.23) with a Pauli eigenspinor, according to (2.11).

are the analogues formed with $\boldsymbol{\chi}_{+\frac{1}{2}} \to \xi_{\mathrm{p}}$ and $\boldsymbol{\chi}_{-\frac{1}{2}} \to \xi_{\mathrm{n}}$. Denoting $\xi_{\mathrm{p,n}}$ by p and n, simply:

$$\left.\begin{aligned} \xi^{\mathrm{A}} &= 2^{-\frac{1}{2}}(\mathrm{pn}-\mathrm{np})\mathrm{p} \\ \xi^{\mathrm{S}} &= 6^{-\frac{1}{2}}[(\mathrm{pn}+\mathrm{np})\mathrm{p}-2\mathrm{ppn}] \end{aligned}\right\}. \tag{5.77}$$

A unique description of the three $s_{\frac{1}{2}}$ nucleons is obtained by requiring anti-symmetry in the interchange of any pair:

$$\begin{aligned} |I(M)T(T_3)\rangle &\to 2^{-\frac{1}{2}}(\xi^{\mathrm{A}}\boldsymbol{\chi}^{\mathrm{S}}-\xi^{\mathrm{S}}\boldsymbol{\chi}^{\mathrm{A}}) \\ &= 6^{-\frac{1}{2}}[(\mathrm{ppn})(\uparrow\downarrow-\downarrow\uparrow)\uparrow-(\mathrm{pnp})(\uparrow\uparrow\downarrow-\downarrow\uparrow\uparrow)+(\mathrm{npp})\uparrow(\uparrow\downarrow-\downarrow\uparrow)], \end{aligned} \tag{5.78}$$

for $I = M = T = T_3 = \frac{1}{2}$. As to be expected, in each term the like nucleons have antiparallel spins. The $T_3 = -\frac{1}{2}$ eigenstate can be obtained via

$$|I(M)\tfrac{1}{2}(-\tfrac{1}{2})\rangle = T_{-}|I(M)\tfrac{1}{2}(+\tfrac{1}{2})\rangle, \tag{5.79}$$

and this sets the arbitrary relative phase of the two states so that the singlet moment becomes $\langle 1\rangle = +1$, as in (5.67) for $T = \frac{1}{2}$.

The triplet moment is to be obtained from (5.20):

$$\begin{aligned} \langle\sigma\rangle &= \langle I(I)1(0)|I(I)\rangle^{-1}\Big\langle I(I)\tfrac{1}{2}(\pm\tfrac{1}{2})\Big|\sum_a \sigma_0^a\,\tau_{\pm}^a\Big|I(I)\tfrac{1}{2}(\mp\tfrac{1}{2})\Big\rangle \\ &= [(I+1)/I]^{\frac{1}{2}}\Big\langle I(I)\tfrac{1}{2}(\pm\tfrac{1}{2})\Big|\sum_a \sigma_0^a\,\tau_{\pm}^a\,T_{\mp}\Big|I(I)\tfrac{1}{2}(\pm\tfrac{1}{2})\Big\rangle \end{aligned} \tag{5.80}$$

for $\mathrm{e}^{\mp}$ emissions, respectively. The operators here can be transposed with the help of the commutation relations $[\tau_{+}^a, \tau_{-}^b] = \delta_{ab}\,\tau_3$, so that $\sum_a \sigma_0^a\,\tau_{\pm}^a\,T_{\mp} = T_{\mp}\sum_a \sigma_0^a\,\tau_{\pm}^a \pm \sum_a \sigma_0^a\,\tau_3^a$. The first terms of this lead to a vanishing expectation value since

$$\langle I(I)\tfrac{1}{2}(\pm\tfrac{1}{2})|T_{\mp} = (T_{\pm}|I(I)\tfrac{1}{2}(\pm\tfrac{1}{2})\rangle)^{\dagger} = 0. \tag{5.81}$$

Consequently,

$$\langle\sigma\rangle = (-)^{T_3-\frac{1}{2}}[(I+1)/I]^{\frac{1}{2}}\Big\langle\sum_a \sigma_z^a\,\tau_3^a\Big\rangle, \tag{5.82}$$

where the last factor is the expectation value in the state $|I(I)\frac{1}{2}(T_3)\rangle$. Actually, the two alternatives in (5.80) are obviously each others' complex conjugates and yet represent a real number. This means that the same sign of $\langle\sigma\rangle$ will emerge whether it applies to $\mathrm{e}^-$ or $\mathrm{e}^+$ emission (or whether (5.82) is evaluated in the $T_3 = +\frac{1}{2}$ or $T_3 = -\frac{1}{2}$ member of the doublet). For the $I = \frac{1}{2}$ state (5.78), it is now easy to compute that $\langle\sigma\rangle = -3^{\frac{1}{2}}$ is to be expected, applicable to both the $\mathrm{H}^3$ and $\mathrm{Ne}^{19}$ cases. This outcome agrees with the experimental finding for $\mathrm{Ne}^{19}$, quoted above.

A striking conclusion here is that, whereas a polarized free neutron emits negatrons almost isotropically ($A = -0{\cdot}11$ in (1.58)), the singlet (hence isotropic) pair of neutrons bound in ${}_1H_2^3$ are predicted to co-operate in producing negatrons with a strong directionality of emission. With the above conclusion that the interference product $\langle 1\rangle\langle\sigma\rangle$ is negative, and the observed $ft(H^3)$, (5.42) can be shown to yield the prediction

$$A(H^3) = -0{\cdot}99 \pm 0{\cdot}04 \tag{5.83}$$

for the electron anisotropy coefficient. It is suggestive that a free proton, if it had energy available, would exhibit $A_p \approx +1$.

Perhaps the most reliable way to obtain the correct signs for all the mirror moments is through the use of their relationships to the observed magnetic moments as given by (5.75). This extra usefulness for their relation warrants presenting its derivation here (ref., p. 149). The magnetic moment operator is quite obviously

$$\boldsymbol{\mu} = \sum_a \left[\tfrac{1}{2}(1+\tau_3^a)(\mu_p \boldsymbol{\sigma}^a + \mathbf{l}^a) + \tfrac{1}{2}(1-\tau_3^a)\mu_n \boldsymbol{\sigma}^a\right], \tag{5.84}$$

since each unit of proton orbital momentum adds a unit $(e\hbar/2M_p c)$. Experimenters quote the expectation value of $\mu_z$ in the polarized state $|I(I)\tfrac{1}{2}(T_3)\rangle$. Since $\mathbf{l}^a = \mathbf{j}^a - \tfrac{1}{2}\boldsymbol{\sigma}^a$ in the units used here, it is obvious that expectation values $\left\langle \sum_a \sigma_z^a \right\rangle$ and $\left\langle \sum_a j_z^a \right\rangle = I$ will be needed. The contributions of the nucleons in the even-even core certainly vanish, hence only the extra-core nucleons, each with the same $j$, $l+\tfrac{1}{2}$ or $l-\tfrac{1}{2}$, need be considered. If the angular momentum description of one extra-core nucleon is separated off from the remainder, of angular momentum $\mathbf{R}$, say,

$$|I(I)\tfrac{1}{2}(T_3)\rangle \rightarrow \sum_m \chi_{\kappa m} \chi_{R,I-m} \langle R(I-m)j(m)|I(I)\rangle,$$

and it is easy to compute, as in (5.72), that

$$\langle \sigma_z^a \rangle = \pm(l+\tfrac{1}{2})^{-1} \sum_m m\langle R(I-m)j(m)|I(I)\rangle^2 \quad \text{for } j = l \pm \tfrac{1}{2}.$$

The summation factor here will be recognized as just $\langle j_z^a \rangle$ for the one nucleon. If that nucleon is a proton, the relation is equivalent to $\langle \tfrac{1}{2}(1+\tau_3^a)j_z^a \rangle = \pm(l+\tfrac{1}{2})\langle \tfrac{1}{2}(1+\tau_3^a)\sigma_z^a \rangle$. Now, the complete expectation value, $\mu$, for the magnetic moment can be written down as

$$\mu = \tfrac{1}{2}[(\mu_p - \mu_n - \tfrac{1}{2}) \pm (l+\tfrac{1}{2})]\left\langle \sum_a \sigma_z^a \tau_3^a \right\rangle + \tfrac{1}{2}I \pm$$
$$\pm \tfrac{1}{2}(\mu_p + \mu_n - \tfrac{1}{2})I/(l+\tfrac{1}{2}) \quad \text{for } j = l \pm \tfrac{1}{2}.$$

Only the relation (5.82) need be used to express $\langle\sigma\rangle$ exactly as in (5.75). It is readily checked that either

$$\mu(H^3) \approx \mu(F^{19}) \approx \mu_p, \quad \text{or} \quad \mu(He^3) \approx \mu(Ne^{19}) \approx \mu_n,$$

leads to $\langle\sigma\rangle \approx -3^{\frac{1}{2}}$ as found above.

*The unfavoured transitions of odd-A nuclei*

The single-particle model may also be tried out for the odd-$A$ nuclei with $|Z-N| > 1$. No Fermi transitions are expected among these nuclei (i.e. $\langle 1 \rangle \approx 0$) in so far as the isospin selection rule $\Delta T = 0$ remains valid. The lowest states are supposed to have

$$T = |T_3| = \tfrac{1}{2}|Z-N| > \tfrac{1}{2}$$

and then the $\Delta T_3 = \pm 1$ which occurs in a $\beta$-transformation implies that $\Delta T \neq 0$. It can then be supposed that the $ft$-values are direct measures of 'experimental' Gamow–Teller moments:

$$\langle \sigma \rangle^2_{\text{exp}} \approx (4400 \text{ sec})/(ft)_{\text{exp}},$$

according to (5.60). Such are recorded in Table 5.2, in the column headed $\langle \sigma \rangle^2_{\text{exp}}$.

The next two columns of Table 5.2 list the assignments of the odd-nucleon orbitals which follow from (5.74) and the corresponding $\langle \sigma \rangle^2$ values as obtained from the single-particle model formulae (5.73). The ratios‡ $\langle \sigma \rangle^2_{\text{exp}}/\langle \sigma \rangle^2_{\text{theo}}$ are recorded in the last column, labelled 'mismatch factors'. The large discrepancy between experiment and the over-simplified theory is to be expected; the simple single-particle model states can only give 'favoured' values for the moments just as they do for the mirrors, $|Z-N| = 1$. The description of the 'cores' is ignored, and when these have unequal numbers of neutrons and protons, as when $|Z-N| > 1$, they may be very different for the neutron and proton states of the transforming nucleon. Certainly the mismatches cannot be understood without taking into account the behaviour of several nucleons of the nucleus.

Table 5.3 lists still another group of transitions obeying the allowed selection rules, $\Delta I = 0$ or 1, now ones in which the orbital momenta assigned to the transforming nucleon are different in its initial and final states. Under these conditions, both the singlet and triplet moments vanish according to the single-particle model results (5.71), (5.72); an additional selection rule, $\Delta l = 0$, is being violated. The measured $ft$-values listed in the table indicate that the so-called‡ '$l$-forbiddenness' in almost all cases suppresses the ratio much more than is usual among the normal allowed transitions. This outcome attests to some validity for the shell-model assignments. It may be mentioned that the smaller suppression by the $l$-forbiddenness of the decay rates of the nuclei having about fifteen neutrons or protons can be correlated with

‡ Called 'unfavoured factors' by L. W. Nordheim, *Phys. Rev.* **78**, 294 (1950). They may be compared to the expression of observed $\gamma$-lifetimes in so-called 'Weisskopf units', which are simply values which follow from the single-particle model.

TABLE 5.2

*Allowed transitions among odd-A nuclei*

| Parent | Daughter | $\log_{10}(ft)_{\text{exp}}$ | $\langle\sigma\rangle^2_{\text{exp}}$ | Transition | $\langle\sigma\rangle^2_{\text{theo}}$ | Mismatch factor |
|---|---|---|---|---|---|---|
| $_{16}S^{35}_{19}$ | $_{17}Cl_{18}$ | 4·98 | 0·048 | $d_{3/2}\to d_{3/2}$ | 0·6 | 0·080 |
| $_{18}A^{37}_{19}$ | $_{17}Cl_{20}$ | 5·04 | 0·040 | $d_{3/2}\to d_{3/2}$ | 0·6 | 0·067 |
| $_{20}Ca^{45}_{25}$ | $_{21}Sc_{24}$ | 5·94 | 0·005 | $f_{7/2}\to f_{7/2}$ | 1·28 | 0·0039 |
| $_{22}Ti^{45}_{23}$ | $_{21}Sc_{24}$ | 4·59 | 0·110 | $f_{7/2}\to f_{7/2}$ | 1·28 | 0·086 |
| $_{21}Sc^{49}_{28}$ | $_{22}Ti_{27}$ | 5·06 | 0·038 | $f_{7/2}\to f_{7/2}$ | 1·28 | 0·030 |
| $_{23}V^{49}_{26}$ | $_{22}Ti_{27}$ | 5·10 | 0·035 | $f_{7/2}\to f_{7/2}$ | 1·28 | 0·027 |
| $_{27}Co^{61}_{34}$ | $_{28}Ni_{33}$ | 5·20 | 0·028 | $f_{7/2}\to f_{5/2}$ | 1·71 | 0·016 |
| $_{29}Cu^{61}_{32}$ | $_{28}Ni_{33}$ | 4·94 | 0·050 | $p_{3/2}\to p_{3/2}$ | 1·67 | 0·030 |
| $_{30}Zn^{63}_{33}$ | $_{29}Cu_{34}$ | 5·40 | 0·017 | $p_{3/2}\to p_{3/2}$ | 1·67 | 0·010 |
| $_{30}Zn^{69}_{39}$ | $_{31}Ga_{38}$ | 4·37 | 0·186 | $p_{1/2}\to p_{3/2}$ | 2·67 | 0·070 |
| $_{32}Ge^{71}_{39}$ | $_{31}Ga_{40}$ | 4·30 | 0·219 | $p_{1/2}\to p_{3/2}$ | 2·67 | 0·082 |
| $_{33}As^{71}_{38}$ | $_{32}Ge_{39}$ | 5·80 | 0·0069 | $f_{5/2}\to f_{5/2}$ | 0·71 | 0·0097 |
| $_{33}As^{77}_{44}$ | $_{34}Se_{43}$ | 5·76 | 0·0076 | $p_{3/2}\to p_{1/2}$ | 1·33 | 0·0057 |
| $_{35}Br^{77}_{42}$ | $_{34}Se_{43}$ | 5·36 | 0·019 | $p_{3/2}\to p_{1/2}$ | 1·33 | 0·0014 |
| $_{34}Se^{81}_{47}$ | $_{35}Br_{46}$ | 4·72 | 0·083 | $p_{1/2}\to p_{3/2}$ | 2·67 | 0·031 |
| $_{34}Se^{*}_{49}$ | $_{35}Br^{83}_{48}$ | 5·22 | 0·026 | $p_{1/2}\to p_{3/2}$ | 2·67 | 0·010 |
| $_{35}Br^{83}_{48}$ | $_{36}Kr_{47}$ | 5·13 | 0·032 | $p_{3/2}\to p_{1/2}$ | 1·33 | 0·024 |
| $_{42}Mo^{*}_{49}$ | $_{41}Nb^{91}_{50}$ | 5·72 | 0·0083 | $p_{1/2}\to p_{1/2}$ | 0·33 | 0·025 |
| $_{41}Nb^{95}_{54}$ | $_{42}Mo_{53}$ | 5·08 | 0·036 | $g_{9/2}\to g_{7/2}$ | 1·78 | 0·020 |
| $_{41}Nb^{97}_{56}$ | $_{42}Mo_{55}$ | 5·35 | 0·020 | $g_{9/2}\to g_{7/2}$ | 1·78 | 0·011 |
| $_{50}Sn^{111}_{61}$ | $_{49}In_{62}$ | 4·69 | 0·089 | $g_{7/2}\to g_{9/2}$ | 2·22 | 0·040 |
| $_{50}Sn^{121}_{71}$ | $_{51}Sb_{70}$ | 5·00 | 0·044 | $d_{3/2}\to d_{5/2}$ | 2·40 | 0·018 |
| $_{53}I^{121}_{68}$ | $_{52}Te_{69}$ | 5·05 | 0·039 | $d_{5/2}\to d_{3/2}$ | 1·60 | 0·024 |
| $_{50}Sn^{123}_{73}$ | $_{51}Sb_{72}$ | 5·27 | 0·023 | $d_{3/2}\to d_{5/2}$ | 2·40 | 0·009 |
| $_{52}Te^{127}_{75}$ | $_{53}I_{74}$ | 5·66 | 0·0096 | $d_{3/2}\to d_{5/2}$ | 2·40 | 0·004 |
| $_{55}Cs^{131}_{76}$ | $_{54}Xe_{77}$ | 5·50 | 0·014 | $d_{3/2}\to d_{3/2}$ | 0·60 | 0·023 |
| $_{54}Xe^{133}_{79}$ | $_{55}Cs_{78}$ | 5·58 | 0·012 | $d_{3/2}\to d_{5/2}$ | 2·40 | 0·005 |

TABLE 5.3

*Apparent l-forbidden transitions among odd-A nuclei*

| Parent | Daughter | Transition | $\log_{10}(ft)_{\text{exp}}$ |
|---|---|---|---|
| $_{14}Si^{31}_{17}$ | $_{15}P^{31}_{16}$ | $d_{3/2}\to s_{1/2}$ | 5·51 |
| $_{15}P^{33}_{18}$ | $_{16}S^{33}_{17}$ | $s_{1/2}\to d_{3/2}$ | 5·05 |
| $_{28}Ni^{63}_{35}$ | $_{29}Cu^{63}_{34}$ | $f_{5/2}\to p_{3/2}$ | 6·56 |
| $_{28}Ni^{65}_{37}$ | $_{29}Cu^{65}_{36}$ | $f_{5/2}\to p_{3/2}$ | 6·56 |
| $_{30}Zn^{65}_{35}$ | $_{29}Cu^{65}_{36}$ | $f_{5/2}\to p_{3/2}$ | 7·34 |
| $_{29}Cu^{67}_{38}$ | $_{30}Zn^{67}_{37}$ | $p_{3/2}\to f_{5/2}$ | 6·30 |
| $_{32}Ge^{69}_{37}$ | $_{31}Ga^{69}_{38}$ | $f_{5/2}\to p_{3/2}$ | 6·4 |

the unusually large suppression found among the mirror decays with about that number of odd nucleons.‡ It can be understood to arise from the same mixing of $l$-values in both cases.

*Transitions among the even-A nuclei*

As in the odd-$A$ case, a basis of discussion is best provided by first giving attention to the favoured transitions among the even-$A$ nuclei. The purely singlet, $0 \to 0$, decays have already been discussed in connexion with the isospin selection rule, $\Delta T = 0$, which pertains just to the singlet moment, $\langle 1 \rangle$. The remaining favoured cases among the even-$A$ nuclei consist of triplet emissions by members of the $A = 4n+2$ family listed in Table 5.4. These all involve nuclear spin changes $0 \leftrightarrow 1$ together with $1 \leftrightarrow 0$ changes of isospin: $\Delta T = 1$!

TABLE 5.4

*Allowed transitions among the $A = 4n+2$ isobars*

| *Parent* | *Daughter* | *Spins* | $(ft)_{\text{exp}}$ *(sec)* | $(ft)_{LS}$ | $(ft)_{jj}$ |
|---|---|---|---|---|---|
| ${}_2\text{He}_4^6$ | ${}_3\text{Li}_3$ | $0 \to 1$ | $808 \pm 32$ | 730 | 1316 |
| ${}_6\text{C}_4^{10}$ | ${}_5\text{B}_5^*$ | $0 \to 1$ | $1700 \pm 150$ | 730 | 1316 |
| ${}_6\text{C}_4^{10}$ | ${}_5\text{B}_5^{**}$ | $0 \to 0$ | $5900 \pm 2700$ | 3070 | 3070 |
| ${}_6\text{C}_8^{14}$ | ${}_7\text{N}_7$ | $0 \to 1$ | $\sim 10^9$ | 730 | 6580 |
| ${}_8\text{O}_6^{14}$ | ${}_7\text{N}_7$ | $0 \to 1$ | $\sim 10^{7\cdot 6}$ | 730 | 6580 |
| ${}_8\text{O}_6^{14}$ | ${}_7\text{N}_7^*$ | $0 \to 0$ | $3060 \pm 10$ | 3070 | 3070 |
| ${}_9\text{F}_9^{18}$ | ${}_8\text{O}_{10}$ | $1 \to 0$ | $4169 \pm 158$ | 2190 | 2190 $(s_{1/2})$ or 4695 $(d_{5/2})$ |
| ${}_{13}\text{Al}_{13}^{26*}$ | ${}_{12}\text{Mg}_{14}$ | $0 \to 0$ | $3050 \pm 60$ | 3070 | 3070 |
| ${}_{15}\text{P}_{15}^{30}$ | ${}_{14}\text{Si}_{16}$ | $1 \to 0$ | $\sim 10^{5\cdot 2}$ | 2190 | 2190 |
| ${}_{17}\text{Cl}_{17}^{34}$ | ${}_{16}\text{S}_{18}$ | $0 \to 0$ | $3110 \pm 70$ | 3070 | 3070 |
| ${}_{19}\text{K}_{19}^{38}$ | ${}_{18}\text{A}_{20}$ | $0 \to 0$ | $3140 \pm 400$ | 3070 | 3070 |
| ${}_{21}\text{Sc}_{21}^{42}$ | ${}_{20}\text{Ca}_{22}$ | $0 \to 0$ | $\sim 2800$ | 3070 | 3070 |
| ${}_{23}\text{V}_{23}^{46}$ | ${}_{22}\text{Ti}_{24}$ | $0 \to 0$ | 3140 | 3070 | 3070 |

Each of the spin 0 states is a $T_3 = \pm 1$ member of a $T = 1$ isotriplet, of the type participating in the $0 \to 0$ decays. The $I = 1$ states naturally belong to some different isomultiplet, and since they occur in the $T_3 = 0$ $(N = Z)$ isobars, they should almost certainly be assigned to the isosinglet, $T = 0$. The $T = 0$ eigenstate of the extra-core neutron-proton pair may be written $\xi_{00} = 2^{-\frac{1}{2}}(\xi_p \xi_n - \xi_n \xi_p)$, the analogue of the ordinary spin singlet eigenspinor, $\chi^s$ of (2.22). The $T = 1$ eigenstates, $\xi_{1T_3}$, are corresponding analogues of the triplet eigenspinor, $\chi_M^t$ of (2.23).

‡ C. W. Kim, *Nuclear Physics*, **49**, 383 (1963).

If $\chi_{IM}$, some two-particle angular momentum eigenstate, is used for the space-spin part of the description, then it must be symmetric to interchange of the two nucleons in the isosinglet state, $\xi_{00}\chi_{IM}$, since $\xi_{00}$ provides the required antisymmetry. On the other hand, $\chi_{IM}$ must be chosen to be antisymmetric for the isotriplet of states, $\xi_{1T_3}\chi_{IM}$, as befits the two like nucleons of the $T_3 = \pm 1$ members. With such state descriptions it is easy to reduce the matrix element of the Gamow–Teller operator, $\boldsymbol{\sigma}^1\tau^1_{\pm} + \boldsymbol{\sigma}^2\tau^2_{\pm}$ occurring in the definition (5.20) of the triplet moment, to

$$\langle I'(M')1(m)|I(M)\rangle\langle\sigma\rangle = 2^{-\frac{1}{2}}\chi^{\dagger}_{I'M'}(\sigma^1_m - \sigma^2_m)^{\dagger}\chi_{IM}$$
$$= 2^{+\frac{1}{2}}\chi^{\dagger}_{I'M'}(\sigma^1_m)^{\dagger}\chi_{IM}, \qquad (5.85)$$

within an arbitrary overall sign. This result holds for both $T = 0 \to T = 1$ and $T = 1 \to T = 0$ transitions, and for either $e^-$ or $e^+$ emission ($\Delta T_3 = \pm 1$). It is necessary to remember that each angular momentum eigenstate must be appropriately symmetrized or antisymmetrized, depending on which belongs to the unlike, which to the like, nucleons.

When the angular momenta in the two-nucleon states are $I = 1$ or $I = 0$, they may arise entirely from nucleonic spins and the triplet and singlet eigenspinors, $\chi^t_M$ and $\chi^s$, may be used for the $\chi_{IM}$. This neglect of possible contributions from orbital momenta is at least consistent with the fact that the Gamow–Teller operator does not affect any orbital momenta which persist unchanged. The evaluation of (5.85) with the simple eigenspinors directly yields $\langle\sigma\rangle^2 = 6$ for the $I \equiv S = 0 \to 1$ transitions and $\langle\sigma\rangle^2 = 2$ for the $1 \to 0$ cases. The latter value, $\langle\sigma\rangle^2 = 2$ like the result $\langle 1\rangle^2 = 2$ in the $0 \to 0$ decays, may be understood as arising from the fact that the transforming nucleon may become either one of two final like nucleons. There is an extra factor 3 for the $0 \to 1$ cases because a final $I = 1$ state may be produced in any of three orientations.

The results listed as $(ft)_{LS}$ in Table 5.4 are based on the appropriate uses of $\langle\sigma\rangle^2 = 2$ and $\langle\sigma\rangle^2 = 6$. The case of $He^6$ seems to offer a striking confirmation of the ideas used so far. The $He^6$ decay has the lowest $ft$-value known, and it could not be at all understood without attributing to it the largest theoretically possible moment, $\langle\sigma\rangle^2 = 6$. On the other hand, the $0 \to 1$ transitions to the ground state of $N^{14}$ exhibit moments so small that the considerations introduced so far are not at all adequate for explaining them. It has been found‡ possible to concoct mixed states,

‡ A summary of several attempts can be found in a letter by R. Sherr, J. Gerhart, H. Horie, and W. Hornyak, *Phys. Rev.* **100**, 945 (1955).

formed partly with orbital momenta coupled to the nucleon spins, which yield not only the observed *ft*-values but also fit certain electromagnetic data.

That the role of orbital momenta cannot generally be ignored is also indicated by the existence of such states as the $T = 0$, $I = 3$ ground state of $B^{10}$ (the $C^{10} \rightarrow B^{10}$ transition to it has a 2·5 million year half-life in keeping with expectations for a forbidden transition with $\Delta I = 3$). It would be best, consistent with the treatment accorded the odd-$A$ nuclei, to assign orbitals to each of the two extra-core nucleons as suggested by the level order (5.74). Then the two-nucleon configuration appropriate to $A = 6$ and $A = 10$ is $p_{3/2}^2$; to $A = 14$, $p_{1/2}^2$; to $A = 18$, $s_{1/2}^2$ or $d_{5/2}^2$; to $A = 22$ and 26, $d_{5/2}^2$; to $A = 30$, $s_{1/2}^2$; to $A = 34$ and 38, $d_{3/2}^2$; to $A = 42$ and 46, $f_{7/2}^2$. Each of these configurations can yield $I = 0$ states, including those observed, and states of higher angular momentum as well.

There is next the question of how the individual spins and orbital momenta in each configuration combine to form the total $I$. When spin-orbit coupling is strong, the best descriptions should be provided by the '$jj$-coupled' states:

$$\chi_{IM} = \sum_{\mu} \langle j_1(\mu) j_2(M-\mu) | I(M) \rangle \chi_{\kappa_1 \mu}(\hat{\mathbf{r}}_1) \chi_{\kappa_2, M-\mu}(\hat{\mathbf{r}}_2), \tag{5.86}$$

here written for $\mathbf{j}_1 + \mathbf{j}_2 = \mathbf{I}$. As this expression stands, it is generally neither symmetric nor antisymmetric in the two nucleons unless $j_1 = j_2$ and $l_1 = l_2$ (i.e. $\kappa_1 = \kappa_2$). When $\kappa_1 = \kappa_2$, a permutation of the two nucleons is equivalent to multiplication by $(-)^{I-1}$, according to (2.14). This corresponds to the well-known fact that two equivalent nucleons can form antisymmetric states of only *even* total angular momentum, $I$. The isosinglet ($T = 0$) states (neutron-proton pairs antisymmetric in isospin) can have only the odd $I$ values, hence the $I = 1$ and $I = 3$ observed for the middle isobars of the $A = 4n+2$ nuclei.

Eigenstates of $I$ alternative to (5.86) can also be constructed; thus '$LS$ coupling' results in singlet and triplet states, each with a specific $L = |\mathbf{l}_1 + \mathbf{l}_2|$:

$$\chi_{IM} = \sum_{\mu} \langle L(M-\mu) S(\mu) | I(M) \rangle \chi_{\mu}^{s,t} \times$$
$$\times \sum_{m} \langle l_1(m) l_2(M-\mu-m) | L(M-\mu) \rangle Y_{l_1 m}(\hat{\mathbf{r}}_1) Y_{l_2, M-\mu-m}(\hat{\mathbf{r}}_2). \tag{5.87}$$

The interchange of the nucleons in this merely introduces the factor $(-1)^{L+S+1}$ when $l_1 = l_2$. The parities of both the states (5.86), (5.87) are $\pi = (-)^{l_1+l_2}$, hence they are even states for equivalent ($l_1 = l_2$) nucleons.

It is states (5.87) with $L = 0$ which yielded the results $\langle\sigma\rangle^2 = 2$ or 6, above ('$^3S_1 \leftrightarrow {}^1S_0$' transitions); the states (5.86) yield identical results for $l_1 = l_2 = 0$.

The general evidence about nuclei indicates that although the $LS$-coupling may better describe the nuclear states for $A \leqslant 8$, the $jj$-coupling has yielded more consistent descriptions for heavier nuclei (accounting especially well for the exceptional stability attending the filling of the shells of (5.74) at the 'magic numbers' $N$ or $Z = 50$, 82, and 126, at which the 'next' nucleon has its spin flipped relative to its orbital momentum). It is, therefore, appropriate to give attention to moments yielded by (5.85) when the $jj$-coupled states (5.86) are used.

In cases of initial and final states which can be characterized by two equivalent ($\kappa_1 = \kappa_2$) nucleons, the moment $\langle\sigma\rangle$ vanishes unless these $\kappa$-values are also the same initially and finally. It is then easy to find that (5.85) yields $I = 0 \to I' = 1$ transitions with

$$\langle\sigma\rangle^2 = 2(j+1)/j \quad \text{and} \quad \langle\sigma\rangle^2 = 2j/(j+1) \tag{5.88}$$

for $j = l+\frac{1}{2}$ and $j = l-\frac{1}{2}$, respectively; this could have been anticipated from the single-nucleon results (5.73), after allowance for the factor 2 arising from the circumstance that now either of two nucleons can make the transition. For $1 \to 0$ transitions, the results (5.88) should be multiplied by $\frac{1}{3}$ because there are no longer three possible final orientations for the nuclear spin. The $jj$-coupling moments thus obtained were used to calculate the column of $(ft)_{jj}$-values in Table 5.4. It can be seen that this type of evaluation accords better with the $C^{10} \to B^{10*}$ datum ($A > 8$) than does the $LS$-coupling result, but gives a moment which is much too small for $He^6$ ($A < 8$).

States of at least two nucleons are needed to represent the integer angular momenta of all the even-$A$ nuclei. Restriction to just two may seem the way to define the even-$A$ states which is the natural generalization of the one-particle descriptions used to normalize expectations for odd-$A$ nuclei. Thus, for the important $1 \to 0$ decays ${}_5B_7^{12} \to {}_6C_6^{12} \leftarrow {}_7N_5^{12}$, the odd $p_{\frac{1}{2}}$ nucleon in each parent may be taken to be the only transforming one, and an inert $p_{\frac{3}{2}}$ nucleon of the opposite kind is coupled to it to get $I = 1$. This results in $\langle\sigma\rangle = \frac{2}{3}$ and $(ft)_{\text{theo}} \approx 10^4$ as against $(ft)_{\text{exp}} \approx 10^{4\cdot 1}$ and $10^{4\cdot 2}$, respectively. However, proper $T = 1 \to T = 0$ isospin symmetrizations require constructing at least a four-particle description for each state, and this leads to $\langle\sigma\rangle = \frac{4}{3}$ and a four times smaller expectation for $ft$.

The frequent necessity of considering more than two particles in

TABLE 5.5

*Allowed transitions among even-A nuclei*

| *Parent* | *Daughter* | *Odd proton* | *Odd neutron* | $I \to I'$ | $\log_{10}(ft)_{\text{expt}}$ |
|---|---|---|---|---|---|
| ${}_{5}\mathrm{B}^{12}_{7}$ | ${}_{6}\mathrm{C}^{12}_{6}$ | $p_{3/2}$ | $p_{1/2}$ | $1 \to 0$ | 4·1 |
| ${}_{7}\mathrm{N}^{12}_{5}$ | ${}_{6}\mathrm{C}^{12}_{6}$ | $p_{1/2}$ | $p_{3/2}$ | $1 \to 0$ | 4·2 |
| ${}_{7}\mathrm{N}^{16}_{9}$ | ${}_{8}\mathrm{O}^{16*}_{8}$ | $p_{1/2}$ | $d_{5/2}$ | $2 \to 3$ | 4·5 |
| ${}_{9}\mathrm{F}^{20}_{11}$ | ${}_{10}\mathrm{Ne}^{20*}_{10}$ | $d_{5/2}$ | $d_{5/2}$ | $1 \to 2$ | 5·0 |
| ${}_{10}\mathrm{Ne}^{24}_{14}$ | ${}_{11}\mathrm{Na}^{24*}_{13}$ | $d_{5/2}$ | $d_{5/2}$ | $0 \to 1$ | 4·4 |
| ${}_{11}\mathrm{Na}^{24}_{13}$ | ${}_{12}\mathrm{Mg}^{24***}_{12}$ | $d_{5/2}$ | $d_{5/2}$ | $4 \to 4$ | 6·1 |
| ${}_{13}\mathrm{Al}^{28}_{15}$ | ${}_{14}\mathrm{Si}^{28*}_{14}$ | $d_{5/2}$ | $s_{1/2}$ | $3 \to 2$ | 4·9 |
| ${}_{15}\mathrm{P}^{28}_{13}$ | ${}_{14}\mathrm{Si}^{28*}_{14}$ | $s_{1/2}$ | $d_{5/2}$ | $3 \to 2$ | 4·7 |
| ${}_{15}\mathrm{P}^{30}_{15}$ | ${}_{14}\mathrm{Si}^{30}_{16}$ | $s_{1/2}$ | $s_{1/2}$ | $1 \to 0$ | 5·2 |
| ${}_{15}\mathrm{P}^{30}_{15}$ | ${}_{14}\mathrm{Si}^{30*}_{16}$ | $s_{1/2}$ | $s_{1/2}$ | $1 \to 2$ | 5·4 |
| ${}_{15}\mathrm{P}^{32}_{17}$ | ${}_{16}\mathrm{S}^{32}_{16}$ | $s_{1/2}$ | $d_{3/2}$ | $1 \to 0$ | 7·9 |
| ${}_{15}\mathrm{P}^{34}_{19}$ | ${}_{16}\mathrm{S}^{34}_{18}$ | $s_{1/2}$ | $d_{3/2}$ | $1 \to 0$ | 5·2 |
| ${}_{15}\mathrm{P}^{34}_{19}$ | ${}_{16}\mathrm{S}^{34*}_{18}$ | $s_{1/2}$ | $d_{3/2}$ | $1 \to 2$ | 4·5 |
| ${}_{17}\mathrm{Cl}^{34*}_{17}$ | ${}_{16}\mathrm{S}^{34*}_{18}$ | $d_{3/2}$ | $d_{3/2}$ | $3 \to 2$ | 5·8 |
| ${}_{19}\mathrm{K}^{38*}_{19}$ | ${}_{18}\mathrm{A}^{38*}_{20}$ | $d_{3/2}$ | $d_{3/2}$ | $3 \to 2$ | 5·0 |
| ${}_{21}\mathrm{Sc}^{44}_{23}$ | ${}_{20}\mathrm{Ca}^{44*}_{24}$ | $f_{7/2}$ | $f_{7/2}$ | $3 \to 2$ | 5·3 |
| ${}_{21}\mathrm{Sc}^{48}_{27}$ | ${}_{22}\mathrm{Ti}^{48*****}_{26}$ | $f_{7/2}$ | $f_{7/2}$ | $6 \to 6$ | 5·5 |
| ${}_{25}\mathrm{Mn}^{52}_{27}$ | ${}_{24}\mathrm{Cr}^{52******}_{28}$ | $f_{7/2}$ | $f_{7/2}$ | $6 \to 6$ | 5·5 |
| ${}_{25}\mathrm{Mn}^{52*}_{27}$ | ${}_{24}\mathrm{Cr}^{52*}_{28}$ | $f_{7/2}$ | $f_{7/2}$ | $2 \to 2$ | 5·4 |
| ${}_{25}\mathrm{Mn}^{56}_{31}$ | ${}_{26}\mathrm{Fe}^{56*}_{30}$ | $f_{7/2}$ | $p_{3/2}$ or $f_{5/2}$ | $3 \to 2$ | 7·2 |
| ${}_{27}\mathrm{Co}^{56}_{29}$ | ${}_{26}\mathrm{Fe}^{56**}_{30}$ | $f_{7/2}$ | $p_{3/2}$ or $f_{5/2}$ | $4 \to 4$ | 8·7 |
| ${}_{27}\mathrm{Co}^{58}_{31}$ | ${}_{26}\mathrm{Fe}^{58*}_{32}$ | $f_{7/2}$ | $p_{3/2}$ or $f_{5/2}$ | $2 \to 2$ | 6·6 |
| ${}_{27}\mathrm{Co}^{60}_{33}$ | ${}_{28}\mathrm{Ni}^{60****}_{32}$ | $f_{7/2}$ | $p_{3/2}$ or $f_{5/2}$ | $5 \to 4$ | 7·5 |
| ${}_{27}\mathrm{Co}^{60*}_{33}$ | ${}_{28}\mathrm{Ni}^{60*}_{32}$ | $f_{7/2}$ | $p_{3/2}$ or $f_{5/2}$ | $2 \to 2$ | 7·3 |
| ${}_{29}\mathrm{Cu}^{64}_{35}$ | ${}_{28}\mathrm{Ni}^{64}_{36}$ | $p_{3/2}$ | $f_{5/2}$ | $1 \to 0$ | 5·0 |
| ${}_{29}\mathrm{Cu}^{64}_{35}$ | ${}_{30}\mathrm{Zn}^{64}_{34}$ | $p_{3/2}$ | $f_{5/2}$ | $1 \to 0$ | 5·3 |
| ${}_{29}\mathrm{Cu}^{66}_{37}$ | ${}_{30}\mathrm{Zn}_{36}$ | $p_{3/2}$ | $f_{5/2}$ | $1 \to 0$ | 5·3 |
| ${}_{31}\mathrm{Ga}^{68}_{37}$ | ${}_{30}\mathrm{Zn}_{38}$ | $p_{3/2}$ | $f_{5/2}$ | $1 \to 0$ | 5·2 |
| ${}_{31}\mathrm{Ga}^{70}_{39}$ | ${}_{32}\mathrm{Ge}_{38}$ | $p_{3/2}$ | $p_{1/2}$ | $1 \to 0$ | 5·1 |
| ${}_{35}\mathrm{Br}^{80}_{45}$ | ${}_{34}\mathrm{Se}_{46}$ | $p_{3/2}$ | $p_{1/2}$ | $1 \to 0$ | 4·6 |
| ${}_{35}\mathrm{Br}^{80}_{45}$ | ${}_{36}\mathrm{Kr}^{80}_{44}$ | $p_{3/2}$ | $p_{1/2}$ | $1 \to 0$ | 5·5 |
| ${}_{35}\mathrm{Br}^{82}_{47}$ | ${}_{36}\mathrm{Kr}^{82*****}_{46}$ | $p_{3/2}$ | $g_{9/2}$ | $5 \to 4$ | 5·1 |
| ${}_{37}\mathrm{Rb}^{82}_{45}$ | ${}_{36}\mathrm{Kr}^{82}_{46}$ | $f_{5/2}$ | $g_{9/2}$ | $1 \to 0$ | 4·4 |
| ${}_{37}\mathrm{Rb}^{88}_{51}$ | ${}_{38}\mathrm{Sr}^{88**}_{50}$ | $p_{3/2}$ or $f_{5/2}$ | $d_{5/2}$ | $2 \to 3$ | 6·7 |
| ${}_{39}\mathrm{Y}^{88}_{49}$ | ${}_{38}\mathrm{Sr}^{88**}_{50}$ | $p_{1/2}$ | $g_{9/2}$ | $4 \to 3$ | 6·6 |
| ${}_{45}\mathrm{Rh}^{104}_{59}$ | ${}_{46}\mathrm{Pd}^{104}_{58}$ | $g_{9/2}$ | $g_{7/2}$ | $1 \to 0$ | 4·5 |
| ${}_{44}\mathrm{Ru}^{106}_{62}$ | ${}_{45}\mathrm{Rh}^{106}_{61}$ | $g_{9/2}$ | $g_{7/2}$ | $0 \to 1$ | 4·3 |
| ${}_{47}\mathrm{Ag}^{108}_{61}$ | ${}_{48}\mathrm{Cd}^{108}_{60}$ | $g_{9/2}$ | $g_{7/2}$ | $1 \to 0$ | 4·4 |
| ${}_{49}\mathrm{In}^{112}_{63}$ | ${}_{48}\mathrm{Cd}^{112}_{64}$ | $g_{9/2}$ | $g_{7/2}$ | $1 \to 0$ | 4·6 |
| ,, | ${}_{50}\mathrm{Sn}^{112}_{62}$ | $g_{9/2}$ | $g_{7/2}$ | $1 \to 0$ | 4·1 |
| ${}_{49}\mathrm{In}^{114}_{65}$ | ${}_{48}\mathrm{Cd}^{114}_{66}$ | $g_{9/2}$ | $g_{7/2}$ | $1 \to 0$ | 4·7 |
| ,, | ${}_{50}\mathrm{Sn}^{114}_{64}$ | $g_{9/2}$ | $g_{7/2}$ | $1 \to 0$ | 4·4 |
| ${}_{49}\mathrm{In}^{118}_{69}$ | ${}_{50}\mathrm{Sn}^{118}_{68}$ | $g_{9/2}$ | $g_{7/2}$ | $1 \to 0$ | 4·9 |
| ${}_{55}\mathrm{Cs}^{130}_{75}$ | ${}_{54}\mathrm{Xe}^{130}_{76}$ | | | $1 \to 0$ | 5·1 |
| ,, | ${}_{56}\mathrm{Ba}^{130}_{74}$ | | | $1 \to 0$ | 5·4 |
| ${}_{57}\mathrm{La}^{134}_{77}$ | ${}_{56}\mathrm{Ba}^{134}_{78}$ | | | $1 \to 0$ | 4·9 |
| ${}_{59}\mathrm{Pr}^{140}_{81}$ | ${}_{58}\mathrm{Ce}^{140}_{82}$ | | | $(1) \to 0$ | 4·4 |
| ${}_{73}\mathrm{Ta}^{178}_{105}$ | ${}_{72}\mathrm{Hf}^{178}_{106}$ | | | $1 \to 0$ | (∼ 4·7) |
| ${}_{73}\mathrm{Ta}^{180*}_{107}$ | ${}_{74}\mathrm{W}^{180}_{106}$ | | | $1 \to 0$ | 6·9 |

describing the even-$A$ states makes it more difficult to define a general 'mismatch factor' for them than it was for the odd-$A$ cases. However, just the magnitudes of the $ft$-values in Table 5.5, as compared to those in the favoured decays, are sufficient to show that about the same degree of mismatch occurs among even-$A$ as among the odd-$A$ nuclei.

*'Deformed-core' theories*

In general, the theoretical explanations of the 'mismatches' found in the unfavoured decays must be developed case by special case, as is to be expected for effects arising in systems with enormous numbers of degrees of freedom. However, there is one further quite widely applicable and fairly unified view about the nuclear states, and this can be made to account for the greater part of the observed mismatches. Instead of being treated as completely inert, as above, the 'core' of nucleons may be attributed a few 'collective' degrees of freedom: rotations and vibrations as a whole. Particularly in the hands of Bohr and Mottelson, that general picture was shown capable of accounting for a great variety of nuclear phenomena.

Just one parameter need be introduced for each nuclear state when the core is treated as having a static ellipsoidal deformation. Not only is such a deformed core capable of showing rotational angular momentum, which is coupled to that of the extra-core nucleons to form the total **I**, but it presents a deformed field to the extra-core nucleons. This has the effect of mixing orbital momentum values in a way which has been calculated numerically by Nilsson.‡ The one 'deformation parameter' may be evaluated from electromagnetic data, and almost invariably turns out quite reasonable in view of the configurations of the extra-core nucleons, which are regarded as responsible. Such determinations show that in some cases there is even a change from a prolate to an oblate deformation (e.g. $A^{37} \rightarrow Cl^{37}$), or vice versa, during a $\beta$-transition. The resultant misfits of the cores account quite well§ for the factors by which the transitions are unfavoured. Quite large deformations also seem to exist in many favoured transitions, but then the deformations are the same in both the initial and final states.

*The Fermi coupling strength, g*

The most concerted effort to obtain an accurate theoretical evaluation of a $\beta$-moment has been made for the case of $O^{14}$, which has been regarded as providing the most accurate measure of the Vector coupling

‡ S. G. Nilsson, *K. danske vidensk. Selskab. Skr.* **29,** No. 16 (1955).

§ See the reference on p. 158 for a recent summary.

strength. The $0 \to 0$ transition can be trusted to generate only singlet emissions and it is difficult to find (reference, p. 146) effects which could change the expectation $\langle 1 \rangle^2 = 2$ by more than a fraction of 1 per cent. Moreover, an unusually low uncertainty is reported‡ for the measured *ft*-value, $(3060 \pm 10)$ sec. Late evaluations§ give

$$g_\mathrm{V} \equiv gC_\mathrm{V} = (1{\cdot}403 \pm 0{\cdot}002)10^{-49}\ \text{erg-cm}^3. \tag{5.89}$$

This result incorporates a series of small corrections || the largest of which (of order 2 per cent) arise from electromagnetic effects, including bremsstrahlung by the emerging positrons. Typical of the corrections (of order $\frac{1}{3}$ per cent) to $\langle 1 \rangle^2 = 2$ is one due to the different coulomb repulsions in the initial and final nuclear states.

Despite the probability that the determination (5.89) is correct, an eventual accurate evaluation from neutron decay data alone seems desirable, since it would avoid reliance on the understanding of systems as complex as $O^{14}$ and its daughter $N^{14}$. (Actually, the neutron is itself quite complex, except in so far as the representation of that complexity by constant $C_\mathrm{V}$, $C_\mathrm{A}$ can be trusted.) The neutron data presently available, $(ft)_\mathrm{n} = (1180 \pm 35)$ sec, and the anisotropy measurement yielding (1.63), lead to $g_\mathrm{V} = (1{\cdot}37 \pm 0{\cdot}05)\ 10^{-49}$ erg-cm³.

It was seen that $(ft)_\mathrm{n}$ and $(ft)_{\mathrm{O}^{14}}$, in conjunction, led to (1.26), which corresponds to

$$C_\mathrm{A}/C_\mathrm{V} = -1{\cdot}19 \pm 0{\cdot}03 \tag{5.90}$$

for the GT-to-Fermi ratio. This, multiplying $g_\mathrm{V}$ of (5.89), gives a value for the Pseudovector coupling constant $g_\mathrm{A} \equiv gC_\mathrm{A}$.

‡ D. Hendrie and S. Gerhart, *Phys. Rev.* **121**, 846 (1961); this paper contains references to equally important earlier work.

§ R. K. Bardin, C. A. Barnes, W. A. Fowler, and P. A. Seeger, *Phys. Rev.* **127**, 583 (1962).

|| Listed by L. Durand, L. F. Landovitz, and R. B. Marr, *Phys. Rev. Letters*, **4**, 620 (1960), and revised in the preceding reference.

# VI

# EMISSIONS OF ARBITRARY ANGULAR MOMENTUM

FOR the theory of allowed $\beta$-decay, in the preceding chapter, there was not only the well-justified restriction to first-order processes (as discussed in § 4.3), but additional approximations were introduced. In this chapter, results will be derived which are, in principle at least, exact evaluations of first-order emissions. These will not merely furnish small corrections to the transitions obeying the allowed selection rules, but will provide a basis for a theory of forbidden $\beta$-decay.

Two effects were neglected in the 'allowed approximation': the possibility that the leptons can carry off orbital momentum, and that the nuclear parity can be changed by the transforming nucleon's recoil.

The orbital momenta were automatically excluded when the lepton current was evaluated at the nuclear centre (5.2). The ejection of orbital momentum requires a finite 'lever arm', $\mathbf{r} \neq 0$. This may be attained when the lepton current is properly evaluated, at the actual positions of the transforming nucleon, which may be anywhere within the nuclear radius, $R$.

Parity changes were also excluded in the 'allowed approximations' when the nuclear matrix elements $\int \gamma_5$ and $\int \boldsymbol{\alpha} = -\int \gamma_5 \boldsymbol{\sigma}$ were neglected relative to $\int 1$ and $\int \boldsymbol{\sigma}$, in going from (5.2) to (5.4). That this amounts to neglecting the nucleon recoil was shown by the example of neutron decay (§ 4.4). The retaining of all the matrix elements will admit nuclear parity changes even without orbital momentum ejections, since $\gamma_5$ changes sign in space inversions (2.89).

Any desired degree of accuracy can in principle be attained by a procedure which parallels the multipole expansions of electromagnetic theory. The generalization from electric dipole to electric multipole radiations corresponds to allowing for orbital momentum ejections. The inclusion of magnetic multipoles allows for radiations of parity opposite to that of the corresponding electric multipoles.

The analogies with the electromagnetic case make it convenient to treat the process of $\beta$-radiation as a generation of 'Dirac field', in the sense that electromagnetic radiation constitutes a 'Maxwell field', The new point of view does not involve new approximations; it will be seen to yield exactly the same results as does a more straightforward development of the approach introduced in Chapter IV. Thus, we make a fresh start,‡ avoiding the 'allowed approximation' of Chapter V this time.

## 6.1. The generation of electron field

It is sufficient to concentrate on the generation of the electrons; the behaviour of the other particles which participate in the $\beta$-emissions will then emerge automatically.

*The source amplitude*

In the presence of a decaying nucleus, the field of electrons undergoes changes which are not properly treated unless their $\beta$-coupling is included in the Dirac equation (2.72) which governs those changes. The appropriately modified equation may be written (with $m = c = \hbar = 1$):

$$i\partial\psi/\partial t = [-i\boldsymbol{\alpha}.\boldsymbol{\nabla}+\beta+V(r)]\psi+h'(\mathbf{r},t). \tag{6.1}$$

The static potential, e.g. $V(r) = -\alpha Z/r$, redistributes the field, but has no overall generative or absorptive effects (it does not disturb the particle conservation relation (2.76)). Generation of the field may be represented as arising from a suitably chosen 'source amplitude', $h'(\mathbf{r},t)$, an 'inhomogeneity' like the source terms in the Maxwell equations.

To describe a source which generates negatrons by way of the $\beta$-coupling (4.10) to the neutrino and nucleon fields, $h'$ should be given the spinor amplitude form§

$$h' = 8^{\frac{1}{2}}g(\phi_{\mathrm{p}}^{\dagger}\,\beta\gamma_{\alpha}\,\phi_{\mathrm{n}}).\beta\gamma_{\alpha}\,\phi_{\nu}. \tag{6.2}$$

That can be checked by evaluating the energy density involved in (6.1):

$$\psi^{\dagger}(i\partial/\partial t)\psi = \psi^{\dagger}(\boldsymbol{\alpha}.\mathbf{p}+\beta+V)\psi+8^{\frac{1}{2}}g(\phi_{\mathrm{p}}^{\dagger}\,\beta\gamma_{\alpha}\,\phi_{\mathrm{n}})(\psi^{\dagger}\beta\gamma_{\alpha}\,\phi_{\nu}). \tag{6.3}$$

This consists of a pure electron field energy density (see the remark leading to (4.2)) plus the part of the $\beta$-interaction energy density, $h_{\beta}$ of (4.10), which can exchange energy with a specifically negatronic (positive-frequency) field. It is the hermitian conjugate of (6.1) that contains the proton-to-neutron transformation current which generates positrons.

A properly exhaustive (and unmanageable!) treatment would require the simultaneous solution of the electron field equation (6.1)

‡ The reader may prefer to omit this. He may do so by starting with the equation (6.36) of this chapter, referring back only to (6.31) and (6.32) for definitions.

§ This can be derived formally by showing that equation (6.1) is just a canonical equation in the conjugate field variables $\psi$ and $i\psi^*$; the type of formalism needed can be found in textbooks on quantum mechanics (e.g. Schiff, reference on p. 13). The hamiltonian energy function of $\psi$ and $i\psi^*$, needed for the derivation, is just the sum of $h_{\beta} = \psi^{\dagger}h'+\text{h.c.}$, and the pure electron field energy density occurring in (6.3). Notice that $\phi = \frac{1}{2}(1+\gamma_5)\psi = \frac{1}{2}(1+\gamma_5)\phi$, so that $\psi^{\dagger}\beta\gamma_{\alpha}\,\phi \equiv \phi^{\dagger}\beta\gamma_{\alpha}\,\phi$.

and of corresponding equations for the neutrino and nucleon fields as well (indeed, also the equations of any other fields with which these fields interact). The electron, neutrino, and nucleon field equations all contain $\beta$-coupling terms analogous to $h'$. However, the $\beta$-coupling is so weak that almost any sort of extraneous fields (except possibly gravitational ones!) are more important in determining the individual states, at any given moment, as they enter into the evaluation of the negatron source amplitude $h'$. That is especially true for the transforming nucleon, which interacts strongly with its neighbouring nucleons in the nucleus, and with the pion field. Those effects are taken into account, with sufficient accuracy for evaluating the small perturbation $h'$, by using conventional nuclear state descriptions $|\mathrm{i}\rangle$ and $|\mathrm{f}\rangle$, and the 'renormalization constants' $C_{\mathrm{V,A}}$. Thus, $h'$ of (6.2) is evaluated as

$$h'(\mathbf{r},t) = 8^{\frac{1}{2}}g\beta\gamma_{\alpha}\phi_{\nu}^{C}\Big\langle \mathrm{f}\Big|\sum_{a}\delta(\mathbf{r}-\mathbf{r}^{a})\tfrac{1}{2}(C_{\mathrm{V}}-C_{\mathrm{A}}\gamma_{5}^{a})\beta^{a}\gamma_{\alpha}^{a}\tau_{+}^{a}\Big|\mathrm{i}\Big\rangle, \tag{6.4}$$

in consistency with the interaction hamiltonian (4.67). The insertion of the $\delta$-functions is needed for evaluating the transforming nucleon's amplitude at the same position $\mathbf{r}$ as that of the antineutrino and the electron. The antineutrino state $\phi_{\nu}^{C}$ can be justifiably evaluated as in free space. The electron itself interacts appreciably with the electromagnetic field, as taken into account by inserting the potential $V$ into the electron field equation (6.1).

The discussion makes clear that the states $\phi_{\nu}$, $|\mathrm{i}\rangle$ and $|\mathrm{f}\rangle$ used in constructing the source amplitude $h'$ may as well be treated as *given*, and the specific choice made will correspond to a specific case of $\beta$-decay. (Disregarding the perturbation by the $\beta$-coupling, of the given states, corresponds to neglecting second-order processes, as discussed in § 4.3.) The given $h'$ will be shown to lead to an outgoing wave solution of (6.1), which has an outward radial current density, $\psi^{\dagger}\alpha_{r}\psi$ (2.77). It will be convenient to work with states $|\mathrm{i}\rangle$ and $|\mathrm{f}\rangle$ describing the transition of a single nucleus, and to choose such a normalization that

$$\int_{-\infty}^{\infty} dt \oint d\Omega r^{2}(\psi^{\dagger}\alpha_{r}\psi)_{r=\infty} = 1, \tag{6.5}$$

i.e. describing the outflow of a single electron at infinity, during the entire time of the decay.

*Analysis in energy*

If the nuclear energy eigenstates, $|\mathrm{i}\rangle$ and $|\mathrm{f}\rangle$, differ by the energy release $W_0$, then the factor $\langle\mathrm{f}|\ldots|\mathrm{i}\rangle$ of $h'$ (6.4) is proportional to $\exp(-iW_0 t)$.

If, further, we ask for the generation of a negatron in the company of an antineutrino with the definite energy $q$, then $\phi_\nu^C \sim \exp(+iqt)$ and the source amplitude becomes proportional to $h' \sim \exp\{-i(W_0-q)t\}$. This stationary time dependence would lead to an infinite generation of electrons, over the infinite time span allowed it in (6.5), as the development below will confirm (6.10). A source so constructed is incompatible with the overall normalization (6.5).

The choice of stationary, energy-conserving, isolated states in $h'$ can be completely accurate only if they are unaffected by the $\beta$-coupling even over an infinite time span. The weakness of the $\beta$-coupling actually justifies such choices, as approximations, only at any given moment (the states having ample time for spatial and internal readjustments over time intervals which are small compared to the $\beta$-decay time). Over times long compared to the decay time, there is necessary an effective renormalization of the source, and that can be taken into account by a choice of the form

$$h'(\mathbf{r}, t<0) = 0, \qquad h'(\mathbf{r}, t>0) = h'(\mathbf{r}, 0)e^{-i(W_0-q)t-\lambda t/2}, \tag{6.6}$$

with $\lambda$ to be determined by (6.5), after the coupling to the electron field, via (6.1), is taken into account. This describes a source *intensity* decaying as $\exp(-\lambda t)$, hence the parameter $\lambda$ has the interpretation of the decay constant. The choice (6.6) can be regarded as a trial solution‡ in which a parameter is to be adjusted to the demands of the field equations (6.1)

Next, the time dependences will be fourier-analysed. As in the example of (4.25),

$$h'(\mathbf{r}, t) = \int_{-\infty}^{\infty} d\omega h'_\omega(\mathbf{r})e^{-i\omega t}, \tag{6.7 a}$$

if

$$h'_\omega(\mathbf{r}) = \int_{-\infty}^{\infty} (dt/2\pi)h'(\mathbf{r}, t)e^{+i\omega t}$$

$$= h'(\mathbf{r}, 0)/2\pi i(W_0-q-\omega-i\lambda/2). \tag{6.7 b}$$

The last line follows from the time integration of (6.6). For the similar analysis of the electron field,

$$\psi(\mathbf{r}, t) = \int_{-\infty}^{\infty} dW\psi_W(\mathbf{r})e^{-iWt}/2\pi i[W_0-q-W-i\lambda/2], \tag{6.8}$$

‡ A more arbitrary spectrum of energies could be allowed for instead, and a derivation closely paralleling that of (4.34) evolved. The choice (6.6) amounts to forming a 'wave packet' of limited effective duration, providing for a spectrum of possible neutrino energies with $\Delta q \gtrsim \hbar/c\Delta t$, $\Delta t < 1/\lambda$.

the fourier coefficients are given such a form that

$$(W+i\boldsymbol{\alpha}.\boldsymbol{\nabla}-\beta-V)\psi_W(\mathbf{r}) = h'(\mathbf{r},0) \tag{6.9}$$

follows from (6.1), as the equation for $\psi_W(\mathbf{r})$.

For a field of the form (6.8), the condition (6.5) becomes

$$1 = \int_{-\infty}^{\infty} dt \oint d\Omega r^2 \int\int_{-\infty}^{\infty} \frac{dW\,dW'(\psi_W^\dagger\,\alpha_r\,\psi_{W'})_\infty\,e^{i(W-W')t}}{4\pi^2(W_0-W-q+i\lambda/2)(W_0-W'-q-i\lambda/2)}$$

$$= \oint d\Omega r^2 \int_{-\infty}^{\infty} (dW/2\pi)(\psi_W^\dagger\,\alpha_r\,\psi_W)_\infty/[(W_0-W-q)^2+\tfrac{1}{4}\lambda^2], \tag{6.10}$$

after use of the $\delta$-function representation (4.27). The energy integration is elementary when it is extended about the pole at $W = W_0-q+i\lambda/2$:

$$1 = \lambda^{-1}\oint d\Omega r^2(\psi^\dagger\alpha_r\,\psi)_{W=W_0-q,r\to\infty}. \tag{6.11}$$

It is being presumed that there are no other singularities of comparable magnitude, at which the energy does not approach conservation.

Multiplied through by $\lambda$, (6.11) gives an expression for the decay constant, and when the integration over the solid angle is left off, it gives $d\lambda/d\Omega$, the average rate of electron emissions into a unit solid angle. If the antineutrino state used for the source $h'$ of (6.4) is now normalized per unit energy, then the rate into the energy interval

$$|dq = d(W_0-W)| = dW$$

is obtained by multiplying the result for $d\lambda/d\Omega$ by $dW$, so that

$$d\lambda/dWd\Omega = r^2(\psi^\dagger\alpha_r\,\psi)_{r\to\infty}. \tag{6.12}$$

It must be understood that the antineutrino state is normalized per unit energy, in the source of $\psi$, and that the evaluation must be 'on the energy shell': $W = W_0-q$.

*The propagation of the electron*‡

The electron wave arising from the source $h'(\mathbf{r},0) \equiv h'(\mathbf{r})$ in (6.9) can be given the form

$$\psi(\mathbf{r}) = \oint G(|\mathbf{r}-\mathbf{r}'|)h'(\mathbf{r}')(d\mathbf{r}'), \tag{6.13}$$

if the so-called 'propagator', $G$, from the source element $(d\mathbf{r}')$ to the field point $\mathbf{r}$, satisfies the 'unit point source' equation

$$(W+i\boldsymbol{\alpha}.\boldsymbol{\nabla}-\beta-V)G = \rho_0\,\delta(\mathbf{r}-\mathbf{r}'). \tag{6.14}$$

‡ The following parallels, to a great extent, the treatment by M. Rose, L. Biedenharn, and G. Arfken, *Phys. Rev.* **85**, 5 (1953). Some of the results were also anticipated by E. Greuling and M. Meeks, *Phys. Rev.* **82**, 531 (1951).

Here, $\rho_0$ is the $4\times 4$ unit matrix; $G$ must be expected to be a square matrix operating on the spinor column $h'$, to yield a spinor wave amplitude.

For the emission rate (6.12), the solution $\psi$ which is an outgoing wave at infinity is needed. A solution which is outgoing everywhere outside the source can be obtained for $V = 0$, when 'potential scattering' is avoided [see the remark leading to (3.55)]. It is easy to show that

$$G^{(0)} = -(W-i\boldsymbol{\alpha}.\boldsymbol{\nabla}+\beta)e^{ip|\mathbf{r}-\mathbf{r}'|}/4\pi|\mathbf{r}-\mathbf{r}'| \qquad (6.15)$$

satisfies (6.14) with $V = 0$, if $p = (W^2-1)^{\frac{1}{2}}$ is the magnitude of the electron momentum. To make use of this result, we temporarily neglect the Coulomb distortion of the wave.

The outward current in the decay rate (6.12) should be evaluated for $r \to \infty$, hence we need

$$G^{(0)}(r \gg r') \approx -(W+\boldsymbol{\alpha}.\mathbf{p}+\beta)e^{i\mathbf{p}.(\mathbf{r}-\mathbf{r}')}/4\pi r, \qquad (6.16)$$

where $\mathbf{p} = p\mathbf{r}/r$ is the electron momentum vector. This is the same, within a factor, as the density matrix of the plane waves (3.4):

$$\sum_{\rho}\psi_\rho(\mathbf{r})\psi_\rho^\dagger(\mathbf{r}') = (W+\boldsymbol{\alpha}.\mathbf{p}+\beta)e^{i\mathbf{p}.(\mathbf{r}-\mathbf{r}')}/2WV, \qquad (6.17)$$

which may be obtained in any of the same ways as the density matrix of the left-handed components (5.33). [Indeed, (5.33) is a simple adaptation of (6.17).] We may now write the asymptotic form of the electron wave (6.13) as

$$\psi(r\to\infty) \approx -(WV/2\pi r)\sum_{\rho}\psi_\rho(\mathbf{r})\oint\psi_\rho^\dagger(\mathbf{r}')h'(\mathbf{r}')(d\mathbf{r}'). \qquad (6.18)$$

The integral here, after substitution for $h'$ from (6.4), becomes just the transition matrix element $\langle \mathrm{f}|H_\beta|\mathrm{i}\rangle$, of the interaction operator (4.67). As it occurs in (6.18), the electron wave (3.4) is normalized to unity in $V$ while the antineutrino wave $\psi_\nu^C$ is supposed to be normalized per unit energy, as stated below (6.12). The latter normalization can also be changed to unity in $V$ if (6.18) is multiplied with $[q^2(d\hat{\mathbf{q}})V/(2\pi)^3]^{\frac{1}{2}}$, according to (3.43) and the discussion attending it.

The outward current $\psi^\dagger\alpha_r\psi$ in the wave (6.18) will be a superposition of plane wave currents $\psi_\rho^\dagger\alpha_r\psi_{\rho'}$. Since the density is $\psi_\rho^\dagger\psi_\rho = 1/V$, and the velocity is $v_r = p/W$, it should not be surprising that the detailed evaluation using $\psi_\rho$ of (3.4) gives

$$\psi_\rho^\dagger\alpha_r\psi_{\rho'} = \psi_\rho^\dagger\boldsymbol{\alpha}.\hat{\mathbf{p}}\psi_{\rho'} = \delta_{\rho\rho'}p/WV. \qquad (6.19)$$

With this, the decay rate (6.12) can be written

$$\frac{d\lambda}{dp} = 2\pi\frac{p^2(d\hat{\mathbf{p}})V}{(2\pi)^3}\frac{q^2(d\hat{\mathbf{q}})V}{(2\pi)^3}\sum_{\rho}|\langle \mathrm{f}|H_\beta|\mathrm{i}\rangle|^2. \qquad (6.20)$$

This is exactly the same result as follows from (4.36), when we ask for the decay rate into the lepton states here specified. It begins to be obvious that the present approach will have the same outcome as an extension of the one used for the allowed transitions. Complete confirmation will be found below, in (6.36).

## 6.2. The radiation of spherical waves

*Analysis of the propagation*

The free-space electron propagator $G^{(0)}$ (6.15) can be expressed exactly as the density matrix of the spherical waves $\psi_{\kappa\mu}$ (3.20), by making use of the well-known theorem

$$\frac{e^{ip|\mathbf{r}-\mathbf{r}'|}}{ip|\mathbf{r}-\mathbf{r}'|} = 4\pi \sum_{lm} h_l(pr)Y_{lm}(\hat{\mathbf{r}})j_l(pr')Y^*_{lm}(\hat{\mathbf{r}}'). \tag{6.21}$$

This relation is readily shown to reduce‡ to the plane wave expansion (3.44), for $r \gg r'$, by employing the asymptotic form (3.25) of the outgoing wave $h_l(pr)$. The spinor spherical harmonics $\chi_{\kappa\mu}(\hat{\mathbf{r}})$, which help form $\psi_{\kappa\mu}$, may be introduced by constructing the $2\times2$ density matrix

$$\sum_{\kappa(l)\mu} \chi_{\kappa\mu}(\hat{\mathbf{r}})\chi^\dagger_{\kappa\mu}(\hat{\mathbf{r}}') = \mathbf{1}\sum_m Y_{lm}(\hat{\mathbf{r}})Y^*_{lm}(\hat{\mathbf{r}}'), \tag{6.22}$$

where $\kappa(l) = l$ and $-l-1$, and $\mathbf{1}$ is the $2\times2$ Pauli unit matrix (2.45). This is a generalization of the spin density matrix (4.49) which follows from the definition (2.18) of $\chi_{\kappa\mu}$, and an application of unitarity conditions on the vector-addition coefficients (2.12). Next, consider each of the $2\times2$ submatrices, $G^{(0)}_{ij}$, which make up

$$G^{(0)} \equiv \begin{pmatrix} G^{(0)}_{11} & G^{(0)}_{12} \\ G^{(0)}_{21} & G^{(0)}_{22} \end{pmatrix} = -\begin{pmatrix} W+1 & -i\boldsymbol{\sigma}.\boldsymbol{\nabla} \\ -i\boldsymbol{\sigma}.\boldsymbol{\nabla} & W-1 \end{pmatrix}\frac{e^{ip|\mathbf{r}-\mathbf{r}'|}}{4\pi|\mathbf{r}-\mathbf{r}'|}. \tag{6.23}$$

With (6.21), (6.22), the diagonal elements become, respectively,

$$-(W\pm1)ip\sum_{\kappa\mu} h_{l(\kappa)}\chi_{\kappa\mu}(\hat{\mathbf{r}}).j_{l(\kappa)}\chi^\dagger_{\kappa\mu}(\hat{\mathbf{r}}'). \tag{6.24}$$

The summation over $\kappa$ here is no longer restricted, as in (6.22). The expressions for $G^{(0)}_{12} = G^{(0)}_{21}$ are the same except that $(W\pm1)$ are replaced by the operation $-i\boldsymbol{\sigma}.\boldsymbol{\nabla}$. The effect of this operation has already been seen in the step from (3.18) to (3.19), (3.21). The result is further identified in (3.26), and leads to the conclusion:

$$G^{(0)}_{12} = G^{(0)}_{21} = p^2\sum_{\kappa\mu} \hat{\kappa} h_{l(-\kappa)}\chi_{-\kappa\mu}(\hat{\mathbf{r}})j_{l(\kappa)}\chi^\dagger_{\kappa\mu}(\hat{\mathbf{r}}'). \tag{6.25}$$

‡ For $p \to 0$, (6.21) reduces to the defining series for the Legendre polynomials,

$$|\mathbf{r}-\mathbf{r}'|^{-1} = \sum_l [(r')^l/r^{l+1}]P_l(\hat{\mathbf{r}}.\hat{\mathbf{r}}'),$$

as can be seen by using (3.27), (3.29), and (3.45).

It is helpful, and valid, to reverse the sign of the dummy index $\kappa$ in the summations forming $G^{(0)}_{12}$ and $G^{(0)}_{22}$. After that is done, it becomes obvious that the matrix for $G^{(0)}$ is identical with

$$G(|\mathbf{r}-\mathbf{r}'|) = -i2^{\frac{1}{2}}\pi \sum_{\kappa\mu} \psi_{\kappa\mu}(\mathbf{r})\psi^{\dagger}_{\kappa\mu}(\mathbf{r}'), \tag{6.26}$$

where both spinors have the form (3.20), but $\psi_{\kappa\mu}(\mathbf{r})$ contains the outgoing radial waves (3.26), while $\psi_{\kappa\mu}(\mathbf{r}')$ has the regular ones (3.35). That applies when $r \geqslant r'$ ('outside the source'). For $r \leqslant r'$, the arguments $\mathbf{r}$ and $\mathbf{r}'$ need only be interchanged and the matrix transposed (for use in (6.13)).

The notation $G(|\mathbf{r}-\mathbf{r}'|)$ is used for the density matrix (6.26) because the propagator in the presence of a static potential $V$, as in (6.14), has the same form. It is only necessary that now the spherical waves be the regular and outgoing (at infinity) solutions of the Dirac equation containing $V$, and normalized in the same way as the $V = 0$ solutions. It is obvious that (6.26) will then obey (6.14) because this is just the Dirac equation in question, except at the singular point $\mathbf{r} = \mathbf{r}'$. Moreover, the behaviour at the singular point is independent of $V$ unless this potential itself has $\delta$-function singularities. Finally, the expression (6.26), with spherical waves of the types described, has the requisite symmetry in $\mathbf{r}$ and $\mathbf{r}'$.

In the case of the point-charge field, $V = -\alpha Z/r$, the regular solutions are those presented in (3.49). The outgoing wave solutions have not been given, but only their asymptotic behaviour is needed for the decay rate (6.12). The discussion of the equations (3.55)–(3.58) made clear that the outgoing coulomb wave can differ, at infinity, from the free one (3.26), only by the phase shift $\delta'(\kappa)$, as given in (3.58). After the phase-shifted asymptotic radial wave (3.25) is inserted into the form (3.20), this becomes

$$\psi_{\kappa\mu}(\infty) \approx \left(\frac{p}{2\pi}\right)^{\frac{1}{2}} \frac{e^{i[pr+\delta(\kappa)]}}{pr} \begin{pmatrix} (W+1)^{\frac{1}{2}}\chi_{\kappa\mu} \\ -(W-1)^{\frac{1}{2}}\chi_{-\kappa\mu} \end{pmatrix} e^{-iWt}. \tag{6.27}$$

Here, $\delta(\kappa)$ is the total phase shift (3.56), inclusive of the phase, $-[l(\kappa)+1]\pi/2$, characteristic of the free wave (3.25). The eigenfunction $\chi_{-\kappa\mu}$ may be eliminated in favour of $\chi_{\kappa\mu}$ by using the relation (3.63), $\boldsymbol{\sigma}\,.\,\hat{\mathbf{r}}\chi_{\kappa\mu}(\hat{\mathbf{r}}) = -\chi_{-\kappa\mu}(\hat{\mathbf{r}})$. Then

$$\psi_{\kappa\mu}(\infty) \approx \left(\frac{W+1}{2\pi p}\right)^{\frac{1}{2}} \frac{e^{i[pr+\delta(\kappa)]}}{r} \begin{pmatrix} 1 \\ \boldsymbol{\sigma}\,.\,\hat{\mathbf{r}}p/(W+1) \end{pmatrix} \chi_{\kappa\mu}(\hat{\mathbf{r}})e^{-iWt}, \tag{6.28}$$

still normalized per unit energy. When this is evaluated for a specific direction, $\hat{\mathbf{r}}$, that is equivalent to preparation for observing electrons with the momentum $\mathbf{p} = \hat{\mathbf{r}}p$. The close relation to the plane waves $\psi_p$ (3.4) then becomes evident. We only need to introduce the defining relation (2.18), for $\chi_{\kappa\mu}$, to get

$$\psi_{\kappa\mu}(\infty) \approx \left(\frac{WV}{\pi p}\right)^{\frac{1}{2}} \frac{e^{i\delta(\kappa)}}{r} \sum_{\rho} \psi_{\rho} Y_{l,\mu-\rho}(\hat{\mathbf{p}}) \langle l(\mu-\rho)\tfrac{1}{2}(\rho)|j(\mu)\rangle. \tag{6.29}$$

This, in contrast to (3.48), is valid only asymptotically; however, it also includes the coulomb phase shift.

*The emissions and their angular distribution*

With the propagator (6.26), the emitted wave (6.13) takes the form

$$\psi(\mathbf{r}) = -2^{\frac{1}{2}} i\pi \sum_{\kappa\mu} \psi_{\kappa\mu}(\mathbf{r}) \langle \mathrm{f}|H_{\beta}(\kappa\mu)|\mathrm{i}\rangle, \tag{6.30}$$

where
$$\langle \mathrm{f}|H_{\beta}(\kappa\mu)|\mathrm{i}\rangle \equiv 8^{\frac{1}{2}} g \left\langle \mathrm{f} \left| \sum_{a} \tfrac{1}{2}(C_{\mathrm{V}} - C_{\mathrm{A}} \gamma_5^a) \beta^a \gamma_\alpha^a \tau_+^a J_\alpha(\kappa\mu) \right| \mathrm{i} \right\rangle \tag{6.31}$$

is a transition matrix element containing the lepton current,

$$J_\alpha(\kappa\mu) = \psi_{\kappa\mu}^{\dagger} \beta \gamma_\alpha \phi_\nu^C \equiv \phi_{\kappa\mu}^{\dagger} \beta \gamma_\alpha \phi_\nu^C, \tag{6.32}$$

with $\phi^C \equiv \frac{1}{2}(1+\gamma_5)\psi^C$ as in (3.15).

For the decay rate (6.12), the outward current in $\psi$ of (6.30) is needed. That will be a superposition of currents $\psi_{\kappa\mu}^{\dagger} \alpha_r \psi_{\kappa'\mu'}$ in the outgoing waves (6.28). The latter are easily evaluated with

$$\alpha_r \equiv \begin{pmatrix} 0 & \boldsymbol{\sigma}\,.\,\hat{\mathbf{r}} \\ \boldsymbol{\sigma}\,.\,\hat{\mathbf{r}} & 0 \end{pmatrix}, \tag{6.33}$$

the result being

$$\psi_{\kappa\mu}^{\dagger} \alpha_r \psi_{\kappa'\mu'} = e^{i[\delta(\kappa') - \delta(\kappa)]} \chi_{\kappa\mu}^{\dagger} \chi_{\kappa'\mu'} / \pi r^2. \tag{6.34}$$

This is a function of the emission direction $\hat{\mathbf{r}} \equiv \hat{\mathbf{p}}$.

When the currents (6.34) are properly superposed in the decay rate (6.12), they give it the form:

$$d\lambda/dW d\Omega = 2\pi \left| \sum_{\kappa\mu} e^{i\delta(\kappa)} \chi_{\kappa\mu}(\hat{\mathbf{p}}) \langle \mathrm{f}|H_{\beta}(\kappa\mu)|\mathrm{i}\rangle \right|^2. \tag{6.35}$$

This may be made the starting-point for evaluating expectations for observations in a great variety of circumstances.

The same result (6.35) can also be obtained using the approach introduced in Chapter IV, starting with the decay formula (4.36). When the latter has the waves of both leptons normalized per unit energy, as in the transition matrix of (6.35), then it gives a partial decay rate

$$d\lambda/dW = 2\pi |\langle \mathrm{f}|H_{\beta}|\mathrm{i}\rangle|^2. \tag{6.36 a}$$

For comparison with (6.35), this must be summed over all the electron waves headed into $d\Omega \equiv (d\hat{\mathbf{p}}) \equiv (d\hat{\mathbf{r}})$, and over their spins. The 'distorted plane waves' $\Psi_\rho^{\cdot}$ of (3.60) must be used, and when these are substituted into (6.36 a), the result will be

$$\frac{d\lambda}{dW} = d\Omega\,.\,2\pi \sum_\rho \Big| \sum_{\kappa\mu} i^{-l} e^{i\delta''} \langle l(\mu-\rho)\tfrac{1}{2}(\rho)|j(\mu)\rangle Y_{l\,\mu-\rho}(\hat{\mathbf{p}}) \langle \mathrm{f}|H_\beta(\kappa\mu)|\mathrm{i}\rangle \Big|^2. \tag{6.36 b}$$

That this is the same as (6.35) can be seen from the definition (2.18) of the angular momentum eigenfunctions $\chi_{\kappa\mu}$, which gives:

$$\chi^\dagger_{\kappa\mu}\chi_{\kappa'\mu'} = \sum_\rho Y^*_{l\mu-\rho} Y_{l'\mu'-\rho} \langle l(\mu-\rho)\tfrac{1}{2}(\rho)|j(\mu)\rangle \langle l'(\mu'-\rho)\tfrac{1}{2}(\rho)|j'(\mu')\rangle. \tag{6.37}$$

Further $$\exp i[\delta(\kappa')-\delta(\kappa)] \equiv i^{l-l'} \exp\{i[\delta''(\kappa')-\delta''(\kappa)]\}$$

according to the definitions of these phases in (3.56) and (3.59). The form (6.36 b) offers a better starting-point than (6.35) for finding the expectations for polarized electrons; the summation over spin orientations, $\rho$, must merely be omitted. The factors $\chi_{\kappa\mu}(\hat{\mathbf{p}})$ in (6.34) give the electron emissions an angular distribution which is made more explicit in (6.37). The latter may still be expanded into spherical harmonics by making use of (5.12). The result amounts to a generalization of (5.12) to

$$\chi^\dagger_{\kappa\mu}\chi_{\kappa'\mu'} = {\sum_\Lambda}' (-)^{\mu+\frac{1}{2}} \rho_\Lambda(jj') \langle j(\mu)j'(-\mu')|\Lambda(\mu-\mu')\rangle Y_{\Lambda\mu'-\mu}, \tag{6.38}$$

where $$\rho_\Lambda(jj') = \left[\frac{(2j+1)(2j'+1)}{4\pi(2\Lambda+1)}\right]^{\frac{1}{2}} \langle j(-\tfrac{1}{2})j'(\tfrac{1}{2})|\Lambda(0)\rangle. \tag{6·39}$$

The apostrophe on the summation sign is meant to indicate that only terms with even values of $l(\kappa)+l'(\kappa')+\Lambda$ are to be included in the sum. With this, (6.38) is invariant to the simultaneous sign reversal of both $\kappa$ and $\kappa'$; $\chi^\dagger_{-\kappa\mu}\chi_{-\kappa'\mu'} = \chi^\dagger_{\kappa\mu}\chi_{\kappa'\mu'}$. That this must be so follows from (3.63).

The result (6.35) was derived for negatron emission. The expression for positron emission would have exactly the same formal appearance; use of a phase shift $\delta(\kappa)$ for a negatron in the field of a nucleus with charge $-Ze$, rather than $+Ze$, would be implied. Of course, in positron emission, the nuclear states are such that the operative terms of $H_\beta$ are hermitian conjugates of the ones effective in negatron emission. That the factor $\chi_{\kappa\mu}$ need not be changed is especially easy to see from (6.36) and the fact that the electron field appears as $\psi^\dagger_{\kappa\mu}$ in the negatron current and as $C\psi^*_{\kappa\mu}$ in the positron current.

*The lepton currents at the source*

For use in the form (6.35) of the radiation rate, the lepton currents $J_\alpha$ (6.32) must be classified according to electron eigenfunctions of definite $W$, $\kappa(j)$, and $\mu$. To continue with the angular momentum analysis, the antineutrino states will be classified similarly, according to the eigenvalues $q$, $\bar{\kappa}(\bar{j})$, and $\bar{\mu}$, i.e. $\phi_\nu^C \to \frac{1}{2}(1+\gamma_5)\psi^C_{\bar{\kappa}\bar{\mu}}$. The eigenfunction $\psi^C_{\bar{\kappa}\bar{\mu}}$ must be given the form (3.85), with radial waves of the form (3.35), adapted to neutrinos. As in the preceding chapter, the result (4.35) makes possible treating positron emission concurrently, by replacing projections $\frac{1}{2}(1+\gamma_5)$ with $\frac{1}{2}(1-\gamma_5)$ in the negatron emission current. Then

$$\phi^C_{\bar{\kappa}\bar{\mu}} = \tfrac{1}{2}(1\pm\gamma_5)\psi^C_{\bar{\kappa}\bar{\mu}} = 2^{-\frac{1}{2}}\begin{pmatrix}\bar{\mathbf{u}}_{\bar{\kappa}\bar{\mu}}\\ \mp\bar{\mathbf{u}}_{\bar{\kappa}\bar{\mu}}\end{pmatrix}, \tag{6.40}$$

with the Pauli spinors

$$\begin{aligned}\bar{\mathbf{u}}_{\bar{\kappa}\bar{\mu}} &= q(2\pi)^{-\frac{1}{2}}[i^{-\bar{l}(\bar{\kappa})}j_{\bar{l}(\bar{\kappa})}(qr)\chi_{\bar{\kappa},-\bar{\mu}}\pm i^{-\bar{l}(-\bar{\kappa})}j_{\bar{l}(-\bar{\kappa})}\chi_{-\bar{\kappa},-\bar{\mu}}]\\ &= \pm\bar{\mathbf{u}}_{-\bar{\kappa}\bar{\mu}} \quad \text{in } e^{\mp} \text{ emission currents.}\end{aligned} \tag{6.41}$$

The last properties, obtainable only for zero rest-mass, were acquired through suitable choices of the overall phases with which the eigenfunctions may be defined.

The lepton current components may now be written (compare (5.32))

$$\left.\begin{aligned}\mathbf{J}(\kappa\mu;\bar{\kappa}\bar{\mu}) &= -i\phi^\dagger_{\kappa\mu}\boldsymbol{\alpha}\phi^C_{\bar{\kappa}\bar{\mu}} = \pm i\mathbf{u}^\dagger_{\kappa\mu}\boldsymbol{\sigma}\bar{\mathbf{u}}_{\bar{\kappa}\bar{\mu}}\\ J_4 &= \phi^\dagger_{\kappa\mu}\phi^C_{\bar{\kappa}\bar{\mu}} = \mathbf{u}^\dagger_{\kappa\mu}\bar{\mathbf{u}}_{\bar{\kappa}\bar{\mu}}\end{aligned}\right\} \tag{6.42}$$

if

$$\mathbf{u}_{\kappa\mu} = 2^{-\frac{1}{2}}[g_\kappa(\pm Z)\chi_{\kappa\mu}\mp if_{-\kappa}(\pm Z)\chi_{-\kappa\mu}] \quad \text{for } e^{\mp}. \tag{6.43}$$

The electron radial waves here are given by (3.49) when the nucleus is treated as a point charge, but such effects as arise from the finite spread of charge over the nuclear volume, or from screening by atomic electrons, can be taken into account by modifying $g_\kappa$, $f_{-\kappa}(pr)$ suitably. For this reason, the calculations will be carried through for arbitrary $g_\kappa$, $f_{-\kappa}$ and phase-shift, $\delta(\kappa)$.

Because of the simple transformations of the neutrino state in sign changes of $\bar{\kappa}$, the current can be written

$$J_\alpha = q(4\pi)^{-\frac{1}{2}}[i^{-\bar{l}(\bar{\kappa})}\mathscr{J}_\alpha(\kappa\mu;\bar{\kappa}\bar{\mu})\pm i^{-\bar{l}(-\bar{\kappa})}\mathscr{J}_\alpha(\kappa\mu;-\bar{\kappa}\bar{\mu})] \quad \text{for } e^{\mp}, \tag{6.44}$$

with

$$\begin{aligned}\mathscr{J}_4 &= [g_\kappa j_{\bar{l}(\bar{\kappa})}-\hat{\bar{\kappa}}f_{-\kappa}j_{\bar{l}(-\bar{\kappa})}]\chi^\dagger_{\kappa\mu}\chi_{\bar{\kappa},-\bar{\mu}},\\ \mathscr{J} &= \pm i[g_\kappa j_{\bar{l}(\bar{\kappa})}\chi^\dagger_{\kappa\mu}\boldsymbol{\sigma}\chi_{\bar{\kappa},-\bar{\mu}}-\hat{\bar{\kappa}}f_{-\kappa}j_{\bar{l}(-\bar{\kappa})}\chi^\dagger_{-\kappa\mu}\boldsymbol{\sigma}\chi_{-\bar{\kappa}-\bar{\mu}}].\end{aligned} \tag{6.45}$$

The expression for $\mathscr{J}_4$ has been simplified by the invariance of $\chi^\dagger_{\kappa\mu}\chi_{\bar{\kappa},-\bar{\mu}}$ to the simultaneous sign reversal of $\kappa$, $\bar{\kappa}$ exhibited by (6.38).

The next step to be taken is the analysis of the current into spherical tensor operators, which will enable classifications according to selection rules (§ 5.1). For the component $\mathscr{J}_4$, it is only necessary to introduce the spherical harmonic analysis (6.38):

$$\mathscr{J}_4 = (-)^{\bar{\mu}-\frac{1}{2}}P(\kappa\bar{\kappa})\sum_J{}' \rho_J(j\bar{j})\langle j(\mu)\bar{j}(\bar{\mu})|J(\mu+\bar{\mu})\rangle Y^*_{J,\mu+\bar{\mu}}, \tag{6.46}$$

where $$P(\kappa\bar{\kappa}) = g_\kappa(pr)j_{l(\bar{\kappa})}(qr) - \hat{\bar{\kappa}} f_{-\kappa} j_{l(-\bar{\kappa})} \tag{6.47}$$
is real. It is evident that $J$ is the total angular momentum ($\mathbf{J} = \mathbf{j}+\bar{\mathbf{j}}$) carried off by the leptons, in the corresponding radiation component.

The spatial-vector part of the current must be analysed into '*vector* spherical harmonics'. Those‡ constitute a set of vectors defined by

$$\mathbf{T}^L_{Jm} = \sum_{\rho=0,\pm1} \langle L(m-\rho)1(\rho)|J(m)\rangle Y_{L,m-\rho}\,\mathbf{e}_\rho, \tag{6.48}$$

where the unit vectors $\mathbf{e}_{0,\pm1}$ are related to unit vectors $\mathbf{e}_{x,y,z}$ which point out the directions of the coordinate axes by

$$\mathbf{e}_0 \equiv \mathbf{e}_z, \quad \mathbf{e}_{\pm1} \equiv \mp 2^{-\frac{1}{2}}(\mathbf{e}_x \pm i\mathbf{e}_y), \quad [\mathbf{e}^\dagger_\rho\,\mathbf{e}_{\rho'} = \delta_{\rho\rho'}]. \tag{6.49}$$

That the hermitian ($\equiv$ complex) conjugate is

$$(\mathbf{T}^L_{Jm})^* = (-)^{L+J+m+1}\mathbf{T}^L_{J,-m} \tag{6.50}$$

follows readily from

$$Y^*_{LM} = (-)^M Y_{L,-M} \quad \text{and} \quad \mathbf{e}^*_\rho = (-)^\rho \mathbf{e}_{-\rho}. \tag{6.51}$$

The analysis of $\mathscr{J}$ in (6.45) into vector harmonics requires such an analysis of the vectors $\chi^\dagger_{\pm\kappa\mu}\boldsymbol{\sigma}\chi_{\pm\bar{\kappa},-\bar{\mu}}$. That will involve obtaining matrix elements of the spherical tensor operator

$$\boldsymbol{\sigma}\,.\,(\mathbf{T}^L_{Jm})^* = \sum_\rho \langle L(m-\rho)1(\rho)|J(m)\rangle Y^*_{L,m-\rho}\,\sigma^\dagger_\rho = (\boldsymbol{\sigma}\,.\,\mathbf{T}^L_{Jm})^\dagger, \tag{6.52}$$

combining states $\chi_{\kappa\mu}$ and $\chi_{\bar{\kappa},-\bar{\mu}}$. The latter states are characterized by $\mathbf{l}+\frac{1}{2} = \mathbf{j}$ and $\bar{\mathbf{l}}+\frac{1}{2} = \bar{\mathbf{j}}$, respectively. The operator (6.52) adds orbital momentum $\mathbf{L}$ to the orbital momentum balance $\mathbf{l}+\bar{\mathbf{l}}$, and a unit spin to the spin balance. The evaluations therefore involve the 'decoupling' of $(\mathbf{l}+\frac{1}{2})+(\bar{\mathbf{l}}+\frac{1}{2}) = \mathbf{J}$, and a 'recoupling' according to

$$(\mathbf{l}+\bar{\mathbf{l}})+(\tfrac{1}{2}+\tfrac{1}{2}) = \mathbf{L}+\mathbf{S} = \mathbf{J}.$$

The states of $\mathbf{J}$ formed in these alternative ways are related to each other via coefficients known as '9-$j$ symbols', and widely used for transformations from the '$jj$-coupling' to the '$LS$-coupling' of atomic and nuclear spectroscopy. There is no point in burdening this account with further details§ of these formalities, especially since the particular '9-$j$ symbols' needed can be finally expressed‖ in terms of ordinary vector-

‡ The vector spherical harmonics are particularly useful in electromagnetic theory, since the $\mathbf{e}_\rho$ can serve as eigenfunctions of the unit photon spin. The $\mathbf{T}^L_{Jm}$ are in this sense modifications, from spin $\frac{1}{2}$ to spin 1, of the 'spinor spherical harmonics' $\chi_{\kappa\mu}$ (2.18), and from spin 0 to spin 1, of the spherical harmonics $Y_{lm}$ themselves.

§ The technique can be learned from A. R. Edmonds, *Angular Momentum in Quantum Mechanics'* (Princeton Press, 1957).

‖ As found by N. Newby and E. J. Konopinski, *Phys. Rev.* **115,** 434 (1959). See the footnote on p. 441 of this paper.

addition coefficients. The result is

$$\chi^{\dagger}_{\kappa\mu}\boldsymbol{\sigma}\chi_{\bar{\kappa},-\bar{\mu}} = (-)^{\mu+\frac{1}{2}}\sum_{LJ}{}' \rho_J(j\bar{j})\langle j(\mu)\bar{j}(\bar{\mu})|J(\mu+\bar{\mu})\rangle \mathbf{T}^{L}_{J,-\mu-\bar{\mu}}\times$$
$$\times[\langle J(0)1(0)|L(0)\rangle+\hat{\kappa}w_J(j\bar{j})\langle J(1)1(-1)|L(0)\rangle], \quad (6.53)$$

where

$$\left.\begin{aligned} w_J(j\bar{j}) &= [(2j+1)+(2\bar{j}+1)(-)^{j+\bar{j}+J}]/[2J(J+1)]^{\frac{1}{2}} \\ w_0(j\bar{j}) &= 0 \end{aligned}\right\}. \quad (6.54)$$

As in the analysis (6.38), the apostrophe on the summation sign is meant to indicate that only even values of $L+l(\kappa)+\bar{l}(\bar{\kappa})$ are to be included in the sum over $L$. Triangle conditions symbolized by $\mathbf{j}+\bar{\mathbf{j}} = \mathbf{J}$, $\mathbf{l}+\bar{\mathbf{l}} = \mathbf{L}$, and $\mathbf{J} = \mathbf{L}+\mathbf{S}$, must be maintained. While $\mathbf{J}$ is the total lepton angular momentum, $\mathbf{L}$ will be the orbital momentum carried off, in radiation components labelled by $L$, $J$.

Now the spatial components of the current can be written analogously to $\mathscr{J}_4$ of (6.46):

$$\mathscr{J} = \pm i(-)^{\bar{\mu}-\frac{1}{2}}\sum_{LJ}{}' P_{LJ}\,\rho_J\langle j(\mu)\bar{j}(\bar{\mu})|J(\mu+\bar{\mu})\rangle(\mathbf{T}^{L}_{J,\mu+\bar{\mu}})^{\dagger}, \quad (6.55)$$

with $\quad P_{LJ}(\kappa\bar{\kappa}) = \langle J(0)1(0)|L(0)\rangle P+\hat{\kappa}w_J\langle J(-1)1(1)|L(0)\rangle\bar{P}. \quad (6.56)$

Here

$$\bar{P}(\kappa\bar{\kappa}) = g_\kappa\, j_{l(\bar{\kappa})}+\hat{\bar{\kappa}}f_{-\kappa}\, j_{l(-\bar{\kappa})} \quad (6.57)$$

differs from $P$ of (6.47) only by the relative sign of the two terms. $P$ and $\bar{P}$ contain the only dependence on the lepton energies which will occur in the transition matrix elements. Both are real functions of $pr$ and $qr$.

## 6.3. The nuclear β-moments

The transition matrix element (6.31), and its counterpart for positron emission, can be given the forms

$$\langle \mathrm{f}|H_\beta|\mathrm{i}\rangle = q(4\pi)^{-\frac{1}{2}}[i^{-l(\bar{\kappa})}\langle \mathrm{f}|\mathscr{H}(\bar{\kappa})|\mathrm{i}\rangle \pm i^{-l(-\bar{\kappa})}\langle \mathrm{f}|\mathscr{H}(-\bar{\kappa})|\mathrm{i}\rangle], \quad (6.58)$$

when the lepton current is split as in (6.44). By $\langle \mathrm{f}|\mathscr{H}(\bar{\kappa})|\mathrm{i}\rangle$ is obviously meant the same matrix element as $\langle \mathrm{f}|H_\beta|\mathrm{i}\rangle$ except that $\mathscr{J}_\alpha$ of (6.45) replaces the full lepton current $J_\alpha$ of (6.44). This matrix element can be resolved into

$$\langle \mathrm{f}|\mathscr{H}|\mathrm{i}\rangle = 2^{\frac{1}{2}}g\{C_\mathrm{V}[\langle \mathrm{f}|\mathscr{J}_4|\mathrm{i}\rangle - i\langle \mathrm{f}|\boldsymbol{\alpha}\,.\,\mathscr{J}|\mathrm{i}\rangle]-$$
$$-C_\mathrm{A}[\langle \mathrm{f}|\gamma_5\mathscr{J}_4|\mathrm{i}\rangle + i\langle \mathrm{f}|\boldsymbol{\sigma}\,.\,\mathscr{J}|\mathrm{i}\rangle]\} \quad (6.59)$$

as in (5.2), except that now the lepton currents are to be evaluated at the positions of the transforming nucleon in the nucleus. Operations $\sum_a \tau^a_\pm$ and superscripts '$a$' on other nucleon operators, have been omitted only to simplify the writing; their continued presence is to be understood.

When the currents are analysed into spherical tensors, as in (6.46) an (6.55), then the matrix element takes the form:

$$\langle \mathrm{f}|\mathscr{H}|\mathrm{i}\rangle = 2^{\frac{1}{2}}g(-)^{\bar{\mu}-\frac{1}{2}}\sum_J \rho_J(j\bar{j})\langle j(\mu)\bar{j}(\bar{\mu})|J(m)\rangle\times$$
$$\times \sum_L{}' \{\delta_{LJ}\langle \mathrm{f}|P(C_\mathrm{V}-C_\mathrm{A}\gamma_5)Y^*_{Lm}|\mathrm{i}\rangle \pm$$
$$\langle \mathrm{f}|P_{LJ}(C_\mathrm{A}-C_\mathrm{V}\gamma_5)(\boldsymbol{\sigma}\,.\,\mathbf{T}^L_{Jm})^\dagger|\mathrm{i}\rangle\}, \quad (6.60)$$

with the upper sign applying to negatron, the lower to positron, emission.

*Definitions of β-moments*

We deal here with nuclear matrix elements of the form

$$\langle \mathrm{f}|P(r)S^\dagger_{Jm}|\mathrm{i}\rangle = \langle I'(M')J(m)|I(M)\rangle\langle PS_J\rangle. \quad (6.61)$$

where $P(r)$ is a real function of the transforming nucleon's radial position (6.47) or (6.57). $S_{Jm}$ stands for any one of the spherical tensor operator which occur, being proportional either to $Y_{Jm}$ or $\boldsymbol{\sigma}\,.\,\mathbf{T}^L_{Jm}$, with or withou a factor $\gamma_5$. The symbol $\langle PS_J\rangle$ stands for a reduced matrix element independent of the orientations $M$, $M'$, and $m$, of the type defined b the Wigner–Eckart theorem (5.15).

The elements of the type $\langle P(r)S_J\rangle$ depend on the energies of th particular leptons emitted through the factor $P(r)$, which is a function o $pr$ and $qr$. To separate off such dependences, average radii $R$ are defined such that

$$\langle P(r)S_J\rangle = P(R)\langle S_J\rangle. \quad (6.62)$$

This still differs from the 'allowed approximation' in that, for the latter all terms having $P(0) = 0$ were neglected. A vast number of differen average radii $R$ are, in principle, being introduced through the step (6.62) Each ought to be labelled suitably, to indicate the averaging proces from which it arises. In practice, such labelling is unwarranted, as a argument to be completed in § 7.1 will show. Meanwhile, the various $R$' may be regarded as 'labelled' by the moments $\langle S_J\rangle$ with which they wil continue to be associated. As long as this association is maintained, th development can still be regarded as 'exact'.

The separation of the lepton properties from the nuclear matrix element, as in (6.62), is desirable because it leaves elements $\langle S_J\rangle$ which can be regarded as properties of the decaying nucleus. Such quantities will be called nuclear 'β-moments'. In principle, the β-moments should be calculated from nuclear state descriptions, but that is rarely feasible a all and almost never with trustworthy accuracy. In practice, it is prefer able to treat the moments as nuclear parameters to be measured.‡ Th

‡ The same is true of the moments which determine the rate at which a nucleus wil emit γ-radiation, for example.

theoretical expectations are expressed in terms of the $\beta$-moments, and are then compared with appropriate experimental observations; the values of the $\beta$-moments are adjusted until the best possible agreement is obtained, and that constitutes the measurement.

All the types of $\beta$-moments are defined as the reduced matrix elements in the following:

$$\left.\begin{aligned} \left\langle \mathrm{f} \middle| \sum_a \tau_\pm^a (i^J Y_{Jm}(\hat{\mathbf{r}}^a))^* \middle| \mathrm{i} \right\rangle &= (\mathrm{V.A.})\langle Y_J \rangle \\ \left\langle \mathrm{f} \middle| \sum_a \tau_\pm^a \gamma_5^a (i^J Y_{Jm})^* \middle| \mathrm{i} \right\rangle &= (\mathrm{V.A.})\langle \gamma_5 Y_J \rangle \\ \left\langle \mathrm{f} \middle| \sum_a \tau_\pm^a (i^L \boldsymbol{\sigma}^a . \mathbf{T}_{Jm}^L)^\dagger \middle| \mathrm{i} \right\rangle &= (\mathrm{V.A.})\langle \boldsymbol{\sigma} . \mathbf{T}_J^L \rangle \\ \left\langle \mathrm{f} \middle| \sum_a \tau_\pm^a (i^L \boldsymbol{\alpha}^a . \mathbf{T}_{Jm}^L)^\dagger \middle| \mathrm{i} \right\rangle &= (\mathrm{V.A.})\langle \boldsymbol{\alpha} . \mathbf{T}_J^L \rangle \end{aligned}\right\}, \tag{6.63}$$

where
$$(\mathrm{V.A.}) \equiv \langle I'(M')J(m)|I(M)\rangle$$

in every case. It must be emphasized that the reduced elements on the right are highly unspecific symbols; these relations must always be referred to whenever their specific significances are sought. As before, $I$ is the spin of the initial nuclear state, and $I'$ that of the final one. The motive for including the phase factors $i^L$ in these definitions will appear to the next subsection. It will be found to permit treating the matrix elements, hence also the $\beta$-moments, as real numbers.

*Reality of the $\beta$-moments*

If the $\beta$-moments are to be used as adjustable parameters in comparisons with observations, then it is important to know about any limits to their adjustability. Since they are constituted of non-diagonal matrices of non-hermitian spherical tensor operators, it is possible for their theoretical evaluations to yield complex numbers, and that ostensibly permits regarding each $\beta$-moment as equivalent to two real, adjustable parameters. That much arbitrariness is illusory, however. Any given $\beta$-moment can be made real with a suitable choice of the arbitrary phase with which the initial nuclear state enters interaction. The problem then becomes one of finding the relative phases with which the various $\beta$-moments should be defined in order that all those arising from a given initial state are made real simultaneously, for the same initial phase. The significant point is that the suitable relative phase factors can be shown to be independent of the particular nuclear states involved, if all these are assumed to be constructed in agreement with certain admissible conventions.

To find the conditions under which matrix elements of the types (6.63) are real, i.e.

$$\langle I'(M')|S^{\dagger}_{Jm}|I(M)\rangle = \langle I'(M')|S^{\dagger}_{Jm}|I(M)\rangle^*, \tag{6.64}$$

we must inquire into what formal significance should be given the complex conjugate of a state. The inquiry can be narrowed to concern with the descriptions of the angular momentum, since all the $\beta$-moments for a given nuclear transition contain the same description of other variables. Any complex phase independent of the angular momenta will be common to all the matrix elements, hence can be cancelled merely by a suitable choice of the arbitrary phase which the initial state may be given. Such phases, common to all terms, at any rate cancel in forming the absolute squares which give the final intensities.

The complex conjugate, $\chi^*_{IM}$, of an angular momentum eigenstate must be an eigenstate for the same angular momentum reversed in orientation, just as in the well-known special case $Y^*_{lm} = (-)^m Y_{l,-m}$. The general conclusion follows from examining the description formed by subjecting all the angular momentum relations (§ 2.1) to complex conjugation. Those relations are all built up from the fundamental commutators of the type $\mathbf{I}\times\mathbf{I} = i\hbar\mathbf{I}$, and $\mathbf{I}^*\times\mathbf{I}^* = -i\hbar\mathbf{I}^*$ are just the commutators satisfied if $\mathbf{I}^* = -\mathbf{I}$. Now, $-\mathbf{I}$ is already described by the original set of eigenstates, in the forms $\chi_{I,-M}$. This does not mean, however, that $\chi^*_{IM}$ needs to be identical with $\chi_{I,-M}$ (within a phase). A given physical situation can always be equivalently described by an infinite variety of representations which are related to each other by unitary transformations (examples were mentioned in the footnotes on pp. 65 and 67). This means that the relation between $\chi^*_{IM}$ and $\chi_{I,-M}$ may be a proportionality $U\chi^*_{IM} \sim \chi_{I,-M}$, where $U = (U^\dagger)^{-1}$ is some unitary operation, depending on the representation used for $\chi_{IM}$. The unitarity permits the 'proportionality' here to be an equality within a phase. Whether a phase factor depending on $I$, $M$ intervenes in this equality depends on the phases with which the various members of the set $\chi_{IM}$ are defined, before being put to use. A convention adopted in the literature, standardizing the phases to be adopted in defining the sets, requires making such choices that

$$U\chi^*_{IM} = (-)^{I+M}\chi_{I,-M}. \tag{6.65}$$

The unitarity of $U$ will then insure the preservation of normalizations:

$$(\tilde{\chi}_{IM}\,U^\dagger)U\chi^*_{IM} = (\chi^*_{IM})^\dagger\chi^*_{IM} = \chi^\dagger_{I,-M}\chi_{I,-M}.$$

The transformation by the complex conjugation and $U$ is supposed to be such that, for example $I_z\chi_{I,-M} \sim I_z(U\chi^*_{IM}) = -M\hbar(U\chi^*_{IM})$ is consistent with $I_z^*\chi_{IM}^* = M\hbar\chi_{IM}^*$. Thus, $U$ must be so chosen that $UI_z^* = -I_z U$, or, more generally, $\mathbf{I}^* = -U^{-1}\mathbf{I}U$. That the latter is a more general solution of $\mathbf{I}^*\times\mathbf{I}^* = -i\hbar\mathbf{I}^*$, than is $\mathbf{I}^* = -\mathbf{I}$, is obvious. The elaboration to $U \neq 1$ is unnecessary in dealing only with orbital degrees of freedom, for which the operator representations $\mathbf{l}^* = i\hbar\mathbf{r}\times\boldsymbol{\nabla} = -\mathbf{l}$ are used. However, for spin degrees of freedom it is customary to use representations $\mathbf{s} = \frac{1}{2}\hbar\boldsymbol{\sigma}$ with $\boldsymbol{\sigma}^* \neq -\boldsymbol{\sigma}$. Consequently, for each of the latter degrees of freedom, a factor must be included in $U$ such that

$$U\sigma_{x,z}^* \equiv U\sigma_{x,z} = -\sigma_{x,z}U \quad \text{while } U\sigma_y^* = U(-\sigma_y) = -\sigma_y U.$$

Such a factor is $i\sigma_y$ itself, which is also unitary. The phase of this factor of $U$ has been so chosen that, for the spin eigenfunctions as defined in (2.30),

$$i\sigma_y\chi_\rho^* = (-)^{\frac{1}{2}+\rho}\chi_{-\rho}, \tag{6.66}$$

in conformity with the convention (6.65). If merely a factor unity is included in $U$ for each orbital degree of freedom, as the property $\mathbf{l}^* = -\mathbf{l}$ permits, then the convention (6.65) requires $i^lY_{lm}$ to be used as the orbital eigenfunction set, rather than $Y_{lm}$ itself.

To utilize the results here, the complex conjugate matrix element (6.64) should be written

$$(\langle I'M'|)^*\tilde{S}_{Jm}(|IM\rangle)^* = (\langle I'M'|)^*U^\dagger U\tilde{S}_{Jm}U^{-1}U(|IM\rangle)^*,$$

since $U^\dagger U = U^{-1}U = 1$. The above discussion shows that the right side is equivalent to

$$(-)^{I+M-I'-M'}\langle I', -M'|(US_{Jm}^*U^{-1})^\dagger|I, -M\rangle. \tag{6.67}$$

Thus, it remains to investigate the transformations undergone by the spherical tensors.

Since $U$ affects only spin degrees of freedom,

$$U(i^{+J}Y_{Jm})^*U^{-1} = (i^{+J}Y_{Jm})^* = (-)^{J+m}(i^{+J}Y_{J,-m}).$$

However,

$$U(i^{+L}\boldsymbol{\sigma}\,.\,\mathbf{T}_{Jm}^L)^*U^{-1} = \sum_\rho \langle L(m-\rho)1(\rho)|J(m)\rangle(i^{+L}Y_{L,m-\rho})^*U\sigma_\rho^*U^{-1}.$$

Now, from the definitions of $\sigma_{\pm 1}$ we have $U\sigma_{\pm 1}^*U^{-1} = \sigma_{\mp 1}$, whereas $U\sigma_z^*U^{-1} = -\sigma_z \equiv -\sigma_0$, so that the last expression becomes

$$(-)^{J+m}\sum_\rho \langle L(-m+\rho)1(-\rho)|J(-m)\rangle(i^{+L}Y_{L,-m+\rho})\sigma_{-\rho}$$
$$= (-)^{J+m}(i^{+L}\boldsymbol{\sigma}\,.\,\mathbf{T}_{J,-m}^L),$$

with the help of the vector-addition relations (2.14). The inclusion of a factor $\gamma_5$ in the spherical tensors here, as for $\boldsymbol{\alpha}\,.\,\mathbf{T}_{Jm}^L = -\gamma_5\boldsymbol{\sigma}\,.\,\mathbf{T}_{Jm}^L$, makes no difference to their transformations since $U\gamma_5^*U^{-1} = \gamma_5^* = \gamma_5$ is real, and commutes with $\sigma_y$. Thus, with spherical tensors having definitions like

$$S_{Jm} = (\gamma_5)i^{+J}Y_{Jm} \quad \text{or} \quad (\gamma_5)i^{+L}\boldsymbol{\sigma}\,.\,\mathbf{T}^L_{Jm}, \tag{6.68}$$

the complex conjugate (6.67) of the matrix element (6.64) becomes

$$(-)^{I+M-I'-M'-J-m}\langle I', -M'|(S_{J,-m})^\dagger|I, -M\rangle$$
$$= (-)^{I-I'-J}\langle I'(-M')J(-m)|I(-M)\rangle\langle S_J\rangle,$$

according to (6.61). Because of the vector-addition coefficient properties (2.14), this is just equal to the matrix element (6.64) before its complex conjugation. Accordingly, the $\beta$-moments will be real if they are defined with spherical tensors having phase factors as chosen in (6.68).

It may be mentioned that the transformation investigated here is also the one which replaces the description of a given state by a description of the same state with all the motions reversed in time.‡ This is not surprising, in view of its reversing the angular momenta. It does account for the fact that the usual practice, when treating the effects of complex conjugation, is to start with a consideration of invariances under time-reversal.§

*Selection rules for the $\beta$-moments*

The chief restrictions on the $\beta$-moments as parameters come from selection rules.

The rules arising from total angular momentum conservation, $\mathbf{I} = \mathbf{I}'+\mathbf{J}$, are implicit in the vector-addition coefficient which enters the definition (6.63) of each $\beta$-moment, $\langle S_J\rangle$. The triangle condition (2.10) requires $I'+J \geqslant I$, $I+J \geqslant I'$, and $I+I' \geqslant J$, simultaneously. Consequently, for a given nuclear transition $I \rightarrow I'$:

$$\left.\begin{aligned} \langle S_J\rangle &= 0 \quad \textit{unless } \Delta I \equiv |I'-I| \leqslant J \\ \langle S_J\rangle &= 0 \quad \textit{also if } I+I' < J \end{aligned}\right\}. \tag{6.69}$$

Examples of these rules, for $J = 0$ and 1, were given in (5.8).

The rules arising from nuclear parity conservation can be found by considering the effects of 'space-inversion'. This may be regarded as a change of reference frame in which the axes are reversed in direction. For vectors, it is equivalent to reversing polar ones, like the position vectors ($\mathbf{r} \rightarrow -\mathbf{r}$) or the linear momenta ($\mathbf{p} = -i\hbar\boldsymbol{\nabla} \rightarrow -\mathbf{p}$). Axial vectors, like the orbital momentum ($\mathbf{l} = \mathbf{r}\times\mathbf{p} \rightarrow (-\mathbf{r})\times(-\mathbf{p}) = +\mathbf{l}$), and the

‡ E. P. Wigner, *Group Theory* (Academic Press, 1959).

§ It is thus that C. Longmire and A. Messiah first approached the problem of real $\beta$-moments (*Phys. Rev.* **83**, 464 (1951)).

spin $\boldsymbol{\sigma}$, are unaffected. (The defining relation $\boldsymbol{\sigma}\times\boldsymbol{\sigma} = 2i\boldsymbol{\sigma}$ must remain valid in the new frame.) The space-inversion of a nuclear state is equivalent to a parity operation $P$ (5.7) on it, since $P\mathbf{r} = -\mathbf{r}$ and $P\boldsymbol{\sigma} = +\boldsymbol{\sigma}$ as in space-inversions, and nucleonic configurations can be described entirely in terms of the $\mathbf{r}$ and $\boldsymbol{\sigma}$ variables. Thus, the result

$$P|\mathrm{i}\rangle = \pi_\mathrm{i}|\mathrm{i}\rangle, \tag{6.70}$$

giving the parity $\pi_\mathrm{i}$ of a state $|\mathrm{i}\rangle$, can be equivalently regarded as a parity operation or a space-inversion, and be represented by the same operator, $P$.

The space-inversion of a spherical tensor like $S_{Lm} = i^{+L}Y_{Lm}$, or $S_{Jm} = i^{+L}\boldsymbol{\sigma}\,.\,\mathbf{T}^L_{Jm}$, multiplies it by a sign $(-)^L$, since

$$Y_{Lm}(-\hat{\mathbf{r}}) = (-)^L Y_{Lm}(\hat{\mathbf{r}})$$

according to (5.18), and $P\boldsymbol{\sigma} = +\boldsymbol{\sigma}$. When the pseudoscalar $\gamma_5$ is present, it suffers a sign change, $P\gamma_5 = -\gamma_5$ according to (2.89); that is consistent with $P\boldsymbol{\alpha} = P(-\gamma_5\,\boldsymbol{\sigma}) = -\boldsymbol{\alpha}$ for the polar vector $\boldsymbol{\alpha}$. Considering, further, that a $\beta$-moment combines nuclear states $|\mathrm{i}\rangle$ and $|\mathrm{f}\rangle$,

$$P\langle S_J\rangle = \pm(-)^L\pi_\mathrm{i}\pi_\mathrm{f}\langle S_J\rangle$$

should result from the space inversion of a $\beta$-moment; the lower sign applies only when $\gamma_5$, or $\boldsymbol{\alpha} = -\gamma_5\,\boldsymbol{\sigma}$, is present in the $\beta$-moment. On the other hand, a number like $\langle S_J\rangle$ is not altered in a mere change of reference frame. We must conclude that

$$\left.\begin{array}{ll} \langle Y_L\rangle, \langle \boldsymbol{\sigma}\,.\,\mathbf{T}^L_J\rangle & \textit{vanish unless } \pi_\mathrm{i}\pi_\mathrm{f} = (-)^L \\ \langle \gamma_5 Y_L\rangle, \langle \boldsymbol{\alpha}\,.\,\mathbf{T}^J_L\rangle & \textit{vanish unless } \pi_\mathrm{i}\pi_\mathrm{f} = (-)^{L+1} \end{array}\right\}. \tag{6.71}$$

These are the selection rules governing the nuclear parities, $\pi_\mathrm{i}$ and $\pi_\mathrm{f}$, of the states, which can contribute to these $\beta$-moments.

*The $\beta$-emission amplitudes*

When the $\beta$-moments are introduced into the rate formula (6.35), its dependence on the various angular momentum orientations becomes completely explicit. Certain orientation-independent amplitudes $A_J(\kappa\bar{\kappa})$ become distinguishable and these are best introduced into the matrix element (6.60) first:

$$\langle \mathrm{f}|\mathscr{H}|\mathrm{i}\rangle = \pm 2^{\frac{1}{2}} g i^{\bar{l}(\bar{\kappa})}(-)^{\bar{\mu}-\frac{1}{2}} \sum_J \langle j(\mu)\bar{j}(\bar{\mu})|J(\mu+\bar{\mu})\rangle \times$$
$$\times \langle I'(M')J(\mu+\bar{\mu})|I(M)\rangle \rho_J(j\bar{j})A_J(\kappa\bar{\kappa}) \tag{6.72}$$

if

$$A_J = \sum_L{}' i^{L-\bar{l}}\{\pm\delta_{LJ}\,P\langle (C_\mathrm{V}-C_\mathrm{A}\,\gamma_5)\,Y_L\rangle + P_{LJ}\langle (C_\mathrm{A}-C_\mathrm{V}\,\gamma_5)\boldsymbol{\sigma}\,.\,\mathbf{T}^L_J\rangle\}. \tag{6.73}$$

As usual, the upper signs refer to negatron, the lower to positron, emissions. It is to be understood that

$$\left.\begin{aligned}\langle(C_{\mathrm{V}}-C_{\mathrm{A}}\,\gamma_5)Y_L\rangle &\equiv C_{\mathrm{V}}\langle Y_L\rangle - C_{\mathrm{A}}\langle\gamma_5 Y_L\rangle\\ \langle(C_{\mathrm{A}}-C_{\mathrm{V}}\,\gamma_5)\boldsymbol{\sigma}\,.\,\mathbf{T}_J^L\rangle &\equiv C_{\mathrm{A}}\langle\boldsymbol{\sigma}\,.\,\mathbf{T}_J^L\rangle + C_{\mathrm{V}}\langle\boldsymbol{\alpha}\,.\,\mathbf{T}_J^L\rangle\end{aligned}\right\}. \tag{6.74}$$

At most, only one of the two terms in each of these expressions will actually exist for a given nuclear transition because of the parity selection rules (6.71).

The summation over $L = J,\ J\pm 1$ can be carried out immediately, and the results will be most useful if in them the radial waves $g_\kappa, f_{-\kappa}(pR)$ and $j_l(qR)$, of (6.47) and (6.57), are made explicit. Several cases must be distinguished because of the restriction to even $L+l(\kappa)+\bar{l}(\bar{\kappa})$ values which is indicated by the apostrophe on the summation sign in (6.73). For $\kappa$, $\bar{\kappa}$ of the same sign *and* $J+j+\bar{j}$ even, *or* for $\kappa$, $\bar{\kappa}$ of opposite signs *and* $J+j+\bar{j}$ odd:

$$A_J(\kappa\bar{\kappa}) = i^{J+1-l(\bar{\kappa})}[g_\kappa j_{l(\bar{\kappa})}\,B_J(\hat{\kappa}) - \hat{\kappa} f_{-\kappa} j_{l(-\bar{\kappa})} B_J(-\hat{\kappa})]. \tag{6.75 a}$$

For $\kappa$, $\bar{\kappa}$ of the same sign *and* $J+j+\bar{j}$ odd, *or* for $\kappa$, $\bar{\kappa}$ of opposite signs *and* $J+j+\bar{j}$ even:

$$A_J(\kappa\bar{\kappa}) = \pm i^{J-l(\bar{\kappa})}[g_\kappa j_{l(\bar{\kappa})} C_J(\pm\hat{\kappa}) - \hat{\kappa} f_{-\kappa} j_{l(-\bar{\kappa})} C_J(\mp\hat{\kappa})]. \tag{6.75 b}$$

Here, $B_J$ and $C_J$ stand for the $\beta$-moment combinations:

$$\begin{aligned}B_J(\hat{\kappa}) = (2J+1)^{-\frac{1}{2}}\{[J^{\frac{1}{2}} - \hat{\kappa}(J+1)^{\frac{1}{2}} w_J/2^{\frac{1}{2}}]\langle(C_{\mathrm{A}}-C_{\mathrm{V}}\,\gamma_5)\boldsymbol{\sigma}\,.\,\mathbf{T}_J^{J-1}\rangle + {}\\ +[(J+1)^{\frac{1}{2}} + \hat{\kappa} J^{\frac{1}{2}} w_J/2^{\frac{1}{2}}]\langle(C_{\mathrm{A}}-C_{\mathrm{V}}\,\gamma_5)\boldsymbol{\sigma}\,.\,\mathbf{T}_J^{J+1}\rangle\},\end{aligned} \tag{6.76}$$

$$C_J(\hat{\kappa}) = \langle(C_{\mathrm{V}}-C_{\mathrm{A}}\,\gamma_5)Y_J\rangle - \hat{\kappa}(w_J/2^{\frac{1}{2}})\langle(C_{\mathrm{A}}-C_{\mathrm{V}}\,\gamma_5)\boldsymbol{\sigma}\,.\,\mathbf{T}_J^J\rangle. \tag{6.77}$$

These combinations are real if the $\beta$-moments are properly constructed.

Straightforward substitution of these results into (6.35) would yield a rate for decays in which neutrinos are produced in the special state designated by $\bar{\kappa}\bar{\mu}$. We shall want to include every neutrino which can contribute, formed in any phase, hence will sum (incoherently) over all $\bar{\kappa}\bar{\mu}$. Furthermore, interference among electron waves with different $\mu$ need not be provided for, as done in (6.35). Final nuclear orientations $M'$ in arbitrary phase will be acceptable, together with the incoherent $\bar{\mu}$, and then each $\mu = M - M' - \bar{\mu}$ which arises from a given initial nuclear orientation $M$ cannot be coherent with any other. Mathematical proof of this is implicit in the ensuing development. With these considerations, the use of (6.58) and (6.72) in (6.35) can be seen to yield:

$$\begin{aligned}d\lambda/dW\,d\Omega = g^2 q^2 \sum_{\bar{\kappa}\bar{\mu}\mu}\Big|\sum_{\kappa J} e^{i\delta(\kappa)}\chi_{\kappa\mu}[A_J(\kappa,\bar{\kappa}) \pm A_J(\kappa,-\bar{\kappa})]\times\\ \times\rho_J(j\bar{j})\langle j(\mu)\bar{j}(\bar{\mu})|J(\mu+\bar{\mu})\rangle\langle I'(M')J(\mu+\bar{\mu})|I(M)\rangle\Big|^2.\end{aligned} \tag{6.78}$$

The quantity which is squared here is symmetric in sign changes of $\bar{\kappa}$ for negatron emission, and antisymmetric for positrons. Its square is the same for the two values, $\bar{\kappa} = \pm(\bar{j}+\frac{1}{2})$, which $\bar{\kappa}$ has for a given $\bar{j}$; thus the sum over $\bar{\kappa}$ is equivalent to twice a sum over $\bar{j}$.

The form (6.78) is now ready for adaptation to a series of more specific observational circumstances.

## 6.4. The electron spectra

The results it is simplest to examine first are for emissions from randomly oriented nuclei, as given by the rate formula (6.78) after this is subjected to the averaging operation $(2I+1)^{-1}\sum_M$. Since the formula, as it stands, includes summations over all possible lepton states $(\kappa\mu,\ \bar{\kappa}\bar{\mu})$ of given energies, it will yield no further details than just the distribution of the electrons in energy, i.e. the spectra.

The dependence on the initial nuclear orientations $M$, in (6.78), is confined to the factors in

$$(2I+1)^{-1}\sum_M \langle I'(M-\mu-\bar{\mu})J(\mu+\bar{\mu})|I(M)\rangle\times$$
$$\times\langle I'(M-\mu-\bar{\mu})J'(\mu+\bar{\mu})|I(M)\rangle = \delta_{JJ'}/(2J+1). \quad (6.79)$$

The result here follows from the properties of the vector-addition coefficients (2.14) and (2.13). It shows that radiation components with different total angular momenta $J$ do not interfere with each other when coming from randomly oriented nuclei. This is a generalization of the finding for the allowed ($L = 0$) transitions, that there is no singlet-triplet interference unless the initial nuclei are oriented.

Like considerations show that the summation over the neutrino orientations involves only the factors in

$$\sum_{\bar{\mu}} \langle j(\mu)\bar{j}(\bar{\mu})|J(\mu+\bar{\mu})\rangle\langle j'(\mu)\bar{j}(\bar{\mu})|J(\mu+\bar{\mu})\rangle = \delta_{jj'}(2J+1)/(2j+1), \quad (6.80)$$

for any given $\mu$. There is left the summation over the electron orientations:

$$\delta_{jj'}\sum_{\mu} \chi^{\dagger}_{\kappa\mu}\,\chi_{\kappa'\mu} = \delta_{\kappa\kappa'}(2j+1)/4\pi. \quad (6.81)$$

The result here is a generalization of $\sum_m |Y_{lm}|^2 = (2l+1)/4\pi$ (3.45) which follows from (6.37). The factor (6.81) is just the one which was to determine the angular distribution of the electrons, according to (6.38). It is constant here because of the lack of interference between electrons of different $j$ found in (6.80), and it is thus that the isotropy to be expected of randomly oriented nuclei emerges.‡

After the summations over all the angular momentum orientations have been completed, the rate formula (6.78) is reduced to:§

$$d\lambda/dW = g^2q^2 \sum_{\kappa\bar{\kappa}J} \rho_J^2 |A_J(\kappa\bar{\kappa}) \pm A_J(\kappa, -\bar{\kappa})|^2. \tag{6.82}$$

It has been multiplied by $4\pi = \oint d\Omega$, so that it now counts the electrons which emerge (isotropically) into all directions.

*The spectrum shape-factors*

The electron spectra are generally discussed in terms of so-called 'shape-factors', $S(W, Z)$, defined in such a way that

$$d\lambda/dW = [g^2q^2pWF/2\pi^3]S(W, Z), \tag{6.83}$$

where $F(\pm Z, W)$ is just the electron density ratio (1.14). Comparison with the allowed spectrum (5.45) shows that its shape-factor is

$$S_0(W, Z) = C_V^2\langle 1\rangle^2 + C_A^2\langle\sigma\rangle^2, \tag{6.84}$$

independent of the energy ($S_0 \equiv \xi$ of (5.39)). More general shape-factors do depend on energy and thus indicate deviations from the 'statistical shape' (1.10). Experimental shape-factors can be obtained, in arbitrary normalization, by dividing observed numbers of electrons per unit energy range, $n(W)$, by the calculable quantities $pWF(W_0 - W)^2$. Results so treated are extremely sensitive to observational uncertainties, particularly to errors in $W_0$ when dealing with the sparsely populated region near the spectrum end-point. For that reason, theories are frequently tested by plotting $[n(W)/pWFS]^{\frac{1}{2}}$, using numbers $S$ proportional to theoretical expectations. The theoretical hypotheses yielding each $S$ are then confirmed when the plot results in a straight line $\sim q = W_0 - W$. This is a modification of the 'Kurie plot' treatment discussed on p. 14.

The theoretical shape factors which follow from (6.82) can be put into the form

$$S(W, Z) = \sum_{Jj\bar{j}} S_{Jj\bar{j}}(W, Z), \tag{6.85 a}$$

‡ All the results here can be obtained by a slightly different route, starting with an average of (6.78) over all electron directions, as befits expectations for randomly oriented nuclei. Then only the term $\Lambda = 0$ survives in the angular distribution (6.38) and the remaining results follow easily.

§ The same result could have been obtained more directly from

$$d\lambda/dW = 2\pi \sum_{\kappa\mu\bar{\kappa}\bar{\mu}} |\langle \mathrm{f}|H_\beta|\mathrm{i}\rangle|^2,$$

the suitable summation of (6.36). However, (6.78) serves as a basis for a greater variety of results, explored in succeeding sections.

with

$$S_{Jj\bar{j}} = \{16\pi^2/(1+\gamma_0)\}\rho_J^2\, R^{2j-1}[D_-^2\, L_{j-\frac{1}{2}} + D_+^2\, \overline{M}_{j-\frac{1}{2}} + 2D_-\, D_+\, \overline{N}_{j-\frac{1}{2}}]. \qquad (6.85\text{ b})$$

Here, $L$, $M = \overline{M}/R^2$ and $N = \overline{N}/R$ are combinations of electron radial waves introduced in the original paper‡ on forbidden $\beta$-decay and, since then, extensively tabulated§ as functions of electron energy $W$ and nuclear charge $Z$:

$$\left.\begin{aligned} L_{k-1} &= [\pi(1+\gamma_0)/4pWFR^{2(k-1)}](f_{-k}^2+g_{-k}^2) \\ \overline{M}_{k-1} &= [\pi(1+\gamma_0)/4pWFR^{2(k-1)}](f_k^2+g_k^2) \\ \overline{N}_{k-1} &= [\pi(1+\gamma_0)/4pWFR^{2(k-1)}](f_k\, g_{-k}-f_{-k}\, g_k) \end{aligned}\right\}. \qquad (6.86)$$

Approximations of these functions will be introduced in the next chapter. In the above,

$$\gamma \equiv \gamma_{j-\frac{1}{2}} = [(j+\tfrac{1}{2})^2-(\alpha Z)^2]^{\frac{1}{2}}, \qquad (6.87)$$

of (3.53).

The quantities $D_\pm$ are combinations of neutrino radial waves with $\beta$-moments:

$J+j+\bar{j}$ even

$$\left.\begin{aligned} D_+ &= j_{\bar{j}+\frac{1}{2}}(qR)B_J(+1)+j_{\bar{j}-\frac{1}{2}}\, C_J(\pm 1) \\ D_- &= j_{\bar{j}-\frac{1}{2}}B_J(-1)-j_{\bar{j}+\frac{1}{2}}C_J(\mp 1) \end{aligned}\right\}; \qquad (6.88\text{ a})$$

$J+j+\bar{j}$ odd

$$\left.\begin{aligned} D_+ &= j_{\bar{j}-\frac{1}{2}}\, B_J(+1)-j_{\bar{j}+\frac{1}{2}}\, C_J(\pm 1) \\ D_- &= -j_{\bar{j}+\frac{1}{2}}\, B_J(-1)-j_{\bar{j}-\frac{1}{2}}\, C_J(\mp 1) \end{aligned}\right\}. \qquad (6.88\text{ b})$$

The quantities $B_J$, $C_J$ are still the $\beta$-moment combinations given in (6.76), (6.77). The transformation $C_J(+1) \longleftrightarrow C_J(-1)$ is all that remains of the difference between negatron and positron spectra (the upper signs of (6.88) referring to negatrons), aside from the nuclear charge reversal $Z \longleftrightarrow -Z$.

The shape factor formula (6.85) is still exact for first-order emissions in the sense that sufficiently careful evaluations of the radial waves and $\beta$-moments in it can yield results of indefinitely high accuracy. Practical applications of it require making approximations which are left to the next chapter. The remainder of this chapter will be devoted to bringing other results to a stage comparable to (6.85). The advantage of having available such 'exact' formulae is that the approximations to be introduced in the next chapter will be sufficiently accurate for almost all

‡ E. J. Konopinski and G. E. Uhlenbeck, *Phys. Rev.* **60,** 308 (1941).

§ M. E. Rose, C. Perry, and N. Dismuke, *Oak Ridge National Lab. Report ORNL*-1459, (1953). In *ORNL*-3207 (1962), C. P. Bhalla and Rose have published tables of $f_\kappa$, $g_\kappa$ and phase shifts, on a uniformly charged sphere of radius $R = 1{\cdot}2A^{\frac{1}{3}}(10)^{-13}$ cm. Their notation differs in the sign of the subscript on $f_\kappa(\leftrightarrow f_{-\kappa})$ and their normalizations differ by the factor $[\pi p/W]^{\frac{1}{2}}$.

applications but not all of them. There are 'anomalous' cases which require extraordinary treatment, and the systematic corrections needed for them can always be obtained by reverting to the 'exact' results of this chapter, and specializing them for the case in question.

### 6.5. The longitudinal polarizations of the electrons

To find expectations for the polarization of electrons from randomly oriented nuclei, we proceed as for the spectra in the preceding section up to the step (6.81), at which orientations of the electrons were summed together. Just short of that step, the rate formula (6.78) is left in the form:

$$d\lambda/dW\,d\Omega = 2g^2q^2 \sum_{Jj\bar{j}} \rho_{\bar{j}}^2(2j+1)^{-1} \sum_{\mu} \left| \sum_{l} e^{i\delta(\kappa)} \chi_{\kappa\mu}[A_J(\kappa\bar{\kappa}) \pm A_J(\kappa, -\bar{\kappa})] \right|^2, \tag{6.89}$$

in which either one of the $\bar{\kappa}$ values $\pm(\bar{j}+\frac{1}{2})$ may be used. The electron angular momentum eigenfunctions $\chi_{\kappa\mu}(\hat{\mathbf{p}})$ must now be analysed into spin orientations $\rho = \pm\frac{1}{2}$, as in the definition (2.18). They enter (6.89) in the forms $\sum_{\mu} \chi^{\dagger}_{\kappa\mu}\,\chi_{\kappa'\mu}$ with $\kappa' = \pm\kappa$ for a given $j = |\kappa| - \frac{1}{2}$. These sums over $\mu$ are just traces (sums over $\rho = \pm\frac{1}{2}$) of $2\times 2$ density matrices $\sum_{\mu} \chi_{\kappa'\mu}\,\chi^{\dagger}_{\kappa\mu}$.

The latter density matrix must obviously be isotropic in the case $\kappa' = +\kappa$. It must be diagonal and its two non-vanishing elements must be equal. Since its trace is just $(2j+1)/4\pi$ according to (6.81),

$$\sum_{\mu} \chi_{\kappa\mu}\,\chi^{\dagger}_{\kappa\mu} = [(2j+1)/8\pi].\mathbf{1}. \tag{6.90 a}$$

The remaining case, $\kappa' = -\kappa$, follows from this one and the relation $\boldsymbol{\sigma}.\hat{\mathbf{p}}\chi_{\kappa\mu}(\hat{\mathbf{p}}) = -\chi_{-\kappa\mu}$ (3.63):

$$\sum_{\mu} \chi_{-\kappa\mu}\,\chi^{\dagger}_{\kappa\mu} = -[(2j+1)/8\pi]\boldsymbol{\sigma}.\hat{\mathbf{p}}. \tag{6.90 b}$$

This has the vanishing trace needed for accord with (6.81).

As it stands, (6.89) contains the traces (sums over $\rho = \pm\frac{1}{2}$) of the density matrices (6.90). A diagonal element (i.e. when the sum over $\rho$ is now left off) will help give the rate for producing the specific orientation designated by e. The result can be written as a modification of the spectrum expression (6.82) to

$$(d\lambda/dW\,d\Omega)_{\mathrm{e}} = (d\lambda/4\pi dW).\tfrac{1}{2}(1+\mathscr{P}.\boldsymbol{\sigma}_{\mathrm{e}}), \tag{6.91}$$

where $\boldsymbol{\sigma}_{\mathrm{e}} \equiv \chi^{\dagger}_{\mathrm{e}}\,\boldsymbol{\sigma}\chi_{\mathrm{e}}$ again, as in (5.51). The polarization vector here is, not unexpectedly, a longitudinal one

$$\mathscr{P} = \mp\hat{\mathbf{p}}\bar{S}/S \quad (\text{for } \mathrm{e}^{\mp}), \tag{6.92}$$

with $S$ just the spectrum shape-factor (6.85).

The 'polarization shape', $\bar{S}$ of (6.92), differs from $S$ in that it is a product of the interference of amplitudes with $\kappa = \pm(j+\frac{1}{2})$, rather than a sum of their squares:

$$\bar{S} = [4\pi^3/pWF] \sum_{J\kappa\bar{\kappa}} \rho_J^2 \, e^{i[\delta(\kappa)-\delta(-\kappa)]} A_J(\kappa\bar{\kappa})[A_J(-\kappa,-\bar{\kappa}) \pm A_J(-\kappa,\bar{\kappa})]^*. \tag{6.93}$$

When the amplitudes (6.75) are inserted into this, the result can be written

$$\bar{S}(W,Z) = \sum_{Jj\bar{j}} \bar{S}_{Jj\bar{j}}(W,Z) \tag{6.94 a}$$

with

$$\bar{S}_{Jj\bar{j}} = [16\pi^2/(1+\gamma_0)]\rho_J^2 \, R^{2j-1}[D_-^2 \, \lambda_{j-\frac{1}{2}} + D_+^2 \, \mu_{j-\frac{1}{2}} + 2D_- D_+ \nu_{j-\frac{1}{2}}]. \tag{6.94 b}$$

This is just the spectrum shape-factor formula (6.85) except that new electron radial function combinations $\lambda$, $\mu$, $\nu$ replace $L$, $\bar{M}$, $\bar{N}$:

$$\left.\begin{aligned} \lambda_{k-1} &= [\pi(1+\gamma_0)/4pWFR^{2(k-1)}]2f_{-k}\,g_{-k}\sin[\delta(-k)-\delta(k)] \\ \mu_{k-1} &= [\pi(1+\gamma_0/)4pWFR^{2(k-1)}]2f_k\,g_k\sin[\delta(k)-\delta(-k)] \\ \nu_{k-1} &= [\pi(1+\gamma_0)/4pWFR^{2(k-1)}](f_k f_{-k}-g_k\,g_{-k})\sin[\delta(-k)-\delta(k)] \end{aligned}\right\}. \tag{6.95}$$

It will be found in the next chapter that, to a high order of approximation, $\lambda/L = \mu/\bar{M} = \nu/\bar{N} = v/c$. This means that the longitudinal polarization $\mathscr{P} = \mp v/c$, for $e^{\mp}$, normally persists even when high angular momenta are being carried away by the electrons.

## 6.6. Angular distributions of the electrons

High angular momentum ejections may result in more complicated angular distributions of the electrons, relative to oriented nuclei, than those found for the allowed decays in § 1.8 and § 5.2.

The expectations can be derived from the rate expression (6.78), which depends on the electron's emission direction through the eigenfunctions $\chi_{\kappa\mu}(\hat{\mathbf{p}})$. The distribution of the intensity among the directions can be expressed in terms of the spherical harmonics

$$Y_{\Lambda 0}(\hat{\mathbf{p}}) \equiv [(2\Lambda+1)/4\pi]^{\frac{1}{2}} P_\Lambda(\cos\theta)$$

through the use of the expansion (6.38). The evaluation of the terms, as (6.78) shows, will require summing over the lepton orientations $\mu\bar{\mu}$. That can be done with techniques initiated by Racah (see the reference § on p. 176, for example) and the results are expressed in terms of 'Racah coefficients' $W$, each a function of six angular momenta, for which extensive tabulations exist. The procedure outlined here converts (6.78) into:

$$d\lambda/dW\,d\Omega = 2g^2q^2(2I+1)\sum_{\Lambda}(-)^{I'-M}\langle I(M)I(-M)|\Lambda(0)\rangle Y_{\Lambda 0}\times$$
$$\times\sum_{\bar{\jmath}jj'JJ'}(-)^{\bar{\jmath}+\frac{1}{2}}[(2J+1)(2J'+1)]^{\frac{1}{2}}\rho_J(j\bar{\jmath})\rho_{J'}(j'\bar{\jmath})\rho_\Lambda(jj')\times$$
$$\times W(IJIJ';\,I'\Lambda)W(jJj'J';\,\bar{\jmath}\Lambda)F^{\Lambda}_{JJ'}(\bar{\jmath}jj'), \qquad (6.96)$$

where

$$F^{\Lambda}_{JJ'} = \sum_{\kappa\kappa'}{}' e^{i[\delta(\kappa')-\delta(\kappa)]}[A_J(\kappa\bar{\kappa})\pm A_J(\kappa,-\bar{\kappa})]^*[A_{J'}(\kappa'\bar{\kappa})\pm A_{J'}(\kappa',-\bar{\kappa})] \qquad (6.97)$$

is a sum over two pairs of the values $\kappa = \pm(2j+1)$, $\kappa' = \pm(2j'+1)$ such that only terms with even values of $l(\kappa)+l'(\kappa')+\Lambda$ are included, as follows from the restriction on the sum (6.38). Only $\bar{\kappa} = +(2\bar{\jmath}+1)$ *or* $\bar{\kappa} = -(2\bar{\jmath}+1)$ is to be used. The entire expression (6.96) is invariant to the interchange $j, J \longleftrightarrow j', J'$ except that $F^{\Lambda}_{J'J}(\bar{\jmath}j'j)$ equals $F^{\Lambda}_{JJ'}{}^*(\bar{\jmath}jj')$, in general, and this is enough to guarantee a properly real rate. As usual, the upper signs in (6.97) refer to negatron emission, the lower to positrons.

The quantity $F^{\Lambda}_{JJ'}(\bar{\jmath}jj')$ is a combination of radial lepton waves and nuclear $\beta$-moments which can be made more explicit by substitutions from (6.75). The cases of interferences $j' \neq j$ will clearly require the introduction of new electron radial function combinations, generalized from the tabulated ones $L$, $M$, $N$ of (6.86). The new combinations are normally negligible as the next chapter will show, hence only the cases of $j' = j$ will be made more explicit here. Then, for *even* $\Lambda$ (when $\kappa' = \kappa$ only, in (6.97)):

$$F^{\Lambda}_{JJ'}(\bar{\jmath}jj) = \epsilon(J-J')[4pWFR^{2j-1}/\pi(1+\gamma_0)]\times$$
$$\times\{D_-D'_-\,L_{j-\frac{1}{2}}+D_+D'_+\,M_{j-\frac{1}{2}}+(D_+D'_-+D_-D'_+)N_{j-\frac{1}{2}}\}, \qquad (6.98)$$

where $D_+$ and $D'_+$ are again just the combinations of neutrino radial functions and nuclear $\beta$-moments of (6.88), evaluated for $J$ and $J'$ respectively. The sign factor $\epsilon(J-J')$ is $i^{J'-J}$ when $J$, $J'$ are both even or both odd; $\epsilon(J-J') \equiv \pm i^{J'-J+1}\,(e^{\mp})$ when $J+j+\bar{\jmath}$ is even and $J'+j+\bar{\jmath}$ is odd. The $\epsilon$'s are always real, $\pm 1$. For *odd* $\Lambda$ (when $\kappa' = -\kappa$ only, in (6.97)):

$$F^{\Lambda}_{JJ'}+F^{\Lambda}_{J'J} = \pm\epsilon(J-J')[8pWFR^{2j-1}/\pi(1+\gamma_0)]\times$$
$$\times\{D_-D'_-\,\lambda_{j-\frac{1}{2}}+D_+D'_+\,\mu_{j-\frac{1}{2}}+(D_+D'_-+D_-D'_+)\nu_{j-\frac{1}{2}}\}. \qquad (6.99)$$

These expressions reduce to just the shape-factors of (6.85) and (6.94) in the absence of all interference, i.e. $J' = J$ as well as $j' = j$. Precisely,

$$\left.\begin{aligned}\rho_J^2(j\bar{j})F_{JJ}^{\Lambda}(\bar{j}jj) &= [pWF/4\pi^3]S_{Jj\bar{j}} && (\Lambda \text{ even})\\ &= \pm[pWF/4\pi^3]\bar{S}_{Jj\bar{j}} && (\Lambda \text{ odd})\end{aligned}\right\}. \tag{6.100}$$

The $\Lambda = 0$ case helps to show that the angular distribution (6.96) properly reduces to the spectrum (6.83), (6.85) upon integration over the electron emission directions.

In the allowed approximation, the radial functions are evaluated for $R = 0$, and then only terms with $j = j' = \bar{j} = \frac{1}{2}$ survive. The quantities $J$, $J'$ and $\Lambda$ are restricted to the values 0 and 1 by the Racah coefficients of (6.96). The resulting angular distribution takes the form:

$$d\lambda/dW\,d\Omega = [g^2q^2pWF/8\pi^4]\left\{S_{0\frac{1}{2}\frac{1}{2}}+S_{1\frac{1}{2}\frac{1}{2}}+\right.$$
$$\left.+\frac{\langle M\rangle}{I}\cos\theta\left[\mp\langle M_{\mathrm{S}}\rangle\bar{S}_{1\frac{1}{2}\frac{1}{2}}+\delta_{II'}\left(\frac{I}{3(I+1)}\right)^{\frac{1}{2}}\frac{2\pi^2}{pWF}(F_{01}^1+F_{10}^1)\right]\right\}. \tag{6.101}$$

It can be readily checked that the version of this for no parity change coincides with the allowed approximation result (5.49), when the latter is integrated over neutrino directions. The form (6.101) will also apply to cases of parity change, the so-called 'parity-forbidden' transitions discussed in the next chapter.

## 6.7. The electron-neutrino correlations

The directional correlation of electrons and neutrinos emitted without orbital momentum were discussed in § 1.9, and presented in (5.44) as a result of the allowed approximation to the theory. Here, the 'exact' theory will be considered.

The emission direction $\hat{\mathbf{q}}$ of the neutrino must be made as specific as the electron's direction $\hat{\mathbf{p}}$ already is in the rate expression (6.35). That may be accomplished as for the electron, in the development from (6.36). A plane wave of definite momentum $\mathbf{q}$ must be used for the lepton current implicit in the transition matrix $\langle \mathrm{f}|H_\beta|\mathrm{i}\rangle$. The plane wave must be analysed into spherical component waves, as in (3.47), if advantage is to be taken of the results already derived for $\langle \mathrm{f}|H_\beta(\kappa\mu\bar{\kappa}\bar{\mu})|\mathrm{i}\rangle$ of (6.58) and (6.72). The latter contains spherical neutrino waves in a special phase adopted in (6.41) for reasons of symmetry. To obtain the $\phi_{\bar{\kappa}\bar{\mu}}^C$ in the special relative phases, the analysis (3.47) of the plane wave must be modified to

$$\phi_{\nu=\pm\frac{1}{2}}^C = \pm\sum_{\bar{\kappa}\bar{\mu}}\hat{\bar{\kappa}}(-)^{\bar{\mu}+\frac{1}{2}}\langle\bar{l}(\bar{\mu}-\nu)\tfrac{1}{2}(\nu)|\bar{j}(\bar{\mu})\rangle Y_{\bar{l},\bar{\mu}-\nu}(\hat{\mathbf{q}})\phi_{\bar{\kappa}\bar{\mu}}^C. \tag{6.102}$$

The product of the vector-addition coefficient and the spherical harmonic here is just the projection $\chi_\nu^\dagger\,\chi_{\bar\kappa\bar\mu}(\hat{\mathbf{q}})$ on a Pauli eigenspinor, as reference to (2.18) shows. Consequently, (6.35) becomes

$$d\lambda/dW\,d\Omega_e\,d\Omega_\nu = 2\pi\left|\sum_{\kappa\mu\bar\kappa\bar\mu}\hat{\bar\kappa}(-)^{\bar\mu+\frac{1}{2}}e^{i\delta(\kappa)}\chi_{\kappa\mu}(\hat{\mathbf{p}})\chi_{\bar\kappa\bar\mu}(\hat{\mathbf{q}})\langle \mathrm{f}|H_\beta(\kappa\mu\bar\kappa\bar\mu)|\mathrm{i}\rangle\right|^2. \tag{6.103}$$

This form holds for either negatron or positron emission.

The distribution in electron and neutrino directions may be analysed into spherical harmonics by using appropriate versions of (6.38) for each lepton. It must be expected that the two spherical harmonics will finally appear in combinations (see (3.45))

$$\sum_m Y_{\Lambda m}(\hat{\mathbf{p}})Y^*_{\Lambda m}(\hat{\mathbf{q}}) = [(2\Lambda+1)/4\pi]P_\Lambda(\hat{\mathbf{p}}\,.\,\hat{\mathbf{q}}), \tag{6.104}$$

after an average over the initial nuclear orientations and summations over the lepton spins have been carried out. The systematic procedure, much like that used to obtain the angular distribution (6.96), actually leads to such a result:

$$\begin{aligned} d\lambda/dW\,d\Omega_e\,d\Omega_\nu &= (g^2q^2/4\pi)\sum_\Lambda(2\Lambda+1)P_\Lambda(\cos\theta_{e\nu})\times \\ &\quad\times\sum_{Jjj'\bar\jmath\bar\jmath'}(-)^{J+j+j'}\rho_\Lambda(jj')\rho_\Lambda(\bar\jmath\bar\jmath')\rho_J(j\bar\jmath)\rho_J(j'\bar\jmath')\times \\ &\quad\times W(j\bar\jmath j'\bar\jmath';\,J\Lambda)G_J^\Lambda(jj'\bar\jmath\bar\jmath'), \end{aligned} \tag{6.105}$$

where

$$G_J^\Lambda = \sum\hat{\bar\kappa}\hat{\bar\kappa}'e^{i[\delta(\kappa')-\delta(\kappa)]}[A_J(\kappa\bar\kappa)\pm A_J(\kappa,-\bar\kappa)]^*[A_J(\kappa'\bar\kappa')\pm A_J(\kappa',-\bar\kappa')] \tag{6.106}$$

is a sum over the four sets of $\kappa$, $\kappa'$, $\bar\kappa$, $\bar\kappa'$ values, for the given $jj'\bar\jmath\bar\jmath'$, which are consistent with $l(\kappa)+l'(\kappa')+\Lambda$ and $\bar l(\bar\kappa)+\bar l'(\bar\kappa')+\Lambda$ both even. As always for randomly oriented nuclei, there is no interference between different total lepton angular momenta $J$ (see (6.79), for example), but various individual lepton angular momenta do interfere, in general.

As for the angular distributions of the preceding section, the important terms here will be those for which $j'=j$ and $\bar\jmath'=\bar\jmath$, when

$$\left.\begin{aligned} \rho_J^2(j\bar\jmath)\,G_J^\Lambda(jj\bar\jmath\bar\jmath) &= [pWF/2\pi^3]S_{Jj\bar\jmath} \quad (\Lambda\text{ even}) \\ &= -[pWF/2\pi^3]\bar S_{Jj\bar\jmath} \quad (\Lambda\text{ odd}) \end{aligned}\right\}. \tag{6.107}$$

in terms of the shape factors of (6.85) and (6.94). The $\Lambda = 0$ case helps show that the integral of the correlation distribution (6.105) over all lepton directions properly yields the spectrum (6.83) (6.85).

In the allowed approximation, $j'=j=\bar\jmath'=\bar\jmath=\frac{1}{2}$ only. There are then only $\Lambda = 0$ and $\Lambda = 1$ terms in (6.105) and it becomes proportional to $[1+a(v/c)\cos\vartheta_{e\nu}]$ with

$$av/c = (\bar{S}_{0\frac{1}{2}\frac{1}{2}}-\tfrac{1}{3}\bar{S}_{1\frac{1}{2}\frac{1}{2}})/(S_{0\frac{1}{2}\frac{1}{2}}+S_{1\frac{1}{2}\frac{1}{2}}). \tag{6.108}$$

This is readily shown to yield the same electron-neutrino correlation coefficient $a$ as that of (5.42), in the allowed approximation.

Further applications of (6.105), as of all the results of this chapter, will be discussed in the next chapter.

# VII

# FORBIDDEN $\beta$-EMISSIONS

WHEN a nucleus can reach a given more stable state only by violating the allowed selection rules (5.8), then it will undergo a slow 'forbidden' transition to that state. The allowed rules are based on neglecting all radiation components except those generated through the $\beta$-moments $\langle 1\rangle$ and $\langle \sigma\rangle$. Additional moments were exhibited in (6.63); they make possible any transition $I \to I'$, with or without parity change.

Forbidden transitions are classified according to 'degree of forbiddenness', $n$, and as 'parity-forbidden' or 'unique' within a given degree. In a given transition, any of the total lepton angular momenta $J = |I'-I| \equiv \Delta I,\ \Delta I+1,\ \Delta I+2,\ldots,\ I+I'$ may be ejected, and the nuclear parities are such that either $\pi_i \pi_f = (-)^{\Delta I}$ or $\pi_i \pi_f = (-)^{\Delta I-1}$. The transition is called

$$\left.\begin{array}{l}\text{`}\Delta I\text{-times forbidden' if } \pi_i \pi_f = (-)^{\Delta I} \\ \text{`}|\Delta I-1|\text{-times forbidden' if } \pi_i \pi_f = (-)^{\Delta I-1}\end{array}\right\}. \tag{7.1}$$

The motives for this nomenclature will emerge when the relative rates are examined. Of course, the cases $\Delta I = 0$ or 1 with no parity change are termed 'allowed' rather than 'zero-times forbidden'.

An $n$-times forbidden transition has $\pi_i \pi_f = (-)^n$ and its nuclear spin change is either $\Delta I = n$ or $\Delta I = n+1$, except that once-forbidden transitions include $\Delta I = 0$. The cases are differentiated as

$$\left.\begin{array}{l}n\text{-times `parity-forbidden' when } \Delta I = n \\ \text{`unique' } n\text{-times forbidden when } \Delta I = n+1\end{array}\right\}. \tag{7.2}$$

The name 'parity-forbidden' is appropriate because the corresponding transitions differ in parity from cases one degree less forbidden, also having $\Delta I = n$ but with $\pi_i \pi_f = (-)^{n-1}$. The name 'unique' is applied to the cases $\Delta I = n+1$ because each is generated predominantly through a single $\beta$-moment ($\langle \boldsymbol{\sigma} . \mathbf{T}^n_{n+1}\rangle$). The singular once-forbidden case $\Delta I = 0$ is parity-forbidden relative to the allowed $\Delta I = 0$ transitions.

## 7.1. The normal approximation

The exact evaluations of the preceding chapter consist of infinite series of terms, corresponding to various angular momenta. The range of the total angular momenta expected in a given case is limited by $\mathbf{J} = \mathbf{I}-\mathbf{I}'$, but the possible angular momenta of the individual leptons are not so restricted; there is some $\bar{\mathbf{j}} = \mathbf{J}-\mathbf{j}$ for any $\mathbf{j}$ chosen. On the other hand, each added unit of $j$ or $\bar{j}$ represents an additional unit of orbital momentum, and the attendant centrifugal repulsion damps its contribution by a large factor, as has already been pointed out in § 1.6. It must be expected that, normally, all $j$, $\bar{j}$ values will be negligible except those giving a minimum sum $j+\bar{j}$, which itself cannot be less than $(j+\bar{j})_{\min} = J_{\min} = \Delta I$. The case $J = j+\bar{j}$ is the 'extended' configuration of $\mathbf{j}+\bar{\mathbf{j}}$; in it, the lepton spins must be parallel, forming a triplet state. This triplet state has the advantage that, to produce a given $J \geqslant 1$, one less unit of lepton orbital momentum is needed than in the singlet state. Of course, the singlet lepton state must still be considered for the allowed and once-forbidden transitions with $J = 0$.

The way that the centrifugal effect is formally implemented is through the behaviour near the origin of the radial waves, as illustrated in Fig. 1.9. For example, the neutrino waves have the power series expansions

$$j_{\bar{l}}(qr) = [(qr)^{\bar{l}}/(2\bar{l}+1)!!][1-(qr)^2/2(2\bar{l}+3)+...], \tag{7.3}$$

as follows from (3.35) and (3.29), if $(2\bar{l}+1)!! \equiv 1.3.5...(2\bar{l}+1)$. Only values inside the nuclear radius, $r < R$, are relevant, and $R < 1/40$, in units of $\hbar/mc$, according to § 1.6. The reduction of the radial amplitudes by the factor $R$ for each unit of orbital momentum is the centrifugal effect in question.

The forbidden transitions will have been treated to the same relative accuracy as the allowed decay of Chapter V if only the leading terms in the power series expansion in $R$ are retained. Since this presumes $qR \ll 1$ and $pR \ll 1$, a necessary criterion for the validity of this step will be

$$R \ll 1/(W_0-1), \tag{7.4}$$

which is equivalent to $W_0-mc^2 \ll 160/A^{\frac{1}{3}}$ MeV, when $R \approx 1{\cdot}2A^{\frac{1}{3}}(10)^{-13}$ cm is used. This condition is easily fulfilled by every known case of nuclear $\beta$-decay.

Evaluations which retain only the lowest contributing power of $R$ will be called 'normal approximations' because they should be adequate in almost all cases. 'Anomalous' cases may occur because the leading term for parity-forbidden transitions depends on several of the unknown nuclear $\beta$-moments. These may happen to cancel against each other (the corresponding radiation components can then be said to interfere destructively). Such events will be unpredictable as long as the $\beta$-moments continue to serve as unknown parameters. (Cancellations which are complete enough may make themselves observationally evident through anomalously low decay rates.) Treatment of the anomalous cases will simply require carrying out the power series expansions in $R$ to higher degrees.

The fact that usually only the single, leading power of $R$ plays an appreciable role in a given case helps justify‡ treating as equivalent all the radii $R$ introduced in (6.62). All are approximately 'root-mean-square' values of the possible distances of the transforming nucleon from the nuclear centre. This mean cannot be very significantly distinguished from others of the many varieties of 'nuclear radius' which are defined by experiments with nuclei. Certainly it would not be valid to treat each $R$ as a free parameter; each must be about $10^{-13}A^{\frac{1}{3}}$ cm in size.

*Normal spectra*

The normal approximation procedure will be applied to the spectrum shape-factor (6.85) first. For this, it is necessary to know the leading terms of the electron radial waves, which appear in the spectrum results only in the combinations $L$, $\bar{M}$, and $\bar{N}$ of (6.86). Decisions must be made about the precision with which the atomic coulomb field must be treated and those become clearest after results are available for the case of a field due to a point-charge, $+Ze$. In this case, the radial waves of § 3.3 may be used and these give for the leading term of $L_{j-\frac{1}{2}}$:

$$L_{j-\frac{1}{2}} \approx \tfrac{1}{2}(2p)^{2(\gamma-\gamma_0)}\left[\frac{\Gamma(2\gamma_0+1)}{\Gamma(2\gamma+1)}\right]^2\left|\frac{\Gamma(\gamma+i\nu)}{\Gamma(\gamma_0+i\nu)}\right|^2(j+\tfrac{1}{2})(j+\tfrac{1}{2}+\gamma), \quad (7.5\,\text{a})$$

where $\gamma$, $\gamma_0$ are given by (6.87) and $\nu = \pm\alpha ZW/p$ for negatrons and positrons, respectively. A slight residual dependence on $R$ has been omitted (a factor $R$ to the power $2(\gamma-\gamma_0)-(2j-1) \approx 0$). The leading terms of $\bar{M}_{j-\frac{1}{2}}$ and $\bar{N}_{j-\frac{1}{2}}$ can be written as ratios to $L_{j-\frac{1}{2}}$:

$$\bar{M}/L \approx (j+\tfrac{1}{2}-\gamma)/(j+\tfrac{1}{2}+\gamma), \qquad \bar{N}/L \approx \mp\alpha Z/(j+\tfrac{1}{2}+\gamma). \quad (7.5\,\text{b})$$

Notice that $\bar{N} \approx \mp(L\bar{M})^{\frac{1}{2}}$ for negatrons and positrons, respectively, when only leading terms are retained. For $j > \frac{1}{2}$, the approximation $\gamma \approx (j+\frac{1}{2})$ is in error by as much as 5 per cent only for $Z = 92$; even $\gamma_0 \approx 1$ is correct within 5 per cent for $Z \lesssim 44$. When the difference $(j+\frac{1}{2})-\gamma \approx \alpha^2Z^2/(2j+1)$ is retained only for $\bar{M}$:

$$\left.\begin{aligned} &L_{j-\frac{1}{2}} \approx p^{2j-1}/[(2j)!!]^2 \\ &\bar{M}/L \approx \{\alpha Z/(2j+1)\}^2, \qquad \bar{N}/L \approx \mp\alpha Z/(2j+1) \end{aligned}\right\}. \quad (7.6)$$

The first of these expressions is independent of $Z$, under the assumption $(\alpha Z)^2 \ll 1$, and reflects the fact that $L_{j-\frac{1}{2}} = R^{-(2j-1)}j^2_{j-\frac{1}{2}}(pR)$ for free

‡ Attempts to improve on this become relatively more important for corrections to the normal approximations (e.g. § 7.4).

radial waves. The normal approximations of $\bar{M}$ and $\bar{N}$ vanish for $Z = 0$ because they require $l = j+\frac{1}{2}$, hence an extra unit of orbital momentum. Thus $\bar{M}$ and $\bar{N}$ embody a modifying influence of the electrostatic field on the centrifugal effects.

The shape-factor (6.85) can now be written:

$$S \approx [16\pi^2/(1+\gamma_0)] \sum_{Jj\bar{j}} \rho_{\bar{j}}^2 R^{2\bar{j}-1} L_{j-\frac{1}{2}} [D_- \mp (\alpha Z/2j+1) D_+]^2. \quad (7.7)$$

Here $D_{\pm}$ are the combinations of neutrino radial waves and nuclear $\beta$-moments given in (6.88). Their leading terms are proportional to $R^{\bar{j}-\frac{1}{2}}$, according to (7.3) and this makes a typical term of the shape factor proportional to the power $2(j+\bar{j}-1)$ of $R$. It is now clear that consistency with the normal approximation procedure requires that only terms with the minimum values $j+\bar{j} = J = \Delta I$ be retained. Then $j+\bar{j}+J = 2J$ is even and the corresponding expressions for $D_{\pm}$ of (6.88 a) lead to

$$S(J \geqslant 1) \approx [16\pi^2/(1+\gamma_0)] R^{2(J-1)} \sum_{j=\frac{1}{2}}^{J-\frac{1}{2}} \rho_{\bar{j}}^2 (j, J-j) L_{j-\frac{1}{2}} \times$$
$$\times (q^{2(J-j)-1}/[(2J-2j)!!]^2)[B_J(-1) \mp (\alpha Z/2j+1) C_J(\pm 1)]^2, \quad (7.8)$$

for negatron and positron emissions, respectively. The indicated restriction to $J \geqslant 1$ here is necessary because this expression is predicated on $j+\bar{j} = J$ and the $J = 0$ radiation must be obtained from the singlet combination of $j = \bar{j} = \frac{1}{2}$, for which $J \neq j+\bar{j} = 1$. The case $J = 0$ is treated separately in § 7.3; it is pertinent only to the allowed and once-forbidden transitions with $\Delta I = 0$.

There are further consequences of the normal approximation $J = j+\bar{j}$ for the $\beta$-moment combinations $B_J$ and $C_J$ occurring in (7.8) and given in (6.76), (6.77). The weight factor $w_J$, given in (6.54), becomes simply $w_J = [2(J+1)/J]^{\frac{1}{2}}$. Consequently,

$$\left.\begin{aligned} B_J(-1) &= (2+J^{-1})^{\frac{1}{2}} \langle (C_A - C_V \gamma_5) \boldsymbol{\sigma} . \mathbf{T}_J^{J-1} \rangle \\ C_J(\pm 1) &= \langle (C_V - C_A \gamma_5) Y_J \rangle \mp (1+J^{-1})^{\frac{1}{2}} \langle (C_A - C_V \gamma_5) \boldsymbol{\sigma} . \mathbf{T}_J^J \rangle \end{aligned}\right\}. \quad (7.9)$$

Moments with $L = J+1$ are thus entirely eliminated by the normal approximation procedure, obviously because they require an extra unit of orbital momentum for a given $J$. Each moment as written in (7.9) has two parts which are mutually exclusive for a given nuclear parity change, a fact already pointed out in connexion with (6.74).

When the weight factor $\rho_{\bar{j}}^2$ of (6.39) is evaluated‡ for the extended

‡ Use is made of the fact that

$$\langle j(-\tfrac{1}{2})\bar{j}(\tfrac{1}{2})|j+\bar{j}(0)\rangle^2 = \frac{(j+\bar{j})!}{2(2j+2\bar{j}-1)!!} \cdot \frac{(2j)!!(2\bar{j})!!}{(j+\frac{1}{2})!(\bar{j}+\frac{1}{2})!}$$

is deducible from the formula (3.6.12) recorded in Edmonds' treatise (ref., p. 176).

(triplet) configuration $J = j+\bar{j}$, the shape factor becomes ($J = \Delta I \geqslant 1$ only):

$$S \approx \frac{8\pi(J-1)!\,R^{2(J-1)}}{(1+\gamma_0)(2J-1)!!}\sum_j \frac{(2j)!!}{(2J-2j)!!}\,\frac{L_{j-\frac{1}{2}}q^{2(J-j)-1}}{(j-\frac{1}{2})!\,(J-j-\frac{1}{2})!}\mathscr{M}_j^2(J), \quad (7.10)$$

where $\mathscr{M}_j$ is a combination of $\beta$-moments which depends on the parity change in the nuclear transition. For *parity-forbidden* transitions having $J = \Delta I$ and $\pi_i\pi_f = (-)^{\Delta I}$,

$$\mathscr{M}_j(J) = C_V[\langle \boldsymbol{\alpha}.\mathbf{T}_J^{J-1}\rangle \mp (\alpha Z/2j+1)(J/2J+1)^{\frac{1}{2}}\langle Y_J\rangle]+$$
$$+(\alpha Z/2j+1)(J+1/2J+1)^{\frac{1}{2}}C_A\langle \boldsymbol{\sigma}.\mathbf{T}_J^J\rangle \quad \text{for } e^{\mp}. \quad (7.11)$$

It can be seen that the change from negatron to positron emission requires not only $Z \to -Z$, but also a sign change of the Vector-Pseudovector interference $\sim C_V C_A$. Such an interference does not appear in the allowed approximation of the spectra (5.45). The *unique* spectra having $\pi_i\pi_f = (-)^{\Delta I-1}$ are obtained merely by making the interchange $C_V \leftrightarrow -C_A\gamma_5$ in the $\beta$-moment combination $\mathscr{M}_j$, as can be seen from (7.9) and the parity selection rules (6.71).

Particularly in the $(\alpha Z)^2 \ll 1$ approximation (7.6) it is easy to see that the normal shape-factor (7.10) is essentially a homogeneous polynomial, of degree $J-1 = \Delta I-1 \geqslant 0$, in products of $p^2$ and $q^2$. Only when $J > 1$ must be ejected, hence the leptons required to carry off orbital moment $L > 0$, is the shape-factor dependent on the electron energy $W = (p^2+1)^{\frac{1}{2}} = W_0-q$. For $\Delta I \leqslant 1$, the full spectrum is normally expected to have just the statistical shape of (1.10), and to yield a linear Kurie plot.

*Order of magnitude estimates*

Preliminary estimates of expected orders of magnitude are peculiarly important to meaningful applications of the forbidden decay theory. This stems from the necessity for treating the $\beta$-moments as unknown parameters. The addition of higher order terms to the ones expected to predominate may bring with it additional parameters and cause the data fitting to lose all significance. The higher order corrections are sometimes justifiable in individual cases, after careful investigations of the consistency with the data of the procedure adopted.

The expected magnitude of any given decay rate is formally represented by the integral over the spectrum (6.83):

$$\lambda = [g^2/2\pi^3]f(W_0, Z)\langle S(W, Z)\rangle, \quad (7.12\,\text{a})$$

where $f$ is again the integrated statistical spectrum (1.11) while $\langle S\rangle$ is the spectrum average of the shape-factor:

$$\langle S\rangle = f^{-1}\int_0^{p_0} dp\, p^2q^2F(Z,W)S(W,Z). \qquad (7.12\text{b})$$

The comparative half-life $ft \equiv f\ln 2/\lambda$ is not expected to be independent of the energy release $W_0$ unless the shape-factor is independent of lepton energies, hence the spectrum of the statistical form characteristic of the allowed approximation. The fact that $S$ is approximately a homogeneous polynomial of degree $(\Delta I-1)$ in $(pR)^2$ and $(qR)^2$, as pointed out in the preceding subsection, makes it evident that the products $(p_0^2R^2)^{\Delta I-1}ft$ should be expected to be more nearly constant than is $ft$ itself. This is sometimes used as a rough guide in comparing measured decay rates with each other.

Concerned in the expectations are the unknown $\beta$-moments. Those like $\langle Y_L\rangle$ and $\langle \boldsymbol{\sigma}.\mathbf{T}_J^L\rangle$ are essentially averages of normalized harmonics over normalized nuclear states hence may be treated‡ as of 'order of magnitude unity'. When the operator $\gamma_5$ intervenes, as in $\langle\gamma_5 Y_L\rangle$ and $\langle\boldsymbol{\alpha}.\mathbf{T}_J^L\rangle$, the moment is treated as of order $v_N/c \ll 1$, where $v_N$ is a typical nucleonic velocity within nuclear matter. The expectation $v_N \ll c$ is based on the fact that typical nuclear energies are only a few MeV as compared to the 1 GeV nucleonic rest-mass. Sometimes it is estimated that $v_N/c \approx \frac{1}{10}$.

Besides the factor $v_N/c$, the quantities $\alpha Z$ and $R$ parametrize the decays. These three 'parameters of smallness' play the leading roles in motivating the forbidden classifications, which are considered next.

First to be justified is the approximation

$$\mathscr{M}_j(J) \approx C_A^*\langle\boldsymbol{\sigma}.\mathbf{T}_J^{J-1}\rangle \quad (\text{unique, } \Delta I = J \geqslant 1) \qquad (7.13)$$

for the moments to appear in the shape-factor (7.9) when

$$\pi_i\,\pi_f = (-)^{\Delta I-1}.$$

The moments proper to this case are supposed to be obtained from (7.11) by making the interchange $C_V \leftrightarrow -C_A\gamma_5$, as asserted just below (7.11). The first term of (7.11) leads to just (7.13). The remaining terms are neglected because they come down to the small relative magnitude $\alpha Z(v_N/c) \ll 1$. This treatment yields the same relative accuracy as that of the allowed approximation. Indeed, the unique $\Delta I = J = 1$ case is just the Gamow–Teller contribution to allowed decay, for which (7.13)

‡ Older definitions of $\beta$-moments include factors $r^L$, and then the moment is treated as of order $[R/(\hbar/mc)]^L$. Here, the factors $R^L$ have been separated off, as shown in (6.62).

becomes $C_A\langle\boldsymbol{\sigma}.\mathbf{T}_1^0\rangle \equiv C_A\langle\sigma\rangle/(4\pi)^{\frac{1}{2}}$. It is the fact that just a single $\beta$-moment (7.13) is expected to predominate in any $\pi_i\pi_f = (-)^{\Delta I-1}$ transition that has led to the name 'unique'.

Next, consider the parity-forbidden moments (7.11) themselves. The first term is of order $v_N/c$ and the remaining ones of order $\alpha Z$. There is no clear justification for neglecting any one, relative to the others. This is what makes parity-forbidden transitions particularly vulnerable to the anomalies mentioned in the paragraph following (7.4). With three $\beta$-moments, opposite relative signs can cause cancellations which raise the relative importance of terms neglected in the normal approximation procedure.

The most decisive factor in determining the expected magnitudes is $R^{2(J-1)}$, as it appears in the shape-factor (7.10). It is the smallness of the additional factor $R^2$ ($\ll \frac{1}{1600}$) appearing when $J = \Delta I$ is raised by one unit which is responsible for considering the degree of forbiddenness to be raised one unit thereby. Unique forbidden transitions are governed by moments (7.13) of order unity and are ascribed the order $\mathcal{O}[R^{2(\Delta I-1)}]$, $|\Delta I-1|$ degrees forbidden relative to allowed transitions. Parity forbidden transitions may be described as $\mathcal{O}[R^{2(\Delta I-1)}(v_N/c)^2]$ for light nuclei ($Z \to 0$). The additional small factor $(v_N/c)^2$ accounts for their classification as $\Delta I$-times forbidden. They may actually approach a $|\Delta I-1|$-times forbidden magnitude for very heavy nuclei, when their order is better described as $\mathcal{O}[(\alpha Z)^2 R^{2(\Delta I-1)}]$.

A complication now arises. The unique moments $\langle\boldsymbol{\sigma}.\mathbf{T}_{n+1}^n\rangle$ of (7.13) and the parity-forbidden ones $\mathcal{M}_j(n)$ of (7.11) both govern transitions classified as $n$-times forbidden. Both obey the same parity rules, $\pi_i\pi_f = (-)^n$. $\mathcal{M}_j(n)$ vanishes for the unique cases because these require $J = n+1$, but the unique moment does not vanish‡ for the parity-forbidden cases $J = \Delta I = n$, unless $I+I' < n+1$ (see the selection rules (6.69)). Thus, judging by 'degree of forbiddenness' criteria alone, it seems that the terms of the unique shape-factor should be added to the parity-forbidden terms when obtaining expectations for $\Delta I = J = n$ transitions. However, the unique amplitudes are $\mathcal{O}(R^n)$ as against $\mathcal{O}[(v_N/c)R^{n-1}]$ or $\mathcal{O}[(\alpha Z)R^{n-1}]$ of the parity forbidden terms. Consequently, the contributions of the unique amplitudes should after all be neglected if

$$\alpha Z/R \gg W_0-1, \tag{7.14}$$

i.e. the electron's coulomb energy is much greater than its kinetic energy

‡ In general, even $\mathcal{M}_j(J \gg \Delta I)$ contributes to transitions with $I+I' \geqslant J$, but negligibly as compared to $\mathcal{M}_j(\Delta I)$.

(which enters because $R$ appears in the combinations $pR$ or $qR$). This criterion is fulfilled in almost all actual cases because forbidden transitions are rare among light nuclei; moreover, it would become seriously restrictive only for $Z \lesssim 5$, or so. On the other hand, it must always be remembered that the parity-forbidden transitions are vulnerable to the anomalies mentioned above. When these occur, the unique additions to the parity-forbidden transitions can become relatively appreciable after all, despite fulfilment of the criterion (7.14).

A summary of the classifications for $n = 0, 1, 2,...$ is presented in Table 7.1. The horizontal lines in it separate contributions which are normally

TABLE 7.1

*Classifications of transitions*

| *Degree of forbiddenness* | $\Delta I^{\pi_i \pi_f}$ | $J$ | *$\beta$-moments* | *Orders of magnitude (amplitudes)* |
|---|---|---|---|---|
| Allowed | $0^+$<br>$0^+,\ 1^+$<br>(No $0 \to 0$) | 0<br>1 | $C_V\langle 1\rangle$<br>$C_A\langle \sigma\rangle$ | $\mathcal{O}(R^0)$<br>$\mathcal{O}(R^0)$ |
| Once-forbidden | $0^-$<br>$0^-,\ 1^-$<br>(No $0 \to 0$) | 0<br>1 | $\begin{cases} C_A\langle i\boldsymbol{\sigma} . \hat{\mathbf{r}}\rangle \\ C_A\langle \gamma_5\rangle \end{cases}$<br>$\begin{cases} C_V\langle i\hat{r}\rangle, \quad C_A\langle(\boldsymbol{\sigma}\times\hat{\mathbf{r}})\rangle \\ C_V\langle \alpha\rangle \end{cases}$ | $\mathcal{O}(\alpha Z)$<br>$\mathcal{O}(v_N)$<br>$\mathcal{O}(\alpha Z)$<br>$\mathcal{O}(v_N)$ |
| | $2^-$<br>($1F$ Unique) | 2 | $C_A\langle \boldsymbol{\sigma} . \mathbf{T}^1_2\rangle$ | $\mathcal{O}(R)$ |
| Twice-forbidden | $2^+$ | 2 | $\begin{cases} C_V\langle Y_2\rangle,\ C_A\langle \boldsymbol{\sigma} . \mathbf{T}^2_2\rangle \\ C_V\langle \boldsymbol{\alpha} . \mathbf{T}^1_2\rangle \end{cases}$ | $\mathcal{O}(\alpha ZR)$<br>$\mathcal{O}(v_N R)$ |
| | $3^+$<br>($2F$ Unique) | 3 | $C_A\langle \boldsymbol{\sigma} . \mathbf{T}^2_3\rangle$ | $\mathcal{O}(R^2)$ |
| $n$-times forbidden | $n^{(-)^n}$ | $n$ | $\begin{cases} C_V\langle Y_n\rangle,\ C_A\langle \boldsymbol{\sigma} . \mathbf{T}^n_n\rangle \\ C_V\langle \boldsymbol{\alpha} . \mathbf{T}^{n-1}_n\rangle \end{cases}$ | $\mathcal{O}(\alpha ZR^{n-1})$<br>$\mathcal{O}(v_N R^{n-1})$ |
| | $(n+1)^{(-)^n}$ | $n+1$ | $C_A\langle \boldsymbol{\sigma} . \mathbf{T}^n_{n+1}\rangle$ | $\mathcal{O}(R^n)$ |

expected to have successively smaller magnitudes, down through the table. The last column gives the estimates of the amplitudes concerned, in units $\hbar = m = c = 1$. A conveniently economical notation is introduced in the second column. In terms of it, the parity-forbidden formulae should be used for transitions with $\Delta I = 1^-,\ 2^+,\ 3^-,\ 4^+,...$ while the unique formulae apply to $\Delta I = 1^+,\ 2^-,\ 3^+,\ 4^-,....$ Details of the $\Delta I = 0$ cases will be presented in § 7.3.

The lowest order $\beta$-moments listed in Table 7.1 have been represented by somewhat more perspicuous symbols than the more generally applicable ones defined in (6.63). The new symbols are defined according to

$$\left.\begin{aligned}\Big\langle \mathrm{f}\Big| \sum_a \tau^a_{\pm}(\text{scalar})^\dagger\Big|\mathrm{i}\Big\rangle &= \delta_{I'I}\,\delta_{M'M}\langle(\text{scalar})\rangle\\ \Big\langle \mathrm{f}\Big| \sum_a \tau^a_{\pm}(V^a_m)^\dagger\Big|\mathrm{i}\Big\rangle &= \langle V\rangle\langle I'(M')1(m)|I(M)\rangle\end{aligned}\right\}, \tag{7.15}$$

where $V_m$ is a spherical component of a vector. Consequently,

$$\left.\begin{aligned}\langle Y_0\rangle &= \langle 1\rangle/(4\pi)^{\frac{1}{2}}\\ \langle Y_1\rangle &= \langle i\hat{r}\rangle(3/4\pi)^{\frac{1}{2}}\\ \langle \boldsymbol{\sigma}\,.\,\mathbf{T}^0_1\rangle &= \langle \sigma\rangle/(4\pi)^{\frac{1}{2}}\\ \langle \boldsymbol{\sigma}\,.\,\mathbf{T}^1_0\rangle &= -\langle i\boldsymbol{\sigma}\,.\,\hat{\mathbf{r}}\rangle/(4\pi)^{\frac{1}{2}}\\ \langle \boldsymbol{\sigma}\,.\,\mathbf{T}^1_1\rangle &= \langle(\boldsymbol{\sigma}\times\hat{\mathbf{r}})\rangle(3/8\pi)^{\frac{1}{2}}\end{aligned}\right\}. \tag{7.16}$$

Further such relations are obtained by inserting $\gamma_5$ on both sides of each of these and using $\gamma_5\boldsymbol{\sigma} = -\boldsymbol{\alpha}$. The newly defined moments can be treated as real on the same basis as the original ones.

*Normal approximations in the correlation phenomena*‡

There is a very simple relationship between the normal approximations for the spectrum shape-factors $S$ and the 'polarization shape' $\bar{S}$ of (6.94). It follows from the ratios of leading terms of the electron radial waves, that

$$\left.\begin{aligned}f_{-\kappa}/g_{\kappa} &\approx \pm\alpha Z/(\kappa-\gamma)\\ e^{i[\delta(\kappa)-\delta(-\kappa)]}f_{-\kappa}/g_{-\kappa} &\approx (\mp\alpha Z-i\kappa p)/(\kappa W+\gamma)\end{aligned}\right\}, \tag{7.17}$$

which are obtainable (for $e^{\mp}$ respectively) from (3.49) et seq., in the limit $R \to 0$. Inserting these into the definitions (6.95) and (6.86) yields

$$\lambda/L \approx \mu/\bar{M} \approx \nu/\bar{N} \approx cp/W \;(\equiv v/c). \tag{7.18}$$

These normal approximations are independent of the nuclear charge and of the angular momenta involved. They give for the ratio of $\bar{S}$ (6.94) to $S$ of (6.85):

$$\bar{S}/S \approx \bar{S}_{Jj\bar{j}}/S_{Jj\bar{j}} \approx v/c, \tag{7.19}$$

a result which is very useful in evaluating the normal approximations to all the correlation phenomena.

An immediate consequence is that the longitudinal electron polarization $\mathscr{P} = \mp\bar{S}/S$ of (6.92) must normally be expected to be

$$\mathscr{P} = \mp v/c \quad (\text{for } e^{\mp}) \tag{7.20}$$

for the forbidden as well as the allowed decays. Deviations from this result must be rare and this accords with experimental findings. There is one case in which a substantial deviation has been established§

‡ Here, this includes $\boldsymbol{\sigma}_e\,.\,\mathbf{p}$, $\boldsymbol{\sigma}_e\,.\,\mathbf{I}$, and $\mathbf{p}\,.\,\mathbf{q}$ correlations.

§ A. Alikhanov, *et al.*, *J. Exp. Theor. Phys.* **35**, 1061 (1958); W. Buehring-Heinze, *Z. Phys.* **153**, 237 (1958); H. Wegener *et al.*, *Phys. Rev. Letters*, **1**, 460 (1958).

($|\mathscr{P}| < v/c$). That is the parity-forbidden transition ($1^- \to 0^+$) in RaE, which has long been known to depart from normal approximation expectations in every respect (lifetime and spectrum as well as polarization); this apparently happens because of destructive interferences among the several $\beta$-moments which contribute appreciably to the transition. Agreement with the theory can be obtained‡ by evaluating $S$ and $\bar{S}$ through the order $R^2$, instead of stopping at the normal approximation, and adopting suitable values for $\beta$-moment ratios.

The normal approximations to the electron angular distributions from oriented nuclei (6.96) can be expressed entirely in terms of the shape-factors as they enter (6.100), for $\Delta I \geqslant 1$. They can be written, *with* $J = \Delta I \geqslant 1$:

$$d\lambda/dWd\Omega = [g^2q^2pWF/2\pi^3](2I+1)(2J+1)(-)^{I'-M}\times$$
$$\times \sum_{\Lambda} \langle I(M)I(-M)|\Lambda(0)\rangle W(IJIJ;\, I'\Lambda)D_\Lambda Y_{\Lambda 0}(\vartheta), \quad (7.21\,\text{a})$$

where $$D_\Lambda = \sum_{j} (-)^{\bar{j}+\frac{1}{2}}\rho_\Lambda(j\bar{j})W(jJjJ;\,\bar{j}\Lambda)S_{Jj\bar{j}}(W,Z) \quad (7.21\,\text{b})$$

in the terms with *even* $\Lambda$. In the *odd* $\Lambda$ terms, $D_\Lambda$ has the same form but should be multiplied by the additional factor $\pm v/c$ for negatrons and positrons, respectively. It must be understood that

$$\bar{j} = J - j = \Delta I - j$$

in (7.21), as always in the normal approximations for $\Delta I \geqslant 1$. The $\Delta I = 0$ case has already been presented in (6.101); it is complicated by singlet-triplet interference ($J = 0$ vs. $J = 1$), and this cannot be expressed in terms of the shape-factors as these have been defined.

The normal approximations to the electron-neutrino correlation distributions (6.105) also cannot be entirely expressed in terms of the shape-factors, despite the restriction to a single total lepton angular momentum value $J = \Delta I$ for $\Delta I \geqslant 1$. Interferences persist among the several individual lepton angular momenta consistent with

$$j+\bar{j} = j'+\bar{j}' = J > 1.$$

The evaluations for specific cases can perhaps be done best through the use of the normal approximations for the amplitudes in $G_J^\Lambda$ of (6.106):

$$A_J(-k, \bar{j}+\tfrac{1}{2}) \pm A_J(-k, -\bar{j}-\tfrac{1}{2})$$
$$\approx \mp i^{k-1}(2+J^{-1})^{\frac{1}{2}}[(qR)^{\bar{j}-\frac{1}{2}}/(2\bar{j})!!]g_{-k}\mathscr{M}_j(J), \quad (7.22\,\text{a})$$

where $k \equiv j+\frac{1}{2}$ ($= |\kappa|$). The combinations of $\beta$-moments $\mathscr{M}_j(J)$ are

‡ A. Bincer, E. Church, and J. Weneser, *Phys. Rev. Letters*, **1**, 95 (1958); H. Wegener, *Z. Phys.* **151**, 252 (1958); A. Alikhanov, G. Eliseyev, and V. Liubimov, *Nucl. Phys.* **13**, 541 (1959); J. Fujita, *Phys. Rev.* **126**, 202 (1962).

again those given in (7.11) and (7.13), for parity-forbidden and unique transitions, respectively. To obtain just these combinations, the $(\alpha Z)^2 \ll (j+\frac{1}{2})^2$ approximations of (7.17),

$$f_k/g_{-k} \approx \mp\alpha Z/(2j+1) \quad \text{and} \quad g_k/f_{-k} \approx \pm\alpha Z/(2j+1), \tag{7.23}$$

have been used. The amplitudes for $\kappa = +k$ are also needed, but these differ from (7.22 a) only by the factor

$$\pm \mathrm{i} f_{-k}/g_{-k} \quad (\text{for e}^{\mp}), \tag{7.22 b}$$

which is easily evaluated from (7.17).

The final normal approximation result for the electron-neutrino correlations cannot be written appreciably more simply than as in the 'exact' expression (6.105). There is a restriction of the summations in accordance with $j+\bar{j} = j'+\bar{j}' = J = \Delta I$ for $\Delta I \geqslant 1$ (the $\Delta I = 0$ case has already been given in (6.108)). In the $j' = j$ and $\bar{j}' = \bar{j}$ terms, the expressions (6.107) with $\bar{S} = (v/c)S$ can be used for $G_J^\Lambda$. Resort to (7.22) is needed in the interference terms. It is helpful to notice that the restrictions on the summations defining $G_J^\Lambda(jj'\bar{j}\bar{j}')$ in (6.106) imply that only values of $(j+j'+\Lambda)$ and $(\bar{j}+\bar{j}'+\Lambda)$ of the same parity can contribute; both must be even or both odd for a given $\Lambda$ because their sum is necessarily even when $j+j' = \bar{j}+\bar{j}' = J$.

## 7.2. The unique transitions ($\Delta I = 2^-, 3^+, 4^-, ...$)

The unique decays are generated almost exclusively by the Pseudovector coupling $\sim C_A$, as (7.13) shows. Each case is normally governed by a single $\beta$-moment which can be factored out of the shape formula (7.10),

$$S_n^{(n+1)} \approx \frac{4\pi n!\, C_A^2\, R^{2n}}{(2n+1)!!}\langle \boldsymbol{\sigma}\,.\,\mathbf{T}_{n+1}^n\rangle^2 \sum \frac{(2j)!!}{(2\bar{j})!!}\frac{L_{j-\frac{1}{2}}\, q^{2\bar{j}-1}}{(j-\frac{1}{2})!\,(\bar{j}-\frac{1}{2})!}, \tag{7.24}$$

to yield an unambiguous energy-dependence, independent of the unknown $\beta$-moment. As before, the sum extends over all pairs of $j, \bar{j}$ values having $j+\bar{j} = J$, with $J = \Delta I = n+1$ for an $n$-times forbidden unique transition. The notation for the shape-factor (7.24) is one already introduced into the literature;‡ the subscript refers to the degree of forbiddenness and the superscript to the total angular momentum ejected.

In the approximation (7.6) for the electron radial density $L_{j-\frac{1}{2}}$, the shape factor can be written

$$S_n^{(n+1)} \approx 4\pi[C_A\, R^n\langle \boldsymbol{\sigma}\,.\,\mathbf{T}_{n+1}^n\rangle/(2n+1)!!]^2\langle|\mathbf{p}+\mathbf{q}|^{2n}\rangle, \tag{7.25 a}$$

‡ For example, E. J. Konopinski, *Beta- and Gamma-Ray Spectroscopy* (K. Siegbahn, editor). (North-Holland Publ. Co., Amsterdam, 1955), p. 304.

with the definition

$$\langle|\mathbf{p}+\mathbf{q}|^{2(J-1)}\rangle \equiv (2J-1)! \sum_{j+\bar{j}=J} p^{2j-1}q^{2\bar{j}-1}/(2j)!\,(2\bar{j})!. \qquad (7.25\,\text{b})$$

This is valid only for $(\alpha Z)^2 \ll 1$ but the absence of terms linear in $\alpha Z$ implies some insensitivity to the nuclear charge under all conditions. The main dependence of the spectrum on $Z$, as represented by the electron density ratio $F(\pm Z, W)$, was factored out in the definition (6.83) of the shape-factor.

The notation adopted for the definition (7.25 b) is meant to indicate the fact that this quantity can be identified as just an average over all relative directions of the lepton momenta, consistent with a given total $\mathbf{P} = \mathbf{p}+\mathbf{q}$:

$$\langle P^{2n}\rangle = \int_{-1}^{1} \tfrac{1}{2}d(\cos\theta)[p^2+q^2+2pq\cos\theta]^n. \qquad (7.26)$$

This outcome can be readily understood. The Pseudovector coupling generates radiation only through the moment $\int \boldsymbol{\sigma}$ in the allowed approximation, $\mathbf{r} = 0$, of (5.4). This moment is more generally to be replaced by $\int \boldsymbol{\sigma}\exp(-i(\mathbf{p}+\mathbf{q}).\mathbf{r}) \equiv \int \boldsymbol{\sigma}\exp(-i\mathbf{P}.\mathbf{r})$ when $\mathbf{r} \neq 0$ and when the coulomb distortion of the plane electron waves can be ignored, as for (7.25). The successive degrees of forbiddenness require developing the exponential as a power series in $r$, with the results:

$$\sum_N [(-iP)^N/N!] \int \boldsymbol{\sigma} r^N \cos^N\Theta = \sum_{NL} C_{NL}\, P^N \int \boldsymbol{\sigma} r^N Y_{L0}(\cos\Theta). \quad (7.27)$$

The $C_{NL}$ represent whatever coefficients are needed for the indicated expansion into spherical harmonics; the latter is obviously restricted to $L \leqslant N$. Now the moments with $L < n$ vanish by definition of an $n$-times forbidden transition, and the terms with $N > n$ are to be neglected in the normal approximation. Only the term $L = N = n$ is to be kept and it yields a rate proportional to $P^{2n}|\int \boldsymbol{\sigma} r^n Y_{n0}|^2$, integrated over all lepton momentum directions. This is sufficient for the understanding of the proportionality $S_n^{(n+1)} \sim \langle P^{2n}\rangle$, since the relation of $\int \boldsymbol{\sigma} r^n Y_{n0}$ to $R^n\langle \boldsymbol{\sigma}.\mathbf{T}^n_{n+1}\rangle$ is obviously independent of the relative lepton momentum orientations.

*The unique spectra*

For $J = \Delta I = n+1 = 2$, the energy dependence of the unique shape-factor is approximately proportional to

$$S_1^{(2)} \sim \langle|\mathbf{p}+\mathbf{q}|^2\rangle = p^2+q^2. \qquad (7.28)$$

This result has been verified experimentally in more than a score of cases. The first definitive one‡ was the $\frac{1}{2}^- \to \frac{5}{2}^+$ transition of $Y^{91}$, treated in Fig. 7.1. The conventional Kurie plot of $[n(W)/pWF]^{\frac{1}{2}}$ shows a definite departure from the linearity expected of a statistical spectrum shape. When $[n(W)/(p^2+q^2)pWF]^{\frac{1}{2}}$ is plotted instead, approximate linearity is achieved, as to be expected with the shape-factor (7.21).

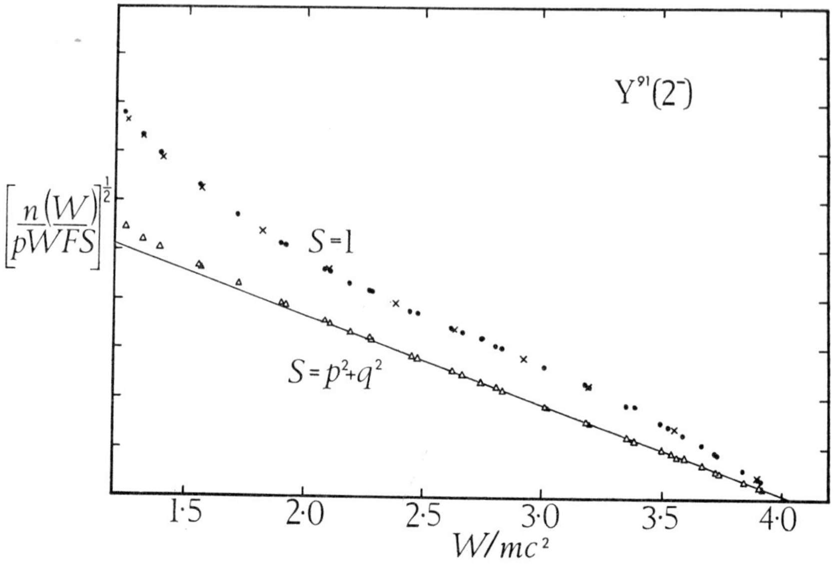


FIG. 7.1. A Kurie plot of the observed $Y^{91}$ spectrum and an attempt to linearize it with the help of the shape-factor (7.28) (courtesy of L. M. Langer).

A small residual effect of the nuclear charge can become detectable, especially for a heavy nucleus like $Tl^{204}$ ($2^- \to 0^+$), which is treated in Fig. 7.2. The necessary modification of the shape-factor can be found from (7.24):

$$S_1^{(2)} \sim q^2+9(L_1/L_0). \tag{7.29}$$

Numerical values for $L_{0,1}$ can be found in the tables of the reference on p. 187. The formula (7.5a) gives

$$9L_1/p^2L_0 \approx [F(Z,W)]^{-1}(1+\nu^2)2\pi\nu/(1-e^{-2\pi\nu}) \tag{7.30}$$

in the approximation $\gamma = (4-\alpha^2Z^2)^{\frac{1}{2}} \approx 2$. This reduces to just the inverse of the electron density ratio $F$ for parts of spectra in which $\nu^2 \equiv (\alpha ZW/p)^2 \ll 1$. The consequence for the spectrum inclusive of

‡ L. M. Langer and H. Price, *Phys. Rev.* **75**, 1109 (1949).

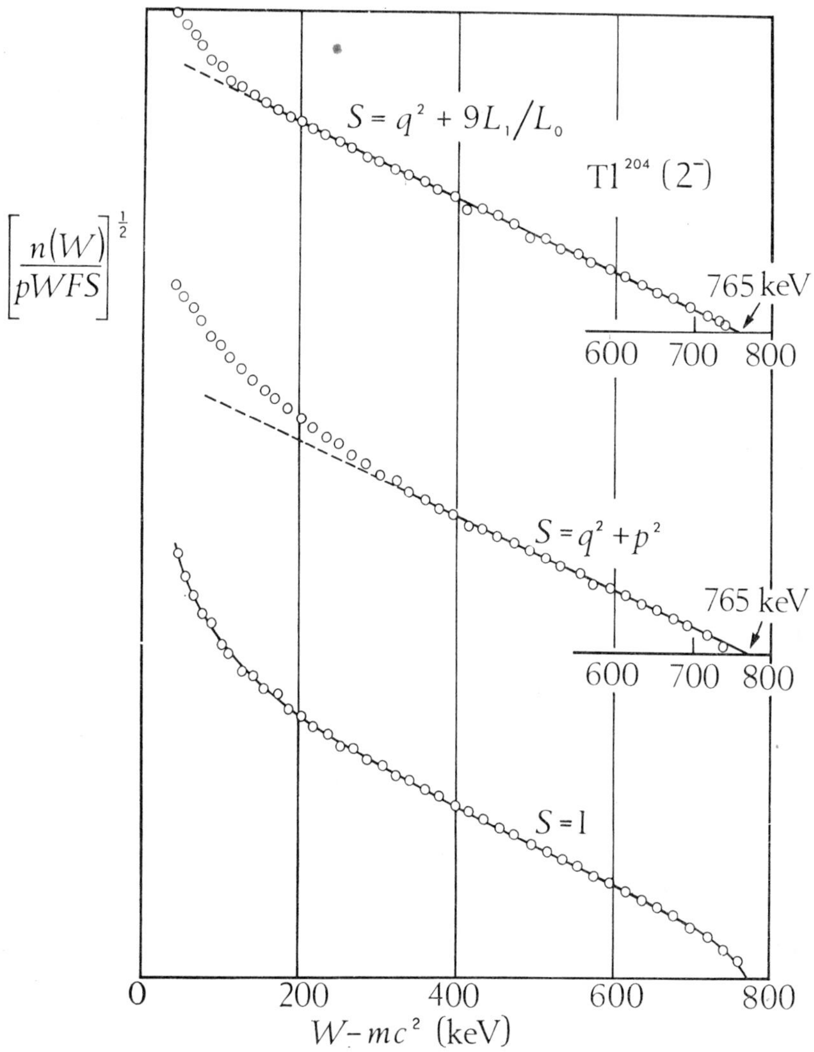


FIG. 7.2. The lowest curve is a Kurie plot of the observed Tl$^{204}$ spectrum ($Z = 81$). The others are attempts at linearization with the help of the shape-factors (7.28) and (7.29). (From L. Lidofsky, P. Macklin, and C. S. Wu, *Phys. Rev.* **87**, 391 (1952).)

the statistical factor is

$$d\lambda/dp \sim p^2q^2(Fq^2+p^2)R^2. \tag{7.31}$$

The nuclear charge effect $\sim F$, first introduced into the allowed spectrum in § 1.4, is here eliminated in the part of the shape-factor $\sim (pR)^2$. This part obviously arises from the centrifugal repulsion of the electron, which throws the particle out of the range of the strongest coulombic effects.

The few cases of unique transitions with degrees of forbiddenness higher than one which have so far been identified all have relatively small nuclear charges (more complex nuclei tend to have more modes of decay available, and these outcompete highly forbidden transitions):

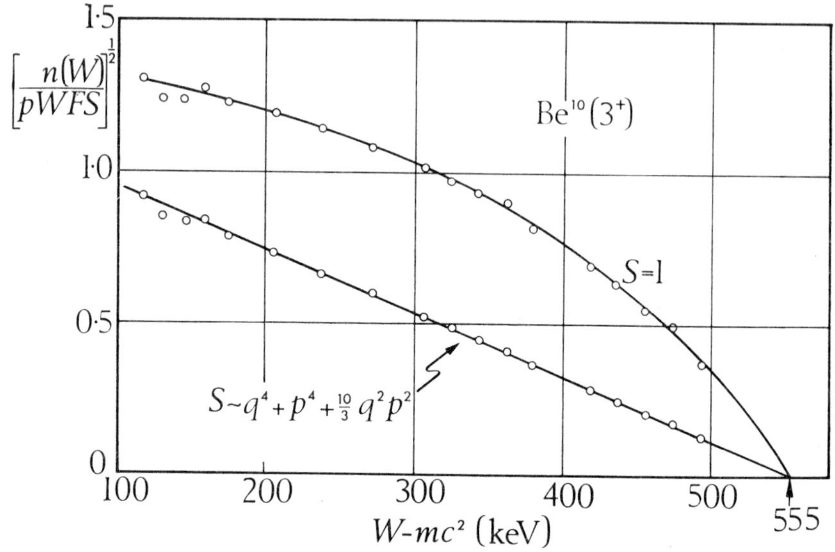


FIG. 7.3. The upper curve is a Kurie plot of the observed $Be^{10}$ spectrum. The lower one demonstrates its linearization with the help of the shape-factor (7.32). (From C. S. Wu, *Rev. Mod. Phys.* **22,** 386 (1950).)

${}_4Be^{10}$ ($0^+ \to 3^+$), ${}_{11}Na^{22}$ ($3^+ \to 0^+$), and ${}_{19}K^{40}$ ($4^- \to 0^+$). Moreover, their decay rates are very low (half-lives of $2{\cdot}5\times10^6$, 4300, and $1{\cdot}5\times10^9$ years, respectively) so that measurements are possible only when thick sources are used. These allow only the high energy portions of the electron spectra to emerge undistorted, parts which are insensitive to the nuclear charge. The low $Z$ approximations (7.25) for the shape-factors become adequate:

$$S_2^{(3)} \sim \langle|\mathbf{p}+\mathbf{q}|^4\rangle = q^4+p^4+(\tfrac{10}{3})q^2p^2, \tag{7.32}$$

$$S_3^{(4)} \sim \langle|\mathbf{p}+\mathbf{q}|^6\rangle = q^6+p^6+7q^2p^2(q^2+p^2). \tag{7.33}$$

The experimental confirmation of these expectations, for $Be^{10}$ and $K^{40}$, respectively, are exhibited in Figs. 7.3 and 7.4.

*Unique transition rates*

Each unique transition is generated through a single $\beta$-moment and the comparative half-life, *ft*, provides a direct measurement of it. The relationship is obtained by substituting the shape-factor (7.25) into the rate expression (7.12):

$$\langle \boldsymbol{\sigma}\,.\,\mathbf{T}^{n}_{n+1}\rangle^2 = \tfrac{1}{2}\ln 2[(2n+1)!!\pi/gC_{\mathrm{A}}]^2[ft\langle|\mathbf{p}+\mathbf{q}|^{2n}R^{2n}\rangle]^{-1}. \quad (7.34)$$

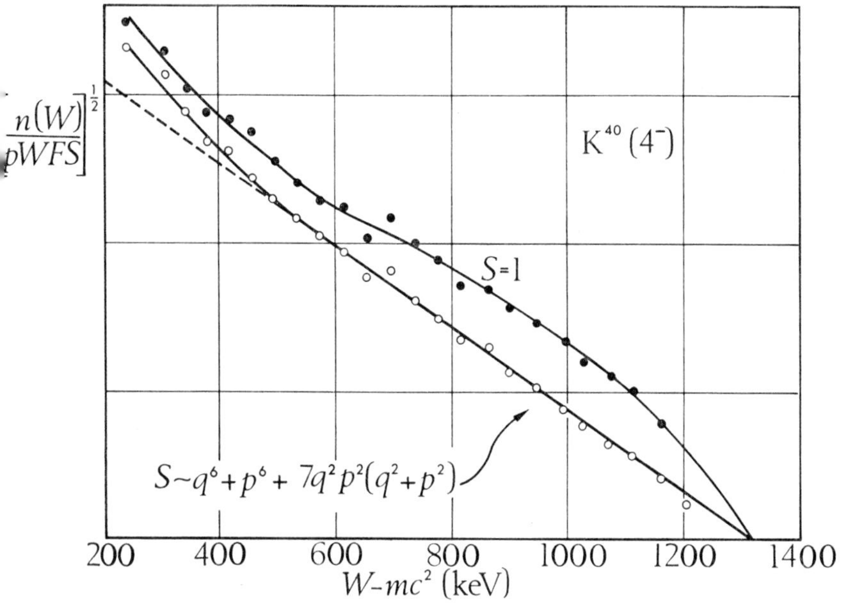


Fig. 7.4. The upper curve is a Kurie plot of the observed $K^{40}$ spectrum. The lower one is an attempt to linearize it with the help of the shape-factor (7.33). (From C. S. Wu, *Rev. Mod. Phys.* **22,** 386 (1950).)

Here, $|\mathbf{p}+\mathbf{q}|^{2n}$ must be averaged not only over all lepton directions, but also over the statistical spectrum, as is $\langle S\rangle$ of (7.12b). A slight improvement in the treatment of the coulomb effects can be made by using, e.g. the spectrum average of (7.29),

$$f^{-1}\int\limits_{0}^{p_0} dp\, p^2q^2F\langle q^2+9L_1/L_0\rangle, \quad (7.35)$$

in place of $\langle|\mathbf{p}+\mathbf{q}|^2\rangle$. Some results for‡ $\langle\boldsymbol{\sigma}\,.\,\mathbf{T}^1_2\rangle^2$, as calculated from observed values $(ft)_{\mathrm{exp}}$, with $R = 1{\cdot}2A^{\frac{1}{3}}(10)^{-13}$ cm, are shown in Tables 7.2 and 7.3. It can be seen that the experimental values of the moments

‡ The relationship to the older definition of the $2^-$ moment is

$$\sum_{ij}|B_{ij}|^2 = (16\pi R^2/3)\langle\boldsymbol{\sigma}\,.\,\mathbf{T}^1_2\rangle^2.$$

TABLE 7.2

*Unique* ($2^-$) *transitions among odd-A nuclei*

| *Parent* | *Daughter* | $\log_{10}(ft)_{exp}$ | $\langle \boldsymbol{\sigma}.\mathbf{T}^1_2\rangle^2_{exp}$ | *Transition* | $\langle \boldsymbol{\sigma}.\mathbf{T}^1_2\rangle^2_{theo}$ | *Mismatch factor* |
|---|---|---|---|---|---|---|
| $_{16}S^{37}_{21}$ | $_{17}Cl_{20}$ | 7·07 | 0·023 | $f_{7/2} \to d_{3/2}$ | $18/35\pi$ | 0·14 |
| $_{17}Cl^{39}_{22}$ | $_{18}A_{21}$ | 7·8 | 0·009 | $d_{3/2} \to f_{7/2}$ | $36/35\pi$ | 0·026 |
| $_{18}A^{39}_{21}$ | $_{19}K_{20}$ | 9·85 | 0·0017 | $f_{7/2} \to d_{3/2}$ | $18/35\pi$ | 0·010 |
| $_{18}A^{41}_{23}$ | $_{19}K_{22}$ | 8·47 | 0·0036 | ,, | ,, | 0·022 |
| $_{19}K^{43}_{24}$ | $_{20}Ca_{23}$ | 9·9 | 0·0042 | $d_{3/2} \to f_{7/2}$ | $36/35\pi$ | 0·013 |
| $_{36}Kr^{85}_{49}$ | $_{37}Rb_{48}$ | 9·09 | 0·0052 | $g_{9/2} \to f_{5/2}$ | $12/21\pi$ | 0·029 |
| $_{38}Sr^{89}_{51}$ | $_{39}Y_{50}$ | 8·57 | 0·0047 | $d_{5/2} \to p_{1/2}$ | $2/5\pi$ | 0·037 |
| $_{38}Sr^{91}_{53}$ | $_{39}Y_{52}$ | 7·91 | 0·0069 | ,, | ,, | 0·055 |
| $_{39}Y^{91}_{52}$ | $_{40}Zr_{51}$ | 8·52 | 0·0043 | $p_{1/2} \to d_{5/2}$ | $6/5\pi$ | 0·011 |
| $_{39}Y^{93}_{54}$ | $_{40}Zr_{53}$ | 8·0 | 0·0039 | ,, | ,, | 0·010 |
| $_{40}Zr^{95}_{55}$ | $_{41}Nb^{*}_{54}$ | 9·9 | 0·0012 | $d_{5/2} \to p_{1/2}$ | $2/5\pi$ | 0·010 |
| $_{47}Ag^{111}_{64}$ | $_{48}Cd^{*}_{63}$ | 8·8 | 0·0055 | $p_{1/2} \to d_{5/2}$ | $6/5\pi$ | 0·015 |
| $_{50}Sn^{*}_{73}$ | $_{51}Sb^{123}_{72}$ | 8·88 | 0·0020 | $h_{11/2} \to g_{7/2}$ | $20/33\pi$ | 0·010 |
| $_{55}Cs^{137}_{82}$ | $_{56}Ba_{81}$ | 9·41 | 0·0021 | $g_{7/2} \to h_{11/2}$ | $10/11\pi$ | 0·008 |
| ($\Delta l = 3$) | | | | | | |
| $_{34}Se^{79}_{45}$ | $_{35}Br_{44}$ | 10·7 | 0·0009 | $g_{7/2} \to p_{3/2}$ | 0 | .. |
| $_{36}Kr^{81}_{45}$ | $_{35}Br_{46}$ | 10·2 | 0·0001 | ,, | 0 | .. |

TABLE 7.3

*Unique* ($2^-$) *transitions among even-A nuclei*

| *Parent* | *Daughter* | *Transition* | $\log_{10}(ft)_{exp}$ | $\langle \boldsymbol{\sigma}.\mathbf{T}^1_2\rangle^2_{exp}$ |
|---|---|---|---|---|
| $_{17}Cl^{38}_{21}$ | $_{18}A_{20}$ | $2^- \to 0^+$ | 7·44 | 0·0129 |
| $_{19}K^{42}_{23}$ | $_{20}Ca_{22}$ | ,, | 8·02 | 0·0055 |
| $_{33}As^{72}_{39}$ | $_{32}Ge_{40}$ | ,, | 8·21 | 0·0028 |
| $_{33}As^{74}_{41}$ | $_{32}Ge_{42}$ | ,, | 8·29 | 0·0105 |
| ,, | $_{34}Se_{40}$ | ,, | 8·44 | 0·0060 |
| $_{33}As^{76}_{43}$ | $_{34}Se_{42}$ | ,, | 8·20 | 0·0032 |
| $_{37}Rb^{84}_{47}$ | $_{36}Kr_{48}$ | ,, | 8·64 | 0·0030 |
| $_{37}Rb^{86}_{49}$ | $_{38}Sr_{48}$ | ,, | 8·51 | 0·0039 |
| $_{37}Rb^{88}_{51}$ | $_{38}Sr_{50}$ | ,, | 7·25 | 0·0094 |
| $_{38}Sr^{90}_{52}$ | $_{39}Y_{51}$ | $0^+ \to 2^-$ | 9·06 | 0·0052 |
| $_{39}Y^{90}_{51}$ | $_{40}Zr_{50}$ | $2^- \to 0^+$ | 8·03 | 0·0079 |
| $_{39}Y^{92}_{53}$ | $_{40}Zr_{52}$ | ,, | 7·64 | 0·0085 |
| $_{51}Sb^{122}_{71}$ | $_{50}Sn_{72}$ | ,, | 8·78 | 0·0042 |
| $_{53}I^{124}_{71}$ | $_{52}Te_{72}$ | ,, | 7·77 | 0·0108 |
| $_{59}Pr^{142}_{83}$ | $_{60}Nd_{82}$ | ,, | 7·39 | 0·028 |

are considerably smaller than the 'order of magnitude unity' which was ascribed to them as a basis for classifying the various forbidden transitions. The classifications are not invalidated by this outcome since the observed suppression is of the same order of magnitude for all transitions outside the exceptional, 'favoured', cases among light nuclei.

Theoretical expectations for the unique moments are no more reliably calculable than they were for the allowed moments of § 5.3. The simple, one-particle model formulae (5.73) for the allowed moment

$$\langle\sigma\rangle = (4\pi)^{\frac{1}{2}}\langle\boldsymbol{\sigma}\,.\,\mathbf{T}_1^0\rangle$$

are easy to generalize to the forbidden cases. They are directly applicable only to odd-$A$ nuclei and, for the half-integer nuclear spins $I = l-\frac{1}{2} \rightarrow I' = l'+\frac{1}{2} = I+(n+1)$,

$$(2I'+1)^{-1}\langle\boldsymbol{\sigma}\,.\,\mathbf{T}_{n+1}^n\rangle^2 = \frac{(2n+1)!}{2\pi(n!)^2}\frac{(2I+1)!}{(2I')!}\left[\frac{(I'-\frac{1}{2})!}{(I+\frac{1}{2})!}\right]^2. \qquad (7.36)$$

It is only necessary to interchange $I$ and $I'$ on the right-hand side to obtain the result for $I = l+\frac{1}{2} \rightarrow I' = l'-\frac{1}{2} = I-(n+1)$. The cases $I'-I = \pm(n+1)$ are the only ones of interest since smaller absolute differences are governed by formulae of a lower order of forbiddenness. It can be checked that putting $n = 0$ into (7.36) properly yields the last of the results (5.73).

As the presentation of (7.36) implies, the rule $\Delta I \equiv |I'-I| = n+1$ is, in the single transforming nucleon picture, accompanied by the orbital momentum rule $\Delta l = |l'-l| = n$; this is quite understandable since the unique transitions always generate triplet radiation and the lepton spins account for the extra unit of $\Delta I$. The effect of the parity rule, $\pi_i \pi_f = (-)^n$, is such that $I'-I = +(n+1)$ is achievable only for changes from an antiparallel spin-orbit orientation, $I = l-\frac{1}{2}$, to the parallel one, $I' = l'+\frac{1}{2}$; correspondingly, $I'-I = -(n+1)$ only for $I = l+\frac{1}{2} \rightarrow I' = l'-\frac{1}{2}$. These facts agree with the assignments of orbitals listed in Table 7.2, which were made as consistent with the general evidence responsible for the ordering (5.74) as this was adequate.

As in the application to the allowed transitions of Table 5.2, a 'mismatch factor' between the measured moments and the single-particle expectations for odd-$A$ nuclei, can be calculated. This ratio of the 'measured' $\langle\boldsymbol{\sigma}\,.\,\mathbf{T}_2^1\rangle^2$ to the theoretical values following from (7.36) is given in the last column of Table 7.2. It can be seen that the mismatch factors here are of the same order as in the allowed transitions.

Two cases which are fairly well identifiable as '$l$-forbidden unique', having $\Delta l = 3$, are exhibited last in Table 7.2. They do have the highest $ft$-values in the table, although not spectacularly so.

## 7.3. Parity-forbidden‡ transitions ($\Delta I = 0^-, 1^-, 2^+,...$)

*The normal* $1^-$ *shape-factor*, $S_1^{(1)}$

Normally, three β-moments, such as shown in (7.11), must be expected to make comparable contributions to any parity-forbidden transition with $\Delta I \geqslant 1$. In the case $\Delta I = 1$, the β-moments may be symbolized as in (7.16), and then the normal shape-factor becomes

$$S_1^{(1)} = 4\pi \mathscr{M}_{\frac{1}{2}}^2(1) = [C_V\langle\alpha\rangle + \tfrac{1}{2}\alpha Z(C_A\langle(\boldsymbol{\sigma}\times\hat{\mathbf{r}})\rangle \mp C_V\langle i\hat{r}\rangle)]^2, \quad (7.37)$$

since $L_0 = \frac{1}{2}(1+\gamma_0)$ in the normal approximation (7.5 a). As in the unique cases (7.24), the subscript on the shape-factor symbol here designates the degree of forbiddenness; the superscript denotes the total angular moment ejected ($J$). The upper sign in (7.37) refers to negatron, the lower to positron, emission, as usual.

Like the allowed shape factor (6.84), $S_1^{(1)}$ is independent of lepton energy and leads to the statistical form of spectrum. The $\Delta I = 1^-$ transitions are like the allowed Gamow–Teller $\Delta I = 1^+$ cases in that they yield only triplet lepton emissions, without orbital momentum, in the normal approximation. They differ in requiring a nuclear parity change; on this account they are generated through $\langle\alpha\rangle$ rather than $\langle\sigma\rangle$, and additionally through $\langle i\hat{r}\rangle$ and $\langle(\boldsymbol{\sigma}\times\hat{\mathbf{r}})\rangle$ because the coulomb modification of the centrifugal effects can make the contributions of the latter moments comparable to that of $\langle\alpha\rangle$, or even larger, in size.

The moments in $S_1^{(1)}$ also contribute to $\Delta I = 0^-$ transitions, just as the allowed, Gamow–Teller moment $\langle\sigma\rangle$ contributes to $\Delta I = 0^+$ cases. For $\Delta I = 0$, there is a supplementation by singlet radiation even in the normal approximation, since $\Delta I = J = 0$ requires no orbital momentum ejection. The shape-factor formulae (7.10) and (7.37) do not include the $J = 0$ radiation and this must now be examined.

*The normal* $0^-$ *shape-factor*, $S_1^{(0)}$

When the leptons carry off no angular momentum ($J = 0$), the exact shape-factor (6.85) becomes

$$S^{(0)} = [4\pi/(1+\gamma_0)] \sum_j (2j+1)R^{2j-1}[D_-^2 L_{j-\frac{1}{2}} + D_+^2 \overline{M}_{j-\frac{1}{2}} + 2D_- D_+ \overline{N}_{j-\frac{1}{2}}]. \quad (7.38)$$

The individual lepton angular momenta must be equal and opposite

‡ Frequently referred to as 'non-unique' in the literature.

in direction, $\bar{\mathbf{j}} = -\mathbf{j}$, so that $j+\bar{j}+J = 2j$ is odd and the formulae (6.88 b) for $D_{\pm}$ apply:

$$D_{\pm} = \pm j_{j\mp\frac{1}{2}}(qR)B_0 - j_{j\pm\frac{1}{2}}C_0, \tag{7.39}$$

where

$$\left.\begin{aligned} B_0 &= \langle (C_A - C_V\gamma_5)\boldsymbol{\sigma}.\mathbf{T}_0^1\rangle = -(4\pi)^{-\frac{1}{2}}\langle (C_A - C_V\gamma_5)i\boldsymbol{\sigma}.\hat{\mathbf{r}}\rangle \\ C_0 &= \langle (C_V - C_A\gamma_5)Y_0\rangle = (4\pi)^{-\frac{1}{2}}\langle (C_V - C_A\gamma_5)\rangle \end{aligned}\right\} \tag{7.40}$$

alike for negatron and positron emissions. Only the Pseudovector terms $\sim C_A$ here survive for $0^-$ transitions; the Vector terms $\sim C_V$ yield the allowed $0^+$ emissions.

In the normal approximation, only the $\sim R^0$ contributions of $j = \bar{j} = \frac{1}{2}$ need be retained. The shape-factor (7.38) then becomes

$$S_1^{(0)} \approx C_A^2[\langle\gamma_5\rangle \pm \tfrac{1}{2}\alpha Z\langle i\boldsymbol{\sigma}.\hat{\mathbf{r}}\rangle]^2 \quad \text{for } e^{\mp}. \tag{7.41}$$

This is the entire shape-factor for $0^- \leftrightarrow 0^+$ transitions, but more general $\Delta I = 0^-$ transitions also receive contributions from $S_1^{(1)}$ of (7.37), hence

$$S_1 = S_1^{(0)} + S_1^{(1)} \tag{7.42 a}$$

should be written for the normal shape-factor of any once-parity-forbidden transition ($S_1^{(0)} \to 0$ automatically when $\Delta I = 1$). This parallels the situation among allowed transitions, where the shape-factor (6.84) also consists of two parts:

$$S_0^{(0)} \equiv C_V^2\langle 1\rangle^2 \quad (\to 0 \text{ for } \Delta I = 1^+),$$

$$S_0^{(1)} \equiv C_A^2\langle \sigma\rangle^2 \quad (\to 0 \text{ for } 0^\pm \to 0^\pm),$$

and both parts contribute to the general $\Delta I = 0^+$ transition. Also like the allowed shape-factor, the normal once-parity forbidden shape-factor (7.42) is independent of the lepton energy. It thus furnishes the theoretical explanation for the experimental finding that most $0^-$ and $1^-$ spectra yield linear Kurie plots, as do the allowed spectra. An example is shown in Fig. 7.5: the case of $Pm^{147}$.

Deviations from the normally expected statistical shape have been definitely established in several $0^-$ and $1^-$ spectra. Such can be accounted for by supposing the normal moment combinations, (7.37) and (7.41), to be anomalously small, so that higher order terms of the expansions in $R$ become relatively appreciable. In at least one case (the $1^- \to 0^+$ transition of RaE), effects of as high order as $\mathcal{O}(R^2)$ have been detected.‡ Because the 'unique' shape-factor, $S_1^{(2)}$ of (7.24), contributes

‡ The experimental results have apparently been stabilized at those of E. Plassmann and L. Langer, *Phys. Rev.* **96,** 1593 (1954); many attempts to fit the spectrum have culminated in the work of J. Fujita, M. Yamada, Z. Matumoto, and S. Nakamura, *Prog. Theoret. Phys.* **20,** 287 (1958).

to $0^-$ and $1^-$ transitions (but not $0 \to 0$, $\frac{1}{2} \to \frac{1}{2}$, or $1 \leftrightarrow 0$ cases), as wel as to the $2^-$ ones, in order $R^2$, it must generally be included in the tota shape factor:

$$S_1 = S_1^{(0)} + S_1^{(1)} + S_1^{(2)}. \qquad (7.42\,b$$

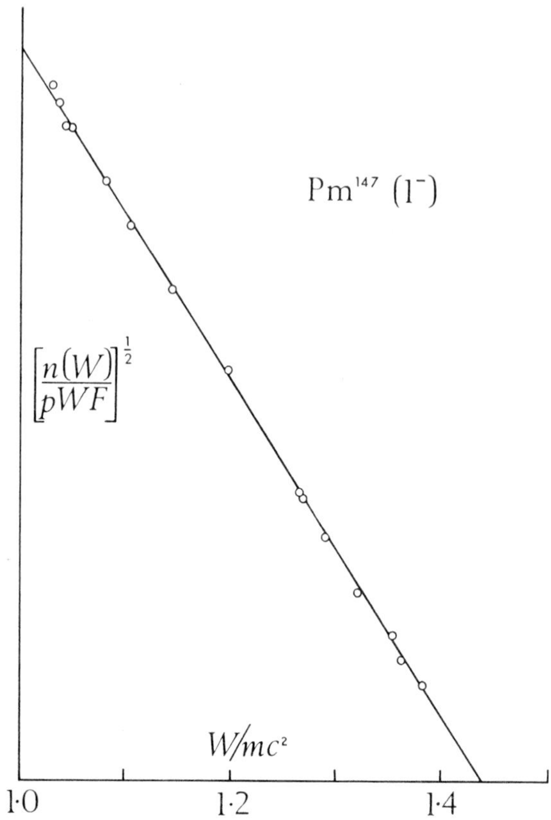


FIG. 7.5. Kurie plot of the once-parity-forbidden spectrum of $Pm^{147}$ (courtesy of L. M. Langer).

Expressions of any desired accuracy for $S_1^{(0)}$ and $S_1^{(1)}$ may be obtained from the 'exact' formulae (7.38) and (6.85); their very lengthy explicit forms are of interest only to specialists and will not again be recorded here.‡ One advantage gained from the study of the anomalies is that they provide data for the determination of the nuclear β-moments; a merely statistical shape is of no help in this regard.

‡ See the second edition of K. Siegbahn, *Beta- and Gamma-Ray Spectroscopy* (North-Holland Press, Amsterdam, 1965) for a late record.

*Once-parity-forbidden angular correlations*

The normal expectations for the electron-(nuclear spin) and electron-neutrino correlations in $0^-$ and $1^-$ transitions are as simple as they are for allowed transitions. Again they have distributions proportional to $\sim [1+(A \text{ or } a)(v/c)\cos\theta]$. The electron anisotropy coefficient, $A$, and the electron-neutrino correlation coefficient, $a$, can be expressed exactly as in (5.42) except for the replacements

$$C_V\langle 1\rangle \to -C_A[\langle\gamma_5\rangle \pm \tfrac{1}{2}\alpha Z\langle i\boldsymbol{\sigma}.\hat{\mathbf{r}}\rangle],$$
$$C_A\langle\sigma\rangle \to C_V\langle\alpha\rangle + \tfrac{1}{2}\alpha Z(C_A\langle(\boldsymbol{\sigma}\times\hat{\mathbf{r}})\rangle \mp C_V\langle i\hat{r}\rangle). \tag{7.43}$$

This follows from (6.101) and (6.108). The transformation (7.43) would be equivalent to the usual one, $C_A \leftrightarrow -C_V\gamma_5$, connecting results for opposite nuclear parity changes, $\pi_i\pi_f \to -\pi_i\pi_f$, if only the allowed results had been given to higher order (§ 7.4).

*Twice-parity-forbidden spectra* ($2^+$)

For the cases with $\Delta I = 2$ and no parity change, the normal shape-factor (7.10) has an energy dependence subject to a single positive parameter which will be denoted $y^2$:

$$S_2^{(2)} = (4\pi/9)\mathscr{M}_{\frac{1}{2}}^2(2)R^2(q^2+9y^2L_1/L_0)$$
$$\approx (4\pi/9)\mathscr{M}_{\frac{1}{2}}^2(2)R^2(q^2+y^2p^2) \quad \text{for } (aZ)^2 \ll 1, \tag{7.44}$$

where $\mathscr{M}_{\frac{1}{2}}(2)$ is the appropriate combination of $\beta$-moments (7.11). The new parameter may best be written in terms of a substitute $z$, as

$$\left.\begin{aligned} y &\equiv \mathscr{M}_{\frac{3}{2}}(2)/\mathscr{M}_{\frac{1}{2}}(2) = (1+\tfrac{1}{2}\alpha Zz)/(1+\tfrac{1}{4}\alpha Zz) \\ z &\equiv [(\tfrac{3}{5})^{\frac{1}{2}}C_A\langle\boldsymbol{\sigma}.\mathbf{T}_2^2\rangle \mp (\tfrac{2}{5})^{\frac{1}{2}}C_V\langle Y_2\rangle]/C_V\langle\boldsymbol{\alpha}.\mathbf{T}_2^1\rangle \end{aligned}\right\}. \tag{7.45}$$

It is not at all implausible that $y \approx 1$ and the spectrum resemble closely the unique $2^-$ spectra. A value $y^2 \approx 1{\cdot}6$ has been reported‡ to fit the observed spectrum of $Cl^{36}(2^+ \to 0^+)$, $y^2 \approx 0{\cdot}5$ for $Tc^{99}$ $(\frac{9}{2}^+ \to \frac{5}{2}^+)$, and $y^2 \approx 0{\cdot}1$ for $Cs^{135}$ $(\frac{7}{2}^+ \to \frac{3}{2}^+)$.

*Parity-forbidden transition rates*

Cases which are reasonably well identified as $0^-$ or $1^-$ transitions are listed in Tables 7.4–7.6. Most have $ft \approx 10^{6-8}$ sec, as compared to a majority of unfavoured allowed values $10^{4-6}$ sec, reviewed in Tables 5.2 and 5.5. The normal theoretical expectations for $ft$-values of $0^-$ or $1^-$ transitions can be given the same form (5.60) as for the allowed decays, except that the allowed shape-factor, $\xi = C_V^2\langle 1\rangle^2 + C_A^2\langle\sigma\rangle^2$, must be replaced by $S_1^{(0)}+S_1^{(1)}$ of (7.41) and (7.37).

‡ C. S. Wu in *Beta- and Gamma-Ray Spectroscopy* (editor K. Siegbahn) (North-Holland Press, Amsterdam, 1955).

TABLE 7.4

$\Delta I = 0^-$ *transitions in odd-A nuclei*

| *Parent* | *Daughter* | *Transition* | $\log_{10}(ft)_{\text{exp}}$ |
|---|---|---|---|
| ${}_{6}C_{9}^{15}$ | ${}_{7}N_{8}$ | $s_{1/2} \to p_{1/2}$ | 6·1 |
| ${}_{19}K_{24}^{43}$ | ${}_{20}Ca_{23}^{**}$ | $d_{3/2} \to p_{3/2}$ | 7·3 |
| ${}_{47}Ag_{66}^{113}$ | ${}_{48}Cd_{65}$ | $p_{1/2} \to s_{1/2}$ | 6·8 |
| ${}_{49}In_{66}^{115m}$ | ${}_{50}Sn_{65}$ | ,, | 6·6 |
| ${}_{49}In_{68}^{*}$ | ${}_{50}Sn_{67}^{117}$ | ,, | 6·5 |
| ${}_{57}La_{84}^{141}$ | ${}_{58}Ce_{83}$ | $g_{7/2} \to f_{7/2}$ | 7·3 |
| ${}_{58}Ce_{83}^{141}$ | ${}_{59}Pr_{82}^{*}$ | $f_{7/2} \to g_{7/2}$ | 6·9 |
| ${}_{66}Dy_{99}^{165}$ | ${}_{67}Ho_{98}$ | ,, | 6·2 |
| ${}_{81}Tl_{126}^{207}$ | ${}_{82}Pb_{125}$ | $s_{1/2} \to p_{1/2}$ | 5·16 |
| ${}_{82}Pb_{127}^{209}$ | ${}_{83}Bi_{126}$ | $g_{9/2} \to h_{9/2}$ | 5·6 |

TABLE 7.5

$\Delta I = 1^-$ *transitions in odd-A nuclei*

| *Parent* | *Daughter* | *Transition* | $\log_{10}(ft)_{\text{exp}}$ |
|---|---|---|---|
| ${}_{19}K_{24}^{43}$ | ${}_{20}Ca_{23}^{*}$ | $d_{3/2} \to f_{5/2}$ | 8·2 |
| ${}_{36}Kr_{51}^{87}$ | ${}_{37}Rb_{50}^{*}$ | $g_{7/2} \to f_{5/2}$ | 7·5 |
| ${}_{43}Tc_{52}^{95}$ | ${}_{42}Mo_{53}^{*}$ | $p_{1/2} \to d_{3/2}$ | 7·5 |
| ${}_{47}Ag_{64}^{111}$ | ${}_{48}Cd_{63}^{*}$ | $p_{1/2} \to d_{3/2}$ | 7·3 |
| ${}_{48}Cd_{67}^{*}$ | ${}_{49}In_{66}^{115}$ | $h_{11/2} \to g_{9/2}$ | 8·8 |
| ${}_{49}In_{68}^{117*}$ | ${}_{50}Sn_{67}^{*}$ | $p_{1/2} \to d_{3/2}$ | 6·7 |
| ${}_{49}In_{70}^{119}$ | ${}_{50}Sn_{69}^{**}$ | $g_{9/2} \to h_{11/2}$ | 6·3 |
| ${}_{59}Pr_{84}^{143}$ | ${}_{60}Nd_{83}$ | $d_{5/2} \to f_{7/2}$ | 7·6 |
| ${}_{58}Ce_{83}^{141}$ | ${}_{59}Pr_{82}$ | $f_{7/2} \to d_{5/2}$ | 7·8 |
| ${}_{81}Tl_{126}^{207}$ | ${}_{82}Pb_{125}^{**}$ | $s_{1/2} \to p_{3/2}$ | 6·1 |

Some attempts‡ have been made to obtain theoretical estimates for ratios among the several $\beta$-moments which contribute: $\langle\alpha\rangle$, $\langle i\hat{r}\rangle$, and $\langle(\boldsymbol{\sigma}\times\hat{\mathbf{r}})\rangle$ in the $1^-$ cases, plus $\langle\gamma_5\rangle$ and $\langle i\boldsymbol{\sigma}.\hat{\mathbf{r}}\rangle$ in the general $0^-$ case. Since $\langle\alpha\rangle$ is a measure of nucleonic velocity, it might be expected to be related to the time-derivative of the transforming nucleon's position, $\mathbf{r}^a$, as given by the commutator $i[H,\mathbf{r}^a] \equiv i(H\mathbf{r}^a-\mathbf{r}^a H)$ with the nuclear hamiltonian $H$. For any operator $\mathcal{O}$ occurring in the nuclear matrix elements,

$$\langle f|[\mathcal{O},H]|i\rangle = (E_i-E_f)\langle f|\mathcal{O}|i\rangle \equiv W_0\langle f|\mathcal{O}|i\rangle, \tag{7.46}$$

where $W_0$ is the usual energy release in the $\beta$-transformation. A first

‡ D. L. Pursey, *Phil. Mag.* **42,** 1193 (1951); T. Ahrens and E. Feenberg, *Phys. Rev.* **86,** 64 (1952); M. Yamada, *Proc. Theoret. Phys.* **9,** 268 (1953); M. Rose and R. Osborn, *Phys. Rev.* **93,** 1326 (1954).

TABLE 7.6

*Once-parity-forbidden transitions among even-A nuclei*

| *Parent* | *Daughter* | $\log_{10}(ft)_{\text{exp}}$ | *Parent* | *Daughter* | $\log_{10}(ft)_{\text{exp}}$ |
|---|---|---|---|---|---|
| $(0^- \to 0^+)$ | | | $(2^- \to 2^+)$ | | |
| ${}_{58}\mathrm{Ce}^{144}_{86}$ | ${}_{59}\mathrm{Pr}_{85}$ | 7·6 | ${}_{17}\mathrm{Cl}^{38}_{21}$ | ${}_{18}\mathrm{A}^{*}_{20}$ | 6·9 |
| ${}_{59}\mathrm{Pr}^{144}_{85}$ | ${}_{60}\mathrm{Nd}_{84}$ | 6·6 | ${}_{19}\mathrm{K}^{42}_{23}$ | ${}_{20}\mathrm{Ca}^{*}_{22}$ | 7·5 |
| ${}_{67}\mathrm{Ho}^{166}_{99}$ | ${}_{68}\mathrm{Er}_{98}$ | 8·1 | ${}_{33}\mathrm{As}^{74}_{41}$ | ${}_{32}\mathrm{Ge}^{*}_{42}$ | 7·9 |
| ${}_{81}\mathrm{Tl}^{206}_{125}$ | ${}_{82}\mathrm{Pb}_{124}$ | 5·1 | ,, | ${}_{34}\mathrm{Se}^{*}_{40}$ | 7·5 |
| ${}_{82}\mathrm{Pb}^{212}_{130}$ | ${}_{83}\mathrm{Bi}^{*}_{129}$ | 5·2 | ${}_{39}\mathrm{Y}^{92}_{53}$ | ${}_{40}\mathrm{Zr}_{52}$ | 8·0 |
| $(1^- \to 0^+)$ | | | ${}_{51}\mathrm{Sb}^{122}_{71}$ | ${}_{52}\mathrm{Te}_{70}$ | 7·6 |
| ${}_{69}\mathrm{Tm}^{170}_{101}$ | ${}_{70}\mathrm{Yb}_{100}$ | 8·9 | $(4^- \to 4^+)$ | | |
| ${}_{75}\mathrm{Re}^{188}_{113}$ | ${}_{76}\mathrm{Os}_{112}$ | 8·1 | ${}_{57}\mathrm{La}^{140}_{83}$ | ${}_{58}\mathrm{Ce}^{**}_{82}$ | 8·5 |
| ${}_{82}\mathrm{Pb}^{212}_{130}$ | ${}_{83}\mathrm{Bi}_{129}$ | 6·6 | $(6^- \to 6^+)$ | | |
| ${}_{83}\mathrm{Bi}^{210}_{127}$ (RaE) | ${}_{84}\mathrm{Po}_{126}$ | 8·0 | ${}_{53}\mathrm{I}^{130}_{77}$ | ${}_{54}\mathrm{Xe}^{***}_{76}$ | 6·4 |
| $(1^- \to 2^+)$ | | | $(5^- \to 4^+)$ | | |
| $\mathrm{Tm}^{170}$ | $\mathrm{Yb}^{*}$ | 9·3 | ${}_{53}\mathrm{I}^{132}_{79}$ | ${}_{54}\mathrm{Xe}^{**}_{78}$ | 7·5 |

part of the nuclear hamiltonian is the kinetic energy,

$$H_T = \sum_a [\boldsymbol{\alpha}^a . \mathbf{p}^a + (\beta^a - 1)M],$$

as formulated in Dirac's terms (2.71). With the operators occurring in $\langle i\hat{r}\rangle$ and $\langle i\boldsymbol{\sigma}.\hat{\mathbf{r}}\rangle$,

$$\left.\begin{aligned} \Big\langle \mathrm{f}\Big|\Big[\sum_a \tau^a_{\pm}\mathbf{r}^a, H_T\Big]\Big|\mathrm{i}\Big\rangle &= i\Big\langle \mathrm{f}\Big|\sum_a \tau^a_{\pm}\,\boldsymbol{\alpha}^a\Big|\mathrm{i}\Big\rangle \\ \Big\langle \mathrm{f}\Big|\Big[\sum_a \tau^a_{\pm}\,\boldsymbol{\sigma}^a.\mathbf{r}^a, H_T\Big]\Big|\mathrm{i}\Big\rangle &= -i\Big\langle \mathrm{f}\Big|\sum_a \tau^a_{\pm}\gamma^a_5[3+2\boldsymbol{\sigma}^a.(\mathbf{r}^a\times\mathbf{p}^a)]\Big|\mathrm{i}\Big\rangle \\ &= -i\Big\langle \mathrm{f}\Big|\sum_a \tau^a_{\pm}\gamma^a_5(1-2\varkappa^a)\Big|\mathrm{i}\Big\rangle \end{aligned}\right\}, \tag{7.47}$$

follow from the elementary commutation properties. The last line contains the spin-orbit operator, $\varkappa = -[1+\boldsymbol{\sigma}.(\mathbf{r}\times\mathbf{p})]$ of (2.17). Plainly, relationships of $\langle i\hat{r}\rangle$ to $\langle\alpha\rangle$, and $\langle i\boldsymbol{\sigma}.\hat{\mathbf{r}}\rangle$ to $\langle\gamma_5\rangle$, are emerging.

Next, the effects of the remainder of the nuclear hamiltonian, $H' = H - H_T$, must be weighed. Its contribution to the commutator in (7.46) may be evaluated with the help of

$$\begin{aligned} \langle \mathrm{f}|[\mathcal{O}, H']|\mathrm{i}\rangle &= \sum_{\mathrm{i}'} \langle \mathrm{f}|\mathcal{O}|\mathrm{i}'\rangle\langle \mathrm{i}'|H'|\mathrm{i}\rangle - \sum_{\mathrm{f}'} \langle \mathrm{f}|H'|\mathrm{f}'\rangle\langle \mathrm{f}'|\mathcal{O}|\mathrm{i}\rangle \\ &\approx \langle \mathrm{f}|\mathcal{O}|\mathrm{i}\rangle[\langle \mathrm{i}|H'|\mathrm{i}\rangle - \langle \mathrm{f}|H'|\mathrm{f}\rangle] \equiv \langle \mathrm{f}|\mathcal{O}|\mathrm{i}\rangle\Delta\langle H'\rangle, \end{aligned} \tag{7.48}$$

where the operations like $\sum_{\mathrm{i}'} |\mathrm{i}'\rangle\langle \mathrm{i}'| = 1$ denote projections on complete sets of nuclear states. The last line is known as the 'Ahrens–Feenberg approximation' and embodies the reasonable assumption that the diagonal elements of $H'$, which are responsible for stabilizing the nuclear states $|i\rangle$ and $|f\rangle$ against dispersal by the nucleonic kinetic energies,

$$H_T = H - H',$$

will be the most important ones. The problem thus reduces to finding *differences*, $\Delta\langle H'\rangle$, of nuclear energy contributions, between states differing by a neutron-proton substitution. The charge-independence of the specifically nuclear binding forces tends to minimize the difference of their contributions. Moreover, their short ranges and general 'saturating' properties (each nucleon tends, through them, to interact with only a few others) depress the differences of their contributions relative to the long-range electrostatic repulsion of the extra proton, in the one nucleus, by all the other protons. It is such effects which seem to be responsible for Pursey's much more detailed and quantitative estimates resulting in the conclusion that the differences of the nuclear force contributions are small as compared to the electrostatic effect. If they are neglected,‡ $\Delta\langle H'\rangle$ will consist solely of a neutron-proton mass difference, $\pm(M_n - M_p)$, and of the electrostatic repulsion of one proton by the nuclear charge $Ze$; the energy difference arising from the electrostatic effect is closely $\mp\alpha Z/R$ ($c = \hbar = 1$) for charge spread fairly uniformly over a nucleus of 'radius' $R$. Under the various assumptions here, it is simple to bring the relation (7.46) to the conclusions

$$\frac{\langle\alpha\rangle}{\langle i\hat{r}\rangle} \approx -\frac{\langle\gamma_5(1-2\varkappa)\rangle}{\langle i\boldsymbol{\sigma}.\hat{\mathbf{r}}\rangle} \approx \left[W_0 \pm \left(\frac{\alpha Z}{R} - M_n + M_p\right)\right] R, \qquad (7.49)$$

for $e^{\mp}$ emissions, respectively. The bracket on the right obviously represents a difference $\Delta\langle H_T\rangle$ made to the kinetic energy by the neutron-proton substitution. The term $\alpha Z/R$, which is the 'extra depth' of the coulomb potential in the nucleus having the extra proton, is usually by far the largest one in (7.49), a fact essentially already expressed in (7.14). Ahrens and Feenberg defined a parameter

$$\Lambda \equiv (\pm 2R/\alpha Z)\Delta\langle H_T\rangle \qquad (7.50\,\text{a})$$

in terms of which the above ratios are written as

$$\langle\alpha\rangle/\langle i\hat{r}\rangle = -\langle\gamma_5\rangle/\langle i\boldsymbol{\sigma}.\hat{\mathbf{r}}\rangle = \pm\tfrac{1}{2}\Lambda\alpha Z. \qquad (7.50\,\text{b})$$

The argument for leaving out the term $2\langle\gamma_5\varkappa\rangle$ will be given below. When the coulomb energy difference is indeed the dominant one, $\Lambda \approx 2$

‡ It may be noted here that a 'gauge-invariant' Vector $\beta$-coupling, such as is expected under the 'Conserved Current Hypothesis' (§ 12.5), seems to require omitting the nuclear force terms from the relationships here. This is the conclusion of J. Fujita, *Phys. Rev.* **126**, 202 (1962).

is expected, and this is called 'Pursey's estimate' since he found the nuclear force effects to be relatively negligible. As against this, Ahrens and Feenberg estimate $\Lambda \approx 1$ more nearly. They took into account a partial cancellation (about a halving) of the extra electrostatic repulsion in the nucleus with one more proton by the readjustments which tend to arise in stabilizing it (they did this through using the so-called 'semi-empirical formula' for the stable nuclear masses).

Pursey also found a relationship between $\langle(\boldsymbol{\sigma}\times\hat{\mathbf{r}})\rangle$ and $\langle i\hat{r}\rangle$ by noticing that

$$[\varkappa, \mathbf{r}] = -[\boldsymbol{\sigma}.\mathbf{l}, \mathbf{r}] = i(\boldsymbol{\sigma}\times\mathbf{r}) \tag{7.51}$$

follows from the fundamental commutation relations. Consequently, whenever a definite eigenvalue $\kappa = \pm(j+\frac{1}{2})$, with $l = j\pm\frac{1}{2}$, can be assigned to the transforming nucleon,

$$\langle(\boldsymbol{\sigma}\times\hat{\mathbf{r}})\rangle = (\kappa'-\kappa)\langle i\hat{r}\rangle, \tag{7.52}$$

where $\kappa'$ belongs to the final state of the transformed nucleon. Usually $\kappa' \neq \kappa$ is to be expected since $\kappa$ is different in every distinct orbital (of (5.74), say), and the transforming nucleon usually undergoes a change of orbital in any forbidden transition. Another consequence of $\kappa' \neq \kappa$ is the reduction of the moment $\langle\gamma_5(1-2\varkappa)\rangle$ in (7.49) to $\langle\gamma_5\rangle$ simply, as in (7.50); $\varkappa = -(1+\boldsymbol{\sigma}.\mathbf{l})$ commutes with $\gamma_5$, hence the term with $\varkappa$ could survive only if $\kappa' = \kappa$ were possible.

The findings about the $\beta$-moment ratios make it possible to reduce the normal shape-factors (7.37) and (7.41) to

$$\left.\begin{aligned} S_1^{(1)} &\approx \tfrac{1}{4}(\alpha Z)^2\langle i\hat{r}\rangle^2[C_{\mathrm{A}}(\kappa'-\kappa)\pm C_{\mathrm{V}}(\Lambda-1)]^2 \\ S_1^{(0)} &\approx \tfrac{1}{4}(\alpha Z)^2\langle i\boldsymbol{\sigma}.\hat{\mathbf{r}}\rangle^2 C_{\mathrm{A}}^2(\Lambda-1)^2 \end{aligned}\right\}. \tag{7.53}$$

The latter of these indicates a particularly great sensitivity of $0^- \leftrightarrow 0^+$ transition rates to deviations from the estimate $\Lambda \approx 1$. The cases listed in Table 7.6 seem to indicate that the $0^- \to 0^+$ rates can be as large as other $0^-$ or $1^-$ rates, but $\Lambda \approx 2$, for example, could already account for that.

It can be hoped that discussions in such terms as led to (7.53) may have wider validity than in terms of the one-particle model used for (5.73) and (7.36). However, nothing can be said about absolute rates until some evaluations of $\langle i\hat{r}\rangle^2$ and $\langle i\boldsymbol{\sigma}.\hat{\mathbf{r}}\rangle^2$ are made. When (for 'normalization' purposes, as before) one-particle descriptions like‡ $i^l\chi_{\kappa M}(\hat{\mathbf{r}})$ of (5.72a) are again adopted for each nuclear state, then the results

‡ Here it becomes necessary to observe a convention like (6.65) when defining the phases of the nuclear states, in order to obtain real $\beta$-moments, hence the extra factor $i^l$. (See remarks following (6.66).)

will again apply directly only to odd-$A$ nuclei, and are easily found to be:

$$\left.\begin{aligned}\langle i\boldsymbol{\sigma}.\hat{\mathbf{r}}\rangle &= \pm\delta_{I'I}\,\delta_{l',l\pm1}\\ \langle i\hat{r}\rangle &= \pm\delta_{l',l\pm1}\langle I(\tfrac{1}{2})1(0)\,|\,I'(\tfrac{1}{2})\rangle\end{aligned}\right\}, \tag{7.54}$$

the upper and lower signs here referring to $l' = l\pm1$, respectively. The unit magnitude of $\langle i\boldsymbol{\sigma}.\hat{\mathbf{r}}\rangle$ follows immediately from the property $\boldsymbol{\sigma}.\hat{\mathbf{r}}\chi_{\kappa M} = -\chi_{-\kappa,M}$ recorded in (3.63). These results can be used to evaluate 'mismatch factors' for the $0^-$ and $1^-$ transitions, as for the allowed and unique cases, and when that is done the 'mismatches' are again found to be of roughly the same order as in the allowed and unique cases. The specific numbers are less significant here because of the ambiguities in the estimates of $\Lambda$. The 'deformed-core' theory of the mismatches, alluded to near the end of Chapter V, could be applied‡ to one or two cases and has about the same success as in the unfavoured allowed transitions.

The theoretical results for the once-parity forbidden moments, as outlined above, can be generalized to an arbitrary degree of forbiddenness. Thus, the commutator

$$[r^L Y_{Lm}, \mathbf{p}] = i\boldsymbol{\nabla}(r^L Y_{Lm}) = i[L(2L+1)]^{\frac{1}{2}} r^{L-1}\mathbf{T}^{L-1}_{Lm} \tag{7.55}$$

can be used to generalize (7.50) to

$$[J(2J+1)]^{\frac{1}{2}}\langle\boldsymbol{\alpha}.\mathbf{T}^{J-1}_{J}\rangle = \pm\tfrac{1}{2}\Lambda\alpha Z\langle Y_J\rangle. \tag{7.56}$$

The generalization of the commutator (7.51),

$$[\varkappa, Y_{Lm}] = -[\boldsymbol{\sigma}.\mathbf{l}, Y_{Lm}] = -[L(L+1)]^{\frac{1}{2}}\boldsymbol{\sigma}.\mathbf{T}^{L}_{Lm}, \tag{7.57}$$

can be used to find

$$[J(J+1)]^{\frac{1}{2}}\langle\boldsymbol{\sigma}.\mathbf{T}^{J}_{J}\rangle = (\kappa'-\kappa)\langle Y_J\rangle. \tag{7.58}$$

Finally, the one-particle result (7.54) can be generalized to

$$\langle Y_L\rangle = (-)^{\frac{1}{2}(l'-l-L)}[(2L+1)/4\pi]^{\frac{1}{2}}\langle I(\tfrac{1}{2})L(0)\,|\,I'(\tfrac{1}{2})\rangle \tag{7.59}$$

if $l+l'+L$ is even ($\langle Y_L\rangle$ is zero otherwise). The reader should be cautioned that great over-simplifications of the nuclear states are assumed for these results, hence large discrepancies with experimental measurements are only too likely; the value of these results is in the fact that almost any of the much more detailed considerations needed in every individual case uses them as 'points of departure'.

‡ See the reference on p. 158, for example. An interesting point is that the deformed-core theory seems to predict generally slower rates for $1^-$ than for $0^-$ transitions. The experimental observation that the $1^-$ rates are generally somewhat slower (see tables) at one time led to the no longer tenable argument that some Pseudoscalar $\beta$-coupling may exist (see § 10.2).

Similar considerations may be applied to the more highly forbidden cases of Table 7.7.

TABLE 7.7

*Transitions of higher forbiddenness*

| *Parent* | *Daughter* | *Transition* | $\log_{10}(ft)_{\text{exp}}$ |
|---|---|---|---|
| (*Twice-parity-forbidden, 2*$^+$) | | | |
| ${}_{11}\text{Na}^{24}_{13}$ | ${}_{12}\text{Mg}_{12}$ | $4^+ \to 2^+$ | 12·7 |
| ${}_{17}\text{Cl}^{36}_{19}$ | ${}_{18}\text{A}_{18}$ | $2^+ \to 0^+$ | 13·5 |
| ${}_{21}\text{Sc}^{46}_{25}$ | ${}_{22}\text{Ti}_{24}$ | $4^+ \to 2^+$ | 13·1 |
| ${}_{26}\text{Fe}^{59}_{33}$ | ${}_{27}\text{Co}_{32}$ | $\frac{3}{2}^- \to \frac{7}{2}^-$ | 10·9 |
| ${}_{28}\text{Ni}^{59}_{31}$ | ” | ” | 11·9 |
| ${}_{38}\text{Sr}^{89}_{51}$ | ${}_{39}\text{Y}^*_{50}$ | $\frac{5}{2}^+ \to \frac{9}{2}^+$ | 10·9 |
| ${}_{40}\text{Zr}^{93}_{53}$ | ${}_{41}\text{Nb}_{52}$ | ” | 11·3 |
| ${}_{43}\text{Tc}^{99}_{56}$ | ${}_{44}\text{Ru}_{55}$ | $\frac{9}{2}^+ \to \frac{5}{2}^+$ | 12·3 |
| ${}_{53}\text{I}^{129}_{76}$ | ${}_{54}\text{Xe}_{75}$ | $\frac{7}{2}^+ \to \frac{3}{2}^+$ | 13·5 |
| ${}_{55}\text{Cs}^{135}_{80}$ | ${}_{56}\text{Ba}_{79}$ | ” | 13·2 |
| ${}_{55}\text{Cs}^{137}_{82}$ | ${}_{56}\text{Ba}_{81}$ | ” | 12·0 |
| (*Unique, 3*$^+$) | | | |
| ${}_{4}\text{Be}^{10}_{6}$ | ${}_{5}\text{B}_{5}$ | $0^+ \to 3^+$ | 13·7 |
| ${}_{11}\text{Na}^{22}_{11}$ | ${}_{10}\text{Ne}_{12}$ | $3^+ \to 0^+$ | 13·1 |
| ${}_{13}\text{Al}^{26}_{13}$ | ${}_{12}\text{Mg}^*_{14}$ | $5^+ \to 2^+$ | 11·5 |
| ${}_{27}\text{Co}^{60}_{33}$ | ${}_{28}\text{Ni}_{32}$ | ” | 12·5 |
| (*Parity-forbidden, 3*$^-$) | | | |
| ${}_{37}\text{Rb}^{87}_{50}$ | ${}_{38}\text{Sr}_{49}$ | $\frac{3}{2}^- \to \frac{9}{2}^+$ | 17·6 |
| ${}_{57}\text{La}^{138}_{81}$ | ${}_{56}\text{Ba}^*_{82}$ | $5^- \to 2^+$ | ~ 17 |
| ” | ${}_{58}\text{Ce}^*_{80}$ | ” | ~ 19 |
| ${}_{83}\text{Bi}^{210}_{127}$ | ${}_{84}\text{Po}_{126}$ | ” | ~ 19 |
| ($4^-$, $4^+$ *cases*) | | | |
| ${}_{19}\text{K}^{40}_{21}$ | ${}_{20}\text{Ca}_{20}$ | $4^- \to 0^+$ | 18·1 |
| ${}_{49}\text{In}^{115}_{66}$ | ${}_{50}\text{Sn}_{65}$ | $\frac{9}{2}^+ \to \frac{1}{2}^+$ | ~ 24 |

## 7.4. 'Forbidden corrections' to allowed transitions

The theory of allowed β-decay, as presented in Chapter V, is a 'normal approximation' to the complete theory of $0^+$ and $1^+$ transitions. It is a very good approximation, but highly refined observations have detected slight deviations from it. The size of the deviations to be expected‡ should be gauged by examining contributions $\mathcal{O}(v_N)$ and $\mathcal{O}(R)$.

*For* $0 \to 0$ *transitions*

The exact shape-factor for transitions in which the leptons carry off no angular momentum ($J = 0$) is given by (7.38). It leads to correc-

‡ M. Morita, *Phys. Rev.* **113,** 1584 (1959).

tions of the allowed approximation $S_0^{(0)} \approx C_V^2\langle 1\rangle^2$ which can also be obtained to $\mathcal{O}(v_N)$ from the normal once-parity-forbidden shape-factor $S_1^{(0)}$ of (7.41), by transforming it according to $C_A \to -C_V\gamma_5$ (as reference to (7.40) shows):

$$S_0^{(0)} \approx C_V^2[\langle 1\rangle \mp \tfrac{1}{2}\alpha Z\langle i\boldsymbol{\alpha}.\hat{\mathbf{r}}\rangle]^2. \tag{7.60}$$

This obviously leaves the normally expected statistical spectrum shape undisturbed, but has an influence on the rate (7.12) which depends on the size of the radial velocity moment, $\langle i\boldsymbol{\alpha}.\hat{\mathbf{r}}\rangle$.

A ratio of $\langle i\boldsymbol{\alpha}.\hat{\mathbf{r}}\rangle$ to $\langle 1\rangle$ may be estimated by the type of procedure used to obtain $\langle\alpha\rangle$ of (7.50). From the commutator

$$[r^2, \boldsymbol{\alpha}.\mathbf{p}] = 2i\boldsymbol{\alpha}.\mathbf{r}, \tag{7.61}$$

it follows that

$$\Big\langle \mathrm{f}\Big|\sum_a \tau_\pm^a[(\mathbf{r}^a)^2, H_T]\Big|\mathrm{i}\Big\rangle = 2i\Big\langle \mathrm{f}\Big|\sum_a \tau_\pm^a\, \boldsymbol{\alpha}.\mathbf{r}\Big|\mathrm{i}\Big\rangle.$$

The right side is just $-2R\langle i\boldsymbol{\alpha}.\hat{\mathbf{r}}\rangle$ [see (6.62)], while the left side is $\langle r^2\rangle = R^2\langle 1\rangle$ multiplied with the kinetic energy difference

$$\Delta\langle H_T\rangle = \pm\Lambda(\alpha Z/2R),$$

according to the estimation procedure which led to (7.49). Thus,

$$\langle i\boldsymbol{\alpha}.\hat{\mathbf{r}}\rangle = \mp\tfrac{1}{4}\Lambda\alpha Z\langle 1\rangle \tag{7.62}$$

with the parameter $\Lambda$ of (7.50). This makes the correction factor of $C_V\langle 1\rangle$ in (7.60) equal to $1-\frac{1}{8}\Lambda(\alpha Z)^2$. In the crucial $0 \to 0$ decay of $O^{14}$, which was used to measure the fundamental coupling strength (see last subsection of Chapter V), the correction amounts to a negligible $0{\cdot}03\Lambda$ per cent.

Some departure from the statistical spectrum shape is generated in the usually smaller $\mathcal{O}(R)$. To find it, the electron densities $L_0$, $\bar{M}_0$, and $\bar{N}_0$ of (7.38) must be evaluated to $\mathcal{O}(R)$ by extending the procedures which yielded the normal approximations (7.5):

$$\left.\begin{aligned} L_0 &\approx \tfrac{1}{2}(1+\gamma_0)[1\mp\tfrac{1}{3}\alpha ZR(5W+W^{-1})+...] \\ \bar{M}_0 &\approx \tfrac{1}{2}(1+\gamma_0)[\tfrac{1}{4}(\alpha Z)^2\pm\tfrac{1}{3}\alpha ZRp^2/W+...] \\ \bar{N}_0 &\approx \tfrac{1}{2}(1+\gamma_0)[\mp\tfrac{1}{2}\alpha Z-\tfrac{1}{3}Rp^2/W+...] \end{aligned}\right\}, \tag{7.63}$$

where $p = (W^2-1)^{\frac{1}{2}}$ is the electron momentum in units $mc$. Then the correction $\sim \langle 1\rangle^2 R$ which is to be added to $S_0^{(0)}$ of (7.60) is

$$\Delta S_0^{(0)} = \mp\tfrac{1}{3}\alpha ZRC_V^2\langle 1\rangle^2[5W+W^{-1}+q], \tag{7.64 a}$$

where $q = W_0 - W$ is the neutrino energy. This may be regarded as the result of an interference between $\langle 1\rangle$ and a moment $\langle r^2\rangle$ which has been treated as equivalent to $R^2\langle 1\rangle$ according to the definitions (6.62) of $R$. An effort is sometimes made to take into account the distinctions between the $R$'s defined relative to different $\beta$-moments: Yamada's‡ 'finite de Broglie wavelength effect'. This has led to estimations of $\langle r^2\rangle$ as $\frac{3}{5}R^2\langle 1\rangle$, as for a transforming nucleon spread uniformly over a radius $R$, and then a factor $\alpha ZR\langle 1\rangle$ of (7.64 a) is treated as

$$(\alpha Z/R)\langle r^2\rangle = \tfrac{3}{5}\alpha ZR\langle 1\rangle.$$

Considering that it may be better to treat the transforming nucleon as one of the superficial ones, with $\langle r^2\rangle \approx R^2\langle 1\rangle^2$, and the uncertainties about the quantitative meaning of 'nuclear radius', it is difficult to put the distinctions into well-justified practice.

Since the correction (7.64 a) has turned out to be better characterized as of order $(\alpha ZR)$, corrections of nominal order $(v_N R)$ may be quite comparable (see the estimate $v_N \sim \alpha Z$ in (7.62)). Such arise in proportion to interferences of $\langle i\boldsymbol{\alpha}.\hat{\mathbf{r}}\rangle$ with $\langle 1\rangle$:

$$\Delta' S_0^{(0)} = -C_V^2\langle 1\rangle\langle i\boldsymbol{\alpha}.\hat{\mathbf{r}}\rangle.\tfrac{2}{3}\{(p^2/W)+q\}R, \tag{7.64 b}$$

to be added to (7.60) and (7.64 a).§ Some evidence of spectral deviations corresponding to $\Delta S_0^{(0)}+\Delta' S_0^{(0)}$ seems to have been found|| in the $0 \to 0$ decay of ${}_{31}\mathrm{Ga}^{66}_{35}$ to ${}_{30}\mathrm{Zn}_{36}$.

*For the general* $0^+$ *or* $1^+$ *transitions*

The $1^+$ transition rates are proportional to a shape factor $S_0^{(1)}$ which also contributes to $0^+$ decays in which $I' = I \neq 0$. Its allowed approximation, $S_0^{(1)} \approx C_A^2\langle\sigma\rangle^2$, is corrected to order $(v_N/c)$ when it is formed by the substitutions $C_V \leftrightarrow -C_A\gamma_5$ into the normal approximation (7.37) of $S_1^{(1)}$:

$$S_0^{(1)} = [C_A\langle\sigma\rangle+\tfrac{1}{2}\alpha Z(C_V\langle(\boldsymbol{\alpha}\times\hat{\mathbf{r}})\rangle \pm C_A\langle i\gamma_5\hat{r}\rangle)]^2. \tag{7.65}$$

Like $S_0^{(0)}$ of (7.60), this leads to no spectral deviations (energy-dependences of the shape-factor) unless corrections $\mathcal{O}(\alpha ZR)$ and $\mathcal{O}(v_N R)$ are added to it. The correction $\mathcal{O}(\alpha ZR)$, analogous to $\Delta S_0^{(0)}$ of (7.64 a) is

$$\Delta S_0^{(1)} = \mp\tfrac{1}{3}\alpha ZRC_A^2\langle\sigma\rangle^2[5W+W^{-1}-\tfrac{1}{3}q]\pm$$
$$\pm\tfrac{2}{9}\alpha ZRC_A^2\langle\sigma\rangle\langle\sigma-3\hat{r}(\boldsymbol{\sigma}.\hat{\mathbf{r}})\rangle q. \tag{7.66 a}$$

The last line arises from an interference of the ${}^3S_1$ lepton wave, generated through the allowed triplet moment $\langle\sigma\rangle$, with the ${}^3D_1$ wave generated through the new $\beta$-moment

$$\langle\sigma-3\hat{r}(\boldsymbol{\sigma}.\hat{\mathbf{r}})\rangle = -(8\pi)^{\frac{1}{2}}\langle\boldsymbol{\sigma}.\mathbf{T}_1^2\rangle. \tag{7.67}$$

‡ M. Yamada, *Prog. Theoret. Phys.* **10**, 252 (1953).

§ Corrections to the once-parity-forbidden shape-factor $S_1^{(0)}$ of (7.41), corresponding to $\Delta_0^{(0)}S$ and $\Delta' S_0^{(0)}$, may be obtained through the transformation $C_V \to -C_A\gamma_5$ (see (7.40)).

|| D. Camp and L. M. Langer, *Phys. Rev.* **129**, 1782 (1963).

The corrections $\mathcal{O}(v_N R)$ analogous to $\Delta' S_0^{(0)}$ of (7.64 b) will be written in two parts

$$\Delta' S_0^{(1)} = C_A^2 \langle\sigma\rangle\langle i\gamma_5 \hat{r}\rangle . \tfrac{2}{3}\{(p^2/W)+q\}R, \tag{7.66 b}$$

$$(\Delta S)_{\text{wm}} = \pm C_A C_V \langle\sigma\rangle\langle(\boldsymbol{\alpha}\times\hat{\mathbf{r}})\rangle . \tfrac{2}{3}\{(p^2/W)-q\}R. \tag{7.66 c}$$

for $e^{\mp}$ emissions, respectively. The subscript 'wm' refers to the identification of the last correction as a 'weak-magnetic' effect, to be discussed in the next subsection.

Attempts to relate the relativistically defined $\beta$-moments, $\langle i\gamma_5 \hat{r}\rangle$ and $\langle(\boldsymbol{\alpha}\times\hat{\mathbf{r}})\rangle$, to the others by the procedures used for $\langle i\boldsymbol{\alpha}.\hat{\mathbf{r}}\rangle/\langle 1\rangle$ of (7.62) result in the intrusion of the spin-orbit operator $\varkappa$ as in (7.49). To avoid the consequent necessity to assign definite orbitals (values of $\kappa$) to the transforming nucleons, a procedure followed by Yamada and Morita will be used (refs., p. 216. Rose and Osborn attain the same ends by using the so-called 'Foldy–Wouthuysen' transformation). The new procedure, although nominally starting with a new type of approximation, yields the same results (7.50) for $\langle\alpha\rangle/\langle i\hat{r}\rangle \approx -\langle\gamma_5\rangle/\langle 1\rangle$. It is explicitly recognized that a non-relativistic description of the nucleons should really be adequate, and that corrections $\mathcal{O}(v_N/c = P/Mc)$ can be made by including 'small components' of the nuclear wave functions which are generated from the main ones by operations $(\boldsymbol{\sigma}.\mathbf{P})/2Mc$. This is the proper way to relate the small to the large components for free nucleons with $P^2 \ll (Mc)^2$ as reference to (3.2) or (3.18) shows; it is also proper when the interactions are small compared to‡ $Mc^2 \approx 1$ GeV, as can be seen from (5.57). Now, when the dependence on the internal variables of some one nucleon is displayed,

$$\psi_{\mathrm{i,f}} = \begin{pmatrix} 1 \\ \boldsymbol{\sigma}.\mathbf{P}/2Mc \end{pmatrix} \boldsymbol{\varphi}_{\mathrm{i,f}}, \tag{7.68}$$

where the $\boldsymbol{\varphi}$'s stand for large components of the nuclear states, forming the non-relativistic descriptions. It then follows, for example, that

$$\psi_{\mathrm{f}}^{\dagger}\boldsymbol{\alpha}\psi_{\mathrm{i}} \approx \boldsymbol{\varphi}_{\mathrm{f}}^{\dagger}\boldsymbol{\sigma}[(\boldsymbol{\sigma}.\mathbf{P}/2Mc)\boldsymbol{\varphi}_{\mathrm{i}}]+[(\boldsymbol{\sigma}.\mathbf{P}/2Mc)\boldsymbol{\varphi}_{\mathrm{f}}]^{\dagger}\boldsymbol{\sigma}\boldsymbol{\varphi}_{\mathrm{i}}$$

$$\approx (2Mc)^{-1}\boldsymbol{\varphi}_{\mathrm{f}}^{\dagger}\{\boldsymbol{\sigma},(\boldsymbol{\sigma}.\mathbf{P})\}\boldsymbol{\varphi}_{\mathrm{i}} = \boldsymbol{\varphi}_{\mathrm{f}}^{\dagger}(\mathbf{P}/Mc)\boldsymbol{\varphi}_{\mathrm{i}}, \tag{7.69}$$

where $\{\boldsymbol{\sigma},(\boldsymbol{\sigma}.\mathbf{P})\}$ is the *anti*commutator $\boldsymbol{\sigma}(\boldsymbol{\sigma}.\mathbf{P})+(\boldsymbol{\sigma}.\mathbf{P})\boldsymbol{\sigma}$. Thus '$\mathbf{v}_N$' $= \mathbf{P}/M = -i(\hbar/M)\boldsymbol{\nabla}$ becomes the non-relativistic operator equivalent to $c\boldsymbol{\alpha}$. The same approximation for a kinetic energy operator

‡ If the interactions themselves depend on $c\boldsymbol{\alpha}$ in some way, then their effects must be small compared to the kinetic energy effects of primary concern here, for the approximation to be valid.

$H_T = c\boldsymbol{\alpha}.\mathbf{P}+(\beta-1)Mc^2$, of the type used in (7.47), is seen from

$$\psi_f^\dagger H_T \psi_i \approx \boldsymbol{\varphi}_f^\dagger[P^2/M-2Mc^2(\boldsymbol{\sigma}.\mathbf{P}/2Mc)^2]\boldsymbol{\varphi}_i$$
$$= \boldsymbol{\varphi}_f^\dagger(P^2/2M)\boldsymbol{\varphi}_i. \quad (7.70)$$

This should be used in the Ahrens–Feenberg approximation (7.48), (7.50),

$$\langle f|[\mathcal{O}, H_T]|i\rangle = \Delta\langle H_T\rangle\langle f|\mathcal{O}|i\rangle \quad (7.71)$$

(where $\Delta\langle H_T\rangle = \pm\frac{1}{2}\Lambda\alpha Zmc^2$) when the non-relativistic equivalents are used for all the other operations.

The non-relativistic equivalent of the operation in $\langle i\gamma_5\,\hat{r}\rangle$ can be seen from

$$\psi_f^\dagger\gamma_5\,\mathbf{r}\psi_i = -\boldsymbol{\varphi}_f^\dagger\{\mathbf{r},(\boldsymbol{\sigma}.\mathbf{P})\}\boldsymbol{\varphi}_i/2Mc$$
$$= -(2Mc)^{-1}\boldsymbol{\varphi}_f^\dagger[2(\boldsymbol{\sigma}.\mathbf{P})\mathbf{r}+i\hbar\boldsymbol{\sigma}]\boldsymbol{\varphi}_i. \quad (7.72)$$

The first part, as the experience in obtaining $\langle\gamma_5\rangle$ from (7.47) suggests, can be related to the commutator

$$[\mathbf{r}(\boldsymbol{\sigma}.\mathbf{r}), P^2/2M] = i(\hbar/M)[(\boldsymbol{\sigma}.\mathbf{P})\mathbf{r}+(\boldsymbol{\sigma}.\mathbf{r})\mathbf{P}]. \quad (7.73)$$

The matrix elements of each of these two terms have the same Ahrens–Feenberg approximations (7.71), namely

$$-(\hbar/M)^2(\Delta\langle H_T\rangle)^{-1}\langle f|(\boldsymbol{\sigma}.\mathbf{P})\mathbf{P}|i\rangle,$$

making the operation (7.73) effectively equivalent to

$$2\hbar c[-i\gamma_5\,\mathbf{r}+(\hbar/2Mc)\boldsymbol{\sigma}]$$

of (7.72). It then follows that

$$R\langle i\gamma_5\,\hat{r}\rangle = -\langle\sigma\rangle(\hbar/2Mc)\pm\tfrac{1}{4}\Lambda\alpha ZR\langle\hat{r}(\boldsymbol{\sigma}.\hat{\mathbf{r}})\rangle. \quad (7.74)$$

The last of the moments here can be separated into $S$-wave and $D$-wave generating parts by replacing it with $\frac{1}{3}[\langle\sigma\rangle-\langle\sigma-3\hat{r}(\boldsymbol{\sigma}.\hat{\mathbf{r}})\rangle]$.

The non-relativistic equivalent of the operator in $\langle(\boldsymbol{\alpha}\times\hat{\mathbf{r}})\rangle$ can be seen from

$$\boldsymbol{\alpha}\times\mathbf{r} \approx (2Mc)^{-1}\{(\boldsymbol{\sigma}\times\mathbf{r}),(\boldsymbol{\sigma}.\mathbf{P})\}$$
$$= -(\mathbf{l}+\boldsymbol{\sigma})\hbar/Mc = -2(\boldsymbol{\mu}_1\,\hbar/2Mc), \quad (7.75)$$

where $\mathbf{l}\hbar = \mathbf{r}\times\mathbf{P}$ is the orbital momentum operator and $\boldsymbol{\mu}_1\hbar/2Mc$ should be recognized as just a magnetic moment operator for a mass $M$ bearing a unit charge and a 'normal' intrinsic magnetic moment (as against such 'anomalous' ones as do physical nucleons; compare $\boldsymbol{\mu}_1$ to $\boldsymbol{\mu}$ of (5.84) with $\mu_p = 1$, $\mu_n = 0$). The relation of this to Gell-Mann's 'weak-magnetism' will be discussed in the next subsection. Meanwhile, estimates of the $\beta$-moments $\langle(\boldsymbol{\alpha}\times\hat{\mathbf{r}}\rangle) \approx -\langle\mu_1\rangle\hbar/McR$ may be derived with the help of the anticommutator

$$\{\varkappa,\boldsymbol{\sigma}\} = -2\boldsymbol{\sigma}-\{\boldsymbol{\sigma}.\mathbf{l},\boldsymbol{\sigma}\} = -2(\boldsymbol{\sigma}+\mathbf{l}), \quad (7.76)$$

having matrix elements like

$$\langle \mathrm{f}|\varkappa\boldsymbol{\sigma}+\boldsymbol{\sigma}\varkappa|\mathrm{i}\rangle = (\kappa'+\kappa)\langle \mathrm{f}|\boldsymbol{\sigma}|\mathrm{i}\rangle,$$

hence

$$\langle(\boldsymbol{\alpha}\times\hat{\mathbf{r}})\rangle \approx (\kappa'+\kappa)\langle\sigma\rangle(\hbar/2McR), \tag{7.77}$$

when definite orbitals labelled by $\kappa$ and $\kappa'$ can be assigned to the initial and final states of the transforming nucleon. (Notice that $\kappa' = -\kappa$ would correspond to an unallowed change of the orbital parity: $l' = l\pm 1$.) With this, all the $\beta$-moments have been reduced to forms which may be evaluated with conventional, non-relativistic, nuclear state descriptions.

*Weak magnetism*

Gell-Mann‡ has demonstrated the value of identifying a part of the corrections $\mathcal{O}(v_N/c)$ to the allowed approximations as an analogue of magnetic effects in the electromagnetic interaction (magnetic fields arise only from charges with non-vanishing velocity!). How the magnetic field $\mathbf{B} = \boldsymbol{\nabla}\times\mathbf{A}$ enters an electromagnetic interaction like (4.1) can be seen from the non-relativistic equivalent of the operator $H_\gamma = e(\phi-\boldsymbol{\alpha}.\mathbf{A})$ formed in the same way as was $\boldsymbol{\alpha} \approx \mathbf{P}/Mc$ of (7.69):

$$\begin{aligned} H_\gamma &\approx e\phi-(e/2Mc)\{\boldsymbol{\sigma}.\mathbf{A},\boldsymbol{\sigma}.\mathbf{P}\} \\ &= e\phi-(e/2Mc)(\mathbf{A}.\mathbf{P}+\mathbf{P}.\mathbf{A})-(e\hbar/2Mc)\boldsymbol{\sigma}.\mathbf{B}, \end{aligned} \tag{7.78}$$

where the linearization in $\boldsymbol{\sigma}$ was performed with the help of (4.52). This becomes appropriate for a nucleon, with its anomalous magnetic moments, if $e$ is replaced by $\frac{1}{2}(1+\tau_3)e$ except in the magnetic term, where the replacement

$$\boldsymbol{\sigma} \rightarrow [\tfrac{1}{2}(1+\tau_3)\mu_{\mathrm{p}}+\tfrac{1}{2}(1-\tau_3)\mu_{\mathrm{n}}]\boldsymbol{\sigma} \tag{7.79}$$

should be made (compare (5.84)). It will later have interest that the electromagnetic interactions of nucleons, thus formulated, can give rise to 'magnetic dipole $\gamma$-radiation' (identifiable through its conformity to selection rules of the Gamow–Teller type) at the rate:§

$$\lambda_\gamma = \tfrac{1}{3}\alpha(Mc^2/\hbar)(E_\gamma/Mc^2)^3\langle\mu\rangle_\gamma^2, \tag{7.80}$$

where

$$\langle\mu\rangle_\gamma = \langle I'(M')1(m)\mid I(M)\rangle^{-1}\langle I'(M')|\mu_m^\dagger|I(M)\rangle \tag{7.81}$$

a moment formed analogously to $\langle\sigma\rangle$ of (5.20), but here connecting states of one nucleus. The vector $\boldsymbol{\mu}$ is just the nuclear magnetic moment operator (5.84), $E_\gamma$ is the $\gamma$-ray energy, and $\alpha = e^2/\hbar c$.

A comparison of the $\gamma$-interaction, especially when written in the

‡ M. Gell-Mann, *Phys. Rev.* **111,** 362 (1958).

§ See, e.g., S. A. Moszkowski, chapter xix of *Beta- and Gamma-Ray Spectroscopy* (editor K. Siegbahn) (North-Holland Press, Amsterdam, 1955).

form $H_\gamma = -ie\beta\gamma_\alpha A_\alpha$ of (4.7) with $H_\beta$ of (4.67), shows that the electron-neutrino current $iJ_\alpha$ plays the role of a 4-vector potential for the $\beta$-interactions of nucleons: $\phi \leftrightarrow J_4$ and $\mathbf{B} \leftrightarrow \nabla \times i\mathbf{J}$. The non-relativistic (in nucleons only) approximation to $H_\beta$, formed analogously to $H_\gamma$ of (7.78), is

$$H_\beta \approx 2^{\frac{1}{2}}g \sum_a \tau_\pm^a\{C_\mathrm{V} J_4 - iC_\mathrm{A}\,\boldsymbol{\sigma}.\mathbf{J}+ \\ +(2Mc)^{-1}[(C_\mathrm{A} J_4\boldsymbol{\sigma} - iC_\mathrm{V}\mathbf{J}).\mathbf{P}+\mathbf{P}.(C_\mathrm{A} J_4\boldsymbol{\sigma} - iC_\mathrm{V}\mathbf{J})] - \\ -(C_\mathrm{V}\hbar/2Mc)\boldsymbol{\sigma}.(\nabla\times i\mathbf{J})\}_a. \quad (7.82)$$

The last line may be appropriately called the *intrinsic* weak-magnetic interaction, arising from the nucleon spin.

When the currents are evaluated at the nuclear centre only, the first two terms of (7.82) obviously yield the allowed approximation (5.4). When the neglect of the gradients of the lepton currents is continued, the remaining terms yield corrections $\mathcal{O}(v_N/c)$ as in (5.2); it must be remembered that $\boldsymbol{\alpha} \approx \mathbf{P}/Mc$ and $\gamma_5 \approx -(\boldsymbol{\sigma}.\mathbf{P})/Mc$ in the non-relativistic approximation.

When the currents are evaluated to $\mathcal{O}(R)$, i.e. $J_\alpha \approx J_\alpha^0 + \mathbf{r}^a.(\nabla J_\alpha)^0$, the interaction form (7.82) can be shown to yield precisely the corrections to the allowed approximation discussed in the preceding two subsections. Further attention will be given here only to the terms which survive in $1 \leftrightarrow 0$ transitions with no nuclear parity change, and, initially, the coulomb distortion of the electron wave will be neglected ($Z = 0$). The latter simplification allows using plane wave descriptions for the leptons, so that $J_\alpha \sim \exp(-i\mathbf{k}.\mathbf{r}^a)$ with $\hbar\mathbf{k} = \mathbf{p}+\mathbf{q}$ and $\nabla J_\alpha = -i\mathbf{k}J_\alpha$. Written for e$^-$ emissions, $J_4 = \phi_\mathrm{e}^\dagger\phi_\nu^C$ and $i\mathbf{J} = \phi_\mathrm{e}^\dagger\boldsymbol{\alpha}\phi_\nu^C = -\phi_\mathrm{e}^\dagger\boldsymbol{\sigma}\phi_\nu^C$, as follows from (4.30) for example. Now the surviving terms‡ of the transition amplitude derivable from (7.82) become

$$\langle \mathrm{f}|H_\beta|\mathrm{i}\rangle \approx -2^{\frac{1}{2}}g\phi_\mathrm{e}^\dagger\Big\{C_\mathrm{A}(\boldsymbol{\alpha}+\hbar\mathbf{k}/2Mc).\int\boldsymbol{\sigma}+(iC_\mathrm{A}/Mc)\mathbf{k}.\int\mathbf{r}(\boldsymbol{\sigma}.\mathbf{P}) - \\ -i(C_\mathrm{V}\hbar/2Mc)(\mathbf{k}\times\boldsymbol{\alpha}).\int(\mathbf{1}+\boldsymbol{\sigma})\Big\}\phi_\nu^C, \quad (7.83)$$

where the nuclear matrix elements have been given in notations of the type (5.3). This is of the form given by Gell-Mann except that he concerned himself only with the corrections $\sim \int\boldsymbol{\sigma}$, hence omitted the

‡ The reduction

$$\sum_{ij} k_i\alpha_j \int x_i P_j = \tfrac{1}{3}(\mathbf{k}.\boldsymbol{\alpha})\int(\mathbf{r}.\mathbf{P})+\tfrac{1}{2}(\mathbf{k}\times\boldsymbol{\alpha}).\int(\mathbf{r}\times\mathbf{P})+\tfrac{1}{2}\sum_{ij} S_{ij}(\mathbf{k},\boldsymbol{\alpha})\int S_{ij}(\mathbf{r},\mathbf{P}),$$

with $S_{ij}(\mathbf{r},\mathbf{P}) = x_iP_j + x_jP_i - \frac{2}{3}\delta_{ij}(\mathbf{r}.\mathbf{P})$ for example, shows that only the middle term, $\sim\int\mathbf{l}\hbar$, survives in $1 \leftrightarrow 0$ transitions. The symmetrical tensor, $\int S_{ij}$, requires radiation of $\mathbf{J} = \mathbf{2}$ for survival.

contribution to the weak-magnetism by the nucleon orbital motions $\sim \int \mathbf{l}$. The full weak-magnetic moment given here is

$$(\hbar/2Mc) \int (\mathbf{l}+\boldsymbol{\sigma}) \approx -\tfrac{1}{2} \int \boldsymbol{\alpha} \times \mathbf{r}$$

per unit '$\beta$-charge', as compared to the classical $(2c)^{-1} \int (d\mathbf{r})\mathbf{r} \times \mathbf{i}$ due to an electromagnetic current density $\mathbf{i}$. It arises solely as a correction to the Vector part of the $\beta$-interaction, $\sim C_{\mathrm{V}}$. The two correction terms $\sim C_{\mathrm{A}}\,\mathbf{k}$ within the brackets of (7.83) can be combined as $C_{\mathrm{A}}\,\mathbf{k}\,.\int (i\gamma_5\,\mathbf{r})^{\dagger}$ according to (7.72).

The shape-factor following from (7.83) may be calculated as

$$S = (V/g)^2 \Big\langle (2I+1)^{-1} \sum_{e\nu MM'} |\langle I'(M')|H_\beta|I(M)\rangle|^2 \Big\rangle, \tag{7.84}$$

where the outside angular brackets indicate averages over lepton directions, as required for the definition of $S$ implicit in (6.83). The energy dependence of the result may be expressed as a proportionality

$$S \sim 1 + AW + B/W, \tag{7.85}$$

as can also be seen from the corrections given in the preceding subsections. The term inversely proportional to the energy comes from $(cp)^2/W = W - (mc^2)^2/W$ and is entirely negligible, especially in its variation with energy, over the measurable portions of high-energy spectra (e.g. only $W \gtrsim 12mc^2$ is well-measured in the spectra of $B^{12}$ and $N^{12}$). As a consequence, the correction $\Delta' S_0^{(1)} \sim \langle i\gamma_5 \hat{r}\rangle$ of (7.66 b), being proportional to $(cp)^2/W + cq \approx W - (W_0 - W) = W_0$, becomes a (very small) part of the constant term. The only dependence on energy left (in the absence of coulomb corrections) arises from the weak-magnetism as measured by $(\Delta S)_{\mathrm{wm}}$ of (7.66 c). This yields for the energy-gradients:

$$A_{\pm} \approx \pm \frac{4}{3} \frac{C_{\mathrm{V}} \langle(\boldsymbol{\alpha} \times \hat{\mathbf{r}})\rangle R}{C_{\mathrm{A}} \langle \sigma \rangle \hbar c} \approx \pm \frac{4}{3} \left| \frac{C_{\mathrm{V}}}{C_{\mathrm{A}}} \right| \frac{\langle l + \sigma \rangle}{\langle \sigma \rangle Mc^2}, \tag{7.86}$$

for $e^{\mp}$ emissions, respectively, in an approximation which is valid for $|AW| \approx W/Mc^2 \ll 1$.

Attempts‡ to measure the weak-magnetic effect on the $B^{12} \rightarrow C^{12} \leftarrow N^{12}$ spectra were inspired by Gell-Mann as a means for testing the 'Conserved Vector-Current Hypothesis', to be discussed in § 12.5. The latest experimental values seem to be $A_{\pm} \approx (0{\cdot}6 \pm 0{\cdot}1)$ per cent MeV.

The results (7.86) represent the predictions of 'conventional' theory. They may be evaluated with the help of the estimate (7.77) for the

‡ T. Mayer-Kuckuck and F. Michel, *Phys. Rev.* **127**, 545 (1962); Y. Lee, L. Mo, and C. S. Wu, *Phys. Rev. Letters*, **10**, 253 (1963).

weak-magnetic moment (times $-2$). Both the ${}_5B_7^{12}$, ${}_7N_5^{12} \to {}_6C_6^{12}$ transitions are expected to involve the transformation of a $p_{\frac{1}{2}}$ to a $p_{\frac{3}{2}}$ nucleon (Table 5.5), thus $\kappa = +1$ and $\kappa' = -2$. The moment $\langle\mu_1\rangle = \langle l+\sigma\rangle$ becomes $+\frac{1}{2}\langle\sigma\rangle$ and $A_{\pm} \approx \pm 0{\cdot}06$ per cent per MeV is the theoretical expectation, only a tenth of that observed.

It should still be checked whether the coulomb correction, $\Delta S_0^{(1)}$ of (7.66 a), can be responsible for the discrepancy. This adds to $A$:

$$\mp(16/9)(\alpha ZR/\hbar c)[1+\langle\sigma-3\hat{r}(\boldsymbol{\sigma}.\hat{\mathbf{r}})\rangle/8\langle\sigma\rangle]. \tag{7.87}$$

Morita's estimates make the last term negligible and the remainder contributes about $\mp 0{\cdot}11$ per cent per MeV. Thus, the coulomb correction here more than cancels the weak-magnetic effect calculated just above, and leads to signs for the energy-gradients which are opposite to those actually observed.

The conclusion is that the conventional theory cannot at all account for either the magnitude or the sign of the energy-gradients found in the $B^{12}$ and $N^{12}$ shape-factors. It will be seen in § 12.5 how, in contrast, the observations exactly fit the expectations from the 'Conserved Vector Current Hypothesis'.

# VIII

# ELECTRON AND NEUTRINO CAPTURE

ONLY spontaneous nuclear $\beta$-emissions have been treated in the preceding chapters. It was pointed out in § 4.3 that 'induced' $\beta$-processes are also possible, when fermions are incident on nuclei. Electron capture by nuclei will be treated in § 8.1 and neutrino absorption in § 8.2.

## 8.1. Orbital electron capture

The best chances for electrons to be absorbed by nucleons arise from the circumstance that atomic electrons spend long times in the vicinity of nuclei, and 'overlap' on them in the course of the orbital motions. When an absorption does occur, a monoenergetic‡ neutrino is emitted and a vacancy created in an atomic shell. The comparatively immediate refilling of such vacancies produces X-rays or Auger electrons (further atomic electrons rather than electromagnetic radiation gaining the energy from the atomic rearrangement). Sometimes, also, the product nucleus is formed in an excited state, so that detectable $\gamma$-radiation ensues (or 'conversion' electrons are ejected from atomic orbits, with the energy gained from the nuclear rearrangement). In addition, 'inner bremsstrahlung' generated by the 'falling' of the captured electron into the nucleus sometimes becomes detectable.§ All the secondary radiations decay exponentially as the capturing nuclei are depleted. A decay constant, $\lambda$, becomes measurable, just as in the detection of $\beta$-electron emissions. The task here is to find the theoretical expectations for the electron capture rates, $\lambda_{EC}$.

The energy requirements for the orbital capture have already been reviewed in § 1.6. The minimum is given by

$$W_0 = [M(Z)-M(Z-1)]c^2 > -mc^2.$$

When the nuclear mass difference $W_0$ is close to this lower limit (the product nucleus heavier than the initial one!), only the capture of the

‡ An experimental confirmation of this expectation was obtained by A. Snell and F. Pleasonton, *Phys. Rev.* **100**, 1396 (1955). They found the $Cl^{37}$ recoils produced in the orbital capture by $A^{37}$ to be monoenergetic, of $9{\cdot}63 \pm 0{\cdot}06$ eV. The expectation based on the emission of a single neutrino was $9{\cdot}64 \pm 0{\cdot}05$ eV, as derived from the $815 \pm 2$ keV energy release (see § 1.3).

§ Papers reporting all these effects have been reviewed by R. Bouchez and P. Depommier, *Rep. Progr. Phys.* **23**, 395 (1960).

outermost, negligibly bound, orbital electrons is energetically possible. For an electron bound with the energy‡ $B = mc^2 - W > 0$ to be captured, $W_0 > -mc^2 + B$ is necessary. Once this requirement is met, the more tightly bound inner atomic electrons are the ones most frequently captured because they overlap on the nucleus best. The capture rate increases rapidly with $W_0$, as will be seen, so that the highest rates occur in cases with $W_0$ large enough for positron emission also to be possible ($W_0 > +mc^2$). It is obvious that positron emission cannot occur without competition from orbital capture. Some of the most complete predictions, independent of uncertainties about $\beta$-moments, are obtainable for ratios of capture to the positron emission.

*Formulation of the capture rate*

The electron capture is generated through the lepton current:

$$J_\alpha(\nu e^-) = (\phi_\nu^\dagger \beta\gamma_\alpha \phi_e)_0 \, e^{-i(W-cq)t/\hbar}, \qquad (8.1)$$

formed like (4.32 c) except that $\phi_e$ and $\phi_\nu$ are interchanged to correspond to $p+e^- \to n+\nu$. The electron state projection can be taken as $\phi_e = \frac{1}{2}(1+\gamma_5)\psi_{\kappa\mu}$ with a $\psi_{\kappa\mu}$ of form (3.20). However, the radial functions $g$, $f$ in this form must now describe electrons in bound atomic states, enumerable by the principal quantum numbers $n = 1, 2, 3,\ldots$, labelling the succession of atomic shells $K, L, M,\ldots$. Each shell may contain as many as $2n^2$ electrons, in states distinguished by

$$\kappa = \pm(j+\tfrac{1}{2}) = \pm 1, \pm 2,\ldots, \pm(n-1), -n,$$

and by

$$\mu = \pm\tfrac{1}{2}, \pm\tfrac{3}{2}, \ldots, \pm j.$$

The absence of $\kappa = l = +n$ corresponds to the elementary fact of atomic structure that electrons with $l > n-1$ have too much centrifugal energy to be bound in the $n$th orbit.

When the nucleus is treated as a point charge, and screening by other atomic electrons is neglected, then the energy of a bound electron may be

$$W_{nj} = [n-(j+\tfrac{1}{2}-\gamma)]mc^2/N \qquad (8.2\,a)$$

with

$$N = \{[n-(j+\tfrac{1}{2}-\gamma)]^2+(\alpha Z)^2\}^{\frac{1}{2}}. \qquad (8.2\,b)$$

‡ This should properly be evaluated as the difference in binding of the whole initial electron cloud and one of a set of final atomic states, to be followed by appropriate summations over the various possible final states. Such precision of treatment is usually unnecessary when there is a substantial energy release $W_0$, but can become important for marginal cases. The latter have interest in connexion with the stability of nuclear isobars. A treatment of the whole atom as the system of interest (P. Benoist-Gueutal, *C.R. Acad. Sci., Paris*, **230**, 624 (1950)) can also be important for studies of the secondary radiations following the capture, and of extranuclear events following electron emissions as well. The reference in the preceding footnote may be consulted for guidance to the literature on such topics.

If $(\alpha Z)^2 \ll 1$, this is approximated by $W_{nj} \approx mc^2(1-\alpha^2Z^2/2n^2)$, the last term of which is just the elementary Balmer formula for the binding energy. The leading terms (as $r = R \to 0$) of the corresponding radial functions are:‡

$$g_n \approx \left[\frac{\Gamma(2\gamma+n-j+\frac{1}{2})}{(n-j-\frac{1}{2})!}\right]^{\frac{1}{2}} \frac{(2Z/Na_0)^{\gamma+\frac{1}{2}}R^{\gamma-1}}{\Gamma(2\gamma+1)} \left[\frac{1+W_{nj}/mc^2}{4N(N-\kappa)}\right]^{\frac{1}{2}} \times$$
$$\times (n-N+\kappa-j-\tfrac{1}{2}), \quad (8.3\,\text{a})$$

$$f_n \approx g_n[(1-W_{nj}/mc^2)/(1+W_{nj}/mc^2)]^{\frac{1}{2}}(n+N-\kappa-j-\tfrac{1}{2})/(n-N+\kappa-j-\tfrac{1}{2}). \quad (8.3\,\text{b})$$

Here $a_0 = \hbar^2/me^2 = \alpha^{-1}\hbar/mc$ is the Bohr radius. With these radial functions, $\psi_{\kappa\mu}$ is normalized to unity in all space.

Notice that in the approximation $\alpha^2Z^2 \ll (j+\frac{1}{2})^2$, when

$$N \approx n-\alpha^2Z^2(n-j-\tfrac{1}{2})/n(2j+1):$$

$$\left.\begin{aligned} f_n/g_n &\approx -\alpha Z/(2j+1) \quad \text{for} \quad \kappa < 0 \quad (l = j-\tfrac{1}{2}) \\ g_n/f_n &\approx +\alpha Z/(2j+1) \quad \text{for} \quad \kappa > 0 \quad (l = j+\tfrac{1}{2}) \end{aligned}\right\}. \quad (8.4)$$

Thus, either $f$ is considerably smaller than $g$, or vice versa. These results are also correct for the negatron states in the continuum (7.17), as might be expected because any finite kinetic energy is negligible in comparison to the potential energy as $r \to 0$. They lie behind the results (7.6) for the combinations of continuum wave functions. All these facts will have an important bearing on the comparisons of the capture to positron decay.

The neutrinos may be described by free spherical waves (3.35), normalized per unit energy. With the choices thus made, (4.36) yields

$$\lambda_{\text{EC}} = (2\pi/\hbar) \sum_{n\kappa\mu\bar{\kappa}\bar{\mu}} |\langle \text{f}|H_\beta|\text{i}\rangle|^2 \quad (8.5)$$

as the capture rate from all the occupied atomic electron states $n\kappa\mu$, resulting in all possible neutrino waves $\bar{\kappa}\bar{\mu}$. This can be evaluated in exactly the same way as were the electron emission rates of Chapter VI, with the result ($\hbar = m = c = 1$)

$$\lambda_{n\kappa\mu} = [2g^2q_{nj}^2/(2j+1)] \sum_{Jj} \rho_J^2[D_\pm g_n \pm D_\mp f_n]^2 \quad \text{for } \kappa \gtrless 0, \quad (8.6)$$

as the capture rate of an electron in the state $n\kappa\mu$. The factors $D_\pm$ here are exactly the same combinations of neutrino radial waves and nuclear $\beta$-moments as for the *positron* emission cases of (6.88). The neutrino

‡ See, for example, H. A. Bethe and E. E. Salpeter, *Quantum Mechanics of One- and Two-Electron Atoms* (Academic Press, N.Y.C., 1957), p. 69. The relative sign of $f$ and $g$ should be changed in their formula (14.37).

energy has been labelled with subscripts indicating its (often negligible) dependence on the atomic binding of the captured electron:

$$q_{nj} = W_0 + W_{nj} \quad (> 0). \tag{8.7}$$

The extra factor $(2j+1)^{-1}$ occurs because (8.6) applies to a single electron, in only one of the $(2j+1)$ possible orientations $\mu$.

The rate expression (8.6) is deducible as a suitable transformation of the positron emission result (6.85 b). The essential part of the transformation procedure follows from the fact that the positrons are generated in a current like (8.1) except that $\phi_e$ is replaced by the charge-conjugate of a continuum state. This means that the lower sign version of the spinor (6.43) is used for the positrons, while the upper sign version applies to the negatron capture (with $g$, $f$ describing discrete states, of course). Accordingly, the essential part of the transformation consists of the substitutions $g(-Z) \leftrightarrow g(+Z)$, $f(-Z) \leftrightarrow -f(+Z)$. Then the summation of the squared bracket in (8.6) over $\kappa = \pm(j+\frac{1}{2})$, after a change in the relative sign of $f$ and $g$, must be such as to give a combination of $\beta$-moment and radial function symbols as is contained in the positron emission result (6.85 b).

*The normal approximations*

As for electron emissions, the 'normal approximation' should usually be adequate. This consists of retaining only the leading power of the nuclear radius $R$ and, as (8.3) shows, the bound electron radial functions are proportional to $R^{\gamma-1}$ exactly as are the free ones of electron emission. A difference now is that $R$ occurs in ratios to the orbital radii $na_0/Z = (n/\alpha Z)(\hbar/mc)$, rather than in products $pR/\hbar \approx R/(\hbar/mc)$. This will usually make the power series in $R$ converge even more rapidly. Of course, the neutrino radial waves again yield power series in $qR/\hbar$.

If only the leading terms of the electron distributions are retained, then the ratios $f/g$ as given by (8.4) should be sufficiently accurate for representing the proportions in which the unknown $\beta$-moments of $D_+$ and $D_-$ are to be included in the rate (8.6). The latter can then be written as

$$\lambda_{n\kappa\mu} \approx [2g^2 q_{nj}^2/(2j+1)]g_n^2 \sum_{J\jmath} \rho_J^2 [D_- + (\alpha Z/2j+1)D_+]^2 \tag{8.8}$$

for electrons in states with $\kappa < 0$; for $\kappa > 0$, the electron density at the nucleus $g_n^2(\kappa < 0)$ should merely be replaced by $f_n^2(\kappa > 0)$. According to (8.3),

$$f_n^2(\kappa > 0)/g_n^2(\kappa < 0) \approx (\alpha Z/2j+1)^2[1-((2j+1)/2n)^2] \tag{8.9}$$

when $(\alpha Z)^2 \ll (j+\frac{1}{2})^2$. This is adequate to show that the $l = j+\frac{1}{2}$

($\kappa > 0$) electron of given $j$ is captured much more slowly than the $l = j-\frac{1}{2}$ ($\kappa < 0$) electron. The $l = j+\frac{1}{2}$ rate escapes suppression by an additional factor $R^2$, arising from the extra unit of centrifugal repulsion, only through the modifying influence of the nuclear charge. A comparison of (8.8) with the positron emission result (7.7) suggests why the capture to positron ratio is frequently independent of the unknown $\beta$-moments contained in $D_{\pm}$.

More explicit results of the normal approximation will now be obtained, with attention concentrated on the capture rate of an electron in a given subshell $n$, $j$ and having $l = j-\frac{1}{2}$ ($\kappa < 0$). The $\kappa > 0$ result will always be obtainable through multiplication with $f_n^2(\kappa > 0)/g_n^2(\kappa < 0)$.

The rate depends on the total angular momentum $J = |\mathbf{j}+\bar{\mathbf{j}}|$ which the nucleus ejects in the given transition, $I \rightarrow I'$. The least value which $J$ can have is $\Delta I = |I'-I|$, and if already this exceeds $j+\frac{1}{2}$, then the neutrino must carry off orbital momentum ($\bar{j} > \frac{1}{2}$) and the process is thereby retarded in proportion to the $2(\bar{j}-\frac{1}{2})$ power of $(qR)$. All $\bar{j}$ will contribute negligibly as compared to the least value, $J-j = \Delta I-j \geqslant \frac{1}{2}$, which $\bar{j}$ can have for the given $j$ and $\Delta I$. Putting in the appropriate normal approximations of $D_{\pm}$ (6.88 a) into (8.8) yields for these cases of $J = \Delta I \geqslant j+\frac{1}{2}$:

$$\lambda_{nj\mu} \approx \frac{g^2 q_{nj}^2}{2\pi} \frac{(J-1)!}{(2J-1)!!} \frac{(2j)!!}{(2J-2j)!!} \frac{(q_{n_j} R)^{2J-2j-1}}{(j+\frac{1}{2})!\,(J-j-\frac{1}{2})!} g_n^2 \mathscr{M}_j^2(J), \tag{8.10}$$

where $g_n^2$ is proportional to the $2(\gamma-1) \approx 2j-1$ power of $R$, as the point-charge nucleus version of it (8.3 a) shows. The $\beta$-moment combination $\mathscr{M}_j(J)$ is the same one which occurs in the positron emission expression (7.10). It is therefore given by the positron (lower sign) version of (7.11) for parity-forbidden transitions, and by (7.13) for unique transitions, inclusive of the allowed $\Delta I = 1^+$ case.

The capture of an electron with so high a $j$ that even the highest available $J$ ($= I+I'$) cannot dissipate it also needs help from neutrino orbital momentum, with the consequent retardation. The least value of $\bar{j}$ needed for such a task is $j-J = j-(I+I') \geqslant \frac{1}{2}$, for the given $j$, $I$, and $I'$. Here the sum $J+j+\bar{j} = 2j$ is odd, in contrast to the even value $J+j+\bar{j} = 2J$ needed for (8.10), and this leads to contributions by different $\beta$-moments, as follows from the version (6.88 b) of $D_{\pm}$ replacing the version (6.88 a). Thus, with $J = I+I' \leqslant j-\frac{1}{2}$:

$$\lambda_{nj\mu} \approx \frac{g^2 q_{nj}^2}{2\pi} \frac{(2J+1)!!}{J!(2J+1)} \frac{(j-\frac{1}{2})!}{(j-J-\frac{1}{2})!} \frac{(q_{n_j} R)^{2j-2J-1}}{(2j)!!\,(2j-2J)!!} g_n^2 \mathscr{N}_j^2(J), \tag{8.11}$$

where, for $\pi_i \pi_f = (-)^J = (-)^{I+I'}$,

$$\mathcal{N}_j(J) = C_V\langle Y_J\rangle - (J/J+1)^{\frac{1}{2}} C_A\langle \boldsymbol{\sigma}.\mathbf{T}_J^J\rangle \tag{8.12 a}$$

in the approximation $\alpha Z(v_N/c) \ll 1$, and for $\pi_i \pi_f = (-)^{J-1} = (-)^{I+I'-1}$,

$$\mathcal{N}_j(J) = C_A\langle \gamma_5 Y_J\rangle + (J/J+1)^{\frac{1}{2}} C_V\langle \boldsymbol{\alpha}.\mathbf{T}_J^J\rangle + \\ +(\alpha Z/2j+1)(2J+1/J+1)^{\frac{1}{2}} C_A\langle \boldsymbol{\sigma}.\mathbf{T}_J^{J+1}\rangle. \tag{8.12 b}$$

It is $\mathcal{N}_j(0)$ as given by (8.12 a) which is responsible for allowed $\Delta I = 0^+$ electron emission and $\mathcal{N}_j(0)$ as given by (8.12 b) which gives the $\Delta I = 0^-$ shape-factor $S_1^{(0)}$ of (7.41). However, except when $I = I' = 0$, entirely different $\beta$-moments $\mathcal{N}_j(J > 0)$ give the only appreciable contributions to the capture during $\Delta I = 0^\pm$ transitions, e.g. $\mathcal{N}_j(2I)$ in (8.11) when $j > 2I+\frac{1}{2}$. The $\mathcal{N}_j(J > 0)$ moments normally play no role in electron emission because the latter never has a minimum electron angular momentum $j > \frac{1}{2}$ to balance out, as do captures out of a given subshell $n, j$.

In general, the moments (8.12 a) operate in $\Delta I$-times parity-forbidden transitions when $I$, $I'$ are integers, and in unique, $|\Delta I - 1|$-times forbidden transitions when $I$, $I'$ are half-integers. The converse is true for the moments (8.12 b). This follows from the fact that $I+I'$ and $\Delta I$ are both even or both odd for integer $I$, $I'$, while half-integers make $\Delta I$ even when $I+I'$ is odd, and vice versa.

The rate expressions (8.10) and (8.11) apply when the captured electron's angular momentum $j$ falls outside the range of values giving the possible angular momentum dissipations $J = \Delta I, \Delta I+1,..., I+I'$ by the nuclear transition. When $j$ falls within this range then *both* the values $J = j\pm\frac{1}{2}$ are available and neither requires neutrino orbital momentum for an angular momentum balance. There is a sum of two appreciable contributions to the capture rate, deducible from (8.10) for $J = j+\frac{1}{2}$ and from (8.11) for $J = j-\frac{1}{2}$. Thus, the total capture rate of an $n, j$ electron is for $\Delta I+\frac{1}{2} \leqslant j \leqslant I+I'-\frac{1}{2}$:

$$\lambda_{nj\mu} \approx [g^2 q_{nj}^2/\pi(2j+1)] g_n^2 [\mathcal{M}_j^2(j+\tfrac{1}{2}) + ((2j+1)/4j)\mathcal{N}_j^2(j-\tfrac{1}{2})]. \tag{8.13}$$

Only the cases of $\Delta I = j+\frac{1}{2}$ as given by (8.10), and $I+I' = j-\frac{1}{2}$ of (8.11), are equally unretarded, $\sim(qR)^0$. A striking consequence is that an electron with $j \geqslant \frac{3}{2}$ is captured more rapidly in 'forbidden' nuclear transitions with $\Delta I = j+\frac{1}{2}$, than in allowed transitions with

$$I+I' \leqslant j-\tfrac{3}{2}.$$

*K-capture vs. positron emission*

The results of the preceding subsection were put in terms comparable to observations which discriminate among captures out of individual subshells $n, j$. It is much easier to measure the total depletion rate of a given nuclear state and this includes a summation‡ of captures out of all the energetically available subshells:

$$\lambda_{\mathrm{EC}} = \sum_{n\kappa} \sigma_{n\kappa}\lambda_{n\kappa}. \tag{8.14}$$

Here, $\sigma_{n\kappa}$ is the occupation number of the $n$, $\kappa$ orbits, having the range of possible values $0 \leqslant \sigma_{n\kappa} \leqslant (2j+1)$. Usually the $K$-capture term $2\lambda_{1,-1} \equiv \lambda_K$ is the dominant one, as will be seen, and the others can be regarded as corrections to it.

An expression for the $K$-capture rate which is valid, in the normal approximation, for any nuclear transition $I \to I' \neq I$ can be obtained from (8.10):

$$\lambda_K = \frac{g^2 q_{1\frac{1}{2}}^2}{\pi} g_K^2 \frac{(q_{1\frac{1}{2}}R)^{2(\Delta I-1)}}{[(2\Delta I-1)!!]^2} \mathscr{M}_{\frac{1}{2}}^2(\Delta I). \tag{8.15}$$

With the additional help of (8.11) and (8.13), an expression applying to the allowed and once-parity-forbidden transitions $\Delta I = 0^{\pm}$, $1^{\pm}$ can be written as:

$$\lambda_K = (g^2 q_{1\frac{1}{2}}^2/4\pi^2) g_K^2 S_{0,1}, \tag{8.16}$$

where

$$S_{0,1} \equiv 4\pi[\mathscr{M}_{\frac{1}{2}}^2(1) + \mathscr{N}_{\frac{1}{2}}^2(0)]. \tag{8.17}$$

Here, advantage is being taken of the fact that these combinations of $\beta$-moments are exactly the ones forming the 'shape-factors' for $\Delta I = 0^{\pm}$, $1^{\pm}$ positron emission. Thus, $S_0 \equiv \xi$ of (6.84) is to be used for the allowed transitions $\Delta I = 0^+, 1^+$, and $S_1 = S_1^{(0)} + S_1^{(1)}$ of (7.42) for the once-parity-forbidden cases $\Delta I = 0^-, 1^-$.

For purposes of discussion, the $(\alpha Z)^2 \ll 1$ approximation of the electron density at a point-charge nucleus will be introduced: $g_K^2 \approx 4(\alpha Z)^3$ according to (8.3 a). Now the allowed and once-parity-forbidden $K$-capture rates (8.16) become

$$\lambda_K \approx (g^2 S_{0,1}/\pi^2)(\alpha Z)^3 (W_0 + W_{1\frac{1}{2}})^2. \tag{8.18}$$

This greatly undervalues the rate for heavy nuclei (by about a factor at $Z = 90$), but gives a fair approximation up to $Z = 40$ or so. It exhibits the rapid rise with $Z$ resulting from the confinement of each electron to smaller volumes around the nucleus as the Bohr radius $a_0/Z$ is drawn in. The rate shows a much slower increase with energy release than does electron emission ($\sim W_0^{\gtrsim 5}$); the two leptons freed in the latter

‡ R. Daudel (*J. Phys. Radium*, **4**, 278 (1955)) called attention to the fact that the rates of capture of two or more electrons are not quite additive because the Pauli principle puts restrictions on how many can impinge on the small nucleus simultaneously. The effect would clearly be null if the individual electron states before and after capture could be treated as members of the same orthogonal set. Actually, there is a non-orthogonality caused by the unit change in the nuclear charge. See the series of papers by J. Bahcall, ending with *Phys. Rev.* **132**, 362 (1963).

process gain more 'phase space' (available final states) with every increment of energy. It might be noted that most often $W_{1\frac{1}{2}} \approx mc^2$ is an adequate approximation. The correction for the atomic binding is negligible as compared to the most typical nuclear energy releases, $W_0$ (Table 8.1).

TABLE 8.1

*Capture-to-positron ratios*

| | $W_0/mc^2$ | *Observed* | *Calculated* |
|---|---|---|---|
| $\Delta I = 0^+, 1^+$‡ | | | |
| $F^{18}$ | 2·27 | 0·030±0·002 | 0·029 |
| $Na^{22}$ | 2·06 | 0·10–0·12 | 0·107 |
| $Sc^{44}$ | 3·88 | 0·02–0·07 | 0·042 |
| $V^{48}$ | 2·35 | 0·068±0·02 | 0·066 |
| $Mn^{52}$ | 2·14 | 1·81±0·07 | 1·77 |
| $Co^{58}$ | 1·92 | 5·4±0·2 | 4·9–5.2 |
| $Cu^{61}$ | 3·37 | 0·18–0·25 | 0·29 |
| $Zn^{65}$ | 1·64 | 25–30 | 30 |
| $Zr^{89}$ | 2·76 | 2·7–3·7 | 2·8 |
| $Cd^{107}$ | 1·63 | 320±30 | 310 |
| $Sn^{111}$ | 3·96 | 2·5±0·25 | 1·5 |
| $\Delta I = 0^-$§ | | | |
| $As^{76}$ | 2·80 | ~1·5 | 1·47 (1·17) |
| $Rb^{84}$ | 2·53 | 5·1±0·4 | 4·2 (3.4) |
| $I^{126}$ | 1·92 | ~148 | 143 (122) |
| $\Delta I = 2^-$§ | | | |
| $Rb^{84}$ | 4·3 | 2·1±0·4 | 0·83 |
| $Sb^{122}$ | 2·11 | 300±50 | 275 ±60 |
| $I^{124}$ | 3·3 | 18±0·3 | 17·3 |

‡ Taken from the reference on p. 230.
§ M. Perlman, J. Welker, and M. Wolfsberg, *Phys. Rev.* **110,** 381 (1958).

The proportionality of the $K$-capture rate (8.16) to the shape-factors of positron emission invites comparison to the rate of the latter, when both can occur in the same nuclear transition ($W_0 > mc^2$). If $\lambda_+$ is the positron emission rate as given by (7.12 a), then for $\Delta I = 0^{\pm}, 1^{\pm}$:

$$\lambda_K/\lambda_+ = \tfrac{1}{2}\pi q_{1\frac{1}{2}}^2 g_K^2/f(W_0, -Z), \tag{8.19}$$

where $f(W_0, -Z)$ is the statistical rate function introduced in (1.11). Thus, the $K$-capture to positron ratio is free of the ambiguities associated with the unknown nuclear $\beta$-moments, at least in the allowed and once-parity-forbidden transitions. The same property is also shared by all the unique forbidden transitions, each of which is proportional to the square of a single $\beta$-moment, $\mathscr{M}^2(\Delta I) = C_A^2\langle\boldsymbol{\sigma}.\mathbf{T}_{\Delta I}^{\Delta I-1}\rangle^2$ according to (7.13). With the shape-factor (7.25), the result for the unique transitions $\pi_i \pi_f = (-)^{\Delta I-1}$ is:

$$\lambda_K/\lambda_+ = \tfrac{1}{2}\pi(2\Delta I-1)^2 q_{1\frac{1}{2}}^{2\Delta I} g_K^2/f(W_0, -Z)\langle|\mathbf{p}+\mathbf{q}|^{2(\Delta I-1)}\rangle. \quad (8.20)$$

Here, the power of $|\mathbf{p}+\mathbf{q}|$ is averaged over the spectrum as well as directions; a slight improvement can be made by replacing it with coulomb-corrected expressions like (7.29). Similar ratios for the parity-forbidden $\Delta I \geqslant 2$ transitions will not be entirely independent of the $\beta$-moments because, as in the unique forbidden transitions, electron angular momenta $j > \frac{1}{2}$ contribute to the positron emission, and this time in proportion to $\beta$-moments combinations (7.11) which may have some dependence on $j$.

The results here are subject to various corrections before they are ready for comparison to accurate experimental data. First, screening and finite nuclear size effects on both $g_K^2$ and $f(W_0, -Z)$ become important for heavy nuclei. Curves for $g(Z)$, obtained by machine computation, have been provided by Brysk and Rose.‡ Next, captures from shells other than $K$ are not entirely negligible for comparison with total measured rates. These contributions will be weighed in the next subsection. Finally, it is customary in treating the parity-forbidden-transitions to include improvements on the normal approximation, i.e. expand the exact expression (8.6) to higher powers in $R$.

Table 8.1 presents some comparisons of the theoretical expectations, obtained by the procedure outlined here, to experimental results. The parenthesized theoretical values for the parity forbidden transitions were obtained without the higher order corrections to the normal approximations.

*L-capture*

The $K$-capture formulae (8.15) and (8.16) can also be used for the captures from the $s$-orbits ($j = \frac{1}{2}$, $\kappa = -1$) of the higher shells ($L_1$, $M_1$,..., etc.). It is only necessary to change $W_{nj}$ suitably and replace the electron density $g_K^2$ by an appropriate $g_s^2$. In the point-charge nucleus case (8.3 a), with $\alpha^2 Z^2 \ll 1$, $g_s^2 \approx 4(\alpha Z/n)^3$. Thus, the $s$-capture from the shells $n = 2, 3, 4,...$ decreases as $n^{-3}$. In particular,

$$\lambda_{L_1}/\lambda_K = [(W_0+W_{L_1})^2/(W_0+W_K)^2]g_{L_1}^2/g_K^2 \approx \tfrac{1}{8}, \quad (8.21)$$

the number being a rough approximation which presumes that the atomic binding is negligible. The ratio $\frac{1}{8}$ is fairly independent of screening and finite-nuclear size effects (see the reference below). Of course,

‡ H. Brysk and M. E. Rose, *Rev. Mod. Phys.* **30**, 1169 (1958).

his ratio of the $L_1$ capture increases as the nuclear energy release $W_0$ s decreased. However, the final nuclear state must be heavier than he initial one by a substantial fraction of the captured electron's mass efore the energy release is small enough for the $L_1$-capture to equal he $K$-capture. Roughly, the equality occurs for

$$(W_0/mc^2)+1 \approx [8(2)^{\frac{1}{2}}-1](\alpha Z)^2/8[2(2)^{\frac{1}{2}}-1], \tag{8.22}$$

vhich gives $W_0 \approx -0{\cdot}7mc^2$ at $Z \approx 90$, but $W_0 \approx -mc^2$ within 1·5 per ent for $Z = 20$ or so. This confirms the negligibility of the atomic inding when positron emission is also possible ($W_0 > +mc^2$).

$L_2$-capture ($j = \frac{1}{2}$, $\kappa = +1$) can be evaluated simply by multiplying he $L_1$-capture rate with $f_{L_2}^2/g_{L_1}^2$, approximately (8.9). However, $L_3$-apture ($n = 2$, $j = \frac{3}{2}$, $\kappa = 2$) involves more extensive formal changes.

'or $\Delta I = 0^{\pm}, 1^{\pm}$:

$$\lambda_{L_3} = (g^2 q_{2\frac{3}{2}}^2/\pi) g_{L_3}^2 [\mathscr{M}_{\frac{3}{2}}^2(2) + \tfrac{2}{3}\mathscr{N}_{\frac{3}{2}}^2(1)]. \tag{8.23 a}$$

'his vanishes for $0 \to 0$ transitions, in which case

$$\lambda_{L_3} = (g^2 q_{2\frac{3}{2}}^2/9\pi) g_{L_3}^2 (q_{2\frac{3}{2}} R)^2 \mathscr{N}_{\frac{3}{2}}^2(0). \tag{8.23 b}$$

'or $\Delta I \geqslant 2$:

$$\lambda_{L_3} = (3g^2 q_{2\frac{3}{2}}^2/\pi) g_{L_3}^2 \frac{(\Delta I-1)(2\Delta I-1)}{[(2\Delta I-1)!!]^2} (q_{2\frac{3}{2}} R)^{2(\Delta I-2)} \mathscr{M}_{\frac{3}{2}}^2(\Delta I). \tag{8.24}$$

TABLE 8.2

*$\lambda_L/\lambda_K$ results*

| | $W_0/mc^2$ | *Observed* | *Calculated* |
|---|---|---|---|
| ($\Delta I = 0^+, 1^+$) | | | |
| $A^{37}$ | 0·59 | 0·100 ±0·003 | 0·099‡ |
| $Cr^{51}$ | 0·47 | 0·1026±0·0004 | 0·101‡ |
| $Mn^{54}$ | 0·04 | 0·098 ±0·006 | 0·102‡ |
| $Fe^{55}$ | −0·57 | 0·106 ±0·003 | 0·106‡ |
| $Co^{57}$ | −0·16 | 0·099 ±0·011 | 0·103‡ |
| $Co^{58}$ | 2·0 | 0·107 ±0·004 | 0·102‡ |
| $Zn^{65}$ | 1·6 | 0·119 ±0·007 | 0·108‡ |
| $Ge^{71}$ | −0·54 | 0·1175±0·002 | 0·114‡ |
| $Kr^{79}$ | 2·16 | 0·108 ±0·005 | 0·111‡ |
| $Cd^{109}$ | ∼ −0·7 | 0·23 ±0·03 | 0·26 |
| $Cs^{131}$ | −0·3 | ∼ 0·15 | 0·15 |
| ($\Delta I = 0^-$) | | | |
| $As^{74}$ | 2·8 | 0·09 ±0·02 | 0·095 |
| $Sn^{113}$ | −0·04 | ∼ 0·17 | 0·225 |
| $I^{126}$ | 3·2 | 0·14 ±0·02 | 0·131 |

‡ These cases include additions up to 15 per cent arising from the greater exclusion ffects on the $K$-electrons (see footnote, p. 236) as calculated by J. Bahcall, *Phys. Rev.* **32,** 362 (1963). The other results were adapted from the reference on p. 230 and . Robinson and R. Fink, *Rev. Mod. Phys.* **32,** 117 (1960).

These have been multiplied by an occupation number 4, appropriate t a filled $L_3$ subshell. All the rates are retarded relative to $L_{1,2}$ capture by the proportionality $g_{L_3}^2 \sim R^2$, arising from the centrifugal effect o the $p$-electron. However, one unit less neutrino orbital momentum i needed for $\Delta I > 2$ transitions than in the $j = \frac{1}{2}$ captures, hence $L_1$ an $L_3$ capture are comparable, $\sim R^{2(\Delta I-1)}$, in those forbidden transitions.

Some theoretical and experimental results for the ratio of $L$- to $K$ capture are listed in Table 8.2.

## 8.2. Antineutrino capture

The observation of $\beta$-processes induced by incident neutrinos is th only known way of detecting these particles, since they have never bee found to engage in any other form of interaction. It is through th induced emission of positrons from protons,

$$\mathrm{p}+\bar{\nu} \rightarrow \mathrm{n}+\mathrm{e}^+, \qquad (8.25$$

that pile antineutrinos have been detected (§ 1.2).

*Formulation of the capture cross-section*

A process like (8.25), initiated by incident particles, must be evaluate for some standard number of these, a 'unit incident beam'. This i defined as having unit current density: one particle passing throug each unit of cross-sectional area per second. The antineutrino wave $\psi$ which describes this situation may be adapted from (3.6); the normaliza tion is changed from one antineutrino in $V$ to a unit beam simply b multiplying with $(c/V)^{-\frac{1}{2}}$, so that $(\psi_\nu^{C\dagger}\psi_\nu^C)c = 1$. Now the rate $d\lambda$ o (4.36) will represent a number of processes per second, per target proton and per unit incident beam. It acquires the dimensions of an area whic is called the cross-section for the process, denoted $d\sigma$ instead of $d\lambda$ It may be thought of as an area at the proton which intercepts as man antineutrinos out of a unit incident beam as there are capture processe of the type to be counted by $d\sigma$.

Antineutrinos coming from nuclear $\beta$-sources have too little energ to cause appreciably energetic recoils of nucleons, hence the reco energy will be neglected just as for the neutron decay process (§ 4.4 The product electron will be essentially monoenergetic, with

$$W = cq - W_0, \qquad (8.2$$

where $W_0 = (M_\mathrm{n} - M_\mathrm{p})c^2 = 2{\cdot}53mc^2$.

Plane wave descriptions may be used for each participant in th process, just as for the neutron decay, but this time there is first counting of positrons which emerge into the momentum rang

$(d\mathbf{p}) = pW\,dW\,d\Omega/c^2$ while the neutron's momentum is in the range $(d\mathbf{P})$. Energy-momentum conservation may again be enforced as in the neutron decay and the result is

$$d\sigma/d\Omega = [pW/(2\pi\hbar^2c)^2].\tfrac{1}{2}\sum_{\text{pne}} V^3|h_\beta|^2, \tag{8.27}$$

with
$$h_\beta = 2^{\frac{1}{2}}g\psi_{\text{n}}^\dagger(C_{\text{V}}-C_{\text{A}}\gamma_5)(J_4-i\boldsymbol{\alpha}.\mathbf{J})\psi_{\text{p}}. \tag{8.28}$$

The resolution $\gamma_\alpha(-i\beta\boldsymbol{\alpha},\beta)$ has been introduced to write

$$\beta\gamma_\alpha J_\alpha = J_4-i\boldsymbol{\alpha}.\mathbf{J},$$

and it is obvious that

$$J_\alpha = \phi_\nu^{C\dagger}\beta\gamma_\alpha\phi_{\text{e}}^C = \psi_\nu^{C\dagger}\tfrac{1}{2}(1+\gamma_5)\beta\gamma_\alpha\psi_{\text{e}}^C \tag{8.29}$$

here (see discussion of (4.30)). The plane wave exponentials disappear in forming $|h_\beta|^2$; their function was completed in the enforcement of the energy-momentum conservation.

The cross-section (8.27) counts productions of both orientations of the neutron, and of the positron, and is averaged over the two possible initial orientations of the proton $\left(\tfrac{1}{2}\sum_{\text{p}}\right)$. These spin sums are easy to perform with the help of the trace techniques (4.48). They may be applied directly to the four-dimensional Dirac matrix products by using density matrices of the type

$$\sum_{\text{e}}\psi_{\text{e}}\psi_{\text{e}}^\dagger = (2V)^{-1}(1+\boldsymbol{\alpha}.\mathbf{v}/c+\beta mc^2/W), \tag{8.30}$$

which follows from (6.17), for example. When the recoil energy is neglected,

$$\sum_{\text{n}}\psi_{\text{n}}\psi_{\text{n}}^\dagger = (1+\beta)/2V = \sum_{\text{p}}\psi_{\text{p}}\psi_{\text{p}}^\dagger. \tag{8.31}$$

The trace of the Dirac unit matrix is 4, while all the other Dirac matrices have tr $= 0$; this makes it easy to find

$$\tfrac{1}{2}\sum_{\text{p,n}}|h_\beta|^2 = (2g^2/V^2)(C_{\text{V}}^2|J_4|^2+C_{\text{A}}^2\,\mathbf{J}.\mathbf{J}^*). \tag{8.32}$$

When the spins of both leptons are summed over, the same techniques give

$$\left.\begin{aligned}\sum_{\text{e}\nu}|J_4|^2 &= (2cV)^{-1}(1+\hat{\mathbf{q}}.\mathbf{v}/c)\\ \sum_{\text{e}\nu}\mathbf{J}.\mathbf{J}^* &= (3/2cV)(1-\tfrac{1}{3}\hat{\mathbf{q}}.\mathbf{v}/c)\end{aligned}\right\}, \tag{8.33}$$

independently of the fact that, with charge conjugate states, the density matrix $\sum_{\text{e}}\psi_{\text{e}}^C\psi_{\text{e}}^{C\dagger}$ differs from (8.30) in the sign of the mass term $\sim\beta$. These results differ from (5.43) only in the neglect of the coulomb distortion ($F = 1$) and because, here, each antineutrino state was normalized to unit current ($V \to c$) instead of the usual unit in $V$.

The sum over antineutrino spins needs special comment, especially since *each* of the two orientations $\nu = \pm\frac{1}{2}$ was normalized to unit current as if a total of two units of current were incident. Ordinarily, in dealing with 'random' beams having equal populations of both orientations, the results should be *averaged* $\left(\frac{1}{2}\sum_{\nu}\right)$ rather than summed $\left(\sum_{\nu}\right)$ over the orientations. However, it is now known that neutrino beams are not random but completely polarized. All sources consisting of $\beta$-processes produce only right-handed antineutrinos, and this polarization persists whatever thicknesses of material may be interposed between source and capturing proton; no interactions exist to disturb the particle except the $\beta$-processes, and these send on only right-handed antineutrinos if they occur at all. Properly, a 'helicity eigenstate' such as discussed in § 3.1 should be used to represent the antineutrino beam. This is easy to construct when the beam direction $\hat{\mathbf{q}}$ is used as the quantization axis so that $\boldsymbol{\sigma}.\hat{\mathbf{q}} = \sigma_z$. The adaptations of (3.6),

$$\psi^C_{\nu=\pm\frac{1}{2}} = (2c)^{-\frac{1}{2}}\begin{pmatrix}\mp 1\\ 1\end{pmatrix}\chi_{\mp\frac{1}{2}}\, e^{-iq(z-ct)/\hbar}, \tag{8.34}$$

represent right- and left-handed antineutrino beams, respectively. Both are written despite the actual existence of only the right-handed one, $\nu = +\frac{1}{2}$, because both can be said to have been included in the spin sums (8.33). There was no harm in this because the $\nu = -\frac{1}{2}$ wave contributes nothing anyway. The interacting current, $J_\alpha$, contains only the positive chirality projection,

$$\phi^C_\nu = \tfrac{1}{2}(1+\gamma_5)\psi^C_\nu = (2c)^{-\frac{1}{2}}\begin{pmatrix}1\\ -1\end{pmatrix}\tfrac{1}{2}(\sigma_z-1)\chi_{-\nu}\, e^{-iq(z-ct)/\hbar}, \tag{8.35}$$

which vanishes for left-handed, $\nu = -\frac{1}{2}$, antineutrino beams. It is, by itself, properly normalized to unit current density for $\nu = +\frac{1}{2}$. Since this intensity is not distributed between both $\nu = +\frac{1}{2}$ and $\nu = -\frac{1}{2}$, as in old calculations made before the beam was known to be polarized, the cross-section now predicted is twice as great (relative to neutron decay, below) as in the old predictions. An experimental check of this factor two would provide evidence of the persistent polarization of neutrinos.

It may be noticed that the result (8.33) gives the positive correlation of the positron's emission direction, with the incident antineutrino's direction, characteristic of the Vector coupling also in positron-neutrino emissions (Fig. 1.12). There is no nucleonic spin flip in the Fermi transitions, hence the right-handed positron must carry on in the same direction (within $v/c$) as the right-handed antineutrino. The predominance of nucleon spin flips in the Gamow-Teller interactions accounts for the negative correlation found in these cases.

When the results (8.32) and (8.33) are now substituted into (8.27), the differential cross-section

$$d\sigma/d\Omega = (g^2/4\pi^2\hbar^4c^3)pW\xi_n(1+a_n\,\hat{\mathbf{q}}\,.\,\mathbf{v}/c) \tag{8.36}$$

is found. Here, $\xi_n = C_V^2+3C_A^2$ and $\xi_n a_n = C_V^2-C_A^2$ are exactly the same strength and correlation coefficients, (4.66) and (1.55), as in the neutron decay. Since $a_n \approx -0{\cdot}08$ only, the angular distribution of the positrons is nearly isotropic.

*The total capture cross-section*

An integration of the angular distribution (8.36) over all positron directions yields the total cross-section

$$\sigma = (g^2/\pi\hbar^4c^3)pW\xi_n, \tag{8.37}$$

for the capture by protons of antineutrinos with the energy

$$cq = W-W_0 = W+(M_n-M_p)c^2.$$

The process is sometimes called 'inverse neutron decay' because of its close connexions with the neutron decay process. The latter has a rate directly measured by its comparative half-life (5.46),

$$(ft)_n = [\ln 2/(mc)^5](2\pi^3\hbar^7c/g^2\xi_n) = (1180\pm35)\text{ sec}, \tag{8.38}$$

hence
$$\sigma = (\hbar/mc)^2[2\pi^2\ln 2(\hbar/mc^2)/(ft)_n](pW/m^2c^3). \tag{8.39}$$

For $cq \approx 3{\cdot}2$ MeV, this gives $\sigma \approx 3(10)^{-43}$ cm$^2$ and now it should be obvious how difficult it is to detect the neutrino. Water has about $2(10)^{22}$ protons per cm$^3$, hence the antineutrino will penetrate through about $1{\cdot}7(10)^{20}$ cm $\approx$ 170 light-years of water before it is intercepted. The detection was nevertheless achieved (§ 1.2) by careful discrimination of the extremely rare capture events from background processes, in a reactor flux of some $10^{13}$ antineutrinos/cm$^2$ sec.

The above value was chosen for the antineutrino energy because it seems to represent about the effective average used in the experiments. A reactor actually provides a continuous spectrum of antineutrino energies over which the cross-section should be averaged. The spectrum arises from a conglomerate of fission-fragment negatron emitters. The overall negatron spectrum could be measured directly and then the antineutrino spectrum could be deduced from it on the basis of the theoretical sharing of the energy in $\beta$-emissions. Only the antineutrinos surpassing the threshold $cq = (M_n - M_p + m)c^2 = 1{\cdot}8$ MeV of the process (8.25) could contribute, and when their relative numbers were taken into account the effective theoretical cross-section, $\sigma = (2{\cdot}9 \pm 0{\cdot}8)10^{-43}$ cm$^2$ was computed.‡ The actual observations (refs., p. 6) yielded $(3 \pm 1)10^{-43}$ cm$^2$. The agreement is sufficiently definite to afford some confirmation that the antineutrino beam was indeed polarized.

‡ R. Carter, F. Reines, J. Wagner, and M. Wyman, *Phys. Rev.* **113,** 280 (1959).

# IX

# QUANTIZED LEPTON FIELDS AND DOUBLE β-DECAY

IT will have practical value to recognize that the lepton fields are subject to quantization, like any basic variables used for describing physical systems, especially in such problems as that posed by 'double β-decay'. When two electrons are emitted simultaneously, they must emerge in a state which is antisymmetric with respect to the interchange of whatever variables are used to specify each. The antisymmetry results automatically in the quantized field description, as will be seen. It could also be arranged for in the more limited type of description used so far, but only with a looser economy of assumptions. It is in any case desirable to examine how the theory of β-decay fits into the more complete formulation of quantum fields, and that becomes particularly attractive to do when immediate physical consequences can be promised.

## 9.1. The description of quantized fermion fields

*The basic quantum conditions*

Each fermion field $\psi(\mathbf{r},t)$ is now to be regarded as an infinite set of variables (each component at each of the continuum of points $\mathbf{r}$), subject to appropriate quantum conditions. To satisfy these, the $\psi$'s will have to be represented by operators, and no longer considered mere given parameters, as in the foregoing chapters. Indeed, it now becomes necessary to justify the former treatment, and how that may be done will be seen in the next section.

The quantum conditions appropriate to fermion field variables were found by Wigner and Jordan. The complex conjugate $\psi^*_\alpha(\mathbf{r},t)$ of each spinor component $\psi_\alpha(\mathbf{r},t)$ must be treated as a variable distinct from $\psi_\alpha(\mathbf{r},t)$, and then

$$\left.\begin{array}{c}\{\psi_\alpha(\mathbf{r},t),\, \psi_\beta(\mathbf{r}',t')\} = 0, \qquad \{\psi^*_\alpha(\mathbf{r},t),\, \psi^*_\beta(\mathbf{r}',t')\} = 0\\ \{\psi_\alpha(\mathbf{r},t),\, \psi^*_\beta(\mathbf{r}',t)\} = \delta_{\alpha\beta}\,\delta(\mathbf{r}-\mathbf{r}')\end{array}\right\}. \tag{9.1}$$

Notice that the last of these conditions is listed here only for the special case of 'equal times', i.e. at a given moment as judged from some particular reference frame. The expression of the relation between arbitrary space-time points, $x_\mu(\mathbf{r},ict)$ and $x'_\mu(\mathbf{r}',ict')$, would require introducing a less familiar singular function than the Dirac $\delta$-function. That will be unnecessary for the considerations here.

The bracket symbols in (9.1) stand for *anti*commutators,

$$\{\psi, \psi'\} \equiv \psi\psi' + \psi'\psi,$$

rather than commutators

$$[\psi, \psi'] \equiv \psi\psi' - \psi'\psi.$$

Thus, the conditions more nearly resemble those on the Dirac $\gamma$'s, or the Pauli $\sigma$'s, than on canonically conjugate variables like $\mathbf{r}$, $\mathbf{p}$. The choice of anticommutators over commutators is a crucial one, necessary to describe fermions consistently, as will be discussed.

Field quantization conditions give rise to commutation relations among more directly observable field variables than the $\psi$'s. The observables are bilinear combinations of $\psi$ with $\psi^\dagger$, e.g. the energy of the field in isolation from other physical systems:

$$H_\psi(t) = \oint (d\mathbf{r})\psi^\dagger(\mathbf{r}, t)[-i\hbar c\boldsymbol{\alpha}.\boldsymbol{\nabla} + \beta mc^2]\psi(\mathbf{r}, t). \tag{9.2}$$

This is an operator by virtue of $\psi$, $\psi^\dagger$ being operators, and has consequent commutation relations with other such observables. Another example is the 'particle number' operator defined by

$$N(t) = \oint (d\mathbf{r})\psi^\dagger\psi. \tag{9.3}$$

Its commutator with $H_\psi$ can be readily seen to vanish as a consequence of (9.1) and, since $i\hbar\dot{N} = [N, H_\psi] = 0$ in the isolated system, the particle number is conserved. The latter result should be required in the absence of interactions, and is typical of some criteria which led to (9.1).

In general, commutation relations among observables like energy-momentum and angular momentum are better established than are those among the $\psi$'s, hence a systematic derivation of the latter from the former would be more desirable than the converse. However, this approach does not lead to a unique result; rather, it shows that the proper commutation relations among observables are equally consistent with (9.1) and with the conditions formed by replacing the anticommutators with commutators. A readily checked example of the invariance to these alternatives is the result $[N, H_\psi] = 0$ seen above. The final choice must rest on further properties, with respect to which the alternatives do exhibit differences.

*The quanta of the field*

Further properties appear in useful forms after a change of variables, from $\psi$, $\psi^\dagger$ to a set of amplitudes found by decomposing $\psi(\mathbf{r}, t)$ into a given complete set of orthogonal modes. The modes to be used for the present are to be normalized eigenstates of the free-particle Dirac hamiltonian, $H = -i\hbar c\boldsymbol{\alpha}.\boldsymbol{\nabla}+\beta mc^2$, and of additional dynamical variables, whatever ones are needed to complete specifying a unique mode. The Dirac spinor modes of positive energy (frequency), $H \equiv +W_e$, will be denoted $u_e(\mathbf{r})$, with $e$ standing for the complete set of eigenvalue labels. The modes needed to make the orthogonal set complete will be taken to be the charge-conjugates $u_e^C = Cu_e^*$; the latter is orthogonal to $u_e$ because it has a different energy eigenvalue,

$$Hu_e^C = -C(Hu_e)^* = -W_e u_e^C,$$

as follows from the definition (3.76) of $C$. The $u_e(r)$ may be just the plane waves (3.4) without the time factors, and then $e \equiv W_e, \mathbf{p}_e, \rho_e$. Alternatively, free spherical waves (3.20) may be chosen, with $e \equiv W_e, \kappa_e, \mu_e$. Any dependence on $\mathbf{r}$, and inner fermion variables, may be analysed in the manner

$$\psi(\mathbf{r},t) = \sum_e [a_e(t)u_e(\mathbf{r})+c_e^\dagger(t)u_e^C(\mathbf{r})], \tag{9.4 a}$$

if the amplitudes $a_e$, $c_e^\dagger$ are suitably determined. The summation is to include integration over any eigenvalues which are continuous. A similar analysis has already been employed in (4.31), but now the time dependence is not specified (the $\psi$ has not yet been subjected to an equation of motion).

The amplitudes $a_e$, $c_e$, $a_e^\dagger$, and $c_e^\dagger$ are to be the new field variables replacing $\psi$ and

$$\psi^\dagger = \sum_e [a_e^\dagger u_e^\dagger + c_e u_e^{C\dagger}]. \tag{9.4 b}$$

They will bear the field-operator properties of $\psi$, $\psi^\dagger$ implicit in the quantum conditions (9.1); it is the modes $u_e$, $u_e^C$ which bear the spinor properties (describe the dependence on 'inner variables' as well as on $\mathbf{r}$). From (9.1), anticommutation relations for the new variables follow:

$$\left.\begin{aligned} \{a_e, a_{e'}^\dagger\} = \delta_{ee'}, \quad \{a_e, a_{e'}\} = \{a_e^\dagger, a_{e'}^\dagger\} = 0 \\ \{c_e, c_{e'}^\dagger\} = \delta_{ee'}, \quad \{c_e, c_{e'}\} = \{c_e^\dagger, c_{e'}^\dagger\} = 0 \\ \{a_e, c_{e'}^\dagger\} = \{a_e^\dagger, c_{e'}\} = \{a_e, c_{e'}\} = \{a_e^\dagger, c_{e'}^\dagger\} = 0 \end{aligned}\right\}. \tag{9.5}$$

The operators $H_\psi$ and $N$ are also easy to put into terms of the new variables:

$$N = \sum_e (a_e^\dagger a_e + c_e c_e^\dagger) = \sum_e (a_e^\dagger a_e - c_e^\dagger c_e + 1), \tag{9.6}$$

$$H_\psi = \sum_e W_e[a_e^\dagger a_e - c_e c_e^\dagger], \tag{9.7}$$

where $\pm W_e$ are the eigenvalues of the Dirac free-particle hamiltonian for the eigenfunctions $u_e$ and $u_e^C$, respectively.

The result (9.6) invites definition of the new operators

$$N_e = a_e^\dagger a_e \quad \text{and} \quad N_e^C = c_e^\dagger c_e. \tag{9.8}$$

Considerations like the fact that $N_e \to N$ when only the mode $u_e(\mathbf{r})$ of the field is excited make it clear that $N_e$ is the operator representative for the 'occupation number' of the mode. The consequence for $N_e$ of the quantum conditions (9.5) is

$$N_e^2 \equiv a_e^\dagger a_e a_e^\dagger a_e = a_e^\dagger(1-a_e^\dagger a_e)a_e = a_e^\dagger a_e = N_e,$$

hence the only eigenvalues which $N_e$ can have are 0 or 1. In the case of eigenvalue 1, it is appropriate to speak of a quantum, or fermion, being present with the energy $W_e$; the corresponding addition to the field energy $H_\psi$ of (9.7) supports this interpretation. The operators $N_e^C = c_e^\dagger c_e$ and $c_e c_e^\dagger = 1-N_e^C$ also have the eigenvalues 0 or 1. It is $c_e c_e^\dagger$ which represents the number of *normal* fermions in the mode $u_e^C$, according to (9.6). When $N_e$ refers to fermions with the properties $W_e$, $\mathbf{p}_e$, $\rho_e$, then $c_e c_e^\dagger$ will give the number with $-W_e$, $-\mathbf{p}_e$, $-\rho_e$. It is obvious that conformity to the Pauli exclusion principle has resulted from the quantum conditions in the form (9.1).

The latter outcome contrasts with the results of replacing the anti-commutators of (9.1) with commutators. Then all the non-negative integers become possible occupation numbers in each mode, whether it has positive or negative energy. After energy exchanges with other physical systems are admitted, there is no way to prevent all the quanta from falling ever deeper in the negative energy scale. On the other hand, the exclusion principle permits treating the field as having all modes filled up to some level of energy, so that stable situations can be described.

In the 'hole picture', the vacuum is described as having all negative energy modes filled, with $c_e c_e^\dagger = 1-N_e^C = 1$ so that $N_e^C = 0$ as well as $N_e = 0$. A field with $N_e^C = 1$ has a 'vacancy' ($c_e c_e^\dagger = 0$) in a negative-energy mode, to be interpreted as the presence of an antifermion. More generally, the energy expression (9.7) becomes

$$H_\psi = \sum_e W_e(N_e+N_e^C-1), \tag{9.9}$$

in which $-\sum_e W_e$ can be treated as merely an additive constant, albeit an infinite one. It will have no observable significance since only energy differences, such as are produced by interactions with observing mechanisms, are detectable. Of course, this alone gives no guarantee that finite results will be forthcoming for every effect of every interaction, but it can serve as a starting-point in constructing a consistent theory.

*Descriptions of the state of the field*

If the symbol $|0\rangle$ is defined to stand for the 'vacuum' state, and $\langle 0|$ is its hermitian conjugate, then the absence of either normal or antiparticles must be expressed by

$$\left.\begin{aligned}\langle 0|N_e|0\rangle &= \langle 0|a_e^\dagger a_e|0\rangle = 0\\ \langle 0|N_e^C|0\rangle &= \langle 0|c_e^\dagger c_e|0\rangle = 0\end{aligned}\right\}. \tag{9.10a}$$

These are projections of $a_e|0\rangle$ and $c_e|0\rangle$ on themselves, hence

$$a_e|0\rangle = 0 \quad \text{and} \quad c_e|0\rangle = 0. \tag{9.10b}$$

On the other hand, the effect of operations by $a_e^\dagger$ or $c_e^\dagger$ on $|0\rangle$ can be seen from

$$N_e(a_e^\dagger|0\rangle) \equiv a_e^\dagger a_e a_e^\dagger|0\rangle = a_e^\dagger(1-a_e^\dagger a_e)|0\rangle = 1.(a_e^\dagger|0\rangle). \tag{9.11}$$

Thus, $a_e^\dagger|0\rangle$ represents a state of the field with eigenvalue 1 for $N_e$, hence containing a single fermion, in the mode of motion $u_e$. Similarly, $c_e^\dagger|0\rangle$ describes a field having one antiparticle, in $u_e^C$. Such results have led to the name 'creation operators' for $a_e^\dagger$ and $c_e^\dagger$. Since

$$a_e(a_e^\dagger|0\rangle) = (1-a_e^\dagger a_e)|0\rangle = |0\rangle, \tag{9.12}$$

$a_e$ and $c_e$ are called 'annihilation operators'.

The connexion between describing a one particle state by $a_e^\dagger|0\rangle$ and by the Dirac spinor $u_e(\mathbf{r})$ can be seen from inverting the decomposition (9.4b), which gives

$$a_e^\dagger(t) = \oint (d\mathbf{r})\psi^\dagger(\mathbf{r},t)u_e(\mathbf{r}). \tag{9.13a}$$

The result

$$a_e^\dagger|0\rangle = \sum_\alpha \oint (d\mathbf{r})\psi_\alpha^*(\mathbf{r},t)|0\rangle u_{e\alpha}(\mathbf{r}) \tag{9.13b}$$

can be regarded as a transformation in the space of states from axes labelled by the $e$'s to axes labelled by the various possible values of $\mathbf{r}$ and $\alpha$. The coefficients $u_{e\alpha}(\mathbf{r})$ are the projections of $a_e^\dagger|0\rangle$ on $\psi_\alpha^*(\mathbf{r},t)|0\rangle$, hence become probability amplitudes for the fermion in mode $e$ to be found at $\mathbf{r}$, with the internal configuration $\alpha$. Then the spinor product $u_e^\dagger(\mathbf{r})u_e(\mathbf{r})$ has the usual interpretation as the probability density in the mode $e$.

A two-fermion state may be described by

$$a_e^\dagger a_{e'}^\dagger|0\rangle = -a_{e'}^\dagger a_e^\dagger|0\rangle = \tfrac{1}{2}(a_e^\dagger a_{e'}^\dagger - a_{e'}^\dagger a_e^\dagger)|0\rangle, \tag{9.14}$$

which vanishes for $e' \equiv e$, in conformity with the Pauli principle. The description exhibits antisymmetry in the interchange of the individual eigenvalue sets $e$, $e'$ being used to specify the fermions. Corresponding to (9.13b) we now have

$$a_e^\dagger a_{e'}^\dagger|0\rangle = \sum_{\alpha_1\alpha_2} \oint\oint \psi_{\alpha_1}^*(\mathbf{r}_1,t)\psi_{\alpha_2}^*(\mathbf{r}_2,t)|0\rangle(d\mathbf{r}_1)(d\mathbf{r}_2)u_{e\alpha_1}(\mathbf{r}_1)u_{e'\alpha_2}(\mathbf{r}_2). \tag{9.15a}$$

The sets of dummy variables $\mathbf{r}_1$, $\alpha_1$ and $\mathbf{r}_2$, $\alpha_2$ being used here can be interchanged without effect. Then, because of (9.14), the expression can be written

$$a_e^\dagger a_{e'}^\dagger|0\rangle = 2^{-\frac{1}{2}} \sum_{\alpha_1\alpha_2} \oint\oint \psi_{\alpha_1}^*(\mathbf{r}_1,t)\psi_{\alpha_2}^*(\mathbf{r}_2,t)|0\rangle(d\mathbf{r}_1)(d\mathbf{r}_2)\times$$
$$\times 2^{-\frac{1}{2}}[u_{e\alpha_1}(\mathbf{r}_1)u_{e'\alpha_2}(\mathbf{r}_2)-u_{e'\alpha_1}(\mathbf{r}_1)u_{e\alpha_2}(\mathbf{r}_2)]. \quad (9.15\,\text{b})$$

The resolution here corresponds to finding the probability amplitudes for some fermion to be at $\mathbf{r}_1$ with $\alpha_1$, simultaneously with another at $\mathbf{r}_2$ with $\alpha_2$, in the state containing two fermions in the modes $e$, $e'$. The result, as represented by the last bracket, is the familiar antisymmetrized wave function used for two particles subject to the Pauli principle. The antisymmetry characterizes 'Fermi–Dirac statistics'; the substitution of commutators for the anticommutators in (9.1) would obviously result in a symmetric wave function, characteristic of 'Einstein–Bose' statistics.

It is clear that similar results can be obtained for states of the field

$$c_e^\dagger|0\rangle \quad \text{and} \quad c_e^\dagger c_{e'}^\dagger|0\rangle, \tag{9.16}$$

containing one and two *anti*particles, respectively.

It will be useful to generalize the modes $u_e$ used in the above analysis to be eigenstates of a Dirac hamiltonian which may include the electrostatic energy arising from the presence of a nuclear charge, $Z$. The considerations must then be somewhat altered because $u_e^C = Cu_e^*$ can no longer be used together with $u_e$, as a member of a complete orthogonal set. The $u_e^C$ describes a normal fermion with negative energy which is in the presence of $-Z$, rather than $Z$, according to § 3.4. Detailed reconsideration will be unnecessary, since it is obvious when we use the results for cases in which only negatrons are present ($N_e^C = 0$), or for cases having positrons alone ($N_e = 0$). Only the parts $u_e$, or only the parts $u_e^C$, of the sets are used in the respective cases. We may take the electrostatic energy to be $-\alpha Z/r$ in the one case, $+\alpha Z/r$ in the other.

## 9.2. The β-coupling as a field operator

The fundamental coupling-energy density expression $h_\beta$ of (4.10) must now be treated as an operator by virtue of the field variables $\psi_{\mathrm{n,p,e,\nu}}$ composing it. It is profitless to treat the nucleons as quanta of fields $\psi_{\mathrm{p,n}}$, for nuclear $\beta$-processes. Any attempt would have to end very soon in simplifying assumptions which allow the use of $H_\beta$ (4.67) as before, except that now the lepton current $J_\alpha$ which it contains is to be treated as an operator having effect on states of the lepton fields.

The lepton current expression

$$J_\alpha(e\nu) = \psi_e^\dagger \beta\gamma_\alpha \tfrac{1}{2}(1+\gamma_5)\psi_\nu \tag{9.17}$$

will first be analysed into electron modes $u_e$, $u_e^C$ of (9.4), and similar neutrino field modes $u_\nu$, $u_\nu^C$. The amplitude operators $a_e$, $c_e$ used for the electron field will be supplemented with corresponding amplitudes $b_\nu$, $d_\nu$ for the neutrino field. Then

$$J_\alpha = \sum_{e\nu}\{(\phi_e^\dagger\beta\gamma_\alpha\phi_\nu)_0 a_e^\dagger b_\nu + (\phi_e^\dagger\beta\gamma_\alpha\phi_\nu^C)_0 a_e^\dagger d_\nu^\dagger + \\ +(\phi_e^{C\dagger}\beta\gamma_\alpha\phi_\nu)_0 c_e b_\nu + (\phi_e^{C\dagger}\beta\gamma_\alpha\phi_\nu^C)_0 c_e d_\nu^\dagger\}, \tag{9.18}$$

where the coefficients of the amplitude operators are just the expressions of (4.32), since $\phi = \frac{1}{2}(1+\gamma_5)u$ at $t = 0$.

The states on which $H_\beta$ and $J_\alpha$ operate, like $|\mathrm{i}\rangle$ and $|\mathrm{f}\rangle$ of (4.36), must now include descriptions of the states of the lepton fields. It will be convenient to continue using the symbols $|\mathrm{i}\rangle$ and $|\mathrm{f}\rangle$ for the conventional nuclear state descriptions, unaffected by the operations of $J_\alpha$. States of the complete physical system, nucleus and fields, will be given representations like

$$|\mathrm{i}\rangle_{e\nu} \equiv |\mathrm{i}\rangle\,|\,\rangle_e\,|\,\rangle_\nu. \tag{9.19}$$

Here $|\,\rangle_e$ and $|\,\rangle_\nu$ stand for possible states of the fields, formed as in (9.11) or (9.14). When no leptons or antileptons are present $|\,\rangle_e = |0\rangle_e$ and $|\,\rangle_\nu = |0\rangle_\nu$.

Consider the case in which a parent nucleus in state $|\mathrm{i}\rangle$ is present, and there are neither leptons or antileptons in the field. To find its decay rate into some state $|\mathrm{f}\rangle_{e\nu} = |\mathrm{f}\rangle\,|\,\rangle_e\,|\,\rangle_\nu$, a transition matrix element of (4.67) must be formed:

$$\langle \mathrm{f}|H_\beta|\mathrm{i}\rangle_{e\nu} = 2^{\frac{1}{2}}g\{\langle \mathrm{f}|\sum_a (C_V - C_A\gamma_5^{(a)})\beta\gamma_\alpha^a\tau_+^a\,{}_e\langle\,|\,{}_\nu\langle\,|J_\alpha(e\nu)|0\rangle_e|0\rangle_\nu|\mathrm{i}\rangle + \\ +\langle \mathrm{f}|\sum_a (C_V - C_A\gamma_5^{(a)})\beta\gamma_\alpha^a\tau_-^a\,{}_e\langle\,|\,{}_\nu\langle\,|J_\alpha(\nu e)|0\rangle_e|0\rangle_\nu|\mathrm{i}\rangle\}. \tag{9.20}$$

Here, (9.18) will yield

$${}_e\langle\,|\,{}_\nu\langle\,|J_\alpha(e\nu)|0\rangle_e|0\rangle_\nu = \sum_{e'\nu'}\langle\,|a_{e'}^\dagger|0\rangle_e\langle\,|d_{\nu'}^\dagger|0\rangle_\nu(\phi_{e'}^\dagger\beta\gamma_\alpha\phi_{\nu'}^C)_0, \tag{9.21 a}$$

$${}_e\langle\,|\,{}_\nu\langle\,|J_\alpha(\nu e)|0\rangle_e|0\rangle_\nu = \sum_{e'\nu'}\langle\,|c_{e'}^\dagger|0\rangle_e\langle\,|b_{\nu'}^\dagger|0\rangle_\nu(\phi_{\nu'}^\dagger\beta\gamma_\alpha\phi_{e'}^C)_0. \tag{9.21 b}$$

Only the first of these two expressions is needed when the request is for the rate of decay into a final nuclear state $|\mathrm{f}\rangle$ differing from $|\mathrm{i}\rangle$ by the substitution of a proton for a neutron; in that case $\langle \mathrm{f}|\tau_-^a|\mathrm{i}\rangle = 0$. Now the final electron field state $|\,\rangle_e$ requested may be $a_{e''}^\dagger|0\rangle_e$ (a negatron in mode $e''$), or $c_{e''}^\dagger|0\rangle_e$ (a positron), or $a_{e''}^\dagger a_{e'''}^\dagger|0\rangle_e$ (two negatrons), or $a_{e''}^\dagger c_{e'''}^\dagger|0\rangle_e$ (a pair), etc. It is easy to see that of all such possibilities only the first will allow $\langle\,|a_{e'}^\dagger|0\rangle_e$ not to vanish (in the term $e' = e''$).

Thus, a first-order process governed by (9.20) can generate only a single electron. Similar arguments lead to the conclusion that only a single *anti*neutrino will be generated in company with the negatron.

During a neutron-to-proton transformation only a lepton field state like $a^{\dagger}_{e''}|0\rangle_{\mathrm{e}}.d^{\dagger}_{\nu''}|0\rangle_{\nu}$ can be requested, and then (9.21 a) reduces to

$$(\phi^{\dagger}_{\mathrm{e}''}\beta\gamma_{\alpha}\phi^{C}_{\nu''})_{0}. \tag{9.22}$$

The transition matrix element becomes

$$2^{\frac{1}{2}}g\langle\mathrm{f}|\sum_{a}(C_{\mathrm{V}}-C_{\mathrm{A}}\gamma_{5}^{a})\beta^{a}\gamma_{\alpha}^{a}\tau_{+}^{a}(\phi^{\dagger}_{e''}\beta\gamma_{\alpha}\phi^{C}_{\nu''})_{0}|\mathrm{i}\rangle, \tag{9.23}$$

which is exactly the same result which followed from (4.32 a) and (4.67), in the earlier treatment. This justifies the procedure then used.

It is obvious how the justification may be extended to positron emission and the capture processes. For instance, when antineutrinos are incident on protons, the initial state of the lepton field has a description like $|0\rangle_{\mathrm{e}}d^{\dagger}_{\nu}|0\rangle_{\nu}$. Only final states like $c^{\dagger}_{e}|0\rangle_{\mathrm{e}}|0\rangle_{\nu}$ can be successfully requested, and the surviving part of the lepton current will be

$$(\phi^{C\dagger}_{\nu}\beta\gamma_{\alpha}\phi^{C}_{\mathrm{e}})_{0}\langle 0|c_{e}c^{\dagger}_{e}|0\rangle_{\mathrm{e}}\langle 0|d_{\nu}d^{\dagger}_{\nu}|0\rangle_{\nu} = (\phi^{C\dagger}_{\nu}\beta\gamma_{\alpha}\phi^{C}_{\mathrm{e}})_{0}. \tag{9.24}$$

The antineutrino has vanished and a positron has appeared. The result for the transition matrix element will be exactly that already used in § 8.2.

## 9.3. Double β-decay

There are cases (Table 9.1) of nuclei which are less stable with only one of their neutrons exchanged for a proton, but which gain stability

TABLE 9.1

*Cases examined for $\beta^{-}\beta^{-}$-decay*

| | $T_0/mc^2$ | *t (years)* Experimental‡ | *t (years)* Theoretical |
|---|---|---|---|
| $_{20}\mathrm{Ca}^{48}$ | 8·4 | $> 2(10)^{18}$ | $8(10)^{20\pm2}$ |
| $_{40}\mathrm{Zr}^{96}$ | 6·5 | $> 5(10)^{17}$ | $4(10)^{21\pm2}$ |
| $_{42}\mathrm{Mo}^{100}$ | 4·5 | $> 3(10)^{17}$ | $8(10)^{22\pm2}$ |
| $_{48}\mathrm{Cd}^{116}$ | 5·3 | $> 1(10)^{17}$ | $2(10)^{22\pm2}$ |
| $_{52}\mathrm{Te}^{130}$ | 5·9 | $1{\cdot}4(10)^{21}$ | $6(10)^{21\pm2}$ |
| $_{60}\mathrm{Nd}^{150}$ | 7·3 | $> 4(10)^{18}$ | $8(10)^{20\pm2}$ |
| $_{92}\mathrm{U}^{238}$ | 2·0 | $> 6(10)^{18}$ | $5(10)^{25\pm2}$ |

‡ From data as collected in reference on p. 255.

when two of their neutrons are replaced by protons. This is understood to be a consequence of strong 'pairing forces', extra attractions between like nucleons when the Pauli principle permits them to have similar spatial distributions within the nucleus.

The availability of energy for the transformations of a pair of neutrons leads to the expectation of double $\beta$-emission, in which two negatrons are emitted simultaneously. The rate should be extremely low, $\sim g^4$ as against the proportionality to $g^2$ of first-order processes, but has a chance of becoming detectable through lack of any other process by which the parent nuclei, when isolated, could have their stability disturbed.

*The second-order process*

We deal now with nuclear states $|\mathrm{i}\rangle$, $|\mathrm{f}\rangle$ for which $\langle\mathrm{f}|H_\beta|\mathrm{i}\rangle = 0$ because $\langle\mathrm{f}|\tau^a_\pm|\mathrm{i}\rangle = 0$ when the states differ by the replacement of more than one neutron by protons. The transition between them cannot be generated as a first-order process in the sense of § 4.3. However, advantage can be taken of the fact that transient states $|\tau\rangle$, differing from $|\mathrm{i}\rangle$ and $|\mathrm{f}\rangle$ in just the character of one nucleon, can be temporarily formed even when the energy is not available to permit their becoming permanent. The first-order amplitude‡ $a_\tau(t)$ can be found as a solution of an equation like (4.24) with $f \to \tau$ and $W_0 \to E_\mathrm{i} - E'_\tau$:

$$a_\tau(t) = \frac{\langle\tau|H_\beta|\mathrm{i}\rangle_{\mathrm{e}\nu}}{E_\mathrm{i}-E'_\tau}\big[e^{i(E'_\tau-E_\mathrm{i})t/\hbar}\big]^t_{t=-\infty}. \tag{9.25}$$

The bracket represents the difference of the exponentials obtained at the indicated limits, arising from the 'initial' condition $a_\tau(-\infty) = 0$. The lower limit value can be dropped since an average of the exponential over even a slight uncertainty in the energies vanishes as $t \to -\infty$. Of course, $E'_\tau \neq E_\mathrm{i}$ is being presumed so that $a_\tau$ can only oscillate and cannot settle on a non-vanishing value; its average tends to vanish in inverse proportion to observation periods $\Delta t \gg \hbar/|E'_\tau - E_\mathrm{i}|$.

For convenience, a departure from the practice of § 4.3 was introduced in (9.25). As indicated by the subscript $\mathrm{e}\nu$, the transition matrix element is now defined to join states $|\mathrm{i},\tau\rangle_{\mathrm{e}\nu}$ which include descriptions of the state of the lepton fields. Accordingly, the transient state energy $E'_\tau$ must include the energies of the electron and neutrino generated in the temporary state,

$$E'_\tau = E_\tau + W + cq \tag{9.26}$$

if $E_\tau$ is the energy of just the nuclear state $|\tau\rangle$. This is necessary also for treating the transition matrix as time-independent, which was done in arriving at (9.25).

‡ For the state of the entire system, as in § 4.3; not to be confused with the operator $a_\mathrm{e}$ of §§ 9.1, 9.2.

Now a permanent state $|\mathrm{f}\rangle_{\mathrm{e}\nu}$ can be generated from the transient states $|\tau\rangle_{\mathrm{e}\nu}$ according to the formula (4.23). When the oscillating amplitude (9.25) is inserted into (4.23), the result is of the type (4.24), the formula from which the permanent first-order transitions were evaluated. One difference is that the first-order transition matrix $\langle\mathrm{f}|H_\beta|\mathrm{i}\rangle$ is now replaced by the second-order expression

$$\sum_\tau \frac{\langle\mathrm{f}|H_\beta|\tau\rangle_{\mathrm{e}\nu}\langle\tau|H_\beta|\mathrm{i}\rangle_{\mathrm{e}\nu}}{E_\mathrm{i}-E'_\tau}. \tag{9.27}$$

Moreover, the nuclear energy release $W_0 = E_\mathrm{i}-E_\mathrm{f}$ is now replaced by $E_\mathrm{i}-E'_\mathrm{f} = W_0-(W_1+W_2+cq_1+cq_2)$, which includes the energies of the four leptons to be anticipated for the final state. The same exponential time-factor enters with every term of (9.27) when the final state sought is to have the definite lepton energies $W_1$, $W_2$, $cq_1$, and $cq_2$. The result for the rate of the second-order process is now obtained in the same way as the first-order rate (4.36)

$$d\lambda = \frac{2\pi}{\hbar}\left|\sum_\tau \frac{\langle\mathrm{f}|H_\beta|\tau\rangle_{\mathrm{e}\nu}\langle\tau|H_\beta|\mathrm{i}\rangle_{\mathrm{e}\nu}}{E_\mathrm{i}-E'_\tau}\right|^2 \delta(W_1+W_2+cq_1+cq_2-W_0). \tag{9.28}$$

The inverse proportionality of the amplitude terms to $E_\mathrm{i}-E'_\tau$ can be regarded as arising from their proportionality to the mean periods $\Delta t \approx \hbar/\,|E'_\tau-E_\mathrm{i}|$ over which the intermediate state can survive.

Next, we reduce the transition matrices to ones involving description of the nuclear states only, by the same procedure as that used to obtain (9.23) from (9.20). The initial and final lepton field states can be given the representations $|0\rangle_\mathrm{e}|0\rangle_\nu$ and‡ $a_1^\dagger a_2^\dagger|0\rangle_\mathrm{e} d_1^\dagger d_2^\dagger|0\rangle_\nu$, respectively. In order to yield the specified final state, the summation in (9.28) must include intermediate states with energies

$$E'_\tau = E_\tau+W_1+cq_1, \qquad E'_\tau = E_\tau+W_2+cq_2,$$
$$E'_\tau = E_\tau+W_1+cq_2, \qquad E'_\tau = E_\tau+W_2+cq_1.$$

When this is taken into account, the decay formula (9.28) can be written:

$$d\lambda = (2\pi/\hbar)\delta(W_1+W_2+cq_1+cq_2-W_0)\times$$
$$\times\left|\sum_\tau \frac{\langle\mathrm{f}|H_\beta(22)|\tau\rangle\langle\tau|H_\beta(11)|\mathrm{i}\rangle}{E_\mathrm{i}-E_\tau-W_1-cq_1}+\frac{\langle\mathrm{f}|H_\beta(11)|\tau\rangle\langle\tau|H_\beta(22)|\mathrm{i}\rangle}{E_\mathrm{i}-E_\tau-W_2-cq_2}-\right.$$
$$\left.-\frac{\langle\mathrm{f}|H_\beta(21)|\tau\rangle\langle\tau|H_\beta(12)|\mathrm{i}\rangle}{E_\mathrm{i}-E_\tau-W_1-cq_2}-\frac{\langle\mathrm{f}|H_\beta(12)|\tau\rangle\langle\tau|H_\beta(21)|\mathrm{i}\rangle}{E_\mathrm{i}-E_\tau-W_2-cq_1}\right|^2. \tag{9.29}$$

‡ $a_2^\dagger\, a_1^\dagger|0\rangle_\mathrm{e}$ differs only in phase (a sign) from $a_1^\dagger\, a_2^\dagger|0\rangle_\mathrm{e}$, hence represents an equivalent, rather than independent, state which might be formed. This introduces a factor $\frac{1}{2}$ into an otherwise unrestricted summation over $\mathbf{p}_1\,\sigma_1\,\mathbf{p}_2\,\sigma_2$. A similar factor $\frac{1}{2}$ arises in the summation over final neutrino states.

The symbols like $\langle\tau|H_\beta(n_e n_\nu)|i\rangle$ stand for results like (9.23), evaluated with lepton modes $u_e(\mathbf{r})$ and $u_\nu^C(\mathbf{r})$, having energies $W_{ne}$ and $cq_{n_\nu}$ respectively. The negative signs on the last two terms arise from the antisymmetry of the final lepton states to the exchange of the two electrons, and of the two neutrinos. The same form (9.29) applies to both double negatron and double positron emissions.

*Expectations for ββ emissions*‡

The evaluation of the rate formula (9.29) will be carried out here only in the allowed approximation (5.4). This will restrict the intermediate nuclear states $|\tau\rangle$ which can contribute to such as have angular momenta $I_\tau$ differing by no more than one unit from $I$ and from $I'$, the nuclear spins in the initial and final states, respectively. It also means that the results can only apply to cases for which $\Delta I = |I'-I| \leqslant 2$. The actual cases (Table 9.1) known to have substantial energy available for the double decay, and none for faster processes, are even–even nuclei with $I = I' = 0$ in their ground states. Further, the allowed approximation permits no nuclear parity changes, and the cases of interest involve only initial and final states of even parity.

It will be convenient to define

$$\left.\begin{aligned} \mathscr{M}^k_{\tau i} &= C_A\Big\langle\tau\Big|\sum_a \tau^a_\pm \sigma^a_k\Big|i\Big\rangle \quad \text{for } k = 1,\,2,\,3 \\ \mathscr{M}^4_{\tau i} &= iC_V\Big\langle\tau\Big|\sum_a \tau^a_\pm\Big|i\Big\rangle \end{aligned}\right\}. \tag{9.30}$$

This permits the allowed approximation (5.4) of the transition matrices to be written in the economical form

$$\langle\tau|H_\beta(n_e, n_\nu)|i\rangle = -2^{\frac{1}{2}}ig\sum_\alpha \mathscr{M}^\alpha_{\tau i} J_\alpha(n_e, n_\nu). \tag{9.31}$$

Another approximation to be made here is the neglect of the distinctions among the lepton energies contributing to the energy denominators of (9.29). The energy spectrum must be symmetric in electron-neutrino pairs, hence the spectrum average of $W_{ne}+cq_{n_\nu}$ must be $\frac{1}{2}W_0$ regardless of the indices $n_e$, $n_\nu$. We therefore put $E'_\tau - E_i \approx E_\tau - E_i + \frac{1}{2}W_0$. If a case should ever be found for which an $E_\tau \approx E_i$ exists, moreover with $|I_\tau - I| \leqslant 1$, then a reconsideration of this point may be justified. Now the squared amplitude in (9.29) can be written

$$4g^4\left|\sum_{\tau\alpha\beta}\frac{\mathscr{M}^\alpha_{f\tau}\mathscr{M}^\beta_{\tau i}}{E'_\tau - E_i}\sum_{n_e n_\nu}(-)^{n_e+n_\nu}J_\alpha(n'_e\, n'_\nu)J_\beta(n_e\, n_\nu)\right|^2 \tag{9.32}$$

‡ First estimates were made by M. Mayer, *Phys. Rev.* **48,** 512 (1935). A comprehensive summary was published by H. Primakoff and S. P. Rosen in *Rep. Progr. Phys.* **22,** 121 (1959); in this, references to other pertinent works can be found.

if $n'_e = 2$ for $n_e = 1$ and $n'_e = 1$ for $n_e = 2$; so also for the pair of labels $n_\nu$, $n'_\nu$.

Plane wave modes are convenient to use for the leptons, in the allowed approximation, with corrections for the nuclear charge effect as in (3.64). Then (9.29) is to be multiplied by the numbers of the modes in the various momentum ranges,

$$\frac{(d\mathbf{p}_1)V}{(2\pi\hbar)^3}\cdot\frac{(d\mathbf{p}_2)V}{(2\pi\hbar)^3}\cdot\frac{(d\mathbf{q}_1)V}{(2\pi\hbar)^3}\cdot\frac{(d\mathbf{q}_2)V}{(2\pi\hbar)^3}.$$

Moreover, summations over all the lepton spins will be carried out.‡ This forgoes finding expectations for the lepton polarizations, but the prospects for their experimental detection are very poor in the very weak double decays, and should not be expected to be of particular interest in any case. This applies to the nuclear recoils as well, hence the neutrino emission directions $\hat{\mathbf{q}}_1$, $\hat{\mathbf{q}}_2$ will be immediately averaged out. Let the symbol $S_{\alpha\beta\alpha'\beta'}(n_e\, n_\nu)$ stand for

$$4V^4 J^*_\alpha(22)J^*_\beta(11)J_{\alpha'}(n'_e\, n'_\nu)J_{\beta'}(n_e\, n_\nu),$$

after this has been summed over the lepton spins and averaged over the neutrino directions. The trace techniques exhibited in § 4.4 can be employed and this results in

$$\left.\begin{aligned} S_{\alpha\beta\alpha'\beta'}(11) &= \tfrac{1}{4}\,\mathrm{tr}[\sigma_{\beta'}\sigma^\dagger_\beta(1-\boldsymbol{\sigma}.\mathbf{v}_1/c)]\mathrm{tr}[\sigma_{\alpha'}\sigma^\dagger_\alpha(1-\boldsymbol{\sigma}.\mathbf{v}_2/c)]\\ S_{\alpha\beta\alpha'\beta'}(22) &= \tfrac{1}{4}\,\mathrm{tr}[\sigma_{\alpha'}\sigma^\dagger_\beta(1-\boldsymbol{\sigma}.\mathbf{v}_1/c)]\mathrm{tr}[\sigma_{\beta'}\sigma^\dagger_\alpha(1-\boldsymbol{\sigma}.\mathbf{v}_2/c)]\\ S_{\alpha\beta\alpha'\beta'}(21) &= \tfrac{1}{4}\,\mathrm{tr}[\sigma_{\beta'}\sigma^\dagger_\beta(1-\boldsymbol{\sigma}.\mathbf{v}_1/c)\sigma_{\alpha'}\sigma^\dagger_\alpha(1-\boldsymbol{\sigma}.\mathbf{v}_2/c)]\\ S_{\alpha\beta\alpha'\beta'}(12) &= \tfrac{1}{4}\,\mathrm{tr}[\sigma_{\alpha'}\sigma^\dagger_\beta(1-\boldsymbol{\sigma}.\mathbf{v}_1/c)\sigma_{\beta'}\sigma^\dagger_\alpha(1-\boldsymbol{\sigma}.\mathbf{v}_2/c)] \end{aligned}\right\}, \tag{9.33}$$

without the coulomb corrections, which will be inserted below. Here $\sigma_{1,2,3}$ are just the 2-dimensional Pauli $\sigma$'s and $\sigma_4 \equiv -i$. Simple symmetries in the interchanges $\alpha \leftrightarrow \alpha'$, $\beta \leftrightarrow \beta'$, and in $\alpha \leftrightarrow \beta$, $\alpha' \leftrightarrow \beta'$, as well as in $\alpha \leftrightarrow \beta$ alone, are easily derived and useful to employ. Next, the electron emission directions will also be averaged over, except that a constant correlation angle $\theta$, between $\mathbf{v}_1$ and $\mathbf{v}_2$, will be maintained in the averaging. This is appropriate for sources of randomly oriented nuclei or for parents of zero nuclear spin, as in the cases of Table 9.1. The following result is thus obtainable:

$$\Big\langle \sum_{n_e n_\nu} (-)^{n_e+n_\nu} S_{\alpha\beta\alpha'\beta'}(n_e\, n_\nu)\Big\rangle = \delta_{\alpha\beta}\,\delta_{\alpha'\beta'}\,F(Z,W_1)F(Z,W_2)(1-\mathbf{v}_1.\mathbf{v}_2/c^2), \tag{9.34}$$

with the angular brackets denoting the electron direction average in question. The vanishing in the cases for which $\alpha' = \alpha \neq \beta = \beta'$ or

‡ With the 'indistinguishability factor', $\frac{1}{4}$, noted in the footnote on p. 254.

$\alpha' = \beta \neq \alpha = \beta'$ is the result of particle exchanges and not merely due to the directional averaging. The same is true for the cases in which $\alpha \neq \beta \neq \alpha' \neq \beta' \neq \alpha$. The functions $F(Z, W)$ are again the electron density ratios first introduced in (1.14). As in first-order decay, the sign of $Z$ must be reversed in going from cases of negatron to positron emission.

The result (9.34) is of immediate use for finding the rate of producing two electrons with their momentum magnitudes in the ranges $dp_1$ and $dp_2$, and with the angle $\theta$ between the two emission directions:

$$\frac{d\lambda}{dp_1\,dp_2} = \frac{8g^4}{15(2\pi)^7\hbar^{13}c^6}\left|\sum_{\tau\alpha}\frac{\mathscr{M}^{\alpha}_{\mathrm{f}\tau}\mathscr{M}^{\alpha}_{\tau\mathrm{i}}}{E'_\tau - E_\mathrm{i}}\right|^2\left(1-\frac{v_1 v_2}{c^2}\cos\theta\right)\frac{d(\cos\theta)}{2}\times$$
$$\times F(\pm Z, W_1)F(\pm Z, W_2)p_1^2 p_2^2(W_0-W_1-W_2)^5 \quad \text{for } \mathrm{e}^{\mp}\mathrm{e}^{\mp}. \quad (9.35)$$

The two electrons emerge predominantly into opposite directions. This is at bottom an effect of the exclusion principle, conjoined with the helicity of the electrons. Their emission into the same direction, especially with both velocities approaching that of light, would entail the unlawful occupation of the same configuration by two fermions spinning in parallel.

In view of the limited accuracy which must be expected in double decay measurements for some time to come, it will suffice to use the crude‡ approximation

$$F \approx \pm(2\pi\alpha ZW/cp)[1-e^{\mp 2\pi\alpha Z}]^{-1} \quad (9.36)$$

for the electron density ratio as given by (1.12). Then a simple integration of (9.35) can give the number of electrons (counting either one per decay) with kinetic energy $T = W-mc^2$ in the range $dT$:

$$\frac{d\lambda}{dT} = \frac{g^4(\alpha Z)^2}{2\pi^5\hbar^{13}c^{12}}[1-e^{\mp 2\pi\alpha Z}]^{-2}\left|\sum_{\tau\alpha}\frac{\mathscr{M}^{\alpha}_{\mathrm{f}\tau}\mathscr{M}^{\alpha}_{\tau\mathrm{i}}}{E'_\tau - E_\mathrm{i}}\right|^2\frac{(T+mc^2)^2}{7!}\times$$
$$\times(T_0-T)^6[(T_0-T)^2+8mc^2(T_0-T)+28m^2c^4], \quad (9.37)$$

with $T_0 = W_0-2mc^2$, the maximum kinetic energy any electron can have. An example of this theoretical 'singles' spectrum is shown in Fig. 9.1. It will be easier to measure the sum of the two electron kinetic energies, $K = W_1+W_2-2mc^2$, emitted in each instance of decay. The 'sum' spectrum should be proportional to

$$d\lambda/dK \sim K(T_0-K)^5[K^4+10K^3+40K^2+60K+30], \quad (9.38)$$

in units of $mc^2 = 1$. This is also illustrated in Fig. 9.1.

‡ It will be adequate except for the low energy portions of positron spectra.

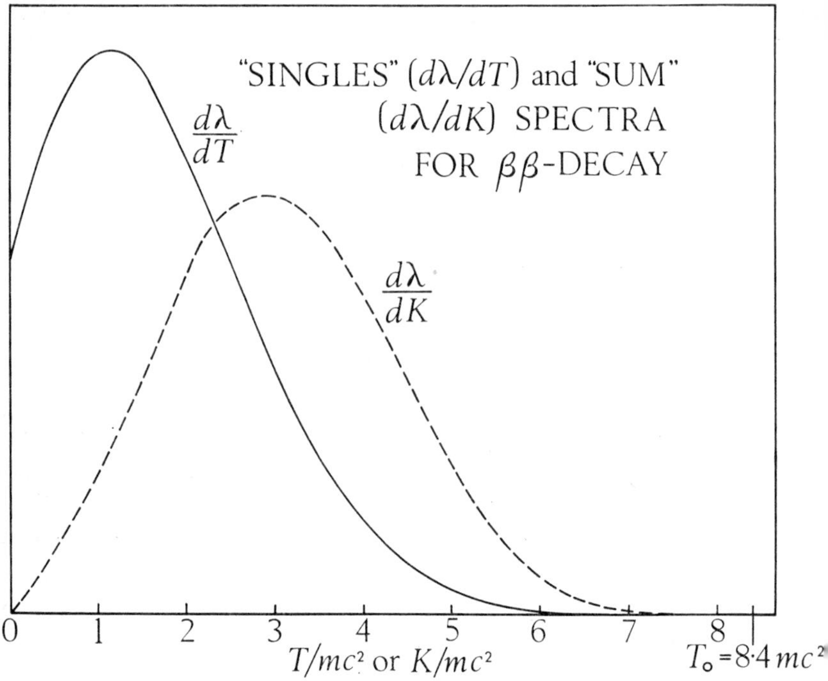


FIG. 9.1

A final integration, over the spectrum (9.37), yields the total decay rate

$$\lambda = \frac{4g^4}{\pi^7\hbar^2 c}\left(\frac{mc}{\hbar}\right)^{11}\left(\frac{2\pi\alpha Z}{1-e^{\mp 2\pi\alpha Z}}\right)^2\left|\sum_{\tau\alpha}\frac{\mathcal{M}^{\alpha}_{\mathrm{f}\tau}\mathcal{M}^{\alpha}_{\tau\mathrm{i}}}{E_\tau - E_\mathrm{i} + \frac{1}{2}W_0}\right|^2 f_{\beta\beta}(T_0), \qquad (9.39)$$

where

$$f_{\beta\beta}(T_0) = \frac{T_0^7}{8!}\left[1+\tfrac{1}{2}T_0+\tfrac{1}{9}T_0^2+\tfrac{1}{90}T_0^3+\tfrac{1}{1980}T_0^4\right], \qquad (9.40)$$

if $T_0 \equiv W_0 - 2$ is measured in units $mc^2$. A diagram of this function is shown in Fig. 9.2. It may be compared to the single $\beta$-decay rate functions of Figs. 1.7 and 1.8.

*Estimates of half-lives*

The greatest uncertainties in evaluating the rates (9.39) stem from ignorance concerning the energy levels of the intermediate nuclear states having $|I_\tau - I| \leqslant 1$, and the sizes of the $\beta$-moments combining these states with the initial and final ones. The moments which have been retained are only the nominally largest, 'allowed' ones, appearing in the combinations

$$\sum_{\alpha}\mathcal{M}^{\alpha}_{\mathrm{f}\tau}\mathcal{M}^{\alpha}_{\tau\mathrm{i}} = C_\mathrm{A}^2\langle \mathrm{f}|\sum_a \tau^a_\pm \boldsymbol{\sigma}^a|\tau\rangle.\langle\tau|\sum_b \tau^b_\pm \boldsymbol{\sigma}^b|\mathrm{i}\rangle -$$
$$- C_\mathrm{V}^2\langle \mathrm{f}|\sum_a \tau^a_\pm|\tau\rangle\langle\tau|\sum_b \tau^b_\pm|\mathrm{i}\rangle. \qquad (9.41)$$

Each of the moment factors is of a type having magnitudes of order unity in the favoured transitions of single $\beta$-decay, but are more commonly found to have squared magnitudes a tenth to a hundredth as great. On this basis, values for (9.41) like $\pm(1/10 \text{ to } 1/100)C^2_{\mathrm{A,V}}$ should be expected to emerge most frequently. The Fermi and Gamow–Teller ransitions in single decays are usually disparate enough so that can-

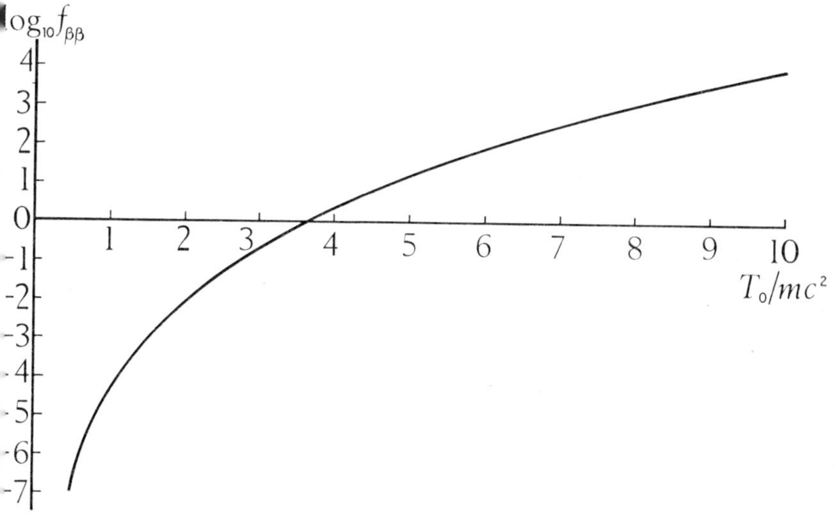


FIG. 9.2

cellations in (9.41), to much smaller values, may be regarded as abnormal.

There is next the problem of summing over the intermediate states which contribute significantly. If the variation of the energy denominaor in (9.39) could be ignored, then the sum over $\tau$ of (9.41) would yield

$$\sum_{\tau\alpha} \mathscr{M}^{\alpha}_{\mathrm{f}\tau}\,\mathscr{M}^{\alpha}_{\tau\mathrm{i}} = \langle \mathrm{f}|\sum_{ab} \tau^a_{\pm}\,\tau^b_{\pm}(C^2_{\mathrm{A}}\,\boldsymbol{\sigma}^a.\boldsymbol{\sigma}^b - C^2_{\mathrm{V}})|\mathrm{i}\rangle \qquad (9.42)$$

because of the completeness of the set of states $|\tau\rangle$ as descriptions of the intermediate nuclear system. The scalar character of the operator n this resultant moment indicates that transitions between states of equal spins, $I' = I$, are most favourable for double $\beta$-decay. Fortunately, the energetically most favourable cases, listed in Table 9.1, have $I' = I = 0$.

The operator $\boldsymbol{\sigma}^a.\boldsymbol{\sigma}^b$ has the value $+1$ in the triplet components of he relative motion of the pair of transforming nucleons. This tends oward a cancellation to $C^2_{\mathrm{A}} - C^2_{\mathrm{V}} \approx \frac{1}{2}C^2_{\mathrm{V}}$ in (9.42). On the other hand, t is the singlet components, with $\boldsymbol{\sigma}^a.\boldsymbol{\sigma}^b = -3$, which are most likely to predominate in the $0^+$ states of the even-even nuclei in Table 9.1; there may well be merely the exchange of a singlet proton pair for a singlet neutron pair. Thus, under favourable circumstances, the resultant (9.42) may have an absolute magnitude of the order $4C^2_{\mathrm{A,V}}$. However, the suppressions by factors 1/10 to 1/100 for the squares of scalar moments like (9.42), found for allowed but unfavoured single decays, should probably be expected to operate.

In view of the above considerations, we shall assume that

$$\left|\sum_{\tau\alpha}\frac{\mathscr{M}^{\alpha}_{\mathrm{f}\tau}\mathscr{M}^{\alpha}_{\tau\mathrm{i}}}{E_\tau-E_\mathrm{i}+\frac{1}{2}W_0}\right|^2 \approx 10^{-2\pm 2}C^4_\mathrm{V}/\langle(E_\tau-E_\mathrm{i}+\tfrac{1}{2}W_0)^2\rangle \qquad (9.43)$$

spans the range of values which might reasonably be expected. The angular brackets here are meant to stand for an average over a range of intermediate nuclear energies which can be expected to contain enough of the states for a fair completion of the relation (9.42). Separate judgements about this should probably be made for each specific case.

When the estimate (9.43) is used in the rate expression (9.39), a result for the half-life $t = \ln 2/\lambda$ can be obtained:

$$t_{\beta\beta} \approx [3(10)^{22\pm 2}\ \mathrm{yrs.}][(1-e^{\mp 2\pi\alpha Z})/2\pi\alpha Z]^2 \mathrm{f}^{-1}_{\beta\beta}(T_0)\langle(E_\tau-E_\mathrm{i}+\tfrac{1}{2}W_0)^2\rangle, \qquad (9.44)$$

with all energies in units of $mc^2$. The formula shows that double negatron decay tends to be most rapid in heavy nuclei ($t \sim Z^{-2}$), an effect of the higher negatron density at larger nuclear charges. The heavy nuclei also tend to have greater densities of nuclear states, which allows lower estimates for $(E_\tau - E_\mathrm{i})$. However, this possible effect has not been taken into account for the estimates listed in Table 9.1, in which a uniform value $\langle(E_\tau-E_\mathrm{i}+\frac{1}{2}W_0)^2\rangle \approx (10mc^2)^2$ is assumed. More detailed studies of individual cases are needed before the estimates can be significantly improved.

The table compares the theoretical estimates with lower limits on the half-lives which have been imposed by experimental attempts to detect the process. There is some positive evidence for the existence of $\beta\beta$-decay only from the case of $\mathrm{Te}^{130}$. It is based on the mass-spectrographic detection‡ of the product $\mathrm{Xe}^{130}$ in the company of Te in very old minerals. Evidence from the detection of the electrons must await improvements in the elimination of background effects. Attempts have also been made to detect double positron decay and double $K$-capture, but with much poorer prospects of success.

‡ M. E. Inghram and J. H. Reynolds, *Phys. Rev.* **78**, 822 (1950).

# X

# SPECULATIONS ABOUT THE $\beta$-COUPLING AND THE NEUTRINO

THE $\beta$-theory has been presented so far as a more or less forthright attempt to describe what the experimenters have found about nuclear $\beta$-processes. Actually, the initiative in the development has at numerous junctures come from quite purely theoretical speculations. These are valuable to review as a means of laying bare general principles on which the present theory can be said to be constructed.

Theoretical speculations are always based on expecting correct descriptions to have symmetries of one kind or another, and these can often be expressed as invariances to appropriate transformations of the entities used for the descriptions. The ideal result would be a set of highly general invariance principles from which a unique law of $\beta$-interaction could follow. It will be found that using only the best-established principles leaves a set of alternatives for the possible interaction forms, among which direct experimental observations must decide. The details of this line of development will be considered first.

Supplementary invariance requirements, designed to lead uniquely to the correct 'V–A Law', will also be considered briefly. The value of these is difficult to assess, since *a priori* equally plausible requirements can lead to different laws of $\beta$-interaction.

The speculations most closely related to the role of the neutrino in the $\beta$-interaction are reserved for the last section of this chapter (§ 10.3).

## 10.1. Alternatives for the law of $\beta$-interaction

All the best developed descriptions of interactions among fields give them forms sometimes called 'contact interactions'. This refers to a proportionality to products of the interacting field amplitudes.‡ The interaction between the electromagnetic field and a fermionic field of charged quanta was the earliest example (4.6). Fermi's proposal for

‡ This specification is not as unambiguous as it may seem because, for example, the gradient of a field is also a field. The early 'KU Theory' (E. J. Konopinski and G. E. Uhlenbeck, *Phys. Rev.* **48,** 7 (1935)) replaced the neutrino field in the $\beta$-coupling with its space-time gradient in order to obtain consistency with early measurements on $\beta$-spectra. After some years, improved measurements began to contradict the first results and the theory eventually had to be discarded (E. J. Konopinski, *Rev. Mod. Phys.* **8,** 82 (1943)).

the $\beta$-interaction (§ 4.2) was the second example, and later proposals such as for the pion-nucleon interaction, have followed the same pattern. All the alternatives to be considered here for the $\beta$-interaction will take it to be proportional to each of the amplitudes $\psi_e$, $\psi_\nu$, $\psi_p$, and $\psi_n$, as is the V–A Law (4.10).

The field amplitudes, as they enter the interaction, will all be evaluated at a common point in space-time. This is characteristic of 'local' interaction. If separated space-time points were involved (the interaction attributed a 'structure') then propagations between them, having finite velocity, would presumably need to be provided for. The propagations would ostensibly be taking place in some kind of 'intermediary' fields.‡ The assumption of a localized interaction among all four fermion fields is best consistent with a conception of the $\beta$-coupling as a basic one not further resolvable into more elementary interactions.

Local interactions may still assume a great variety of specific forms These were investigated before the 'V–A' form (4.10) was finally singled out under the gradually accumulating pressure of the experimental discoveries recounted in Chapter I.

*'Even' couplings and the Fierz transformation*

Varieties of local interactions among spinor fields arise from the fact that, at a given 'point of contact' in space-time, there are still four different components of each spinor field to specify. There are $4^4$ different products of components which can be formed when dealing with the four spinor fields involved in a $\beta$-interaction. However, the number of these products which can constitute terms of a coupling energy density ($\equiv$ interaction lagrangian density) is greatly restricted by demanding relativistic invariance.

The so-called 'even' couplings to be introduced in this subsection are ones to be expected if all spinor fields have *exactly* the same behaviour in changes of the space-time reference frame. The relativistic scalar products needed for the energy density can be found by first constructing the five different covariant products of any pair of the spinors, e.g. $(\bar{\psi}_p \psi_n)$, $(\bar{\psi}_p \gamma_\alpha \psi_n)$, $(\bar{\psi}_p \sigma_{\alpha\beta} \psi_n)$, $(\bar{\psi}_p \omega_\alpha \psi_n)$, and $(\bar{\psi}_p \gamma_5 \psi_n)$. These are, respectively, the Scalar, the Vector, the Tensor, the Pseudovector, and the Pseudoscalar of (2.92). Next, each covariant may be contracted with the corresponding covariant product of the remaining pair of spinors

‡ Such have been proposed repeatedly, first by H. Yukawa in *Proc. Math. Phys. Soc. Japan*, **17**, 48 (1935). These speculations have not contributed directly to the understanding of $\beta$-decay so far, and are perhaps too undeveloped at present for inclusion here. See § 13.4.

$\psi_e, \psi_\nu$). Thus obtained are five different invariant products of the four ields, and an arbitrary linear combination of them may constitute a oupling-energy density:

$$h_\beta = 2^{-\frac{1}{2}}g \sum_X C_X(\bar{\psi}_p \Gamma^X \psi_n).(\bar{\psi}_e \Gamma^X \psi_\nu)+\text{h.c.} \tag{10.1}$$

Here $X$ = S, T, V, A, P and

$$\left.\begin{aligned} \Gamma^S.\Gamma^S &\equiv 1.1 \\ \Gamma^V.\Gamma^V &\equiv \gamma_\alpha.\gamma_\alpha = \beta.\beta-\beta\boldsymbol{\alpha}.\beta\boldsymbol{\alpha} \\ \Gamma^T.\Gamma^T &\equiv \tfrac{1}{2}\sigma_{\alpha\beta}.\sigma_{\alpha\beta} = \boldsymbol{\sigma}.\boldsymbol{\sigma}+\boldsymbol{\alpha}.\boldsymbol{\alpha} \\ \Gamma^A.\Gamma^A &\equiv \omega_\alpha.\omega_\alpha = \beta\boldsymbol{\sigma}.\beta\boldsymbol{\sigma}-\beta\gamma_5.\beta\gamma_5 \\ \Gamma^P.\Gamma^P &\equiv \gamma_5.\gamma_5 \end{aligned}\right\}. \tag{10.2}$$

The operators on the two sides of each dot apply to different internal degrees of freedom, nucleonic and leptonic, respectively.

Alternatives to (10.1) may seem immediately available from the fact that the various spinors might have been paired differently. Consider, therefore, the expressions which can be formed by permuting the four fields in (10.1) among themselves. If $h_\beta$(pne$\nu$) symbolizes the order in which the fields appear in (10.1), then it is first obvious that $h_\beta$(e$\nu$pn) is only a trivial variation in the writing. The reordering $h_\beta$(np$\nu$e) merely interchanges the hermitian conjugate terms of (10.1); that corresponds to interchanging the two sides of the 'lepton conservation relation', $\text{n}+\nu \leftrightarrow \text{p}+\text{e}^-$. The latter symbolism makes particularly clear the fact that certain transpositions, $\text{n} \leftrightarrow \text{p}$ or $\nu \leftrightarrow \text{e}^-$, are forbidden by charge conservation.‡ Finally, transpositions like $\text{n} \leftrightarrow \nu$, or its equivalent $\text{p} \leftrightarrow \text{e}^-$, require more extended discussion.

Fierz§ showed that such an interchange as $\psi_n \leftrightarrow \psi_\nu$ in (10.1) corresponds merely to a renaming of the coupling constants $C_X$. A theorem due to Pauli|| helps show this. It is concerned with 16 numbers $\Gamma^X_{\mu\nu}$ which constitute the elements of each matrix $\Gamma^X$:

$$\sum_X \Gamma^X_{\mu\nu}\Gamma^X_{\rho\sigma} = 4\delta_{\mu\sigma}\delta_{\nu\rho}, \tag{10.3}$$

‡ The formal way to make sure that a description will be consistent with charge conservation is to demand its invariance to 'gauge' transformations. These stem from the familiar fact that the potential $A_\alpha(x_\alpha)+\partial\chi(x_\alpha)/\partial x_\alpha$ describes the same electromagnetic field as does $A_\alpha$ itself, with a $\chi$ which may be chosen arbitrarily if only it is propagated according to the wave equation $\partial^2\chi/\partial x_\alpha^2 = 0$. The concurrent transformation of a field $\psi_a$ with quanta of charge $e_a$ must be $\psi_a \rightarrow \psi_a \exp(ie_a\chi/\hbar c)$ if field equations like the Dirac equation (3.72) are to remain unchanged by the change of gauge. A consequence of the invariance is that the $e_a$'s will be involved only in charge-conserving relationships. To maintain this, every new interaction which is introduced must be invariant to the gauge transformation as extended to all fields.

§ M. Fierz, *Ann. f. Physik*, **104**, 553 (1937).

|| W. Pauli, *Ann. Inst. Poincaré*, **6**, 109 (1936).

with the sum including elements from each of the matrices listed in (10.2). As a consequence:

$$[(\bar{\psi}_{\mathrm{p}}\,\Gamma^X)_\alpha(\psi_\nu)_\alpha][(\bar{\psi}_{\mathrm{e}}\,\Gamma^X)_\beta(\psi_{\mathrm{n}})_\beta]$$
$$= (\bar{\psi}_{\mathrm{p}}\,\Gamma^X)_\alpha\,\delta_{\alpha\gamma}(\psi_\nu)_\gamma(\bar{\psi}_{\mathrm{e}}\,\Gamma^X)_\beta\,\delta_{\beta\delta}(\psi_{\mathrm{n}})_\delta$$
$$= \tfrac{1}{4}\sum_Y [(\bar{\psi}_{\mathrm{p}}\,\Gamma^X)_\alpha\,\Gamma^Y_{\alpha\delta}(\psi_n)_\delta][(\bar{\psi}_{\mathrm{e}}\,\Gamma^X)_\beta\,\Gamma^Y_{\beta\gamma}(\psi_\nu)_\gamma].$$

Thus, pairings $(\psi_{\mathrm{p}}, \psi_\nu)$ and $(\psi_{\mathrm{e}}, \psi_{\mathrm{n}})$ are broken up and replaced by pairings $(\psi_{\mathrm{p}}, \psi_{\mathrm{n}})$ and $(\psi_{\mathrm{e}}, \psi_\nu)$. The new operations coupling each pair are products $\Gamma^X\Gamma^Y$ each of which can only be, within a phase, some one of the 16 matrices $\Gamma^X$ again. In this way, it turns out that transposing $\psi_{\mathrm{n}}$ and $\psi_\nu$ in (10.1) leaves the expression unchanged except for the substitutions:

$$\left.\begin{aligned}
C_{\mathrm{S}} &\to \tfrac{1}{4}(C_{\mathrm{S}}+4C_{\mathrm{V}}+6C_{\mathrm{T}}+4C_{\mathrm{A}}+C_{\mathrm{P}})\\
C_{\mathrm{V}} &\to \tfrac{1}{4}(C_{\mathrm{S}}-2C_{\mathrm{V}}\phantom{+6C_{\mathrm{T}}}+2C_{\mathrm{A}}-C_{\mathrm{P}})\\
C_{\mathrm{T}} &\to \tfrac{1}{4}(C_{\mathrm{S}}\phantom{-2C_{\mathrm{V}}}-2C_{\mathrm{T}}\phantom{+2C_{\mathrm{A}}}+C_{\mathrm{P}})\\
C_{\mathrm{A}} &\to \tfrac{1}{4}(C_{\mathrm{S}}+2C_{\mathrm{V}}\phantom{+6C_{\mathrm{T}}}-2C_{\mathrm{A}}-C_{\mathrm{P}})\\
C_{\mathrm{P}} &\to \tfrac{1}{4}(C_{\mathrm{S}}-4C_{\mathrm{V}}+6C_{\mathrm{T}}-4C_{\mathrm{A}}+C_{\mathrm{P}})
\end{aligned}\right\}. \tag{10.4}$$

There is merely a renaming of coupling constants; the same physical results can be expressed in both ways.

In the particular case $C_{\mathrm{A}} = -C_{\mathrm{V}}$ and $C_{\mathrm{S}} = C_{\mathrm{T}} = C_{\mathrm{P}} = 0$, the energy density expression (10.1) merely changes sign in the transpositions $\mathrm{n} \leftrightarrow \nu$ or $\mathrm{p} \leftrightarrow \mathrm{e}^-$. This circumstance may seem to endow the V–A Law with particular significance. However, four other combinations have comparable properties, as can be found by diagonalizing the matrix implicit in (10.4). The possibility of using invariance under transpositions among the fields as a basis for singling out the correct coupling was explored extensively‡ without decisive results.

*'Odd' couplings and field 'types'*

The energy density expression (10.1) was constructed so as to be invariant to changes of reference frame. Such distinctions as between scalars and pseudoscalars were made in order that invariance could be maintained even in transformations between right- and left-handed frames. However, this presumes that all the spinor fields behave alike in such 'improper' transformations.

The behaviour necessary to a Dirac spinor follows from its having to obey the Dirac equation (3.72), whatever the frame to which it may be

‡ In many papers beginning with C. Critchfield's, *Phys. Rev.* **63,** 417 (1943), and continuing through E. Caianello's, *Nuovo Cim.* **8,** 749 (1952), in which references to earlier work can be found.

referred. It is the behaviour under space-inversion which will be considered specifically since any transformation between right- and left-handed frames (including mirrorings in any plane) can be compounded out of a reversal of the spatial axes and a proper rotation.

The description of the behaviour will be formulated in such a way that the $\gamma_\alpha$ occurring in the Dirac equation is treated‡ as merely providing numerical coefficients for the successive terms of the four component equations. Then

$$[\gamma_\alpha(\partial/\partial x'_\alpha + ieA'_\alpha/\hbar c) + mc/\hbar]\psi'(x') = 0, \tag{10.5}$$

where $x'_\alpha$ $(\mathbf{r}', x'_4)$ has the components $\mathbf{r}' = -\mathbf{r}$, $x'_4 = ict = x_4$, and $e\mathbf{A}' = -e\mathbf{A}$, $eA'_4 = ie\phi = eA_4$. An operator $P$ is to be sought such that $\psi'(x'_\alpha) = P\psi(x_\alpha)$ describes the same state relative to the new frame as $\psi$ describes relative to the old. In order that the equation (10.5) for $P\psi$ follow from (3.72) for $\psi$, application of $P$ to the latter must yield

$$[\boldsymbol{\gamma}\cdot(-\boldsymbol{\nabla} - ie\mathbf{A}/\hbar c) + \gamma_4(\partial/\partial x_4 + ie\mathbf{A}_4/\hbar c) + mc/\hbar]P\psi = 0.$$

Accordingly, $P$ must be such an operator that

$$P\boldsymbol{\gamma} = -\boldsymbol{\gamma}P \quad \text{and} \quad P\gamma_4 = +\gamma_4 P.$$

Any operator which does not commute with all the $\gamma$'s must have some form of the type (2.91). The conditions on $P$ found here are sufficient to narrow (2.91) down to just

$$P = \eta\gamma_4, \tag{10.6}$$

where $\eta$ is an arbitrary complex number. This number must be chosen to have a unit modulus in order to preserve the normalization of $\psi$ (equivalently, $P^\dagger P = 1$ is necessary for the transformation to be unitary).

Phase factors analogous to $\eta$ are easy to determine for the proper, continuous transformations, such as the ordinary rotations. The corresponding operators must properly approach unity in the limit of vanishing rotation angles. However, the best that can be done for discontinuous transformations like space-inversions is to require that two successive applications of the operation restore the original description. If $P^2 = 1$ is thus required, then two types of behaviour are open to the spinor, corresponding to $\eta = \pm 1$. Two distinct (mathematically, at least) types§ of spinor fields become definable, with the properties $P\psi = \gamma_4\psi$

‡ Some such convention must be adopted for definiteness. There is always the possibility of changing the matrix representation simultaneously with the frame. The choice here corresponds to using the same matrix of coefficients for representing $\gamma_{z'}$, say, after the frame change, as was used for $\gamma_z$ before it.

§ A formal term, introduced by C. N. Yang and J. Tiomno (*Phys. Rev.* **79**, 495 (1950)) in the original paper drawing the distinctions discussed here.

and $P\psi = -\gamma_4\psi$, respectively. Actually, $P^2\psi = -\psi$ is equally acceptable. This is because the Dirac, as also the Pauli, spinors provide two-valued descriptions, in the sense that ordinary continuous rotations by 360° result in $\psi \to -\psi$ rather than $\psi \to +\psi$. The 'original description' is sufficiently restored when $P^2 = -1$ and so two more 'types' of spinor field may exist: such that $P\psi = i\gamma_4\psi$ or $P\psi = -i\gamma_4\psi$.

In view of these findings, it becomes a question whether it is $(\bar{\psi}_e\psi_\nu)$ that is a scalar and $(\bar{\psi}_e\gamma_5\psi_\nu)$ a pseudoscalar, or vice versa. Neither may conform to the usual conception of scalars as quantities which change not at all, and of pseudoscalars as changing only in sign, during space inversions. In general,

$$(\bar{\psi}'_e\psi'_\nu) = \eta_e^*\eta_\nu(\bar{\psi}_e\psi_\nu) \quad \text{and} \quad (\bar{\psi}'_e\gamma_5\psi'_\nu) = -\eta_e^*\eta_\nu(\bar{\psi}_e\gamma_5\psi_\nu),$$

since $\gamma_5$ anticommutes with $P = \eta\gamma_4$. Accordingly, the usual classifications apply if the electron and neutrino fields are of the same type, so that $\eta_e^*\eta_\nu = +1$. If $\eta_e^*\eta_\nu = -1$, then it is $(\bar{\psi}_e\gamma_5\psi_\nu)$ that is invariant, and $(\bar{\psi}_e\psi_\nu)$ behaves like a pseudoscalar. Moreover, $\eta_e^*\eta_\nu = \pm i$ are also possible, and then neither product fits the usual classifications. Similar considerations apply to the distinction between vector and pseudovector, and to the question of whether it is the three space–space components of the tensor which form an axial 3-vector (the remaining three a polar one) or the three space-time components. In any event, it becomes clear that the expression

$$\sum_X C'_X(\bar{\psi}_p\Gamma^X\psi_n).(\bar{\psi}_e\Gamma^X\gamma_5\psi_\nu)+\text{h.c.} \tag{10.7}$$

has as valid a claim to invariance as does (10.1). It is unchanged by space inversion if the fields are of such types that $\eta_p^*\eta_n\eta_e^*\eta_\nu = -1$, whereas it is (10.1) which is invariant if $\eta_p^*\eta_n\eta_e^*\eta_\nu = +1$.

The terms of (10.7) are called the 'odd' couplings. Notice that they exhaust the possibilities arising from the present considerations since factors like $(\bar{\psi}_p\Gamma^X\gamma_5\psi_n)$ are already implicit in both (10.1) and (10.7). It may also be remarked that the superposition of odd couplings (10.7) is changed no more essentially by interpermutations of the fields in it than was (10.1); the 'Fierz transformation' yields exactly the same relations among the $C'_X$ as (10.4) among the $C_X$.

The even and odd coupling forms (10.1) and (10.7) can be regarded as differing only by the substitution of $\gamma_5\psi_\nu$ by $\psi_\nu$. This amounts to a relative phase change (by $\pi$) in the way that neutrino wave components of opposite chirality $\gamma_5\phi_{L,R} = \pm\phi_{L,R}$, enter into the coupling. Since

$\gamma_5 \psi_\nu$ and $\psi_\nu$ obey the same, massless Dirac equation,

$$\gamma_\alpha \partial\psi_\nu/\partial x_\alpha = 0, \tag{10.8}$$

it can obviously be arranged for the odd couplings to yield the same physically observable results as the even ones. For this reason the odd couplings were long regarded as merely furnishing an alternative manner of formulating the descriptions, rather than as offering the possibility of ones not encompassable through the use of the even couplings only.

*Parity non-conservation*

There are genuine physical consequences when a combination of the odd with the even couplings is admitted:

$$h_\beta = 2^{-\frac{1}{2}}g \sum_X (\bar{\psi}_p \Gamma^X \psi_n).[\bar{\psi}_e \Gamma^X (C_X + C'_X \gamma_5)\psi_\nu] + \text{h.c.} \tag{10.9}$$

Now, whether the field types are such that $\eta_p^* \eta_n \eta_e^* \eta_\nu$ is $+1$ or $-1$, the expression is *not* invariant to space inversions; there is a relative sign change of the odd and even coupling terms. This will not affect physical results in the form of intensities proportional to any $C_X^2$ or any $(C'_Y)^2$, but odd–even interference contributions proportional to $C_X C'_Y$ will have opposite signs when referred to space-inverted reference frames. Whereas a reflection-invariant formulation can only yield observable intensity components which are proper scalars, expressible as proportional to $\mathbf{q}.\mathbf{v}/c$ or $\boldsymbol{\sigma}.\mathbf{I}$ say, the present one offers the possibility of intensity components with a pseudoscalar behaviour, like $\boldsymbol{\sigma}.\mathbf{v}/c$ or $\mathbf{I}.\mathbf{q}$. (See Chapter 1 for the significances of all these.)

The failure of the physical consequences of a formalism to be invariant to space-inversions was long considered an adequate reason for discarding the formalism. Such a failure was considered comparable to accepting the possibility that experiments done at different locations could give different results (non-invariance to translations in a homogeneous space), or that experimental results could depend on the orientation of the apparatus (failure of invariance to rotations in an isotropic space), or that experiments could give different results at different times (non-invariance to translation in time). It was expected that the mirror image of a given physical process should also be a possible process, whenever arranged for. That this was implied by the accepted theoretical procedures was pointed out by Lee and Yang (ref. p. 3), and they stressed the need for verifying it experimentally for each new type of interaction. The outcome for the $\beta$-processes has already been discussed, beginning with Fig. 1.10. This was concerned with $\beta$-sources which are isotropic, yet produce left-handedly polarized negatrons without an equal production of their ostensible mirror-images: right-handedly polarized ones.

The expectation of invariance to a frame transformation is described in more physical terms as a conservation principle. What remains constant in the transformation can be distinguished for each isolated system, and this leads to the definability of a conserved quantity. Thus, invariance under space-time frame translations enables identifying constants which form the conserved momentum-energy. The definition of a conserved angular momentum is enabled by invariance to frame rotation. Analogously, invariance to space-inversion is spoken of as the conservation of parity, already illustrated for nucleonic systems in formulating the selection rules of Chapters V and VI. The conserved 'quantity' now is simply the evenness or oddness in spatial variables, of descriptions using the variables.

The conservation of parity in the strong internucleonic interactions responsible for nuclear binding, and in the intermediate electromagnetic interactions, has been established to a high degree of precision. It accounts for the efficacy of the parity selection rules, in transitions between nuclear or atomic states. However, the lepton fields produced in $\beta$-processes fail to retain definite parities and this is responsible for the 'non-conservation' of parity exhibited by the results.

The failures of parity conservation are exhibited formally by the behaviour under the space inversion operations,‡ $P$, of the descriptions of the intensities. Thus the analysis of the intensity into negatron polarizations had to be represented by proportionality to $1-\boldsymbol{\sigma}.\mathbf{v}/c$, and $P(1-\boldsymbol{\sigma}.\mathbf{v}/c) = 1+\boldsymbol{\sigma}.\mathbf{v}/c$, rather than $P \equiv 1$. Another instance is provided by the electron angular distribution, proportional to $1+A\hat{\mathbf{I}}.\mathbf{v}/c$, which is changed to $1-A\hat{\mathbf{I}}.\mathbf{v}/c$ by the parity operation $P$, instead of remaining invariant. The electron-neutrino correlation distributions $\sim 1+a\hat{\mathbf{q}}.\mathbf{v}/c$ do remain invariant ($P \equiv 1$ for them) and represent a type of result known long before the failure of parity conservation was discovered.

Any results of the even couplings alone, or the odd couplings by themselves, are invariant to the space inversions. Thus, the discovery of parity non-conservation actually requires description by some combination of odd and even couplings as in (10.9). At least one product of coupling constants like $C_X C'_Y$ must not vanish if the observed results

‡ The *formal* effect of $P$ varies with the type of quantity (scalar, spinor, vector, etc.) on which it operates.

are to be represented. Exactly what combination is needed will be discussed next.

*Experimental evidence about the couplings*

According to the preceding chapters, an adequate description of what is known about the nuclear $\beta$-processes is afforded by the 'renormalized V–A law'. This was adopted initially because it provides for each field to interact in proportion to its $\gamma_5 = +1$ projection, as seemed to be indicated by the experimental evidence. It corresponds to a special case of the generalized law (10.9) for which

$$C_{S,T,P} = C'_{S,T,P} = 0 \quad \text{and} \quad C'_{V,A} = C_{V,A}; \tag{10.10}$$

in (10.9), $C'_X = C_X$ provides for projections by $\frac{1}{2}(1+\gamma_5)$ of the neutrino field, but $C'_{S,T,P} = C_{S,T,P} \neq 0$ would give projections by $\frac{1}{2}(1-\gamma_5)$ of the electron field. The concern now is to see just how necessary, as well as sufficient, this formulation is.

The proper way of bringing the observational evidence to bear is through comparisons with expectations derived from the coupling (10.9), in all its generality, for the specific experiments. This amounts to treating the data as measurements of the various coupling constants $C_X$, $C'_X$, and each is then determined only within some margin of error. However, what is being sought is a consistent theory which it would be promising to use in future applications. Accordingly, whenever some coupling constant, or combination of coupling constants, turns out small enough for its neglect to be compatible with the evidence, then it will be set equal to zero.

How the various expectations are derived from couplings like (10.9) has been adequately illustrated in the preceding chapters, so it will suffice now merely to quote results.‡

First it turns out that the general coupling leads to an *allowed spectrum* which departs from the statistical shape of (1.10) and (5.45), by an extra factor

$$1 \pm \gamma_0 b(mc^2/W) \quad \text{for } e^{\mp}. \tag{10.11}$$

Aside from this factor, the spectrum expression is just (5.45) with $\xi \equiv \xi_F + \xi_{GT}$, these being

$$\left.\begin{aligned} \xi_F &= \tfrac{1}{2}[(|C_V|^2+|C'_V|^2)+(|C_S|^2+|C'_S|^2)]\langle 1\rangle^2 \\ \xi_{GT} &= \tfrac{1}{2}[(|C_A|^2+|C'_A|^2)+(|C_T|^2+|C'_T|^2)]\langle \sigma\rangle^2 \end{aligned}\right\}, \tag{10.12}$$

‡ See the reference of the footnote on p. 129, for example.

in place of (5.39). The so-called 'Fierz interference' coefficient,

$$b \equiv (\xi_F b_F + \xi_{GT} b_{GT})/\xi,$$

is given by

$$\left.\begin{aligned} \xi_F b_F &= \tfrac{1}{2}[C_S^* C_V + (C_S')^* C_V' + \text{c.c.}]\langle 1\rangle^2 \\ \xi_{GT} b_{GT} &= \tfrac{1}{2}[C_T^* C_A + (C_T')^* C_A' + \text{c.c.}]\langle \sigma\rangle^2 \end{aligned}\right\}. \tag{10.13}$$

The constants $C_P$, $C_P'$ are absent from these results because their largest contributions may be classified as once-forbidden rather than allowed; $\Gamma^P \equiv \gamma_5$ in (10.9) and the nucleon 'current' $(\bar{\psi}_p \gamma_5 \psi_n)$ requires the nuclear parity to change if the leptons take no orbital momentum. The subscripts F and GT refer to the experimentally distinguishable Fermi (allowed singlet) and Gamow–Teller (allowed triplet) radiations. Finally, complex values of the coupling constants have been provided for; the significance of that will be taken up in the next section.

The measured allowed spectra conform to the statistical shape within limits narrow enough to permit the conclusion‡ that $|b_F| < 0{\cdot}2$ and $|b_{GT}| < 0{\cdot}2$. More stringent limits are imposed by certain rate measurements. The expectations for the comparative half-life (5.46) are obviously to be modified by the proportionality

$$(ft)^{-1} \sim 1 \pm \gamma_0 b\langle mc^2/W\rangle, \tag{10.14}$$

where $\langle W^{-1}\rangle$ is the spectrum average of the inverse electron energy. This leads to a systematic variation of the comparative half-life, $ft$, with the nuclear energy release. Sherr and Gerhart§ have pointed out that the constancy of the $ft$-values observed for the $0^+ \to 0^+$ transitions among the isobaric triads (§ 1.5) requires $|b_F| < 0{\cdot}1$. Sherr and Miller|| found the narrowest limits on $b_{GT}$ by taking advantage of the fact that the Fierz interference has opposite signs in positron emission and negatron ($K$-) capture. The ratio (8.19) is modified to

$$\lambda_K/\lambda_+ \approx \tfrac{1}{2}\pi(W_0+1)^2 g_K^2(1+b)/f(1-b\langle W^{-1}\rangle) \tag{10.15}$$

by the Fierz interference ($m = c = \hbar = 1$ here). An accurate check was feasible for the $3^+ \to 2^+$ transition of $Na^{22}$, which gave

$$b_{GT} = -0{\cdot}01 \pm 0{\cdot}02.$$

These results make it implausible to continue with a theory for which $b_F$ and $b_{GT}$ exist. The corresponding combinations of coupling constants (10.13) are best assumed to be zero.

Second, consider the general expectations for the allowed *electron-neutrino correlation* distribution, $\sim (1 + a\hat{\mathbf{q}}\,.\,\mathbf{v}/c)$. The correlation coeffi-

‡ H. M. Mahmoud and E. J. Konopinski, *Phys. Rev.* **88,** 1266 (1952).
§ Ibid. **109,** 897 (1958). || Ibid. **93,** 1076 (1954).

cient given by (5.42) is now to be replaced by $a \equiv (\xi_F a_F + \xi_{GT} a_{GT})/\xi$ with

$$\left.\begin{aligned} \xi_F a_F &= \tfrac{1}{2}[(|C_V|^2+|C'_V|^2)-(|C_S|^2+|C'_S|^2)]\langle 1\rangle^2 \\ \xi_{GT} a_{GT} &= -\tfrac{1}{6}[(|C_A|^2+|C'_A|^2)-(|C_T|^2+|C'_T|^2)]\langle \sigma\rangle^2 \end{aligned}\right\}. \tag{10.16}$$

A small coulomb correction may exist, but not exceeding a tenth of present ranges of uncertainty in the measurements, hence it is ignored here. The measurements on the Gamow–Teller transitions exhibited in Fig. 1.14 leave no room for positive values of $|C_T|^2+|C'_T|^2$ at all. This indicates $C'_T = C_T = 0$ and, *a fortiori*, $b_{GT} = 0$ as well. The $A^{35}$ measurement leads to

$$|C_S|^2+|C'_S|^2 < 0{\cdot}1(|C_V|^2+|C'_V|^2),$$

hence $C'_S = C_S = 0$ and $b_F = 0$ are also indicated.

The experiments considered here so far are independent of whether parity is conserved or not, and so have nothing to say about the proportions in which the odd and even couplings may exist. The information must come from measuring pseudoscalar components of intensity, which can be held to owe their existence to interferences between the odd and even couplings. Pertinent data come from *longitudinal electron polarizations*, $\mathscr{P} \equiv (\xi_F \mathscr{P}_F + \xi_{GT} \mathscr{P}_{GT})/\xi$. The expectations for $\mathscr{P}$ include as a factor $(1 \pm \gamma_0 bmc^2/W)^{-1}$, if Fierz interference exists, but $b = 0$ will be assumed already established in the expressions

$$\left.\begin{aligned} \xi_F \mathscr{P}_F &= \mp(v/c).\tfrac{1}{2}[C_V^* C'_V - C_S^* C'_S + \text{c.c.}]\langle 1\rangle^2 \\ \xi_{GT} \mathscr{P}_{GT} &= \mp(v/c).\tfrac{1}{2}[C_A^* C'_A - C_T^* C'_T + \text{c.c.}]\langle \sigma\rangle^2 \end{aligned}\right\} \tag{10.17}$$

applying to $e^{\mp}$ emissions, respectively. Again, an unobservably small coulomb correction has been omitted. These expressions are simpler to contemplate when written in terms of the 'left-' and 'right-handed' combinations:

$$\left.\begin{aligned} L_{V,A} &= \tfrac{1}{2}(C_{V,A}+C'_{V,A}), \qquad & R_{V,A} &= \tfrac{1}{2}(C_{V,A}-C'_{V,A}) \\ L_{S,T} &= \tfrac{1}{2}(C_{S,T}-C'_{S,T}), \qquad & R_{S,T} &= \tfrac{1}{2}(C_{S,T}+C'_{S,T}) \end{aligned}\right\}, \tag{10.18}$$

with which

$$\left.\begin{aligned} \xi_F &= [(|L_V|^2+|L_S|^2)+(|R_V|^2+|R_S|^2)]\langle 1\rangle^2 \\ \xi_{GT} &= [(|L_A|^2+|L_T|^2)+(|R_A|^2+|R_T|^2)]\langle \sigma\rangle^2 \end{aligned}\right\}. \tag{10.19}$$

Then (10.17) becomes

$$\left.\begin{aligned} \xi_F \mathscr{P}_F &= \mp(v/c)[(|L_V|^2+|L_S|^2)-(|R_V|^2+|R_S|^2)]\langle 1\rangle^2 \\ \xi_{GT} \mathscr{P}_{GT} &= \mp(v/c)[(|L_A|^2+|L_T|^2)-(|R_A|^2+|R_T|^2)]\langle \sigma\rangle^2 \end{aligned}\right\}. \tag{10.20}$$

The measurements already quoted in (1.28) give $\mathscr{P} = \mp v/c$ for either Fermi or Gamow–Teller emissions, with margins of error ranging down from $\sim$ 10 per cent. This corresponds to

$$|R_{\mathrm{V,A}}|^2+|R_{\mathrm{S,T}}|^2 < 0{\cdot}1(|L_{\mathrm{V,A}}|^2+|L_{\mathrm{S,T}}|^2). \tag{10.21}$$

The best assumption becomes that the left-hand sides vanish, hence each positive-definite part vanishes: $R_{\mathrm{V}} = R_{\mathrm{A}} = R_{\mathrm{S}} = R_{\mathrm{T}} = 0$. The last two give $C'_{\mathrm{S,T}} = -C_{\mathrm{S,T}}$ but the preceding evidence already indicated that the Scalar and Tensor couplings are negligible. The important additional results are

$$C'_{\mathrm{V}} = C_{\mathrm{V}} \quad \text{and} \quad C'_{\mathrm{A}} = C_{\mathrm{A}}. \tag{10.22}$$

These may hold irrespective of any complexity which these constants may have.

It is the evidence so far outlined here that is chiefly relied on to show that the Scalar and Tensor couplings play no appreciable role in nuclear β-decay, and that it is the 'left-handed' ($\gamma_5 = +1$) combination (see (10.9) and (10.22)) of the odd and even Vector and Pseudovector couplings that operates. This evidence is the most directly interpretable in terms of relationships among the coupling constants, but a vast body of additional evidence lends support to the same conclusions. It consists of the experimental confirmations of all the expectations already found in the preceding chapters.

*The Pseudoscalar coupling*

Two outstanding points remain to be settled. One is the question raised as to the possible complexity of the coupling constants and will be taken up in the next section. The other has to do with the possible existence of the Pseudoscalar coupling, $\sim C_{\mathrm{P}}$, $C'_{\mathrm{P}}$; the evidence reviewed above was not expected to pertain to it.

The transition amplitude generated by the Pseudoscalar parts of the coupling (10.9) may quite obviously be written

$$2^{\frac{1}{2}}gC_{\mathrm{P}} \int \beta\gamma_5 J_{\mathrm{P}}, \tag{10.23 a}$$

in a notation like that of (5.3). The lepton density here is

$$J_{\mathrm{P}} = \tfrac{1}{2}\psi_{\mathrm{e}}^{\dagger}\beta(\gamma_5+C'_{\mathrm{P}}/C_{\mathrm{P}})\psi_{\nu} \tag{10.23 b}$$

for $e^-$ emissions.

The last expression makes clear a property of the Pseudoscalar coupling which is also shared by the Scalar and Tensor couplings. All these produce normal neutrinos and negatrons of opposite handedness (so also for antineutrinos and positrons). When $C'_{\mathrm{P}} = +C_{\mathrm{P}}$ is chosen, the normal neutrinos are left-handed, but, since $\gamma_5$ anticommutes with $\beta$, negatrons are produced in proportion to $\frac{1}{2}(1-\gamma_5)\psi_e$, i.e. with predominantly right-handed helicity. The choice $C'_P = -C_P$ gives predominantly left-handed negatrons, but then the neutrinos are right-handed. Such results are contradicted by the evidence reviewed above, on the electron polarizations conjoined with the electron-neutrino correlations, but that could immediately serve to eliminate only the Scalar and Tensor couplings; the effects of Pseudoscalar coupling were not given a chance to show themselves.

Cases in which the Pseudoscalar coupling may have its greatest effect should be identifiable from the nuclear moments in the amplitude (10.23 a). The largest effects are usually expected to be those which do not depend for their existence on variations of the long lepton wavelengths over the small nuclear volume; that prompted the evaluation of the lepton waves at the nuclear centre when forming the allowed approximation, and carries with it a neglect of leptonic orbital momenta. When $J_P$ is set equal to its value at the nuclear centre in the amplitude (10.23 a), it becomes proportional to the moment $\langle\beta\gamma_5\rangle$. Because of the Pseudoscalar character of the operation in this moment it can contribute only to $0^-$ transitions. For this reason, such putative $0^- \to 0^+$ transitions as those of $Pr^{144}$ and $Ho^{166}$ were examined‡ most thoroughly; in these cases, the possible Pseudoscalar effects suffer substantial competition only from the Pseudovector coupling, through $C_A\langle\gamma_5\rangle$ and $C_A\langle i\boldsymbol{\sigma}.\hat{\mathbf{r}}\rangle$ as in (7.41). The electron polarizations and the spectra have been measured accurately in these cases and no deviations from the V–A Law expectations could be established. However, such considerations put immediate upper limits on the product $|C_P\langle\beta\gamma_5\rangle|$ rather than on $C_P$ itself. Only if it can be presumed that $\langle\beta\gamma_5\rangle$ is of an order comparable to $\langle\gamma_5\rangle$, say, can the experiments be said to contradict the existence of a $C_P$ comparable to $C_A$ in magnitude.

Estimates of the kind which led to $\langle\gamma_5\rangle \approx -\langle\boldsymbol{\sigma}.\mathbf{P}+\boldsymbol{\sigma}.\mathbf{P}\rangle/2Mc$ in § 7.4 here yield $\langle\beta\gamma_5\rangle \approx -\langle\boldsymbol{\sigma}.\mathbf{P}-\boldsymbol{\sigma}.\mathbf{P}\rangle/2Mc = 0$. This is enough to show that $\langle\beta\gamma_5\rangle$ is much smaller than $\langle\gamma_5\rangle$ unless there is reason to question the approximation of taking the small nuclear state components as generated from the large via the operation $(\boldsymbol{\sigma}.\mathbf{P})/2Mc$. There is no incontrovertible evidence on this point, but conventional treatments lead to the conclusion that indeed $|\langle\beta\gamma_5\rangle| \ll |\langle\gamma_5\rangle|$. If this is so, it becomes possible that the largest Pseudoscalar effects may after

‡ Perhaps most exhaustively by C. P. Bhalla and M. E. Rose, *Phys. Rev.* **120,** 1415 (1960).

all depend on the variations of the lepton waves across the nucleus. When this was assumed for the evaluations of the $0^-$ transitions, the upper limit $|C_P| < \frac{1}{20}(M/m)|C_A|$ was found (ref. p. 273). According to this, a Pseudoscalar coupling constant almost 100 times as large as the Pseudovector one would have escaped detection in the experiments.

If, as seems to be the case, the Pseudoscalar coupling has the best chance to show itself through effects arising from variations of the lepton waves across the nucleus, then its easiest detectability may no longer lie in the $0^-$ transitions. The non-relativistic approximation procedure applied above more generally yields

$$\int \beta\gamma_5 J_P \approx \int [\boldsymbol{\sigma}.\mathbf{P}, J_P]/2Mc \approx -(i\hbar/2Mc)\int \boldsymbol{\sigma}.(\nabla J_P). \quad (10.24)$$

By evaluating the lepton density gradient at the nuclear centre, it can be seen that this yields its largest contributions in the allowed triplet ($1^+$) transitions generated through the Gamow–Teller moment, $\int \boldsymbol{\sigma}$. The best chance of detection then arises if this Pseudoscalar contribution is able to interfere with the main triplet emissions $\sim C_A \int \boldsymbol{\sigma}$. Such interference is impossible if $C'_P = -C_P$, for the totally right-handed neutrino wave would be orthogonal to the left-handed waves known to emerge in the main transition. This type of argument does not apply to the electron waves of the $C'_P = C_P$ case since those are polarized only within the fraction $v/c$. Thus, Pseudoscalar couplings with $C'_P \neq -C_P$ should be detectable through the interference effects.

The interference of a Pseudoscalar coupling with allowed triplet emissions would lead to the longitudinal electron polarization

$$\mathscr{P} \approx \mp(v/c)\{1+[(C_P+C'_P)/C_A](m/3M)(1-W_0/2W)\}, \quad (10.25\text{ a})$$

if the correction to $\mp v/c$ is small. The corresponding electron-neutrino correlation coefficient is

$$a \approx -\tfrac{1}{3}\{1-[(C_P+C'_P)/C_A](m/3M)(1+W_0/2W)\}. \quad (10.25\text{ b})$$

About the greatest quoted accuracy is for the correlation measurement on $He^6$, which gives $a = -\frac{1}{3}$ within an uncertainty of only 1 per cent (ref. p. 42). This sets the upper limit $|C_P+C'_P| < \frac{1}{200}(M/m)|C_A|$ on the Pseudoscalar coupling constants. The effect on the spectrum is given by the shape-factor

$$S_0^{(1)} \approx C_A^2\langle\sigma\rangle^2\{1+[(C_P+C'_P)/C_A](m/6M)(W_0/W-1)\}. \quad (10.25\text{ c})$$

With the upper limits already set, the effect would have been undetectable in even the accurate $B^{12}$, $N^{12}$ spectrum measurements designed to detect weak-magnetism (§ 7.4).

The results indicate that even a Pseudoscalar coupling constant ten times as large as the Pseudovector one would have gone undetected in the experiments. However, this is so only if the Pseudoscalar effects appear in proportion to $(m/M)|C_{\mathrm{P}}^{(\prime)}| \approx (1/1836)|C_{\mathrm{P}}^{(\prime)})|$ and this is decidedly negligible. Clearly, the Pseudoscalar coupling should be ignored when genuine expectations are to be advanced.

There are also more speculative arguments against the existence of the Pseudoscalar coupling. It would lose for the $\beta$-processes the simple property of producing only 'left-handed' normal leptons. This is sometimes expressed as a loss of a certain type of invariance (to transformations by $\gamma_5$), as will be seen in the next section. Of course, expectations based on 'simplicity', characteristic of all demands for invariance, are sometimes disappointed (*vide* parity conservation) and cannot be held decisive.

The succeeding chapter will extend applications of the $\beta$-coupling law to processes other than nuclear $\beta$-decay. It will then be found that a Pseudoscalar component in the coupling would yield entirely wrong expectations for pion decay (predicting more electrons than muons as decay products, contrary to observations). Such an argument is naturally predicated on the assumption that the same form of coupling should operate in all the processes being compared.

## 10.2. Time reversal and 'joint' parity conservation

The $\beta$-couplings investigated in the preceding section were all constructed so as to yield physical expectations which are invariant to continuous changes, translations and rotations, of the space-time reference frame. Invariance to the discontinuous reversals of spatial axes had to be abandoned because of experimental findings. This arouses curiosity as to whether symmetries exist, in physically correct descriptions, toward a reversal of the remaining, time, axis. A physically important interpretation of 'time-reversal' has already been illustrated by Fig. 1.15. Convictions that physical descriptions should be invariant under time-reversal have perhaps never been as strong as the comparable expectations relative to space-inversion once were, yet all the basic physical theories always had exhibited invariance of both types, up to the more recent formulations of $\beta$-theory.

*Time-reversal transformations*‡

The interest here is in applications like the one discussed in connexion with Fig. 1.15. Time-reversal will be viewed as a means of transforming

‡ The understanding of these is due chiefly to Wigner (see reference on p. 182).

the description of a given physical situation to another which is different only in having all motions reversed. Advantage can be taken of the fact that the expectations for the situations of interest here are derived from a formalism which uses an individual spinor field for each type of particle.

A given spinor field $\psi(\mathbf{r},t)$ passes through a succession of states, 'phases of motion', as time goes on. It is to be compared to a 'transformed' field $\psi^T$ which describes passage through the same phases, but in reverse order in time. The relation of $\psi^T$ to $\psi$ could not be taken to be simply a proportionality $\psi^T(\mathbf{r},t) \sim \psi(\mathbf{r},-t)$ even if there were no 'inner' motions to describe (i.e. even if $\psi$ were a scalar field). Consider one of the independent, plane-wave components of the field,

$$\psi(\mathbf{r},t) \sim \exp i(\mathbf{p}.\mathbf{r}-Wt)/\hbar.$$

The reversed motion is then described by

$$\psi^T(\mathbf{r},t) \sim \exp i(-\mathbf{p}.\mathbf{r}-Wt)/\hbar.$$

Thus, the proportionality

$$\psi^T(\mathbf{r},t) \sim \psi^*(\mathbf{r},-t)$$

is to be expected as the means for describing the transformation arising from $t \to -t$, of the space-time part of the motion. There must be a concurrent transformation of the dependence on 'inner' variables, if their 'motion' is also to be reversed, and this may be effected by some Dirac operator $T$ such that

$$\psi^T(x_\alpha^T) \equiv \psi^T(\mathbf{r},-t) = T\psi^*(\mathbf{r},t) \equiv T\psi^*(x_\alpha), \tag{10.26}$$

where $x_\alpha(\mathbf{r},ict) \to x_\alpha^T(\mathbf{r},-ict) \equiv x_\alpha^*$. How $T$ is to be defined is considered next.

During phases in which there is no interaction with other fields, $\psi(\mathbf{r},t)$ develops according to the Dirac equation (2.72). The latter can be regarded as a collection of four equations for which $\boldsymbol{\alpha}$, $\beta$ merely provide numerical coefficients,‡ hence relating just space-time dependences. Then $\psi^T$ will describe all motions reversed if it obeys the same set of equations as $\psi(\mathbf{r},t)$ but with $-t$ replacing $t$:

$$-i\hbar\partial\psi^T/\partial t = [-i\hbar c\boldsymbol{\alpha}.\nabla+\beta mc^2]\psi^T. \tag{10.27 a}$$

This is to be compared with the complex conjugate of the equation for $\psi(\mathbf{r},t)$:

$$-i\hbar\partial\psi^*/\partial t = [+i\hbar c\boldsymbol{\alpha}^*.\nabla+\beta^* mc^2]\psi^*. \tag{10.27 b}$$

‡ See footnote on p. 265.

The two equations can be made consistent via the relation $\psi^T = T\psi^*$ if application of $T$ to the second gives the first. It will do so if

$$T\boldsymbol{\alpha}^* = -\boldsymbol{\alpha}T \quad \text{and} \quad T\beta^* = \beta T. \tag{10.28 a}$$

The same relations can be expressed in terms of $\boldsymbol{\gamma} = -i\beta\boldsymbol{\alpha}$ and $\gamma_4 = \beta$:

$$T\gamma_\alpha^* = \gamma_\alpha T. \tag{10.28 b}$$

The normalization is preserved, $(\psi^T)^\dagger\psi^T = \psi^\dagger\psi$, if

$$\tilde{T}T^* = 1 = T^\dagger T. \tag{10.28 c}$$

These conditions are sufficient to determine $T$ within an arbitrary phase, but no relation of $T$ to the $\gamma$'s can be expressed independently of the particular representation adopted for the $\gamma$'s. The reason is the same as in the case of the charge-conjugation (3.7), which also includes complex conjugation as part of the transformation. In the special Dirac representation $\boldsymbol{\alpha} = \rho_1\boldsymbol{\Sigma}$ and $\beta = \rho_3$ (2.66),

$$T = \zeta\Sigma_2, \tag{10.29}$$

where $\zeta$ is the arbitrary phase factor. The latter will be ignored since it plays no more essential a role for the considerations here than did the phase $\eta$ of the space-inversion transformation (10.6). That $T \sim \Sigma_2$ satisfies the conditions on $T$ is obvious; it is readily shown to be a unique way to satisfy them, in the Dirac representation, through finding the restrictions put by (10.28) on a general form like (2.61).

Suppose next that interactions of $\psi$ with an electromagnetic field $A_\alpha(\mathbf{r}, t)$ are admitted. Then $\psi(\mathbf{r}, t)$ is subject to the Dirac equation (3.74), but $\psi^T$ can no longer be said to satisfy the same equation as $\psi$ with $t \to -t$. This is because $A_\alpha(\mathbf{r}, -t)$ will not in general represent the motion-reversed situation any more than $\psi(\mathbf{r}, -t)$ does. Both can be said to have 'inner' degrees of freedom, represented by the multiplicity of components, which must also have their phases reversed in time. Some transformation $A_\alpha(\mathbf{A}, i\phi) \to A_\alpha^T(\mathbf{A}^T, i\phi^T)$ must be allowed for, and then

$$-i\hbar\partial\psi^T/\partial t = \{-i\hbar c\boldsymbol{\alpha}.[\boldsymbol{\nabla}+(ie/\hbar c)\mathbf{A}^T(\mathbf{r}, -t)]+\beta mc^2-e\phi^T(\mathbf{r}, -t)\}\psi^T \tag{10.30 a}$$

is the time-reversed transform of (3.74). The equation for $\psi^*$, after operation with $T$, yields

$$-i\hbar\partial\psi^T/\partial t = \{-i\hbar c\boldsymbol{\alpha}.[\boldsymbol{\nabla}-(ie/\hbar c)\mathbf{A}(\mathbf{r}, t)]+\beta mc^2-e\phi(\mathbf{r}, t)\}\psi^T. \tag{10.30 b}$$

The two equations are consistent when the electromagnetic field is transformed according to

$$\mathbf{A}^T(\mathbf{r}, -t) = -\mathbf{A}(\mathbf{r}, t), \qquad \phi^T(\mathbf{r}, t) = \phi(\mathbf{r}, -t). \tag{10.31}$$

This corresponds to $A^T_\alpha(x^T_\alpha) = -A^*_\alpha(x_\alpha)$, unlike the behaviour $x^T_\alpha = x^*_\alpha$ for a proper four-vector; a 'Pseudovector' behaviour relative to time-reversal can be said to be needed of $A_\alpha$ if there is to be time-reversal invariance in the form sought here. The same kind of behaviour has been implied for momenta, since $p_\alpha(\mathbf{p}, iW/c) \to p^T_\alpha(-\mathbf{p}, iW/c)$ in a motion reversal.

The behaviour $A_\alpha(\mathbf{A}, i\phi) \to A^T_\alpha(-\mathbf{A}, i\phi)$ should have been expected. The electromagnetic field may arise from a source current like $i_\alpha(\mathbf{i}, ic\rho)$; the motions in the source must be reversed, $\mathbf{i} \to -\mathbf{i}$, if their effect on the spinor field is to be reversed as desired. A like behaviour is impressed on the electromagnetic field via $\partial^2_\mu A_\alpha/\partial x^2_\mu = -4\pi i_\alpha/c$. The uniqueness of the entire formalism developed here, for a time-reversal transformation under which symmetry exists, follows from the fact that the electromagnetic current arising in a charged spinor field, $i_\alpha = -iec(\psi^\dagger\beta\gamma_\alpha\psi)$ according to (4.5), conforms to the above behaviour:

$$i^T_\alpha = -iec(\psi^T)^\dagger\beta\gamma_\alpha\psi^T = -iec\tilde{\psi}T^\dagger\beta\gamma_\alpha T\psi^*$$
$$= -iec\tilde{\psi}\beta^*\gamma^*_\alpha\psi^* \equiv -iec\psi^\dagger\gamma_\alpha\beta\psi,$$

since $T^\dagger T = 1$ and $\gamma^*_\alpha = \tilde{\gamma}_\alpha$. This result gives $\mathbf{i}^T = -\mathbf{i}$ and $i^T_4 = i_4$ $(\rho' = \rho)$, since $\boldsymbol{\gamma}\beta = -\beta\boldsymbol{\gamma}$ but $\gamma_4\beta = \beta\gamma_4 = 1$.

*Time-reversal of $\beta$-processes*

There remain to be found the conditions under which $\beta$-interactions will permit the symmetry under motion-reversal to persist. These can be found by comparing the general $\beta$-coupling form (10.9), giving an interaction of the spinor fields $\psi$, to this form when the time reversed states $\psi^T = T\psi^*$ are substituted for the $\psi$'s. The interaction in the latter case will be denoted $h^T_\beta$. When the 'h.c.' terms of (10.9) are written explicitly, they contain the complex conjugates of the coupling constants $C_X$, $C'_X$, if the latter are treated as complex. Then

$$h^T_\beta = 2^{-\frac{1}{2}}g\sum_X \{(\tilde{\psi}_p T^\dagger\beta\Gamma^X T\psi^*_n).[\tilde{\psi}_e T^\dagger\beta\Gamma^X(C_X + C'_X\gamma_5)T\psi^*_\nu] +$$
$$+(\tilde{\psi}_n T^\dagger\Gamma^X\beta T\psi^*_p).[\tilde{\psi}_\nu T^\dagger(C^*_X + C'^*_X\gamma_5)\Gamma^X\beta T\psi^*_e]\}. \quad (10.32)$$

Now $\gamma_5 T = T\gamma^*_5$ follows from $\gamma_\alpha T = T\gamma^*_\alpha$ and

$$\Gamma^{S,V,P}T = T(\Gamma^{S,V,P})^*, \qquad \Gamma^{T,A}T = -T(\Gamma^{T,A})^*$$

can be seen to follow from the definitions (10.2). All the hermitian operators have complex conjugates obtainable merely by transposition: $\Gamma^* = \tilde{\Gamma}$ if $\Gamma^\dagger = \Gamma$. When the spinor products in (10.32) are written in their transposed form, and $T^{\dagger}T = 1$ is eliminated, the expression becomes

$$h_{\beta}^{T} = 2^{-\frac{1}{2}}g\sum_{X}\{(\psi_{\mathrm{n}}^{\dagger}\Gamma^{X}\beta\psi_{\mathrm{p}}).[\psi_{\nu}^{\dagger}(C_{X}+C'_{X}\gamma_{5})\Gamma^{X}\beta\psi_{\mathrm{e}}]+ +(\psi_{\mathrm{p}}^{\dagger}\beta\Gamma^{X}\psi_{\mathrm{n}}).[\psi_{\mathrm{e}}^{\dagger}\beta\Gamma^{X}(C_{X}^{*}+C_{X}'^{*}\gamma_{5})\psi_{\nu}]\}. \quad (10.33)$$

This is the same as the original $h_{\beta}$ except for the interchanges $C_{X}\leftrightarrow C_{X}^{*}$ and $C'_{X}\leftrightarrow C_{X}'^{*}$. Thus, the $\beta$-interaction will generate motion-reversed states equally if the coupling constants are real. If an experimental contradiction of the symmetry were found, it would have to be represented by admitting complex coupling constants.

The above results show that the symmetry under time-reversal can be checked by observing effects of complexity in the coupling constants. It will be sufficient to consider such as follow from the coupling form with complex $C_{\mathrm{V}}$, $C_{\mathrm{A}}$, since the experiments reviewed in the preceding sections make it unpromising to rely on the existence of additional coupling constants. The effects surviving in the above experiments, observing electron-neutrino correlations or electron polarization, depend only on the absolute values of $C_{\mathrm{V}}$, $C_{\mathrm{A}}$. Consider, however, what follows from complex $C_{\mathrm{V,A}}$ for other intensity components of the types included in the general correlation distribution (1.53). The electron and neutrino anisotropy coefficients $A$ and $B$ are given by

$$\left.\begin{aligned} \xi(A-B) &= \mp 2\langle M_{\mathrm{S}}\rangle\langle\sigma\rangle^{2}|C_{\mathrm{A}}|^{2} \\ \xi(A+B) &= -2\langle 1\rangle\langle\sigma\rangle[I/(I+1)]^{\frac{1}{2}}(C_{\mathrm{V}}C_{\mathrm{A}}^{*}+C_{\mathrm{V}}^{*}C_{\mathrm{A}}) \end{aligned}\right\}, \quad (10.34\,\mathrm{a})$$

replacing (5.42), with

$$\xi = |C_{\mathrm{V}}|^{2}\langle 1\rangle^{2}+|C_{\mathrm{A}}|^{2}\langle\sigma\rangle^{2}. \quad (10.34\,\mathrm{b})$$

The purely Pseudovector anisotropy, given by the difference $A-B$, depends only on the absolute magnitude of $C_{\mathrm{A}}$ but the singlet-triplet *interference* effect, $A+B$, does depend on any phase differences between $C_{\mathrm{V}}$ and $C_{\mathrm{A}}$ which may exist, whether these be complex or not. If each coupling constant is given the form $C = |C|\exp i\phi$, then

$$\xi(A+B) = -4\langle 1\rangle\langle\sigma\rangle[I/(I+1)]^{\frac{1}{2}}|C_{\mathrm{V}}||C_{\mathrm{A}}|\cos(\phi_{\mathrm{A}}-\phi_{\mathrm{V}}). \quad (10.35)$$

Both $A$ and $B$ have been measured only for the neutron, as discussed in § 1.10. The numbers are $A+B = 0{\cdot}77\pm0{\cdot}17$, $I = \frac{1}{2}$, $\langle 1\rangle = 1$, $\langle\sigma\rangle = 3^{\frac{1}{2}}$, and $|C_{\mathrm{V}}|\,|C_{\mathrm{A}}|\,/\xi = 0{\cdot}27\pm0{\cdot}02$. They lead to

$$2\pi/3 \lesssim |\phi_{\mathrm{A}}-\phi_{\mathrm{V}}| \lesssim \pi.$$

A much more direct check of the time-reversal invariance was discussed in connexion with Fig. 1.15. It involved observation on the intensity fraction $D\hat{\mathbf{I}}.[\hat{\mathbf{q}}\times\mathbf{v}/c]$, for which the coupling with complex $C_{\mathrm{V,A}}$ has the result

$$\xi D = \langle 1\rangle\langle\sigma\rangle[I/(I+1)]^{\frac{1}{2}}.i(C_V C_{\mathrm{A}}^* - C_{\mathrm{V}}^* C_{\mathrm{A}})$$
$$= 2\langle 1\rangle\langle\sigma\rangle[I/(I+1)]^{\frac{1}{2}}|C_{\mathrm{V}}|\,|C_{\mathrm{A}}|\sin(\phi_{\mathrm{A}}-\phi_{\mathrm{V}}). \qquad (10.36)$$

The measurement $D = 0{\cdot}04 \pm 0{\cdot}07$, already quoted in § 1.10, makes it most plausible that $|\phi_{\mathrm{A}}-\phi_{\mathrm{V}}| = \pi$; the margin of error does not allow it to differ from 180° by more than 10° or so.

With $|\phi_{\mathrm{A}}-\phi_{\mathrm{V}}| = \pi$, the ratio $C_{\mathrm{A}}/C_{\mathrm{V}}$ is a negative real number, as presumed already in Chapter I. It should be remarked that it is sufficient that all ratios of coupling constants be real in order that only results consistent with time-reversal invariance be forthcoming. An overall phase factor in the interaction is not physically meaningful, since at least one of the fields may enter the interaction in arbitrary phase without altering any expectations.

*Charge conjugate β-processes*

The fact that the transformations to the charge conjugate states (3.77) and the time-reversed states (10.26) both include complex conjugation suggests looking for a relationship between them.

As a first step, the β-interaction of a given set of fermion states $\psi$, in the general form $h_\beta$ of (10.9), will be compared to the interaction of the charge conjugates $\psi^C = C\psi^*$ of the same states. Substitution of a $\psi^C$ for each $\psi$ in $h_\beta$ will have a result of the same appearance as $h_\beta^T$ of (10.32) except that the operator $C$ replaces $T$ everywhere. Then use can be made of the fact that

$$\Gamma^X C = \pm C(\Gamma^X)^* = \pm C\tilde{\Gamma}^X \qquad (10.37)$$

follows from the properties (3.76) of $C$, and the definitions (10.2) of the $\Gamma^X$. As indicated, the two sides of the relations (10.37) are of the same sign for some components $\Gamma^X$, of opposite signs for others. The sign does not matter since it is squared in forming the contractions needed in every coupling term of $h_\beta$. When the relations $\gamma_5 C = -C\gamma_5^*$ and $C^\dagger C = 1$ are also used, then

$$h_\beta^C = 2^{-\frac{1}{2}}g\sum_X \{[\psi_{\mathrm{n}}^\dagger \Gamma^X\beta\psi_{\mathrm{p}}].[\psi_\nu^\dagger(C_X - C_X'\gamma_5)\Gamma^X\beta\psi_{\mathrm{e}}] +$$
$$+[\psi_{\mathrm{p}}^\dagger\beta\Gamma^X\psi_{\mathrm{n}}].[\psi_{\mathrm{e}}^\dagger\beta\Gamma^X(C_X^* - C_X'^*\gamma_5)\psi_\nu]\} \qquad (10.38)$$

gives the interaction among the charge-conjugates $\psi^C = C\psi^*$, expressed in terms of the original fields $\psi$. It shows that the interaction is different by the interchanges $C_X \leftrightarrow C_X^*$, $C_X' \leftrightarrow C_X'^*$, and also by the relative signs of the odd and even couplings. The last is a manifestation of a fact already noted in Chapter III, that the charge-conjugate of a component with a definite helicity has the opposite helicity.

Conditions under which the $\beta$-interactions will be invariant to charge-conjugation can now be stated. The invariance will hold if the coupling constants are real and if only even couplings, or only odd couplings, exist. The coupling constants must be effectively real for the symmetry under time-reversal to hold, in agreement with the evidence in the preceding subsection. However, both odd and even couplings must be retained in order that results of the failure of parity conservation be represented. It follows that the *$\beta$-interactions are not invariant to charge-conjugation.*

On the other hand, consider the interaction of states formed by space-inversions of the charge conjugates,

$$\psi^{PC}(-\mathbf{r}, t) = PC\psi^*(\mathbf{r}, t). \qquad (10.39)$$

These differ at most by a phase from charge-conjugates of space-inverted states, since $PC = \eta\beta C = -\eta C\beta^*$. The interaction $h_\beta^{PC}$ among them will plainly be the same as $h_\beta^C$ of (10.38) except for the signs of the odd coupling constants, $C'_X$. Consequently, with the real constants characteristic of the time-reversal symmetry, the interactions among the transformed states $\psi^{PC}$ are the same as among the original ones $\psi$. The interaction is invariant to *joint* transformation by space-inversion and charge conjugation. This may be considered a modified principle of parity conservation, maintenance of a 'joint-parity'. It embodies an idea‡ already mentioned in the discussion attending Fig. 1.10, that the same results should be expected of experimental arrangements which are each other's mirror images if the mirror image of every particle is taken to be its antiparticle.

It appears that a straightforward experimental check of the joint-parity principle is beyond present means. It would require comparing sources such that one consists of antiparticles of the other, e.g. antineutron decay vs. neutron decay. Unfortunately, antineutrons cannot survive long enough in a medium of ordinary matter to allow the slow $\beta$-radiation to develop. (It will be seen later that nucleon and antinucleon sources in the form of pions can be compared.) However, the above results indicate that a finding of time-reversal symmetry is sufficient for confirming the joint-parity principle. The coupling constants would have to be real and then there could be no difference between

‡ L. Landau, *Nuc. Phys.* **3**, 127 (1957), called attention to it immediately after Yang and Lee threw doubts on ordinary parity conservation.

the interactions among any given set of fermion states and the interactions among their mirrored charge-conjugates.

The latter result is a special case of a highly general theorem about local interactions which was developed by Lüders, by Pauli, and by Schwinger.‡ It is known as the '*CPT*-Theorem' and asserts that it is only necessary that all interactions be properly Lorentz-invariant (i.e. in the continuous changes of the space-time reference frame) in order that there be invariance to joint transformation by space-inversion, time-reversal, and charge-conjugation. This holds despite the fact that

$$\psi^{CPT} = C[PT\psi^*]^* \neq \psi, \tag{10.40 a}$$

even within a phase. The latter phenomenon shows itself in the fact that the general, properly invariant $h_\beta$ of (10.9) was found to yield the same interaction among the $\psi^{PC}$ as among the $\psi^T$, yet

$$\psi^{PC} = PC\psi^* \neq \psi^T = T\psi^*. \tag{10.40 b}$$

In other words, a '*CPT*' transformation changes the way fields are described without changing the interactions among them. The transformed description must be considered effectively equivalent to the original one, since nothing is observable except through interactions.

*Symmetries of the* V–A *law*

The debacle of the parity-conservation principle has not damped efforts to find symmetry principles from which a unique and correct law of β-interaction could be said to follow. After all, there has been a broadening of the conception of mirroring which may be regarded as more satisfying than the more narrowly conceived parity principle.

Additional symmetry principles not ordinarily associated with the space-time reference frame must be sought. The invariance to the continuous transformations of the frame permits β-interactions with as many as twenty arbitrary complex coupling constants $C_X$, $C'_X$. The symmetry in time-reversal only narrows these to real ones, and this is also sufficient to maintain the joint invariance to space-inversion and charge-conjugation.

An additional symmetry possessed by the V–A Law in particular has been described throughout this treatise as an engagement in β-interaction of only the positive-chirality ($\gamma_5 = +1$) components,

$$\phi = \tfrac{1}{2}(1+\gamma_5)\psi,$$

of each particle's state. Sudarshan and Marshak (ref. p. 102) describe

‡ G. Lüders, *K. Danske vidensk. Selsk. Skr.* **28** (1954); W. Pauli, *Niels Bohr and the Development of Physics* (Pergamon Press, London, 1955); J. Schwinger, *Phys. Rev.* **91**, 720 (1953).

this symmetry property as conformance to a 'chirality invariance' principle, that the interaction is invariant to the transformation of any participating field by $\psi \to \gamma_5 \psi$. They pointed out that a '$\gamma_5$-invariance' is a natural replacement, representing an extreme of parity *non*-conservation, for the '$\gamma_4$-invariance' lost when the interaction turned out not to be invariant to the space-inversion transformation $P = \eta\gamma_4$ of (10.6). However, such a comparison might be taken to imply that the interaction should be invariant to the *simultaneous* transformation of all the fields by $\gamma_5$, since a spatial frame inversion is represented by a simultaneous transformation of all the fields by $\gamma_4$. This interpretation of chirality invariance would entail a loss of all its effectiveness; even the general form (10.9) is invariant to the simultaneous multiplication of all the fields by $\gamma_5$, whatever $C_X$ and $C'_X$ may exist.

Sakurai‡ suggested that the Sudarshan–Marshak definition of their transformation should be extended to include 'mass-reversal', $m \to -m$. This enables an invariance to the transformation of not only the interactions, but also of the mass term in the Dirac equations (6.1) or (3.74). Such an extension of the symmetry requirements is supported by the fact that it is by mere accident that the Dirac equation is defined with a mass term of the conventional sign; the physical results are independent of the sign used. It can be doubted that there is much point in thus increasing the resemblance of the chirality invariance to a frame transformation when a complete resemblance cannot be admitted without the loss of its effectiveness anyway.

The residue of these considerations is the fact that if the $\beta$-interaction is required to be completely invariant in form, without even a change of phase, to the transformation $\psi \to \gamma_5 \psi$ of *any one* of the fields, then indeed it can only have the V–A Law form. As an *a priori* principle from which the interaction should be derivable, this leaves much to be desired. *A priori*, it could be difficult to see why an interaction form should be discarded because $\psi \to \gamma_5 \psi$ leads merely to a change of phase factor. For example, the '$S+P$ Law',

$$h_\beta(S+P) = 2^{-\frac{1}{2}}g[\bar{\psi}_p(1+\gamma_5)\psi_n][\bar{\psi}_e(1+\gamma_5)\psi_\nu], \tag{10.41}$$

merely changes sign when either $\psi_p$ or $\psi_e$ is multiplied by $\gamma_5$, while remaining completely unchanged when either $\psi_n$ or $\psi_\nu$ is so transformed. Such phase changes lead to no physically observable results (while the space-inversion $\psi \to \eta\gamma_4\psi$ does, even though it admits arbitrary phase changes).

‡ J. Sakurai, *Nuovo Cim.* **7**, 649 (1958).

Feynman and Gell-Mann (ref. p. 102) made another suggestion. They pointed out that what is customarily regarded as only a projection, $\phi = \frac{1}{2}(1+\gamma_5)\psi$, out of a complete spinor field, may be given a role like that of the vector potential, $A_\alpha(x)$, from which the entire electromagnetic field is derivable. Both $\phi$ and $A_\alpha$ are eigenfunctions of the Klein–Gordon operator, $\partial^2/\partial x_\alpha^2 = (mc/\hbar)^2$, with the appropriate mass (zero for photons), in the absence of interactions. While the electromagnetic fields are derivable from $A_\alpha$ via derivative operations alone, the presence of mass requires that the spinor field be derived from $\phi$ via

$$\psi = [1-(\hbar/mc)\gamma_\alpha \partial/\partial x_\alpha]\phi \tag{10.42}$$

if $\psi$ is to obey the Dirac free-particle equation. In the presence of an electromagnetic field, the usual transformation $\partial/\partial x_\alpha \to \partial/\partial x_\alpha + i(e/\hbar c)A_\alpha$ must be introduced.

With the entire formalism derivable from a field-description by $\phi$, it becomes appropriate to expect contact interactions to be proportional to $\phi$ just as the electromagnetic interaction is proportional to $A_\alpha$ in (4.6). Then considerations like those of § 10.1 lead to the V–A form (4.10) of the $\beta$-coupling since, for example, $\phi_p^\dagger \beta\gamma_\alpha \phi_n \equiv i\phi_p^\dagger \beta\omega_\alpha \phi_n$ is the only covariant which can be formed from $\phi_p^\dagger$ and $\phi_n$. The $S$, $T$, and $P$ forms vanish identically when $\phi = \frac{1}{2}(1+\gamma_5)\psi$ is used in place of $\psi$, e.g. the 'Scalar' product is

$$\phi_p^\dagger \beta\phi_n = \phi_p^\dagger \gamma_5 \beta\gamma_5 \phi_n = -\phi_p^\dagger \beta\phi_n = 0,$$

since $\gamma_5 \phi \equiv \phi$ and $\beta$ anticommutes with $\gamma_5$. The degeneration to a single covariant product is a manifestation of the fact that $\phi$ really has only two independent components (half those of $\psi$), being analogous to the Pauli spinor, with its single covariant product $\boldsymbol{\chi}^\dagger\boldsymbol{\sigma}\boldsymbol{\chi}$. From the new point of view, the couplings (10.9) not reducible to $(\phi_p^\dagger \beta\gamma_\alpha \phi_n)(\phi_e^\dagger \beta\gamma_\alpha \phi_\nu)$+h.c. include 'derivative couplings' because of (10.42), hence are degenerate forms of couplings with 'structure'.‡

It must still be admitted that the negative-chirality fields,

$$\phi_R = \tfrac{1}{2}(1-\gamma_5)\psi,$$

could also have been adopted as the 'potentials' of the spinor field. Accordingly, a 'right-handed' $\beta$-interaction becomes as plausible as the 'left-handed' V–A Law. However, it must be expected that observations must decide whether it is the particles heretofore regarded as 'normal' that interact through their 'left-handed' components, while

‡ On the other hand, in the field description by $\phi$, the electromagnetic interaction (4.6) becomes in part a 'derivative coupling'.

their antiparticles interact 'right-handedly', or whether the reverse is true.

## 10.3. Theories of the neutrino

When alternative forms for the β-theory are being considered as in the foregoing sections, it should not be overlooked that whatever is known about neutrinos comes from their β-interactions. This means that the formulation of the β-coupling can be changed, yet consistency with all the experimental data retained, by making compensating changes in the description adopted for the neutrino.

So far, the neutrino has been treated like a chargeless and massless electron; its states have been formally represented like electron states with $m$ and $e$ put equal to zero. A consequence has been the conception of an *anti*-neutrino, to be described by analogues of the positron states. However, Majorana showed long ago that neutral particles need never exist in 'antiparticle' states distinct from 'normal' ones. They may be described as in 'self-charge-conjugate' states, with no particle-antiparticle distinction to be made. It is only if the particles are subject to a type of interaction which, like the electromagnetic coupling, can cause transitions out of a self-charge-conjugate subspace of states, that the existence of antiparticles must be recognized. Whether the β-interaction thus distinguishes between neutrino and antineutrino remains to be seen.

Beyond the presumption that an antineutrino $\bar{\nu}$ distinct from a neutrino $\nu$ exists, it has also been assumed so far that it is $\bar{\nu}$ as defined by the analogues of the positron states that is emitted together with the negatron in the neutron-to-proton transformations, $\mathrm{n} \rightarrow \mathrm{p}+\mathrm{e}^{-}+\bar{\nu}$, while the normal neutrino emerges in positron decay, $\mathrm{p} \rightarrow \mathrm{n}+\mathrm{e}^{+}+\nu$. This seemed to fit most gracefully into the formalism, and permitted the enunciation of a 'lepton conservation principle' with antiparticle emissions treated as absorptions of normal particles. However, it is not difficult to reformulate the β-interaction so that the roles of $\nu$ and $\bar{\nu}$ are interchanged. Such a formulation was used by Fermi in his original introduction of the theory and only later papers (ref. p. 261) adopted the present conventions.

Finally, it is also possible to arrange for the emission of *either* a neutrino or antineutrino in each β-transformation, therewith discarding the particle vs. antiparticle characters as 'good quantum numbers' in β-interactions. Considering this first will provide a basis for discussing all the possibilities for the description of the neutrino.

*Lepton non-conserving formulations*

The way‡ to generalize the coupling forms (10.9) so that they create normal neutrino as well as antineutrino modes out of the vacuum, in neutron-to-proton transformations, is to supplement the 'lepton current',

$$J_X = \bar{\psi}_e \Gamma^X (C_X + C'_X \gamma_5)\psi_\nu, \tag{10.43 a}$$

by adding to it

$$\bar{J}_X = \bar{\psi}_e \Gamma^X (D_X + D'_X \gamma_5) CK\psi_\nu, \tag{10.43 b}$$

with additional coupling constants $D_X$, $D'_X$. Here $K$ stands for the operation of complex-conjugation, so that $CK\psi_\nu = C\psi_\nu^* = \psi_\nu^C$. There is in effect a substitution of the charge-conjugate field operator $\psi_\nu^C$ for $\psi_\nu$ in going from $J_X$ to $\bar{J}_X$. Such a substitution is consistent with the Lorentz invariance and this fact was already presumed in the earlier unquantized field treatments of the lepton-conserving formalism.

The earlier substitutions, for the unquantized fields of their charge conjugates, was consistent with lepton conservation, yet the present one will lead to violations of it. How that can happen is best seen after analysing the quantized field $\psi_\nu$ into its neutrino and antineutrino modes,

$$\psi_\nu = \sum_\nu (b_\nu u_\nu + d_\nu^\dagger u_\nu^C), \tag{10.44}$$

as discussed in §§ 9.1, 9.2. It is essentially the '*c*-number' modes $u_\nu$ and $u_\nu^C$, rather than the '*q*-number' field operators $\psi_\nu$, $\psi_\nu^C$, which were (after multiplication with time factors) denoted $\psi_\nu$ and $\psi_\nu^C$ in the unquantized field treatments.

Suppose first that a neutrino is incident on a neutron so that the initial neutrino field state is $b_1^\dagger|0\rangle_\nu$. The operation on it with $J_X$ will generate those neutrino field states $|\,\rangle_\nu$ for which

$$\langle|J_X b_1^\dagger|0\rangle_\nu = \bar{\psi}_e \Gamma^X (C_X + C'_X \gamma_5) \sum_\nu \langle|(b_\nu u_\nu + d_\nu^\dagger u_\nu^C) b_1^\dagger|0\rangle_\nu$$

does not vanish. The state induced by the incident neutrino will have a neutrino vacuum, $|\,\rangle_\nu = |0\rangle_\nu$, and the interaction will have been proportional to $u_1$. At the same time $\bar{\psi}_e$ will have generated a negatron, and there will have been a straightforward conservation of leptons. On the other hand, consider the states generated by $J_X$ out of an initial neutrino vacuum, $|0\rangle_\nu$. For this, $\langle|b_\nu u_\nu + d_\nu^\dagger u_\nu^C|0\rangle_\nu$ replaces the 'bra-ket' above. The only final states generated now are of the type $|\,\rangle_\nu = d_\nu^\dagger|0\rangle_\nu$, containing an antineutrino, and the interaction will have been proportional to a $u_\nu^C$. This also is consistent with lepton conservation, in the sense that $d_\nu^\dagger|0\rangle_\nu$ is described as the absence of a normal neutrino out

‡ W. Pauli, *Nuovo Cim.* **6**, 204 (1957); many results to be discussed in these pages were also obtained by D. L. Pursey and S. Kahana, ibid., pp. 266 and 1469 (1957).

of a 'negative-energy' state. That is the way that a substitution for the unquantized $u_1$ of its charge-conjugate $u_1^C$ retains consistency with lepton conservation.

Now compare the states generated out of a vacuum by $\bar{J}_X$, instead of $J_X$, so that there is a substitution of a quantized charge-conjugate field *operator* $\psi_\nu^C$, for $\psi_\nu$. Here it is

$$\langle|\bar{J}_X|0\rangle_\nu = \bar{\psi}_e \Gamma^X(D_X + D'_X\gamma_5) \sum_\nu \langle|b_\nu^\dagger u_\nu^C + d_\nu u_\nu|0\rangle_\nu \quad (10.45)$$

which does not vanish in the processes which will occur, since

$$CK\psi_\nu = \sum_\nu (b_\nu^\dagger Cu_\nu^* + d_\nu Cu_\nu^{C*}).$$

Thus, states of the type $b_\nu^\dagger|0\rangle_\nu$, each containing a normal neutrino, are generated, in contrast to the antineutrino states $d_\nu^\dagger|0\rangle_\nu$ arising from the coupling to $J_X$ above. A β-coupling to $J_X + \bar{J}_X$ will generate a mixture of neutrinos and antineutrinos out of the vacuum state, and that ostensibly violates lepton conservation.

To make evident any physical consequences as quickly as possible, the expectations from a coupling to $J_X + \bar{J}_X$, with $D_X$, $D'_X \neq 0$, will be discussed next.

*Expectations for 'single' processes*

All the evidence about the β-coupling used in § 10.1 was based on what Pauli called 'single' processes because they involve just one step of β-interaction, in which one neutral lepton is emitted. The expectations for them when the coupling is generalized to $J_X + \bar{J}_X$ may be obtained without detailed recalculation. Pauli pointed out that the transformation of $J_X$ to a form like that of $J_X + \bar{J}_X$ may be regarded‡ as the result of a substitution

$$\psi_\nu \rightarrow \psi'_\nu = A\psi_\nu + B\gamma_5 \psi_\nu^C \quad (10.46)$$

with arbitrary constants $A$, $B$. If the coupling constants in the original form are called $(C_X)_0$, $(C'_X)_0$, while $(D_X)_0 = (D'_X)_0 = 0$, then the transformed current will have

$$C_X = A(C_X)_0, \qquad C'_X = A(C'_X)_0, \qquad D_X = B(C'_X)_0, \qquad D'_X = B(C_X)_0. \quad (10.47)$$

This implies $D'_X/D_X = C_X/C'_X$, hence the most general case of $J_X + \bar{J}_X$ is not thus obtained. It is nevertheless possible to deduce the expecta-

‡ Similarly, the generalization from $(C'_X)_0 = 0$ to $C_X$, $C'_X \neq 0$ can be obtained by the transformation $\psi_\nu \rightarrow \psi'_\nu = (\exp ia\gamma_5)\psi_\nu = (\cos a + i\gamma_5 \sin a)\psi_\nu$, giving $C_X = (C_X)_0 \cos a$, $C'_X = i(C_X)_0 \sin a$ with the arbitrary ratio $C'_X/C_X = i \tan a$. The transformation here seems to have first been explored by B. Touschek, *Nuovo Cim.* **5**, 1281 (1957).

tions for the general case from those for $(D_X)_0 = (D'_X)_0 = 0$ because of the following.

Representation of a free neutrino by $\psi'_\nu$ is just as valid as by $\psi_\nu$. It is easy to see that $\psi'_\nu$ obeys the free-field equation (10.8) if $\psi_\nu$ does, whatever the choice of $A$ and $B$. Moreover, the anticommutation relations (9.1) will hold among the $\psi'_\nu$, if they do among the $\psi_\nu$, if only

$$|A|^2+|B|^2 = 1$$

(this makes the transformation $\psi_\nu \to \psi'_\nu$ 'canonical'). Thus, any expectations for processes in which a free neutrino description is sufficient should be independent of $A$, $B$; even when calculated with $\psi'_\nu$, any resulting expression for an observable intensity must have

$$A \text{ and } B = \pm(1-|A|^2)^{\frac{1}{2}}$$

somehow cancelled out.

Now calculating expectations from a coupling to $J_X+\bar{J}_X$ with the use of $\psi'_\nu$ is the same as calculating with $\psi_\nu$ the results of a new coupling in which

$$\left.\begin{aligned} C_X &\to AC_X - B^*D'_X, & C'_X &\to AC'_X - B^*D_X \\ D'_X &\to BC_X + A^*D'_X, & D_X &\to BC'_X + A^*D_X \end{aligned}\right\}, \tag{10.48}$$

as follows from the substitution of $\psi'_\nu$ (10.46) into $J_X+\bar{J}_X$ (10.43). The results (10.47) were a special case of this starting from

$$(D_X)_0 = (D'_X)_0 = 0.$$

The relations (10.48) are obviously equivalent to 'rotations' (in a suitably defined space) of two-dimensional column-vectors

$$\mathbf{V}_X = \begin{pmatrix} C_X \\ D'_X \end{pmatrix} \quad \text{and} \quad \mathbf{V}'_X = \begin{pmatrix} C'_X \\ D_X \end{pmatrix} \tag{10.49 a}$$

by the operation

$$U = \begin{pmatrix} A & -B^* \\ B & A^* \end{pmatrix} \tag{10.49 b}$$

which is unitary because $|A|^2+|B|^2 = 1$. Thus, the invariance of physical expectations to choices of $A$, $B$ leads to the conclusion that they can be expressed solely in terms of 'rotationally' invariant combinations of the coupling constants, like

$$\left.\begin{aligned} \mathbf{V}_X^\dagger.\mathbf{V}_X &= |C_X|^2+|D'_X|^2 \\ \mathbf{V}_X^\dagger.\mathbf{V}_Y &= C_X^* C_Y + (D'_X)^* D'_Y \\ \mathbf{V}_X^\dagger.\mathbf{V}'_Y &= C_X^* C'_Y + (D'_X)^* D_Y \end{aligned}\right\}, \tag{10.50}$$

and others obtainable by substitutions $\mathbf{V}_X \to \mathbf{V}'_X$. No one of these invariants vanishes for $D_X = D'_X = 0$, hence it is merely necessary to make substitutions like $|C_X|^2 \to \mathbf{V}_X^\dagger.\mathbf{V}_X = |C_X|^2+|D'_X|^2$ in the results calculated with $D_X = D'_X = 0$ in § 10.1, to obtain the generalized results.

Reconsider now the evidence used in § 10.1 for the conclusion that V–A form of the lepton-conserving interactions (10.9) is best consistent with the data. The idea is to see how the conclusion may be modified when the possibility is admitted that $D_X$, $D'_X \neq 0$ and perhaps there is no lepton conservation.‡

One of the decisive results in § 10.1 came from the electron-neutrino correlations (10.16) and was expressed as $|C_{S,T}|^2+|C'_{S,T}|^2 \to 0$. According to (10.50), this is now to be replaced by§

$$|C_{S,T}|^2+|D'_{S,T}|^2+|C'_{S,T}|^2+|D_{S,T}|^2 \to 0. \qquad (10.51)$$

Thus, the former conclusion that Scalar and Tensor couplings play no appreciable role in the β-interactions still stands. *A fortiori*, the Fierz interferences (10.13) still vanish as the experiments require.

The polarization measurements (10.17) were formerly interpreted as indicating that $|C_{V,A}-C'_{V,A}|^2 \to 0$. This condition is now generalized to

$$|C_{V,A}-C'_{V,A}|^2+|D_{V,A}-D'_{V,A}|^2 \to 0. \qquad (10.52)$$

Thus, the odd and even couplings are still to be related as

$$C'_V = C_V, \quad C'_A = C_A, \quad D'_V = D_V, \quad D'_A = D_A, \qquad (10.53)$$

the generalization of (10.22). The physical significance of the outcome follows from the amplitude expression (10.45), which governs the generation of normal neutrinos in neutron-to-proton transformations (e.g. negatron emissions):

$$\langle 0|b_\nu \bar{J}_X|0\rangle_\nu = D_X \bar{\psi}_e \Gamma^X(1+\gamma_5)CKu_\nu, \qquad (10.54)$$

if $u_\nu$ is the mode in which the neutrino is to appear. Since

$$(1+\gamma_5)CK = CK(1-\gamma_5),$$

‡ C. P. Enz, *Nuovo Cim.* **6,** 250 (1957).

§ It is easy to find that the 4-component 'vectors'

$$\mathbf{V}_X^\dagger = (C_X, C'_X, D_X, D'_X)^* \quad \text{and} \quad (\mathbf{V}'_X)^\dagger = (C'_X, C_X, D'_X, D_X)^*$$

are transformed by the same unitary operation when the substitution

$$\psi_\nu \to (\exp i\alpha\gamma_5)(A\psi_\nu+B\gamma_5\psi_\nu^C)$$

is made (see footnote on p. 287). This leads to the conclusion, more powerful than (10.50), that $C_X^* C_Y$ cannot occur in physical results except in the combination

$$\mathbf{V}_X^\dagger . \mathbf{V}_Y = C_X^* C_Y + C_X'^* C'_Y + D_X^* D_Y + D_X'^* D'_Y;$$

similarly $C_X^* C'_Y \to \mathbf{V}_X^\dagger . \mathbf{V}'_Y$. These are the invariants called

$$K_{XY} (\equiv \mathbf{V}_X^\dagger . \mathbf{V}_Y) \quad \text{and} \quad L_{XY} (\equiv \mathbf{V}_X^\dagger . \mathbf{V}'_Y)$$

by Pauli. Notice that the expressions (10.51) are just $K_{SS}$ and $K_{TT}$ while those of (10.52) are $K_{XX}-L_{XX}$ with $X = $ V, A.

it is the *right*-handed component $\frac{1}{2}(1-\gamma_5)u_\nu$ which is generated. Thu *any neutral leptons emitted together with negatrons must be right-hande* whether they are all antineutrinos as before ($D_X = 0$), or whether the form the superposition of antineutrinos and neutrinos now bein considered.

The remaining evidence used for the conclusions about the β-couplin in § 10.1 consisted of the various anisotropy coefficients $A_n$, $B_n$, $D_n$ of polarized neutron decay. The appropriate generalizations of (10.34) an (10.36) are

$$\left.\begin{aligned} \xi_n(A_n - B_n) &= -4(|C_A|^2 + |D_A|^2) \\ \xi_n(A_n + B_n) &= -2(C_V C_A^* + D_V D_A^* + \text{c.c.}) \\ \xi_n D_n &= i(C_V C_A^* + D_V D_A^* - \text{c.c.}) \end{aligned}\right\}, \qquad (10.5$$

with $$\xi_n = (|C_V|^2 + |D_V|^2) + 3(|C_A|^2 + |D_A|^2).$$

The measured values (1.58) of $A_n$ and $B_n$ presumably deviate fro $A_n = 0$ and $B_n = +1$ only because of extraneous 'renormalizatio effects, according to the interpretation discussed in § 4.4. If

$$A_n - B_n = -1$$

is used in the above formula, it gives unity for the 'GT-to-Fermi ratio formerly denoted $|C_A|^2/|C_V|^2$ but now generalized to

$$(|C_A|^2 + |D_A|^2)/(|C_V|^2 + |D_V|^2);$$

the effect of the 'renormalizations' is only to cause a moderate departur from unity, as in (1.26). When $A_n + B_n = +1$ is taken next, the middl one of the formulae (10.55) yields

$$|C_A + C_V|^2 + |D_V + D_A|^2 = 0,$$

with the consequences $C_A = -C_V$ and $D_V = -D_A$. Finally, the mea surement $D_n \approx 0$ (§ 1.10) is consistent with these results without, how ever, requiring that the individual coupling constants be real; onl $C_V C_A^* + D_V D_A^*$ must be real, and this can be shown sufficient for time reversal invariance.

The final outcome of the evidence from just the single processes is tha an interaction as general as

$$h_\beta = 2^{\frac{1}{2}} g\{[\bar{\psi}_p \gamma_\alpha (C_V - C_A \gamma_5)\psi_n] J_\alpha + [\bar{\psi}_p \gamma_\alpha (D_V - D_A \gamma_5)\psi_n] \bar{J}_\alpha + \text{h.c.}\} \qquad (10.56$$

is possible, with

$$J_\alpha = \bar{\psi}_e \gamma_\alpha \tfrac{1}{2}(1+\gamma_5)\psi_\nu \quad \text{and} \quad \bar{J}_\alpha = \bar{\psi}_e \gamma_\alpha \tfrac{1}{2}(1+\gamma_5) CK\psi_\nu. \qquad (10.57$$

Thus the conventional, 'lepton-conserving' form of the V–A Law ma be modified to admit mixtures of neutrinos and antineutrinos. In th onsequent expressions of results for the single processes there is merely redistribution of coupling strength according to

$$C_X C_Y^* \to C_X C_Y^* + D_X D_Y^*,$$

ithout any restriction on the relative proportions.

*Double' processes*

It should not be surprising that the single processes cannot distinguish etween emissions of neutrinos and antineutrinos. Each of these paricles is massless, chargeless, and of spin $\frac{1}{2}$, and that is all that has een required of the neutral leptons emitted in those processes. It seems bvious that, to establish the distinction, an attempt must be made to detect' the neutral leptons. Then, according to the conventional leptononserving picture for example,‡ neutrinos could be distinguished hrough being absorbable by neutrons and not by protons, whereas ntineutrinos would be absorbable only by protons. 'Double' processes n which neutral lepton emissions are followed by their absorption must e considered.

The one successful detection of neutral leptons from nuclear β-decay, n the Reines–Cowan experiment of § 8.2, could not have been expected o make a neutrino-antineutrino distinction. There was merely a reversal f neutron decays, and whatever neutral leptons are generated together vith the product protons must be reabsorbable by protons. The decription of the neutral lepton beam from emitter to absorber, in that xperiment, becomes quite complicated if mixtures of neutrinos and ntineutrinos are involved, generated by such a coupling as (10.56). That is because coherent§ superpositions of the conjugate particles must e expected. Such superpositions are perhaps easiest|| to represent as tates of the neutral lepton field generated out of the vacuum by the 3-coupling to the emitter:

$$H_\beta|0\rangle_\nu = \sum_\nu [d_\nu^\dagger|0\rangle\langle 0|d_\nu H_\beta|0\rangle_\nu + b_\nu^\dagger|0\rangle\langle 0|b_\nu H_\beta|0\rangle_\nu]. \qquad (10.58)$$

The coherence (relative phase) of the neutrino and antineutrino terms ere will be properly maintained if both are averaged in the same vay, over variables other than those of the neutral leptons. A beam

‡ G. Racah, *Nuovo Cim.* **14**, 322 (1937).

§ Adopting incoherent superpositions, as done by the author in *Ann. Rev. Nuc. Sci.* **9**, 9 (1959), would be equivalent to assuming two kinds of completely unrelated neutral eptons. The author is indebted to correspondence with Dr. S. Bludman for the clarificaion of this point.

|| Readers familiar with the '*S*-matrix' formalism may find it easier to set up the econd-order amplitude for transitions of the entire system of emitter plus absorber, lus the lepton fields.

component arising from plane wave lepton modes may be considered and nothing essential for the objectives here will be lost if detection of 'renormalization' effects is foregone (i.e. $C_A = -C_V$ and $D_A = -D_V$ taken). Then $H_\beta$ of (10.58) may be replaced by

$$2^{\frac{1}{2}} g \mathscr{M}_\alpha [C_V J_\alpha + D_V \bar{J}_\alpha]_{\mathbf{r}=t=0}, \tag{10.59}$$

with $\mathscr{M}_\alpha$ a nuclear matrix element of the emitter,

$$\mathscr{M}_\alpha = \int \beta\gamma_\alpha(1+\gamma_5)\exp\{-i(\mathbf{p}+\mathbf{q}).\mathbf{r}/\hbar\}, \tag{10.60}$$

in a notation like that of (5.3). The lepton current operators, $J_\alpha$ and $\bar{J}_\alpha$ are given by (10.57) for negatron emitters, like those in a nuclear reactor but $\psi_e$ may as well be replaced by a mode $u_e$ since the electron field description is not essential here. The coefficients in the superposition (10.58) may now be evaluated with the help of

$$\left.\begin{aligned} \langle 0|d_\nu(C_V J_\alpha + D_V \bar{J}_\alpha)|0\rangle_\nu &= C_V u_e^\dagger \beta\gamma_\alpha \tfrac{1}{2}(1+\gamma_5)u_\nu^C \\ \langle 0|b_\nu(C_V J_\alpha + D_V \bar{J}_\alpha)|0\rangle_\nu &= D_V u_e^\dagger \beta\gamma_\alpha \tfrac{1}{2}(1+\gamma_5)u_\nu^C \end{aligned}\right\}, \tag{10.61}$$

which follow from the decomposition (10.44) of $\psi_\nu$. Thus, the neutral lepton beam expression (10.58) reduces to one proportional to

$$\sum_\nu (C_V d_\nu^\dagger + D_V b_\nu^\dagger)|0\rangle_\nu \mathscr{M}_\alpha [u_e^\dagger \beta\gamma_\alpha \tfrac{1}{2}(1+\gamma_5)u_\nu^C]_0. \tag{10.62}$$

This will be a factor in the descriptions of the initial states for the subsequent absorption process. Further averaging over source variables (e.g. the negatron spins and momentum directions, as well as nuclear orientations) must be delayed until after the absorption is evaluated. If the emitter undergoes an allowed transition, it is easy to find that the unnormalized beam component (10.62) carries an averaged intensity proportional to

$$(|C_V|^2 + |D_V|^2)(\langle 1\rangle^2_{em} + \langle\sigma\rangle^2_{em}) = \xi_{em}, \tag{10.63}$$

where $\xi_{em}$ is a strength factor like (5.39) generalized to $D_{A,V} \neq 0$, then specialized to $C_A = -C_V$, $D_A = -D_V$. The subscripts 'em' label $\beta$ moments of the emitting nucleus.

Suppose now that the absorbing nucleus is capable of allowed proton-to-neutron transformations, as in the Reines–Cowan experiment. Then an absorption amplitude is found by operating on the neutrino field state (10.62) with

$$2^{\frac{1}{2}} g \mathscr{M}'_{\beta\nu} \langle 0|(C_V^* J_\beta^\dagger + D_V^* \bar{J}_\beta^\dagger), \tag{10.64}$$

as follows from the hermitian conjugate term in the interaction (10.56).

Iere $\mathscr{M}'_\beta$ is a nuclear matrix element of the absorbing nucleus. The operation involves the evaluation:

$$\langle 0|(C_V^* J_\beta^\dagger + D_V^* \bar{J}_\beta^\dagger)(C_V d_\nu^\dagger + D_V b_\nu^\dagger)|0\rangle_\nu$$
$$= (|C_V|^2 + |D_V|^2)[u_\nu^{C\dagger}\beta\gamma_\beta \tfrac{1}{2}(1+\gamma_5)u_{\bar{e}}^C]_0, \quad (10.65)$$

where the label ē refers to the positron produced in the absorption. To complete the formation of the absorption amplitude, the summation over the neutral lepton modes, $\sum_\nu$ of (10.62), must be carried out, and then the square of the result is averaged over the remaining variables to yield the total absorption rate. The formulae (10.63) and (10.65) already make plain the essential result, namely an absorption rate proportional to

$$(|C_V|^2 + |D_V|^2)^2(\langle 1\rangle_{em}^2 + \langle\sigma\rangle_{em}^2)(\langle 1\rangle_{ab}^2 + \langle\sigma\rangle_{ab}^2) = \xi_{em}\,\xi_{ab}, \quad (10.66)$$

where the subscripts 'ab' refer to the absorbing nucleus. The capture cross-section, i.e. the rate per unit incident intensity, is found by dividing the rate by the incident intensity $\sim \xi_{em}$ of (10.63), hence is proportional to

$$\xi_{ab} \to (|C_V|^2 + |D_V|^2)\langle 1\rangle_{ab}^2 + (|C_A|^2 + |D_A|^2)\langle\sigma\rangle_{ab}^2, \quad (10.67)$$

just as in § 8.2 except that $C_X^2 \to |C_X|^2 + |D_X|^2$ when $D_X \neq 0$. Thus, as in the single processes, the coupling strength is merely redistributed in undetermined proportions, without distinguishing between contributions from neutrinos and antineutrinos. All this could have been foreseen from the invariances to the Pauli transformation (10.46), but more detailed insight was sought here for purposes of contrast to the next considerations.

It seemed obvious from the beginning that the decisive way to test whether there is a distinction to be made between 'antineutrinos' emitted in negatron decays, and 'neutrinos' from positron decays or orbital negatron captures, was to see whether the putative antineutrinos can reverse the latter types of transformations. Davis‡ undertook to reverse the well-known orbital capture process,

$$_{18}A_{19}^{37} + e^- \to {}_{17}Cl_{20}^{37} + \nu, \quad (10.68)$$

by exposing thousand-gallon quantities of chlorine to the 'antineutrinos' from a nuclear reactor (the same source of neutral leptons as was used in the Reines–Cowan experiment). The hypothetical reaction sought may be represented as

$$Cl^{37} + \bar{\nu} \xrightarrow{(?)} A^{37} + e^-, \quad (10.69)$$

‡ R. Davis, *Phys. Rev.* **97**, 966 (1955).

which is plainly not just the reverse of (10.68) unless $\bar{\nu} \equiv \nu$. Davis could report no evidence that this process does take place (the little $A^{37}$ found could be attributed to cosmic rays) and was able to put an upper limit on its occurrence: about one-ninth of what was anticipated if every 'antineutrino' were as effective as a 'neutrino' is expected to be.

The Davis experiment does support a distinction between the neutral leptons generated in neutron-to-proton transformations and in their converse. However, since the discovery of the lepton polarizations, it is no longer clear that this distinction is to be interpreted as one between neutrino and antineutrino. It is now known that whatever mixture of these may be emitted in neutron-to-proton transformations, each particle is right-handed, whereas only left-handed neutral leptons are emitted in proton-to-neutron transformations, and only the recapture of such can reverse these transformations. These conclusions from the evidence of the single processes have already been pointed out in the discussion of (10.54), and have led to the formulation (10.56) with $C'_X = C_X$ and $D'_X = D_X$. How the consequences are enforced in forming the absorption amplitude for a process like (10.69) can be seen by replacing the operation (10.64) with one appropriate to absorption in a neutron-to-proton transformation:

$$2^{\frac{1}{2}} g \mathscr{M}'_{\beta\,\nu} \langle 0|(C_V J_\beta + D_V \bar{J}_\beta). \tag{10.70}$$

When this operates on the neutral lepton state (10.62) generated in neutron-to-proton transformations, the evaluation

$$\langle 0|C_V J_\beta + D_V \bar{J}_\beta)(C_V d_\nu^\dagger + D_V b_\nu^\dagger)|0\rangle_\nu = 2C_V D_V[u_{e'}^\dagger \beta\gamma_\beta \tfrac{1}{2}(1+\gamma_5)u_\nu]$$

replaces (10.65), with e$'$ referring to the negatron which would be produced in such a process as (10.69). Now the sum over modes of the mediating neutral lepton, $\sum_\nu$ of (10.62), will be proportional to a spin sum

$$\sum_\nu [u_{e'}^\dagger \beta\gamma_\beta \tfrac{1}{2}(1+\gamma_5)u_\nu][u_e^\dagger \beta\gamma_\alpha \tfrac{1}{2}(1+\gamma_5)u_\nu^C], \tag{10.71 a}$$

which, upon transposition of the second bracket, becomes proportional to the density matrix

$$\tfrac{1}{2}(1+\gamma_5)\sum_\nu u_\nu \tilde{u}_\nu^C \tfrac{1}{2}(1+\gamma_5) = \tfrac{1}{2}(1+\gamma_5)\Big(\sum_\nu u_\nu u_\nu^\dagger\Big)\tfrac{1}{2}(1-\gamma_5)CK, \tag{10.71 b}$$

since $CK\frac{1}{2}(1+\gamma_5) = \frac{1}{2}(1-\gamma_5)CK$ follows from $C\gamma_5^* = -\gamma_5 C$. Now $\gamma_5$ commutes with $\sum_\nu u_\nu u_\nu^\dagger = (2V)^{-1}(1+\boldsymbol{\alpha}.\hat{\mathbf{q}})$, and since $(1+\gamma_5)(1-\gamma_5) = 0$, the absorption in question cannot proceed. It is plainly defeated by the 'wrong' helicities of the neutral lepton beams from negatron decays, regardless of what mixture of neutrinos and antineutrinos they may be conceived to have.

The same conclusions follow from considerations of the process of double $\beta$-decay (§ 9.3). Furry‡ pointed out long ago that if there were no difference between neutrinos and antineutrinos then it may be possible for neutrinoless $\beta\beta$-emission to occur. The process may be treated as going through a transient intermediate state in which one of the neutrons has been transformed, and an electron-neutrino pair formed. Then the transformation of a second neutron may result in a neutrinoless final state if that neutron is able to absorb the neutral lepton emitted by the first neutron. The detection of such a $\beta$-process, if it exists, would be expected to have at least two factors in its favour. First, a monoenergetic peak in the sum of electron energies is much easier to distinguish from background than such a distribution (Fig. 9.1) as is expected when the energy is shared with neutrinos. Second, the absolute rate of the process has a possibility of being much greater than for the four-particle emission because the 'virtual' intermediate neutrinos of the neutrinoless decay are not as restricted in energy, and have a much larger 'phase space' available. It was estimated§ that a lifetime as low as $2(10)^{13}$ years could be possible in the case of $Nd^{150}$ (Table 9.1), and that no longer one than $\sim 10^{17}$ years is at all reasonable if indeed $\bar{\nu} \equiv \nu$. Yet the attempt‖ to find the process failed even though a life as long as $\sim 10^{18}$ years should have been detectable.

Again, the failure to find the neutrinoless double $\beta$-decay is to be expected merely from the fact that any neutral lepton emitted by a neutron has the wrong helicity to be absorbed by a neutron. The formal confirmation of this goes exactly as in (10.71) for the capture process, the only difference being that the intermediate neutral letpons are now 'virtual' ones.

*Lepton conservation and two-component theories*

There is now a basis for discussing the points brought up in the introductory paragraphs of this section, § 10.3. It was asserted that the formulation of the $\beta$-interaction can be changed if compensating changes are made in the way the neutrino is described. The range of alternatives for the coupling, thus provided, is represented in the form (10.56) as an undetermined proportion of the coupling constants $D_V \approx -D_A$ vs. $C_V \approx -C_A$. No neutrino interaction which can determine them more closely is known at present, hence any choice consistent with

‡ W. Furry, *Phys. Rev.* **56**, 1184 (1959).

§ E. J. Konopinski, *Los Alamos Report LAMS*-1949 (1955). See also the reference on p. 255.

‖ C. Cowan, F. Harrison, L. Langer, and F. Reines, *Nuovo Cim.* **3**, 649 (1956).

invariant values for $|D_{V,A}|^2+|C_{V,A}|^2$ and $D_V^* D_A+C_V^* C_A$ can give equal agreement with presently conceivable experiments.

The choice $D_{V,A} = C_{V,A}$ is possible, and it enables writing the total lepton current coupled to the neutron-to-proton current as

$$\bar{\psi}_e \gamma_\alpha(1+\gamma_5).\tfrac{1}{2}(1+CK)\psi_\nu. \qquad (10.72)$$

Now, $\frac{1}{2}(1+CK)$ is a projection operator which picks out just self-charge-conjugate descriptions of the neutrino, invariant to operation by $CK$ because $(CK)^2 = 1$. Since $\frac{1}{2}(1+CK).\frac{1}{2}(1+CK) = \frac{1}{2}(1+CK)$, the neutrino descriptions adopted may be restricted to the self-charge-conjugate subspace of states and no other type need ever be introduced. Thus, a Majorana description of the neutrino may be adopted and no antineutrino-neutrino distinction need be drawn.

The alternative choice $C_{V,A} = 0$ is equally possible. Then the lepton fields would enter interaction through

$$\bar{\psi}_e \gamma_\alpha \tfrac{1}{2}(1+\gamma_5)CK\psi_\nu, \qquad (10.73)$$

and this corresponds to having neutrinos (as against the antineutrinos of the case $D_{V,A} = 0$) emitted in negatron decays, according to the discussion of (10.45). The hermitian conjugate of (10.73) yields antineutrino emissions in positron decays and negatron captures. Fermi's original picture can thus be retained. Of course, all this is predicated on a definition of the antineutrino as the particle described by the states used to describe positrons, with $m, e \to 0$.

Finally, the coupling constant ratios may simply be left undetermined, since this still allows completely defined expectations for presently conceivable experiments. The indeterminacy is merely a manifestation of the invariance to the Pauli transformations‡ (10.46) of all presently known neutrino processes. Indeed, the general interaction form was reduced to a mere Pauli transform of the original V–A Law with $D_X, D'_X = 0$ as soon as the measurements indicated (10.53) that $C'_X = C_X$ and $D'_X = D_X$. That can be confirmed by reference to (10.47) and the statement following it. Thus, the original law may as well be retained; this will have the advantage that constructing neutrino descriptions (relative to the conventional treatments of the other participants in the $\beta$-processes) as complicated as (10.62) will become unnecessary.

The conclusions here put the 'principle of lepton conservation' into an ambiguous position. Because the neutral lepton states produced in neutron-to-proton transformations and their converse are different, at

‡ Those are actually general enough to encompass Majorana descriptions since only projections by $\frac{1}{2}(1+\gamma_5)$ interact and then factors $\gamma_5$ make no essential difference.

least in helicity, it is always possible to interpret the principle so that it is not violated in the $\beta$-processes. A 'leptonic charge unit', $+1$ say, may be defined for the negatron and also assigned to the coherent neutral lepton mixture which replaces it in a process; $-1$ might then be assigned to the charge-conjugates of those states, and then the 'leptonic charge' can be said to be conserved. However, this reduces the principle to a mere restatement of the fact that neutral leptons of opposite helicities are produced in the neutron-to-proton and proton-to-neutron transformations. For lepton conservation to have a distinct meaning, it seems necessary to assign the 'leptonic charge' units to neutrinos and antineutrinos as described by negatron and positron states with $m, e \to 0$. The present situation is, then, that the $\beta$-interaction is at least *reducible* to the straightforward, lepton-conserving one (with $D_{V,A} = 0$). However, the invariance to Pauli transformations which introduce neutrino-antineutrino mixtures is still retained, not only for the free neutrino description, but in the presence of the $\beta$-coupling; this situation will continue unless some new neutrino interaction is found which is not invariant to the Pauli transformation and is thus capable of distinguishing between neutrinos and antineutrinos.

Clearly, the presently more useful distinction to make is between neutral leptons of left- and right-handed helicities. So far, the findings about the neutrino helicities have been treated as properties of the interaction rather than as inherent in the descriptions of the neutrino. From the point of view that only the $\beta$-interaction impresses the observed helicity properties on the neutral leptons, it does so through the operation

$$\tfrac{1}{2}(1+\gamma_5)(C_V+D_V\,CK)\psi_\nu = [C_V\,\tfrac{1}{2}(1+\gamma_5)+D_V\,CK\tfrac{1}{2}(1-\gamma_5)]\psi_\nu \quad (10.74)$$

in the general interaction form (10.56). Thus, if $D_V \neq 0$, both the positive and negative chirality projections, $\tfrac{1}{2}(1\pm\gamma_5)$, of the neutrino field states are being used. This is a formal expression of the fact already noted, that, when mixtures of neutrinos and antineutrinos are produced, then both types of particles must be right-handed in neutron-to-proton transformations, both left-handed in the converse transformations. However, in the original lepton-conserving picture, ($D_{V,A} = 0$), only left-handed neutrino states, and only right-handed antineutrino states, participate.

This last property of the lepton-conserving $\beta$-coupling enables simplifying the theory of the neutrino. The consequence that no right-handed neutrinos, nor left-handed antineutrinos, would be needed for any known process enables discarding even the possibility that the neutral lepton can ever have those two out of the total of four possible 'internal' states. It becomes possible to *identify* the particle-antiparticle distinction with the left- and right-handedness; a physical difference between neutrino and antineutrino will have been conceived.

The picture thus simplified is generally called a 'two-component' theory of the neutrino. Since the neutral lepton now has only two independent internal states, only a two-component spinor is now actually needed to describe its field; this connexion between number of independent internal states and number of spinor components was demonstrated in §§ 2.2 and 2.3.

The field equation for the two-component spinors can be derived from the four-component Dirac equation, $i\hbar\,\partial\psi_\nu/\partial t = c\boldsymbol{\alpha}.\mathbf{q}\psi_\nu$, by using the fact that only solutions with the positive-chirality property,

$$\tfrac{1}{2}(1+\gamma_5)\psi_\nu = \psi_\nu,$$

are now to be kept. For these, the projections $\phi_\nu = \frac{1}{2}(1+\gamma_5)\psi_\nu$, introduced earlier, are identical with the solutions themselves. Then applying the operation $\frac{1}{2}(1+\gamma_5)$ to the Dirac equation yields

$$i\hbar\,\partial\phi_\nu/\partial t = -c\boldsymbol{\sigma}.\mathbf{q}\phi_\nu, \tag{10.75}$$

since $\frac{1}{2}(1+\gamma_5)\boldsymbol{\alpha} = -\frac{1}{2}(1+\gamma_5)\boldsymbol{\sigma} = -\boldsymbol{\sigma}\frac{1}{2}(1+\gamma_5)$. As a four-component equation this has

$$\boldsymbol{\sigma} = \begin{pmatrix} \boldsymbol{\sigma} & 0 \\ 0 & \boldsymbol{\sigma} \end{pmatrix}$$

in terms of the $2\times 2$ Pauli matrices, hence is equivalent to two identical two-component equations, each of the form (10.75). Only two-component solutions $\boldsymbol{\varphi}_\nu$ are needed to characterize the neutral lepton field completely. The solutions for definite momenta, energies and spins have already been given in (3.11) for the more general case of $m \neq 0$.

The equation for a momentum eigenstate, having the positive energy $i\hbar\,\partial\phi_\nu/\partial t = cq\phi_\nu$, may be written

$$(1+\boldsymbol{\sigma}.\hat{\mathbf{q}})\boldsymbol{\varphi}_\nu = 0. \tag{10.76}$$

This is just the two-component form of the equation $(1-\gamma_5)\phi_\nu = 0$ for a massless particle, indicating that the intrinsic velocity and spin stay antiparallel, $\gamma_5 = -\alpha_i\sigma_i = +1$. The massless particle has identical intrinsic and mean velocities, $cq/q = c$, there is no 'zitterbewegung', and both the chirality $\gamma_5 = +1$ and the helicity $\boldsymbol{\sigma}.\hat{\mathbf{q}} = -1$ are simultaneously definite. The normal neutrino can only move left-handedly.

The operation of charge-conjugation, $CK$, anticommutes with the Dirac $\boldsymbol{\sigma} = -\gamma_5\boldsymbol{\alpha}$ since

$$CK\boldsymbol{\sigma} = -C\gamma_5^* K\boldsymbol{\alpha} = +\gamma_5 C\boldsymbol{\alpha}^* K = +\gamma_5\boldsymbol{\alpha}CK = -\boldsymbol{\sigma}CK.$$

This has the consequence that when the antineutrino description

$$\phi_\nu^C = \tfrac{1}{2}(1+\gamma_5)CK\psi_\nu = CK\tfrac{1}{2}(1-\gamma_5)\psi_\nu$$

is reduced to the two-component spinor $\boldsymbol{\varphi}_\nu^C$, then (10.76) is replaced by

$$(1-\boldsymbol{\sigma}.\hat{\mathbf{q}})\boldsymbol{\varphi}_\nu^C = 0. \tag{10.77}$$

The antineutrinos are restricted to right-handedness, as expected.

The two-component theory represented by (10.75) was, in its essential respects, put forward very early by Weyl. It was discarded at the time because it was inconsistent with parity conservation; $\boldsymbol{\sigma}.\mathbf{q}$ changes sign in space inversions, hence (10.75) is clearly not invariant to them. The mirror image of the neutrino is now the antineutrino. Interest in this picture was reawakened‡ when parity non-conservation was discovered.

Adoption of the two-component theory results in a simple lepton-conserving form for the $\beta$-coupling. It yields a lepton current which, when written in terms of the 'doubled' spinor $\phi_\nu$, is

$$\bar{\psi}_e\gamma_\alpha\phi_\nu = \psi_e^\dagger\beta\gamma_\alpha\tfrac{1}{2}(1+\gamma_5)\phi_\nu = \phi_e^\dagger\beta\gamma_\alpha\phi_\nu, \tag{10.78}$$

hence automatically impresses the correct degree of handedness on the electron. Moreover, the theory has the great virtue that it assumes no more about the neutrino than needs to be assumed; it attributes to it only the minimal degrees of freedom needed to account for its so far observable properties. On the other hand, it can be essentially ignored (merely given 'lip service'!) since it changes nothing given by the V–A Law as applied from the beginning. The only difference in the old procedure was that it impressed the restriction to projections by $\tfrac{1}{2}(1+\gamma_5)$ as part of the interaction mechanism. The latter property of the mechanism must still be kept in the two-component theory in so far as the nucleons are concerned. Moreover, it is still far more convenient to introduce four-component representations of even a 'two-component neutrino' in applying the $\beta$-coupling. The symmetry in the way all the four fermions are handled is desirable to keep. In view of all this, and particularly since the interaction has properties of 'handedness' not entirely compassed by the two-component theory, it may well be desirable to retain the possibility of a four-component neutrino. This will be a more viable theory in the contingency that some day the additional neutrino descriptions may be needed. A possible use is suggested in § 13.4.

‡ L. Landau, *Nucl. Phys.* **3,** 127 (1957); T. D. Lee and C. N. Yang, *Phys. Rev.* **105,** 1671 (1957); A. Salam, *Nuovo Cim.* **5,** 299 (1957).

# XI

# PION DECAY

THE preceding chapters were concerned with $\beta$-processes involving only normal nucleons and not the antinucleons: the negative proton ($\bar{p}$) and the antineutron ($\bar{n}$). Free antinucleons can be preserved in the laboratory for only very brief periods after their generation (in high energy collisions of particles) because of their large 'annihilation' cross-sections. These annihilations do not usually result merely in $\gamma$-radiation, as does positron-negatron annihilation, but in the production of 'pions'.

A free antineutron, if protected from contact with matter long enough, should decay spontaneously into an antiproton plus a positron-neutrino pair, according to the version $\bar{n} \rightarrow \bar{p}+e^{+}+\nu$ of the relation (1.21). The energy release and the rate should be the same as in ordinary neutron decay. So slow a rate, corresponding to a 12-minute half-life, makes it difficult to study even the ordinary neutron decay, despite the feasibility of using collisions with matter to slow down the normal neutrons. The difficulties of handling antineutrons are orders of magnitude greater, and observations of their spontaneous decay seem out of reach at present.

## 11.1. The pion

What may be regarded as sources of 'bound' antinucleons are available in the form of pions, particles which can be treated with some degree of success as systems composed of nucleon–antinucleon pairs part of the time. It is the $\beta$-transformations of such 'virtual' nucleons which initially make a consideration of the pions relevant to a study of $\beta$-processes. Most of the information about the pionic states, like the knowledge concerning nuclear states, comes from phenomena not directly related to the $\beta$-interactions, hence those data can be given only a necessary minimum of attention here.

*Properties of the pion and its field*

The pions are spinless bosons having both charged and neutral forms: $\pi^{\pm}$ and $\pi^{0}$. Each charged pion has the mass

$$m_{\pi} = (273{\cdot}25 \pm 0{\cdot}12)m_{e}, \tag{11.1}$$

in units of the electron mass. The neutral pion, which is $(9{\cdot}0 \pm 0{\cdot}3)m_{e}$

less massive, will have only secondary interest here because it decays via electromagnetic interaction, into a photon pair, long before the much weaker $\beta$-interactions can produce detectable results. Whereas the charged pions have the mean life

$$\tau_\pi = (2{\cdot}56 \pm 0{\cdot}05)10^{-8} \text{ sec}, \tag{11.2}$$

the neutral pion lifetime is shorter than $4(10)^{-16}$ sec.

If the pions are to be treated as quanta (*vide* Chapter IX) of a suitably defined field, $\Phi$, then this must be a scalar field in order that its quanta be spinless. A remarkable finding is that the pion field must behave like a *Pseudo*scalar ($\Phi \to -\Phi$) in space inversions. The most directly interpretable evidence for this is provided by the finding that after a negative pion forms a 'pionic atom' with a deuteron as nucleus, the pion can be absorbed by the nucleus with the production of just two neutrons. Such a final state, composed of two identical fermions, is highly restricted in character by the Pauli principle; if it is a singlet state, it is antisymmetric in the spins and must have a symmetric spatial configuration, hence can have only an even relative orbital angular momentum; if the triplet state is formed the orbital momentum must be odd. Now, the initial pionic atom consists of a spinless pion without orbital momentum (the atomic system descends to its lowest level very rapidly), hence all the angular momentum is provided by the deuteron nucleus, which has $\mathbf{I} = \mathbf{1}$ (coming from a triplet orientation of the one neutron and one proton constituting it, together with an *even* orbital momentum). The conservation of this odd unit of angular momentum demands that the final neutron pair be formed in a triplet configuration, since the singlet is limited to even angular momenta by the exclusion effect. Thus, the final outcome must be a triplet state of odd *orbital* momentum and, therefore, *odd parity*. Such a result for the parity is significant because it has been produced from an initial state composed of an even parity nucleus and an even parity orbit ($l = 0$) for the pion. The odd final parity can only have come‡ from an odd 'intrinsic' parity of the pion itself. That is not all the evidence which exists, but does illustrate the kind that is relied on for the conclusion that the pion field should be attributed a Pseudoscalar character.

Suppose, more specifically, that the symbol $\Phi$ is used to denote the

‡ Parity is expected to be conserved in the strong pion-nucleon interactions. These lead to nucleon-nucleon interactions in much the way that interactions of charges with the electromagnetic field lead to forces between charges. It is an experimental fact that the nucleon-nucleon interactions conserve parity to a high order of accuracy. All the more directly observed pion-nucleon interactions have also been consistent with parity conservation.

destruction operator for negative pions, $\pi^-$. The field $\Phi$ must be complex‡ to have charged quanta, and $\Phi^*$ will then have the interpretation of *creating* $\pi^-$. At the same time, $\Phi$ and $\Phi^*$ are decomposable into positive and negative frequency components, hence there is room for the interpretations that $\Phi$ may not only destroy $\pi^-$ but create $\pi^+$, while $\Phi^*$ may destroy $\pi^+$ in addition to creating $\pi^-$. That will amount to treating $\pi^-$ and $\pi^+$ as each others' charge-conjugates ('antiparticles') with mere complex conjugation as the charge-conjugation operation. Real Pseudoscalar field components $\Phi_{1,2}$ may be defined in such a way that

$$\Phi = 2^{-\frac{1}{2}}(\Phi_1+i\Phi_2) \quad \text{and} \quad \Phi^* = 2^{-\frac{1}{2}}(\Phi_1-i\Phi_2). \tag{11.3}$$

A third, real 'self-charge-conjugate' field, $\Phi_3$, must be introduced to take care of the creation and destruction of the neutral pions. Thus, although the pion field is merely a (Pseudo)scalar as regards behaviour in ordinary space, it is yet held resolvable into three components, $\Phi_{1,2,3}$. The resolution is not along ordinary spatial axes, but corresponds to the three different charges which a pion may have. The field may be regarded as an 'isovector' in the three-dimensional 'charge-space' already introduced in connexion with (4.11), and to be discussed further, below.

*Pions as quanta*

In describing various excitations (generations or absorptions of quanta) of the pion field, the amplitudes $\Phi(\mathbf{r},t)$ must be treated as variables subject to appropriate quantum conditions. For the purposes here, it will suffice to present these conditions only for the amplitudes of plane wave modes into which $\Phi$ may be analysed. The decomposition will be written

$$\Phi = c[\hbar/(2\pi)^3]^{\frac{1}{2}} \oint [(d\mathbf{k}/2\omega](A_{\mathbf{k}}\, e^{i(\mathbf{k}.\mathbf{r}-\omega t)}+B^*_{\mathbf{k}}\, e^{-i(\mathbf{k}.\mathbf{r}-\omega t)}), \tag{11.4}$$

with
$$\omega(\mathbf{k}) = +c[k^2+(m_\pi c/\hbar)^2]^{\frac{1}{2}}. \tag{11.5}$$

Separating off the factor $\omega^{-1}$ allows the amplitudes $A_{\mathbf{k}}$ and $B_{\mathbf{k}}$ to remain invariant, like $\Phi$ itself, in proper Lorentz transformations. That follows from the fact that $(d\mathbf{k})/2\omega$ forms an invariant, as can be seen from the property

$$\oint (d\mathbf{k})/2\omega = \oint d^4k\, \delta[\omega^2-(ck)^2-(m_\pi c^2/\hbar)^2], \tag{11.6}$$

where $d^4k \equiv (d\mathbf{k})\, d\omega = (d\mathbf{k})\, d\omega^2/2\omega$ is an obviously invariant four-dimensional element. The invariant delta-function serves to restrict

‡ Fundamentally because participation in gauge-invariant electromagnetic interactions by the charged quanta requires the availability of complex phase changes, as outlined in the footnote on p. 263. This formal language has an essential role in representing charge conservation in general.

the four-dimensional integration to the so-called 'mass-shell' defined by (11.5). The normalizing factors in front of (11.4) are so chosen that a correct expression ensues for the energy, below.

The decomposition (11.4) may be compared to the introduction of the fermion-destroying operators $a$, and antifermion-creating operators $c^\dagger$, in (9.4a). Here, $A_{\mathbf{k}}$ will become a $\pi^-$-destroying operator, and $B^*_{\mathbf{k}}$ a $\pi^+$-creating one, if these amplitudes are subjected to the quantum conditions

$$[A_{\mathbf{k}}, A^*_{\mathbf{k}'}] = [B_{\mathbf{k}}, B^*_{\mathbf{k}'}] = 2\omega\delta(\mathbf{k}-\mathbf{k}'), \tag{11.7}$$

with all other *commutators* of $A^{(*)}_{\mathbf{k}}$, $B^{(*)}_{\mathbf{k}}$ vanishing. The right-hand side in (11.7) is properly invariant, being the inverse of $(d\mathbf{k})/2\omega$, and is the appropriate modification of the Kronecker deltas used in expressing the quantum conditions (9.5) when the continuity of the labels $\mathbf{k}$ is specifically recognized. Imposing such conditions on commutators like $[A_{\mathbf{k}}, A^*_{\mathbf{k}'}] = A_{\mathbf{k}} A^*_{\mathbf{k}'} - A^*_{\mathbf{k}'} A_{\mathbf{k}}$, rather than on anticommutators as in (9.5), is appropriate to a change from Fermi to Bose statistics, as already discussed in § 9.1. It will follow from the commutation properties (11.7) that the 'number operators' defined by

$$N(\pi^-) = \oint [(d\mathbf{k})/2\omega] A^*_{\mathbf{k}} A_{\mathbf{k}}, \qquad N(\pi^+) = \oint [(d\mathbf{k})/2\omega] B^*_{\mathbf{k}} B_{\mathbf{k}} \tag{11.8}$$

will have any of the non-negative integers as eigenvalues.

The interpretation of $A_{\mathbf{k}}$ as annihilating a $\pi^-$ quantum, while $B^*_{\mathbf{k}}$ of (11.4) creates $\pi^+$, is obviously appropriate to the 'charge-conjugacy' of the opposite charges as mentioned in the preceding subsection. It leads to $\Phi$ annihilating $\pi^-$ quanta and generating $\pi^+$, while $\Phi^*$ creates $\pi^-$ and destroys $\pi^+$, just as discussed. A state of the field with $m$ negative quanta and $n$ positive ones is representable by

$$A^*_{\mathbf{k}_1} A^*_{\mathbf{k}_2} \ldots A^*_{\mathbf{k}_m} B^*_{\mathbf{K}_1} \ldots B^*_{\mathbf{K}_n} |0\rangle, \tag{11.9}$$

if the quanta constitute excitations of the modes indicated. Any two or more of the modes may be identical without leading to a vanishing of (11.9), as in the fermion case, because the creation operators all commute. Using

$$A_{\mathbf{k}}|0\rangle = 0 \quad \text{and} \quad B_{\mathbf{k}}|0\rangle = 0, \tag{11.10}$$

it is easy to show that operating on the state (11.9) with $N(\pi^-)$ merely multiplies it by the number $m$, while the eigenvalue $n$ results from an operation by $N(\pi^+)$.

No essential use will be made here of the energy operator, $H_\pi$, for the non-interacting (plane wave) pions. It is presented briefly only because it serves to determine the appropriate normalization constants already put in front of the field operator (11.4). Such procedures as mentioned in the footnote § on p. 166 show that the hamiltonian

$$H_\pi = \tfrac{1}{2}\oint (d\mathbf{r}) \sum_{i=1}^{3} [(\nabla\Phi_i)^2+(\dot{\Phi}_i/c)^2+(m_\pi\, c/\hbar)^2\Phi_i^2] \tag{11.11}$$

leads to appropriate canonical (hamiltonian) equations in the variables $\Phi_{1,2,3}$. One of each pair of canonical equations serves merely to define a conjugate variable, $\Pi_i = \dot{\Phi}_i/c^2$. The remaining one becomes a Klein–Gordon equation,

$$[\nabla^2-\partial^2/c^2\partial t^2-(m_\pi\, c/\hbar)^2]\Phi_i = 0, \tag{11.12}$$

which must be satisfied (see (2.73), for example) by any field having non-interacting quanta of mass $m_\pi$. The two terms of $H_\pi$ containing $\Phi_1 = 2^{-\frac{1}{2}}(\Phi+\Phi^*)$ and $\Phi_2 = -i2^{-\frac{1}{2}}(\Phi-\Phi^*)$ yield

$$\oint [(d\mathbf{k})/2\omega](A_\mathbf{k}^* A_\mathbf{k}+B_\mathbf{k}^* B_\mathbf{k})\hbar\omega(\mathbf{k}), \tag{11.13}$$

after a substitution of (11.4) for $\Phi$ and $\Phi^*$, and with the multiplying constants as chosen. This is obviously appropriate for the energy of the charged quanta in view of the definitions (11.8) of their numbers. A similar term arises for the energy of the (self-charge-conjugate) $\pi^0$ quanta, described by the real field $\Phi_3$; there will be no need to make this specific. It should be mentioned, however, that the full expression (11.11) also contains a 'zero-point energy', present even when the field is unexcited,

$$\oint \frac{\hbar^3(d\mathbf{k})V}{(2\pi\hbar)^3}\,\tfrac{1}{2}\hbar\omega(\mathbf{k}) \tag{11.14}$$

for each of the three types of quanta. This will be ignored just as the infinite constant in the fermion energy (9.9) was ignored.

*The pion-nucleon interaction*

The common sources of pions are processes which are initiated when nucleons suffer the impact of other particles (such as other nucleons). The processes are just such as might be expected if nucleons interact strongly with the pion field and are capable of radiating pionic quanta, once sufficient energy is made available. A nucleon may then be pictured as a system which oscillates among various temporary states containing pions, e.g.:

$$\left.\begin{aligned} &\mathrm{p}\leftrightarrow \mathrm{n}+\pi^+\leftrightarrow \mathrm{p}+\pi^0\leftrightarrow \mathrm{p}+\pi^-+\pi^+\leftrightarrow \ldots\\ &\mathrm{n}\leftrightarrow \mathrm{p}+\pi^-\leftrightarrow \mathrm{n}+\pi^0\leftrightarrow \mathrm{p}+\pi^-+\pi^0\leftrightarrow \ldots\end{aligned}\right\}. \tag{11.15}$$

These states can only be transient, 'virtual', ones in an isolated nucleon, because there is not enough energy available for the constituents to separate from each other. (The virtual transfer of charge to the lighter pions is supposed to account for the greater magnetic moments which nucleons are observed to have, as compared to expectations for the heavy proton mass, $e\hbar/M_p c \ll e\hbar/m_\pi c$.) The pions may be freed when the nucleons engage in sufficiently energetic collisions, or when energy is supplied by an incident $\gamma$-ray in a type of 'photo-effect'. It may also be pointed out that the nucleon-antinucleon annihilations alluded to above are variants of the processes implicit in (11.15), such as $\bar{n}+p \rightarrow 2\pi^+ + \pi^-$ or $\pi^+ + \pi^0$, etc., all of which can proceed to completion because of the abundance of energy available, $\geqslant 2Mc^2$.

The pion-nucleon interaction responsible for such transitions as in (11.15) is supposed to have the fundamental form

$$h_{N\pi} = iG(\bar{\Psi}\gamma_5 \tau_i \Psi)\Phi_i, \tag{11.16}$$

in so far as it is representable in the language of fields. Here, $\Psi$ is the 'isospinor' already introduced in (4.11), to represent the nucleon field; it is a 'direct product' of Dirac spinors, resulting in a function of isospin variables on which the isospin operators $\tau_{1,2,3}$ can have effect. Each pion field component $\Phi_{1,2,3}$ is a pseudoscalar which can be invariantly coupled only to such a pseudoscalar nucleon field density as is here represented with the help of the operation by $\gamma_5$; the factor $i$ serves to make the resultant coupling-energy density (or interaction lagrangian), $h_{N\pi}$, hermitian, since $\gamma_5$ anticommutes with the $\beta$ of $\bar{\Psi} \equiv \Psi^\dagger\beta$.

The components $\Phi_i$ are contracted with the components of the nucleonic isospin operator, $\boldsymbol{\tau}$, in $h_{N\pi}$. Thus, the pion field is being treated as an isovector in the charge space, with $\tau_i \Phi_i$ forming an 'isoscalar product'. The invariance of this to arbitrary rotations in the charge space introduces a 'charge-independence' (§ 5.3).‡ As part of this, consistency with charge conservation is insured. That is easiest to see in terms of the 'spherical isovector components', $-\Phi$ and $\Phi^*$, which are analogues (isomorphs) of the spherical harmonic components $rY_{1,\pm 1}$ of the position vector $\mathbf{r}$ of ordinary space. The isoscalar product in $h_{N\pi}$ can be written

$$\tau_i \Phi_i = \tau_3 \Phi_3 + 2^{\frac{1}{2}}(\tau_- \Phi + \tau_+ \Phi^*), \tag{11.17}$$

where $\tau_\pm \equiv \frac{1}{2}(\tau_1 \pm i\tau_2)$ transform neutron into proton states and vice versa. The $\Phi^*$ and $\Phi$ create $\pi^-$ and $\pi^+$ (or destroy $\pi^+$ and $\pi^-$) in correct correspondence.

The charge-invariant property may be formalized as a conservation of total isospin, $\mathbf{T}$, to which not only each nucleon's isospin, $\frac{1}{2}\boldsymbol{\tau}$,

‡ The consequence is that the contribution of the pion–nucleon interactions to the nucleon–nucleon force, already mentioned in the footnote on p. 301, will be charge-independent in the way discussed in § 5.3.

contributes, but also each pion. An isolated, isovector pion field may be decomposed into individual pion-quantum components which are eigenfunctions of $T_\pi^2 = 2$ and $T_3 = 0$ or $\pm 1$, for neutral and charged quanta (hence $Q = eT_3$ for a pion vs. $Q = (T_3 + \frac{1}{2})\, e$ for a nucleon). The charge-independent interaction, $h_{N\pi}$ above, will generate only processes in which the total isospin, e.g.

$$\mathbf{T} = \sum_{a=1}^{A} \tfrac{1}{2}\boldsymbol{\tau}^a + \sum \mathbf{T}_\pi, \tag{11.18}$$

is conserved, in magnitude $T^2$ as well as in the component $T_3$ which helps maintain consistency with charge-conservation.

To complete the presentation of the pion-nucleon interaction (11.16), the magnitude of the coupling constant $G$ ought to be specified. It should be the result of measuring the intensity of some specific process (such as the direct scattering of a pion on a nucleon) and comparing it to expectations from the interaction form (11.16). This form is such that the value attributed to $G$ will depend on just what are taken to be the correct descriptions, $\Psi$ and $\Phi_i$, of the nucleons and pions as they engage in the interaction. Satisfactorily accurate descriptions are difficult to construct, primarily because even the most elementary physical situation presents an essential many-body problem. The pion-nucleon interaction turns out to be so strong that, for example, even an isolated physical nucleon must be described as in such transient states as are indicated in (11.15), with their many degrees of freedom, for substantial fractions of the time.

What are currently believed to be the most trustworthy approaches (so-called 'dispersion-theoretic' techniques) to the pion-nucleon problem avoid becoming specific about the full descriptions $\Psi$ and $\Phi_i$, relying instead on what seem to be reasonable assumptions about the consequences that a proper description would have. Then the conclusion from evidence about pion-nucleon scattering and the photoproductions of pions from nucleons is that

$$G^2/4\pi\hbar c \approx 15 \tag{11.19}$$

should be taken as the 'renormalized' value of the coupling strength. The contrast of this large value to $e^2/\hbar c \approx 1/137$ for electromagnetic interactions suggests why 'transient states' do not play as vital a role in the weaker interactions.

For later reference, it will be helpful to write the total nucleon-pion interaction energy as

$$H_{N\pi} = \oint (d\mathbf{r}) h_{N\pi} = H(\pi^-) + H(\pi^+) + H(\pi^0) + \text{h.c.}, \tag{11.20}$$

where each $H(\pi)$ is proportional to the annihilation operator for pions of the type indicated; the hermitian conjugate terms, h.c., have the corresponding creation operators. It follows from (11.16), (11.17), and (11.4) that

$$H(\pi^-) = 2^{\frac{1}{2}} icG[\hbar/(2\pi)^3]^{\frac{1}{2}} \oint [(d\mathbf{k})/2\omega] \times \times \oint (d\mathbf{r})(\psi_n^\dagger \beta\gamma_5 \psi_p) A_{\mathbf{k}}\, e^{i(\mathbf{k}.\mathbf{r}-\omega t)}. \quad (11.21)$$

$H(\pi^+)$ differs in having $A_{\mathbf{k}} \to B_{\mathbf{k}}$, $\psi_n \leftrightarrow \psi_p$. $H(\pi^0)$ is constructed in a similar obvious way.

*The π-decay modes*

The pion-nucleon interaction must be expected to induce transients also in the isolated-pion system. These transients will be results of processes which are variants of such as are symbolized in (11.15):

$$\left.\begin{aligned} \pi^+ &\leftrightarrow \mathrm{p}+\bar{\mathrm{n}}\ (\leftrightarrow \mathrm{p}+\bar{\mathrm{p}}+\pi^0+\pi^+ \leftrightarrow \ldots) \\ \pi^- &\leftrightarrow \mathrm{n}+\bar{\mathrm{p}}\ (\leftrightarrow \mathrm{n}+\bar{\mathrm{p}}+\pi^++\pi^- \leftrightarrow \ldots) \end{aligned}\right\}. \quad (11.22)$$

It is in this sense that a physical pion can be regarded as partially composed of nucleon-antinucleon pairs. The transients indicated in the parentheses need not be specified separately if the nucleon pairs specified first are taken to be appropriately 'dressed' with pion clouds and additional nucleon pairs.

While in the nucleon-containing states, the system must be expected‡ to be subject to β-transformations, with the possibility of results like

$$\left.\begin{aligned} \pi^+ &\to \mathrm{p}+\bar{\mathrm{n}} \to \mathrm{e}^++\nu \\ \pi^- &\to \mathrm{n}+\bar{\mathrm{p}} \to \mathrm{e}^-+\bar{\nu} \end{aligned}\right\}, \quad (11.23)$$

the final steps being appropriate versions of (1.21). The lepton states here have the possibility of becoming permanent because the pion rest-mass furnishes plenty of energy for their completion. Thus, the pion must be expected to decay occasionally into an electron-neutrino pair, with the electron getting the unique energy,

$$W = (m_\pi^2+m_e^2)c^2/2m_\pi \approx \tfrac{1}{2}m_\pi c^2 = 69{\cdot}83\ \mathrm{MeV}, \quad (11.24)$$

from a pion at rest. This can be easily seen to follow from the necessary equality of the electron and neutrino momenta.

The expected electron decay mode (11.23) of the pion escaped detection for many years, but was found§ eventually. The detection was

‡ M. R. Ruderman and R. Finkelstein, *Phys. Rev.* **76**, 1458 (1949).

§ T. Fazzini, G. Fidecaro, A. W. Merrison, H. Paul, and A. V. Tollestrup, *Phys. Rev. Letters*, **1**, 247 (1958); G. Impeduglia, R. Plano, A. Prodell, N. Samios, M. Schwartz, and J. Steinberger, *Phys. Rev. Letters*, **1**, 249 (1958).

difficult because another decay mode of the pion is about 10 000 times as frequent. This primary mode consists of

$$\left.\begin{array}{l}\pi^+ \rightarrow \mu^+ + \mu^0 \\ \pi^- \rightarrow \mu^- + \bar{\mu}^0\end{array}\right\}. \tag{11.25}$$

where the symbols $\mu^\pm$ stand for *muons*, particles longer known than the pions themselves, while $\mu^0$ and $\bar{\mu}^0$ stand for ordinarily undetected neutral particles. That only one such neutral is emitted together with each muon is known from the fact that the muons are found to be mono-energetic, each having 4·2 MeV of kinetic energy when arising from a pion at rest.

## 11.2 The muon-neutretto current

*Properties of the muon*

The muons, $\mu^\pm$, are much more massive than electrons,

$$m_\mu = (206{\cdot}77 \pm 0{\cdot}03)m_e, \tag{11.26}$$

but, if due allowances for this are made, they seem to be identical with electrons in all their interactions. Thus, when $m_e$ is replaced by $m_\mu$ in the formulae describing electromagnetic interactions of electrons, the results are found to apply very precisely to the electromagnetic behaviour observed in muons. The magnetic moment of the muon is found to be that characteristic of a spin-$\frac{1}{2}$ particle, even as regards certain very small 'radiative corrections'. Muonic atoms (analogous to the pionic atoms mentioned in the preceding section) have been formed by the capture of negative muons into Bohr orbits around nuclei, and X-rays characteristic of transitions among such orbits have been observed.

The muons are unstable, with a mean life

$$\tau_\mu = (2{\cdot}210 \pm 0{\cdot}003)\ \mu\text{sec}, \tag{11.27}$$

but again this difference from electrons may be attributed to the greater muonic mass, which makes sufficient energy available for the formation of appropriate product particles. Indeed, the existence of the instability turns into evidence for further similarities between electronic and muonic interactions. As will be seen in Chapter XII, the instability seems to arise from a $\beta$-interaction of a form analogous to that engaged in by electrons.

A final property of the muons points to a still further similarity with electrons, and is particularly important for understanding the $\pi$-decay modes. As will be discussed in Chapter XIII, muons are captured by nucleons in processes

$$\mathrm{p}+\mu^- \to \mathrm{n}+\mu^0, \tag{11.28 a}$$

paralleling orbital electron capture. It is presumed that

$$\mathrm{n}+\mu^+ \to \mathrm{p}+\bar{\mu}^0 \tag{11.28 b}$$

can also occur and has not actually been observed only because the requisite initial state has too short a duration.

The current conclusion from the experimental evidence is that muons may be treated as if they are merely 'heavy electrons'. They seem to engage only in beta-, electromagnetic, and (presumably) gravitational interactions, just as electrons do. This has raised questions as to the origin of the large mass difference between the two types of particles. According to long-current ideas, the inertial mass of any particle should be traceable to a kind of 'drag' resulting from its interactions, and, on this basis, the muon-electron mass difference remains a great mystery (perhaps no greater than the particular mass attained by any particle, however).

*The neutretto*

The neutral particles symbolized by $\mu^0$ and $\bar{\mu}^0$ in (11.25) and (11.28) will be called the neutretto and the antineutretto here. Separate evidence about each property and each role assigned to these particles is difficult to adduce because they are as near-unobservable as neutrinos. A series of hypotheses about them must be made before observable consequences can be drawn, and then the set of assumptions must be tested as a whole.

The neutretto mass should be quite directly measurable by observing the muon energies from the $\pi$-decays (11.25). Because the neutretto and muon momenta must have equal magnitudes, the muon energy (inclusive of rest-mass) should be

$$W_\mu = (m_\pi^2+m_\mu^2-m_0^2)c^2/2m_\pi \tag{11.29}$$

if $m_0$ is the neutretto's rest-mass. In case $m_0 = 0$, the kinetic energy is expected to be $W_\mu - m_\mu c^2 = (m_\pi - m_\mu)^2c^2/2m_\pi = (4{\cdot}13\pm0{\cdot}02)$ MeV, with $m_\pi$ and $m_\mu$ as given in (11.1) and (11.26). This $m_0 = 0$ expectation is quite consistent with the directly observed kinetic energy, $(4{\cdot}17\pm0{\cdot}06)$ MeV, hence the neutretto may well have a zero rest-mass like the neutrino. However, there still is enough uncertainty,

$$\Delta W_\mu \approx 0{\cdot}04 m_\mathrm{e} c^2,$$

for a neutretto mass as large as $m_0 = (2m_\pi \Delta W_\mu/c^2)^{\frac{1}{2}} \approx 5m_e$ to be possible.

The neutretto must have a half-integer spin in order to fit into the angular momentum balances with the spin-$\frac{1}{2}$ particles (and the spinless pions) necessary for the processes (11.28) and (11.25). It is assumed to have just the spin $\frac{1}{2}$, like all known elementary particles of half-integer spin. The assumption is supported by successes achieved with giving muon-neutretto pairs roles analogous to electron-neutrino pairs, in explaining the various processes to be examined in this and succeeding chapters.

The consistency of the data with a zero mass and a spin $\frac{1}{2}$ for the neutretto led to its being identified with the neutrino for many years. This identification became untenable when it was eventually shown‡ that the capture of neutrettos by nucleons yields muons, but not electrons. Reversals of the processes (11.28) seem to take place, but not the inducement of electron emissions as by the pile neutrinos used in the Reines–Cowan experiment (§§ 1.2 and 8.2). The experiments thus establish one difference between neutrettos and neutrinos: their capture by nucleons lead to different products. The theoretical treatment of the neutretto capture will be reviewed in Chapter XIII.

The sources of the neutrettos for the capture experiments were the pion decays (11.25). Thus, their success in reversing the $\mu$-capture processes (11.28) signifies that the neutral particles resulting from the $\pi \to \mu$ decays and from the $\mu$+nucleon captures are indeed the same types of neutrettos, as was already presumed when the expressions (11.25) and (11.28) were set down. Now it can be further asserted that at least part of the $\pi \to \mu$ decays may proceed through the temporary states symbolized in

$$\left.\begin{array}{l} \pi^+ \to \mathrm{p}+\bar{\mathrm{n}} \to \mu^+ + \mu^0 \\ \pi^- \to \mathrm{n}+\bar{\mathrm{p}} \to \mu^- + \bar{\mu}^0 \end{array}\right\}, \qquad (11.30)$$

where the last steps are variants of the capture processes (11.28). The first steps are identical with those shown in (11.23), there leading to electron emissions.

*The coupling of muon-neutretto to nucleon*

The observed similarities of muon and neutretto to electron and neutrino suggest trying out the hypothesis that the nucleon transformation current is coupled to a muon-neutretto current in the same way that

‡ G. Danby, J. M. Gaillard, K. Goulianos, L. M. Lederman, N. Mistry, M. Schwartz, and J. Steinberger, *Phys. Rev. Letters*, **9**, 36 (1962). See § 13.3.

it is coupled to the electron-neutrino current in the ordinary $\beta$-interaction (4.10). This involves assuming that a coupling-energy density of the form (4.9),

$$h_{N_\mu} = 8^{\frac{1}{2}} g J_\alpha(\text{pn}) J_\alpha(\mu\mu^0) + \text{h.c.}, \tag{11.31 a}$$

exists, with $J_\alpha(\text{pn})$ just the nucleon transformation current (4.8) and

$$J_\alpha(\mu\mu^0) = \phi_\mu^\dagger \beta\gamma_\alpha \phi_{\mu^0} \equiv \bar{\psi}_\mu \gamma_\alpha \tfrac{1}{2}(1+\gamma_5)\psi_{\mu^0}, \tag{11.31 b}$$

in analogy to $J_\alpha(e\nu)$ of (4.30). The subscript '$N\mu$' will identify the interaction-energy density as coupling nucleons '$N$' to $\mu^\pm$ and $\mu^0$, $\bar{\mu}^0$. A primary task for it will be to account for the muon and neutretto captures which will be discussed in Chapter XIII.

It should be recognized that the form $h_{N_\mu}$ is a law of the 'V–A' type as is $h_\beta$, restricting the various fermions to participation only through state components of specific chirality ($\gamma_5 = +1$). This assumption, as well as the assumption that the coupling constant $g$ has the same magnitude as in the ordinary $\beta$-decay, is not directly justified by the evidence presented so far. For this reason, alternative formulations will have to be considered at suitable stages, in order to see how far the basic assumptions are checked by the evidence which will be developed in this and the next two chapters.

## 11.3. The ratio of the π-decay modes

The chief uncertainty in the theoretical expectations concerning $\pi$-decay will stem from the difficulty of describing the isolated pion state, in view of the essential roles indicated in (11.23) and (11.30) for its transient modes. This makes it desirable to see first what conclusions can be drawn independently of details of the state description, as for the *ratio* of the two $\pi$-decay modes.

*Formulation of the decay rates*

Procedures which avoid the explicit construction of parent and daughter states are already familiar from the treatment of nuclear $\beta$-decay. The initial, physical pion state, $|\text{i}\rangle$, will be regarded as an eigenstate of an 'unperturbed hamiltonian' which is descriptive of the entire system aside from the 'radiated' fields, i.e. excluding here the electron, the neutrino, the muon, and the neutretto. It will be unnecessary for the present to specify that hamiltonian beyond asserting that it must involve not only pionic but also nucleonic degrees of freedom, and must include such strong pion–nucleon interaction as are represented by (11.16). The nucleonic variables must appear in the description of even the isolated pion state, $|i\rangle$, if couplings to the lepton fields, $h_\beta$ of (4.10) and $h_{N\mu}$ of (11.31), are to take hold. That description corresponds to the picture of the pion as oscillating among such transients as are indicated in (11.22), and will, for the present, constitute the only recognition of the role presumably played by such intermediate states as are indicated in (11.23) and (11.30). Moreover, the same hamiltonian will have to possess, as another eigenstate, the final state $|f\rangle$ of the $\pi$-decay. The latter state must be descriptive of a 'pion-nucleon vacuum', since this is all that remains aside from the leptons.

If the states $|i\rangle$ and $|f\rangle$ are taken to be descriptions of excited and unexcited pion-nucleon field states then the coupling energies in the presence of *given* lepton fields are representable by

$$\langle f|H_{Ne(\mu)}|i\rangle \equiv \langle f|\oint (d\mathbf{r})h_{\beta(N\mu)}|i\rangle, \tag{11.32}$$

with only the nucleon field amplitudes implicit in $h_\beta$ or $h_{N\mu}$ acting as field operators. The lepton fields are thus treated as unquantized, but this can be justified as simply as it was done in § 9.2 for the nuclear $\beta$-processes. It is now easy to understand that the differential $\pi$-decay rates can be given forms of the type (4.36):

$$d\lambda_{\pi e(\mu)} = (2\pi/\hbar)\delta(W+K-m_\pi c^2)|\langle f|H_{Ne(\mu)}|i\rangle|^2. \tag{11.33}$$

Here $W = c(p^2+m^2c^2)^{\frac{1}{2}}$ is the electron ($m = m_e$) or muon ($m = m_\mu$) energy, while $K = cq$ for the neutrino, but may be $K = c(q^2+m_0^2c^2)^{\frac{1}{2}}$ for a neutretto of mass $m_0 \neq 0$. When decays into plane wave modes are thus to be calculated, the transition amplitude takes the form

$$\langle f|H_{Ne(\mu)}|i\rangle = 2^{\frac{1}{2}}gJ_\alpha^0 \oint (d\mathbf{r})e^{-i(\mathbf{p}+\mathbf{q}).\mathbf{r}/\hbar}\langle f|\psi_p^\dagger \beta\gamma_\alpha(1+\gamma_5)\psi_n|i\rangle \tag{11.34}$$

for $\pi^-$-decay ($n \leftrightarrow p$ for $\pi^+$-decay). This follows from the definition (11.32) of the coupling energy operators $H_{Ne(\mu)}$, and from the forms (4.10) and (11.31) of $h_\beta$ and $h_{N\mu}$. The symbol $J_\alpha^0$ stands for either the electron-neutrino or the muon-neutretto current, evaluated for plane wave modes at $\mathbf{r} = 0$, $t = 0$.

*Effects of the conservation laws*

Momentum conservation in decays of pions at rest will require that the charged and neutral products have equal and opposite momenta: $\mathbf{p} = -\mathbf{q}$. The expression (11.34) for the transition amplitude makes it evident how that result will emerge from the formalism. The last matrix element factor must turn out to be independent of the interaction-position $\mathbf{r}$ (as it will be if only nucleon-pair components of zero total momentum contribute) so that the space integration becomes simple:

$$\left.\begin{aligned} \oint (d\mathbf{r})\exp(-i(\mathbf{p}+\mathbf{q}).\mathbf{r}/\hbar) &= (2\pi\hbar)^3\delta(\mathbf{p}+\mathbf{q}) \\ \text{or} \qquad &= V \quad \text{at } \mathbf{p} = -\mathbf{q} \end{aligned}\right\}. \tag{11.35}$$

($V$ is the usual indefinitely large 'normalization volume' $\equiv \oint (d\mathbf{r})$.) With this the squared amplitude may be written

$$|\langle \mathrm{f}|H_{N\mathrm{e}(\mu)}|\mathrm{i}\rangle|^2 = 2g^2(2\pi\hbar)^3\delta(\mathbf{p}+\mathbf{q})V\times$$
$$\times|\sum_\alpha J^0_\alpha \langle \mathrm{f}|\psi^\dagger_\mathrm{p}\,\beta\gamma_\alpha(1+\gamma_5)\psi_\mathrm{n}|\mathrm{i}\rangle_0|^2. \tag{11.36}$$

The subscript '0' refers to an evaluation of the nucleon fields at $\mathbf{r} = 0$ and $t = 0$. There is no possibility here of 'forbidden' effects arising from relative lepton orbital momenta, since the residual matrix element is independent of all lepton variables. Of course, no relative orbital momenta should be generated when the linear momenta are exactly opposed, $\mathbf{p} = -\mathbf{q}$.

With the prospective final states resolved into plane lepton wave modes, the total decay rates into each mode, $\lambda_{\pi\mathrm{e}(\mu)}$, are obtained by multiplying the partial rates (11.33) by the usual factors representing counts of eigenstates in specific momentum space elements, then integrating over the momenta. The result is the occurrence of a 'statistical factor',

$$\oint [4\pi p^2\,dp\,V/(2\pi\hbar)^3]\delta(W+K-m_\pi c^2)\oint [(d\mathbf{q})V/(2\pi\hbar)^3]\delta(\mathbf{p}+\mathbf{q})$$
$$= [4\pi V^2/(2\pi\hbar)^6]p^2\,dp/d(W+K), \tag{11.37 a}$$

where now $K = c(p^2+m_0^2c^2)^{\frac{1}{2}}$ because $q = p$, and $m_0 = 0$ for the neutrino at least. The fact that emissions from a spinless pion must be isotropic has also been used. Because $W+K \rightarrow m_\pi c^2$,

$$d(W+K) = c^2p\,dp[W^{-1}+K^{-1}] = m_\pi c^4p\,dp/WK. \tag{11.37 b}$$

The expression (11.37 a) is a measure of the 'phase space' available to the decay products and is proportional to

$$p^2\,dp/d(W+K) = p^2W/m_\pi c^3 = c(m_\pi^2-m^2)^2(m_\pi^2+m^2)/8m_\pi^4 \tag{11.38}$$

in the case of $m_0 = 0$, with $m = m_\mathrm{e}$ for the electron mode and $m = m_\mu$ for the muon emission. The last equality follows from the expression (11.24), or (11.29) with $m_0 = 0$, for the energy of the charged lepton. It can be seen at this point that

$$(p^2W)_\mathrm{e}/(p^2W)_\mu \approx m_\pi^6/(m_\pi^2+m_\mu^2)(m_\pi^2-m_\mu^2)^2 \approx 3{\cdot}5 \tag{11.39}$$

would be expected for the ratio of electron to muon emissions on the basis of the relative 'phase spaces' available, alone. A finite neutretto mass would only decrease the phase space available to the muon, hence increase the above ratio even further. Since this is in complete disagreement with the ratio, $\sim 10^{-4}$, actually observed, the measured number should provide a significant test of further details in the theory.

The above momentum-space analysis takes into account only the energy-momentum conservation. Angular momentum must also be conserved, and this in consistency with the $0^- \rightarrow 0^+$ transition, $|\mathrm{i}\rangle \rightarrow |\mathrm{f}\rangle$, of the 'pion-nucleon system'. Now, it is known from the Wigner–Eckart theorem (5.13) that only a spatial-scalar operator combining the states, like

$$J_4(\mathrm{pn}) = \phi_\mathrm{p}^\dagger \beta\gamma_4 \phi_\mathrm{n} = \tfrac{1}{2}\psi_\mathrm{p}^\dagger(1+\gamma_5)\psi_\mathrm{n} \tag{11.40}$$

of (11.36), (4.8), will yield any $0 \rightarrow 0$ transitions. Moreover, only the spatial-pseudoscalar part, $\frac{1}{2}\psi_\mathrm{p}^\dagger \gamma_5 \psi_\mathrm{n}$, will give the necessary parity change of the odd, isolated-pion state to the pion-nucleon vacuum. When the terms thus shown to vanish are omitted from (11.36), and this is put into the differential rate expression (11.33) together with the result (11.37), then the rate into either mode becomes expressible as

$$\lambda_{\pi\mathrm{e}(\mu)} = [2g^2/\pi(\hbar c)^4](pWK/m_\pi)|\langle\gamma_5\rangle_\pi|^2 \sum_{\text{spins}} V^2|J_4^0|^2, \tag{11.41 a}$$

where

$$\langle\gamma_5\rangle_\pi \equiv V^{\frac{1}{2}}\langle\mathrm{f}|\psi_\mathrm{p}^\dagger \gamma_5 \psi_\mathrm{n}|\mathrm{i}\rangle \tag{11.41 b}$$

for $\pi^-$-decay (with $\mathrm{n} \leftrightarrow \mathrm{p}$ for $\pi^+$-decay). It can now be seen that the entire dependence on details of the pion state description is confined to the $\pi$-decay 'moment', $\langle\gamma_5\rangle_\pi$, and that this will cancel out in the ratio $\lambda_{\pi\mathrm{e}}/\lambda_{\pi\mu}$.

*The Pseudovector ratio,* $\lambda_{\pi\mathrm{e}}/\lambda_{\pi\mu}$

The residual moment (11.41 b) shows that only the fourth component of the Pseudovector part, $\frac{1}{2}\psi_\mathrm{p}^\dagger \beta\gamma_\alpha\gamma_5\psi_\mathrm{n}$, of the nucleon transformation current (4.8) contributes to the $0^- \rightarrow 0^+$ pion decays. Contributions by the Vector part of this 'V–A' nucleon current are forbidden.

Aside from the 'statistical' (phase space) factors $pWK$, the expressions (11.41) for the two $\pi$-decay rates differ only as to the lepton current factors, $\sum |J_4^0|^2$. These sums over spins are easy to evaluate by the trace techniques first introduced for the neutron decay problem (§ 4.4). In the case of $\pi^- \rightarrow \mu^- + \bar{\mu}^0$,

$$\sum |J_4^0|^2 = \tfrac{1}{4}\sum_{\mu\mu^0} |\psi_\mu^\dagger(1+\gamma_5)\psi_{\mu^0}^C|^2 = (2V^2)^{-1}(1+\mathbf{v}\,.\,\mathbf{v}_0/c^2), \tag{11.42}$$

where $\mathbf{v} = c^2\mathbf{p}/W$ and $\mathbf{v}_0 = c^2\mathbf{q}/K$ are the muon and antineutretto velocities. The $\pi^+ \rightarrow \mu^+ + \mu^0$ case can be represented merely by changing the sign of $\gamma_5$, as in (4.35), and this makes no difference to the result. When $m_0 = 0$, the result also applies to the electron-neutrino modes:

$$\sum |J_4^0|^2 = (2V^2)^{-1}(1+\hat{\mathbf{q}}\cdot\mathbf{v}/c) = (2V^2)^{-1}(1-v/c), \tag{11.43}$$

the last because $\mathbf{q}$ is antiparallel to $\mathbf{v} = c^2\mathbf{p}/W$. The middle one of these expressions exhibits just the positive correlation distribution between the electron and neutrino which is characteristic of the $0 \to 0$ (Fermi) transitions in nuclear $\beta$-decay (Fig. 1.12). This should be expected, but a difference develops now because the leptons are forced into a negative correlation, $\mathbf{q} = -\mathbf{p}$, by having to conserve momentum by themselves. As a consequence, the intensity is saved from vanishing only because $v < c$ for a particle of finite rest-mass like the electron or muon.

The fact just noted is responsible for reversing the conclusion from the phase space considerations (11.39). Now it becomes advantageous to an emission to have less kinetic energy available, as does the muon relative to the electron. It follows from (11.41) and (11.43) that, for $m_0 = 0$:

$$\frac{\lambda_{\pi e}}{\lambda_{\pi\mu}} = \frac{[p^2W(1-v/c)]_e}{[p^2W(1-v/c)]_\mu} = \left(\frac{m_e}{m_\mu}\right)^2\left(\frac{m_\pi^2-m_e^2}{m_\pi^2-m_\mu^2}\right)^2. \tag{11.44}$$

This yields $\lambda_{\pi e}/\lambda_{\pi\mu} = (1{\cdot}280 \pm 0{\cdot}003)10^{-4}$, which agrees with the observed value $(1{\cdot}1 \pm 0{\cdot}2)10^{-4}$ within its limits of accuracy.

If the neutretto mass should turn out to be finite, then the muon emission rate, $\lambda_{\pi\mu}$, must be corrected by the factors:

$$\left[1+\frac{m_0^2(m_\pi^2+2m_\mu^2-m_0^2)}{m_\mu^2(m_\pi^2-m_\mu^2)}\right]\left[1-\frac{m_0^2(2m_\pi^2+2m_\mu^2-m_0^2)}{(m_\pi^2-m_\mu^2)^2}\right]^{\frac{1}{2}}. \tag{11.45}$$

In the limit $m_0^2 \ll (m_\pi^2 - m_\mu^2) \approx (179m_e)^2$, the ratio $\lambda_{\pi e}/\lambda_{\pi\mu}$ is decreased by the fraction $0{\cdot}09(m_0/m_\mu)^2$, making this an even less sensitive measure of the neutretto mass than is the energy measurement (11.29), which is decreased about four times as much.

*The polarizations*

The striking result that the low energy muon emission is more probable than the high energy electron mode can be understood in greater detail with the help of Fig. 11.1. This indicates the angular momenta to be expected from the coupling (11.31) and from its counterpart for the electron mode, in the emissions by a positive pion. The couplings

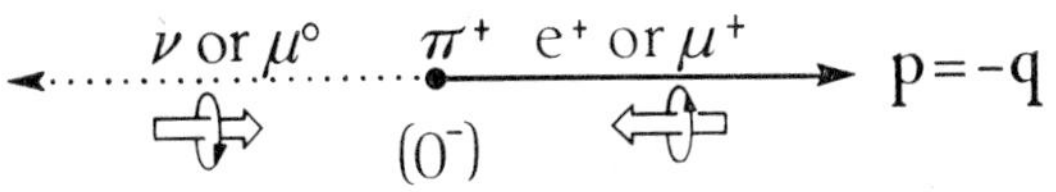


FIG. 11.1

generate lepton states in proportion to their projections by $\frac{1}{2}(1+\gamma_5)$, hence favour left-handed normal leptons and right-handed antileptons over their opposites, in ratios $(1+v/c)(1-v/c)$. The massless normal neutrinos, as well as neutrettos in so far as $m_0 \to 0$, are thus required to have complete left-handed polarizations. Then the positively charged leptons are also forced to be completely left-handed, to conserve linear and angular momentum. Thus, an 'unnatural' handedness, possible only in so far as $v < c$, is being demanded of the charged particles. This outcome is much more restrictive on the fast electrons than on the slower muons:

$$(1-v/c)_{\mathrm{e}} \approx 1/37\,300 \text{ vs. } (1-v/c)_{\mu} \approx 2m_{\mu}^2/(m_{\pi}^2+m_{\mu}^2) \approx 0{\cdot}73.$$

The polarized emissions are to be expected on the basis of the couplings assumed, but the foregoing picture is misleading if it is taken to imply that resultant polarizations, and parity non-conservation, are essential to obtaining the small electron-to-muon ratio. All that is really necessary is for the coupling to be such that, whenever a component of given helicity for one lepton is examined, then the opposite helicity of the accompanying lepton be preferred; the total superposition may even have a zero resultant for the polarization. The latter outcome is exactly what would follow from a coupling to a purely 'Vector' lepton current, like $C_{\mathrm{A}}\bar{\psi}_{\mathrm{e}}\gamma_{\alpha}\psi_{\nu}$, or to a purely 'Pseudovector' one like $C'_{\mathrm{A}}\bar{\psi}_{\mathrm{e}}\gamma_{\alpha}\gamma_5\psi_{\nu}$; either case would yield an intensity proportional to $(1-v/c)$ yet no resultant polarizations. The property essential to a small electron-to-muon ratio is possessed by any combination of the Vector and Pseudovector lepton currents (i.e. with arbitrary $C_{\mathrm{A}}$, $C'_{\mathrm{A}}$), and was already found in § 10.1. This is the fact that no Vector or Pseudovector currents exist between state components of opposite chirality, $\frac{1}{2}(1\pm\gamma_5)\psi$:

$$\psi_{\mathrm{e}}^{\dagger}\tfrac{1}{2}(1\pm\gamma_5).\beta\gamma_{\alpha}(\gamma_5).\tfrac{1}{2}(1\mp\gamma_5)\psi_{\nu} \equiv 0. \tag{11.46 a}$$

In contrast, Scalar, Tensor, and Pseudoscalar densities do not vanish when the chirality changes, but

$$\psi_{\mathrm{e}}^{\dagger}\tfrac{1}{2}(1\pm\gamma_5).\beta(\gamma_5).\tfrac{1}{2}(1\pm\gamma_5)\psi_{\nu} \equiv 0. \tag{11.46 b}$$

Couplings to such densities would find 'natural' the relative spin alignments demanded for the $\pi$-decay process by the conservation principles, and would favour electron over muon emissions. A systematic consideration of the evidence on possible alternatives for the coupling is left to the next subsection.

The considerations here were sufficient to indicate that there is no necessary connexion between the small observed electron-to-muon ratio and the polarizations to be expected. It is, therefore, important to have independent experimental checks of the polarizations predicted from the couplings assumed so far. The predictions are already indicated in Fig. 11.1, but a more formal presentation has interest, because the same formalism which yielded left-handed negatrons and right-handed positrons in emissions by unpolarized nuclei is now to be responsible for right-handed negatrons and left-handed positrons from the unpolarizable pions. The formal expectations follow from the evaluation of $\sum |J_4^0|^2$ in (11.41) when the sum over the spins of the charged lepton is withheld. Then, for example, (11.42) is replaced by

$$\sum |J_4^0|^2 = \tfrac{1}{4}\sum_{\mu^0} |\psi_\mu^\dagger(1\pm\gamma_5)\psi_{\mu^0}|^2 \quad (\text{for } \pi^\mp)$$
$$= (2V)^{-2}\left\{1+\mathbf{v}.\mathbf{v}_0/c^2 \mp (\langle\boldsymbol{\sigma}\rangle.\mathbf{v}/c)\left[1+\frac{\mathbf{v}_0.\mathbf{p}}{W+mc^2}\right] \mp \langle\boldsymbol{\sigma}\rangle.\mathbf{v}_0\, mc/W\right\}, \tag{11.47}$$

where, as in (5.36) for instance, $\langle\boldsymbol{\sigma}\rangle \equiv \boldsymbol{\chi}^\dagger\boldsymbol{\sigma}\boldsymbol{\chi}$ with $\boldsymbol{\chi}$ the Pauli spinor describing the muon spin state relative to whatever quantization axis has been chosen. Thus, $\langle\boldsymbol{\sigma}\rangle = \pm\hat{\mathbf{p}}$ respectively, when emission intensities for a muon spinning parallel vs. antiparallel to its direction of motion is desired.

If the neutral lepton directions could be averaged out, i.e.

$$\mathbf{v}_0 \to \langle\mathbf{v}_0\rangle = 0,$$

as in the observations on nuclear $\beta$-decay, then (11.47) would yield a proportionality to $(1\mp\langle\boldsymbol{\sigma}\rangle.\mathbf{v}/c)$, just the left- and right-handed polarizations of negative vs. positive leptons found in the nuclear decays. However, the same expression leads to the opposite conclusions when, as in $\pi$-decay, $\mathbf{v}_0$ is restricted to the direction opposite to the charged lepton's momentum: $\mathbf{v}_0 = c^2\mathbf{q}/K = -c^2\mathbf{p}/K$. Now, in the limit of zero neutral mass, which is valid at least for the electron mode, (11.47) reduces to

$$\sum |J_4^0|^2 = (2V)^{-2}(1-v/c)(1\pm\langle\boldsymbol{\sigma}\rangle.\hat{\mathbf{p}}) \quad \text{for } \pi^\mp. \tag{11.48}$$

Thus emerge the 'unnatural' helicities of the charged leptons, as discussed in connexion with Fig. 11.1. Notice that the polarization implicit in (11.48) is not restricted to $v/c$ in magnitude, but is complete, $|\mathscr{P}| = 1$. This is the consequence of the angular momentum balance with the completely polarized spin of a massless neutral lepton.

The effect of a finite neutretto mass, $m_0 \neq 0$, would be to reduce the unit muon polarization slightly. It becomes, for negative and positive muons, respectively:

$$\mathscr{P} = \pm cp(W-K)/(WK-c^2p^2)$$
$$= \pm\left(1-\frac{m_0^2}{m_\mu^2}\right)\left(1+\frac{m_0^2}{m_\mu^2}\cdot\frac{m_\pi^2+m_\mu^2}{m_\pi^2-m_\mu^2}\right)^{-1}[1-...]^{\frac{1}{2}}, \tag{11.49}$$

where the last square-root factor is exactly the same one as in (11.45). For $m_0^2 \ll (m_\pi^2 - m_\mu^2)$, the polarization is reduced from unity by the fraction $9{\cdot}6(m_0/m_\mu)^2$. This makes it about 25 times as sensitive to the neutretto mass as is the energy measurement (11.29). Nevertheless, it is only a 0·6 per cent effect for $m_0 \approx 5m_e$.

Confirmations of the right-handed helicity expected for the $\mu^-$ products of $\pi$-decay have been reported.‡ The observations were all consistent with a unit magnitude of the longitudinal polarization, but no better than about a 30 per cent accuracy has so far been obtained in these difficult measurements.

*Pseudoscalar coupling*

The foregoing has shown that the observed ratio of muon to electron emissions, and the observed helicities of the product muons, can be understood very well as consequences of the 'V–A' form of coupling, $h_{N\mu}$ of (11.31). Possible alternatives for this should still be considered in order to gauge how uniquely necessary that coupling form is.

A set of alternatives is presented by an arbitrary superpositon of 'even' and 'odd' coupling forms like (10.9). They rapidly become circumscribed when it is recognized that only a nucleon density which is a Pseudoscalar in ordinary (3-) space can combine the isolated pion with the pion-nucleon vacuum state, in a $0^- \rightarrow 0^+$ transition, $|\mathrm{i}\rangle \rightarrow |\mathrm{f}\rangle$, which is not forbidden. Thus, only the Pseudoscalar term of (10.9), besides the fourth component of the Pseudovector already employed, needs be considered as a possible contributor to the $\pi$-decay, i.e.

$$h_{N\mu} \rightarrow 2^{-\frac{1}{2}}g\{-(\psi_\mathrm{p}^\dagger \gamma_5 \psi_\mathrm{n})[\psi_\mu^\dagger(C_\mathrm{A}\gamma_5 + C'_\mathrm{A})\psi_{\mu^0}] + \\ +(\psi_\mathrm{p}^\dagger \beta\gamma_5 \psi_\mathrm{n})[\psi_\mu^\dagger \beta(C_\mathrm{P}\gamma_5 + C'_\mathrm{P})\psi_{\mu^0}] + \mathrm{h.c.}\} \quad (11.50)$$

can be the effective part of the general form (10.9). It leads to

$$\lambda_{\pi\mu} = (g^2/2\pi\hbar^4c^3)(p^2W/m_\pi)[|\mathscr{A}|^2 + |\mathscr{A}'|^2] \quad (11.51\,\mathrm{a})$$

for $m_0 = 0$, with

$$\mathscr{A} = C_\mathrm{A}\langle\gamma_5\rangle_\pi(1-v/c)^{\frac{1}{2}} - C_\mathrm{P}\langle\beta\gamma_5\rangle_\pi(1+v/c)^{\frac{1}{2}} \quad (11.51\,\mathrm{b})$$

and $\mathscr{A}'$ exactly the same except for the replacements $C_\mathrm{A}, C_\mathrm{P} \rightarrow C'_\mathrm{A}, C'_\mathrm{P}$. The corresponding expectation for the longitudinal polarization of the $\mu^\mp$ can be written:

$$\mathscr{P} = \pm 2\,\mathrm{Re}[C_\mathrm{A}^* C'_\mathrm{A}|\langle\gamma_5\rangle|^2(1-v/c) + \\ + C_\mathrm{P}^* C'_\mathrm{P}|\langle\beta\gamma_5\rangle|^2(1+v/c)]/(|\mathscr{A}|^2 + |\mathscr{A}'|^2). \quad (11.52)$$

‡ A. Alikhanov, Yu. Galaktionov, Yu. Gorodkov, G. Eliseev, and V. Lyubimov, *Sov. J.E.T.P.* **11**, 1380 (1960); G. Backenstoss, B. D. Hyams, G. Knop, P. Marlin, and V. Stierlin, *Phys. Rev. Letters*, **6**, 415 (1961); M. Bardon, P. Franzini, and J. Lee, ibid. **7**, 23 (1961).

An interference contribution $\sim(C_A^* C'_P + C'^*_A C_P)$ has been omitted since it is proportional to $(W - m_\mu c^2)/2W \approx \frac{1}{40}$ in place of $(1 \pm v/c) > 0{\cdot}73$ and is surely negligible in the present considerations.

The observable features of $\pi$-decay are too few to exclude the possibility that arbitrary proportions of the Pseudoscalar couplings $\sim C_P, C'_P$ exist in $h_{N\mu}$. There is the objection that admitting them would entail giving up a 'universal' form for all couplings of the Fermi type, i.e. $h_{N\mu}$ would no longer be identical with the V–A Law, $h_\beta$, except for the replacement of electron-neutrino pair by a muon-neutretto pair. On the other hand, there is still the possibility that some Pseudoscalar coupling exists also in the ordinary $\beta$-interaction, $h_\beta$. That there is no entirely conclusive *observational* evidence against this was pointed out in § 10.1.

To see one consequence of admitting Pseudoscalar couplings into the 'universal' interaction form, consider the electron-to-muon ratio which would result in the limit of a dominating proportion of Pseudoscalar coupling. It follows from (11.51) that this 'Pseudoscalar ratio' would be

$$\left(\frac{\lambda_{\pi e}}{\lambda_{\pi\mu}}\right)_P = \frac{[p^2 W(1+v/c)]_e}{[p^2 W(1+v/c)]_\mu} = \frac{p_e^2}{p_\mu^2} = \left(\frac{m_\pi^2 - m_e^2}{m_\pi^2 - m_\mu^2}\right)^2 \approx 5.5, \qquad (11.53)$$

in gross contradiction to the observed ratio. This outcome is a consequence of the fact that the like helicities of particle and antiparticle demanded by $\pi$-decay are not 'unnatural' to the Pseudoscalar interactions as they are to the Vector or Pseudovector ones; this was implicit in (11.46) and accounts for the replacement of $(1-v/c)$ in the 'Pseudovector ratio' (11.44) by $(1+v/c)$ here.

The large difference between the Pseudovector and Pseudoscalar ratios arises mainly from the replacement of $(1-v/c)_e$ by $(1+v/c)_e$ in the rate of the *electron* mode. When the well-established V–A part of the coupling $h_\beta$ is taken into account, the ratio to its contribution of the purely Pseudoscalar one is given by

$$\frac{(\lambda_{\pi e})_P}{(\lambda_{\pi e})_A} = \left|\frac{C_P^{(\prime)}\langle\beta\gamma_5\rangle_\pi}{C_A^{(\prime)}\langle\gamma_5\rangle_\pi}\right|^2 \left(\frac{1+v/c}{1-v/c}\right)_e. \qquad (11.54\,\text{a})$$

The last factor here is of order 37 000, as compared to $(1{\cdot}27/0{\cdot}73) \approx 1{\cdot}7$ for the muon mode. Thus, approximately

$$|C_P^{(\prime)}\langle\beta\gamma_5\rangle_\pi / C_A^{(\prime)}\langle\gamma_5\rangle_\pi|^2 \leqslant 10^{-4} \qquad (11.54\,\text{b})$$

is necessary to avoid disturbing the agreement with the observed electron-to-muon ratio which had been achieved when $C_P = C'_P = 0$ was taken. This may be interpreted as evidence that $|C_P^{(\prime)}| < 10^{-2}|C_A|$, because $|\langle\beta\gamma_5\rangle_\pi/\langle\gamma_5\rangle_\pi|$ may be expected to have at least an order of magnitude unity.

The last assertion is not in contradiction with the finding

$$\langle\beta\gamma_5\rangle/\langle\gamma_5\rangle \approx 0$$

for the moments of nuclear $\beta$-decay, in the last subsection of § 10.1. This is because the operations $\beta\gamma_5$ and $\gamma_5$ combine nucleon with *anti*-nucleon states in the $\pi$-decay moments, whereas only the normal nucleon states are involved in the nuclear moments, and, moreover, the latter at least may be treated non-relativistically. It may also be that only low-momentum, non-relativistic nucleon-antinucleon pairs contribute appreciably to the $\pi$-decay. Then the members of a pair will have descriptions like

$$\psi_\mathrm{n} \approx \begin{pmatrix} 1 \\ \boldsymbol{\sigma}.\mathbf{p}_\mathrm{n}/2Mc \end{pmatrix}\chi_\mathrm{n}, \qquad \psi_\mathrm{p}^C \approx \begin{pmatrix} \boldsymbol{\sigma}.\mathbf{p}_\mathrm{p}/2Mc \\ 1 \end{pmatrix}\chi_\mathrm{p},$$

modelled on (7.68) and (3.6). These lead to

$$|\psi_\mathrm{p}^{C\dagger}\beta\gamma_5\psi_\mathrm{n}| \approx \chi_\mathrm{p}^\dagger\chi_\mathrm{n} \approx |\psi_\mathrm{p}^{C\dagger}\gamma_5\psi_\mathrm{n}|$$

and $|\langle\beta\gamma_5\rangle_\pi/\langle\gamma_5\rangle_\pi| \approx 1$, in the non-relativistic limit. In the extreme relativistic limit,

$$\psi_\mathrm{n} \approx 2^{-\frac{1}{2}}\begin{pmatrix} 1 \\ \boldsymbol{\sigma}.\hat{\mathbf{p}}_\mathrm{n} \end{pmatrix}\chi_\mathrm{n}, \qquad \psi_\mathrm{p}^C \approx 2^{-\frac{1}{2}}\begin{pmatrix} \boldsymbol{\sigma}.\hat{\mathbf{p}}_\mathrm{p} \\ 1 \end{pmatrix}\chi_\mathrm{p},$$

yielding

$$\left.\begin{aligned} |\psi_\mathrm{p}^{C\dagger}\beta\gamma_5\psi_\mathrm{n}| &\approx \tfrac{1}{2}\chi_\mathrm{p}^\dagger(1-\hat{\mathbf{p}}_\mathrm{p}.\hat{\mathbf{p}}_\mathrm{n})\chi_\mathrm{n} \\ |\psi_\mathrm{p}^{C\dagger}\gamma_5\psi_\mathrm{n}| &\approx \tfrac{1}{2}\chi_\mathrm{p}^\dagger(1+\hat{\mathbf{p}}_\mathrm{p}.\hat{\mathbf{p}}_\mathrm{n})\chi_\mathrm{n} \end{aligned}\right\}. \tag{11.55}$$

Now members of high-momentum pairs must largely supply each others' recoil momenta, hence $\mathbf{p}_\mathrm{p} = -\mathbf{p}_\mathrm{n}$ is to be expected, and then

$$\langle\beta\gamma_5\rangle_\pi > \langle\gamma_5\rangle_\pi$$

seems most plausible.

It should be emphasized that the arguments against the existence of Pseudoscalar interaction here are predicated on a hypothesis that the four-fermion couplings have a 'universal' form, i.e. $h_{N\mu}$ differs from $h_\beta$ only in the replacement of $\psi_\mathrm{e}$, $\psi_\nu$ by $\psi_\mu$, $\psi_{\mu^0}$. The observational evidence from the $\pi$-decay, by itself, is equally consistent with even a purely Pseudoscalar form for $h_{N\mu}$ (i.e. (11.50) with $C_\mathrm{A} = C'_\mathrm{A} = 0$) if only the V–A form is retained for $h_\beta$. The observed right-handedness of the negative muon products would be obtained if $C'_\mathrm{P} = C_\mathrm{P}$, and the observed electron-to-muon ratio if $|g_\mathrm{P}\langle\beta\gamma_5\rangle_\pi|^2 \approx \frac{2}{3}|g_\mathrm{A}\langle\gamma_5\rangle_\pi|^2$.

## 11.4. The pion lifetime

To derive theoretical expectations for the absolute rate of $\pi$-decay, the decay 'moment', $\langle\gamma_5\rangle_\pi$ of (11.41), must be evaluated. The problem is full of ambiguities because of uncertainties as to just how an isolated, 'physical' pion is to be described, and it is best to begin with an idea of the size of $|\langle\gamma_5\rangle_\pi|$ which is needed to obtain the observed pion-lifetime. The rate $\lambda_{\pi\mu}$ of producing the muon mode is the total rate within 0·01 per cent and its relation to the moment is

$$\lambda_{\pi\mu} = (g^2c/4\pi\hbar^4)m_\mu^2[1-(m_\mu/m_\pi)^2]^2|\langle\gamma_5\rangle_\pi|^2, \tag{11.56}$$

as follows from (11.41) after substitutions from (11.43) and (11.29). The neutretto mass is taken to be zero since any $m_0 \neq 0$ value consistent with the evidence would have negligible effect (11.45). With $g \to g_A = 1{\cdot}7(10)^{-49}$ erg-cm$^3$ (5.89), (5.90), comparison to the observed mean life $\tau_\pi \approx \lambda_{\pi\mu}^{-1}$ of (11.2) yields the 'measurement':

$$|\langle\gamma_5\rangle_\pi|^2 \approx \tfrac{1}{3}(\hbar/m_\pi c)^{-3}. \tag{11.57}$$

The pion compton wavelength, $\hbar/m_\pi c$, is used as a unit here merely for convenience.

The theoretical consideration of $\langle\gamma_5\rangle_\pi$ is best started from its relationship to the basic decay amplitude, implicit in the development from (11.34) to (11.41):

$$\langle \mathrm{f}|H_{N\mu}|\mathrm{i}\rangle = 2^{\frac{1}{2}}gJ_4^0[(2\pi\hbar)^3\delta(\mathbf{p}+\mathbf{q})]^{\frac{1}{2}}\langle\gamma_5\rangle_\pi, \tag{11.58}$$

with

$$H_{N\mu} = 2^{\frac{1}{2}}gJ_4^0 \oint (d\mathbf{r})(\psi_\mathrm{p}^\dagger \gamma_5 \psi_\mathrm{n})e^{-i(\mathbf{p}+\mathbf{q}).\mathbf{r}/\hbar}, \tag{11.59}$$

this being just the part of the lepton-generating coupling energy which is effective in the $\pi$-decay. It is immaterial for $\langle\gamma_5\rangle_\pi$ whether it be calculated for $\pi^-$ or for $\pi^+$ decay (the entire formalism to be used is charge-invariant), or whether the muon or electron mode is considered (since $\langle\gamma_5\rangle_\pi$ is independent of lepton variables). For the sake of concreteness, the ensuing will refer specifically to $\pi^- \to \mu^- + \bar{\mu}^0$.

### *Lowest-order perturbation effects*

The earliest work on the $\pi$-decay (ref. p. 307) was an attempt to see how well it could be accounted for as a 'lowest-order' perturbation of a 'bare' pion by

$$V = H_{N\pi} + H_{N\mu}, \tag{11.60}$$

where $H_{N\pi}$ is a pion-nucleon interaction like (11.16). The great strength expected of the latter makes the approach inadequate, but it is still worth reviewing because it serves to introduce several evaluations which are important in discussions.

By the 'bare' pion is meant an eigenstate of the non-interacting pion field hamiltonian, $H_\pi$ of (11.11), e.g.

$$|\mathbf{k}\rangle \equiv A^*_{\mathbf{k}}|0\rangle \tag{11.61 a}$$

in the notation of (11.9). The continuous normalization,

$$\langle\mathbf{k}|\mathbf{k}'\rangle = \langle 0|A_{\mathbf{k}}\,A^*_{\mathbf{k}'}|0\rangle = 2\omega\delta(\mathbf{k}-\mathbf{k}'), \tag{11.61 b}$$

following from (11.7), makes it necessary to represent a bare pion at rest ($\hbar\mathbf{k}_0 = 0$) as a superposition:

$$|\pi\rangle = \oint [(d\mathbf{k}_0)/2\omega_0]A^*_{\mathbf{k}_0}|0\rangle\langle\mathbf{k}_0|\pi\rangle. \tag{11.62 a}$$

Then, the choice

$$|\langle\mathbf{k}_0|\pi\rangle|^2 = 2\omega_0\,\hbar^3\delta(\hbar\mathbf{k}_0) \tag{11.62 b}$$

will yield $\langle\pi|\pi\rangle = 1$, as needed for counting the decays from a single pion. In the same approximation that $|\mathrm{i}\rangle \approx |\pi\rangle$, the final state of the $\pi$-decay becomes the 'bare' vacuum, $|\mathrm{f}\rangle \approx |0\rangle$.

Because the perturbation cannot generate the direct transition, $\langle 0|V|\pi\rangle = 0$, the lowest order contribution to the $\pi$-decay amplitude is the second-order one represented by

$$\langle\mathrm{f}|H_{N\mu}|\mathrm{i}\rangle^{(2)} = \sum_\tau \langle 0|V|\tau\rangle\langle\tau|V|\pi\rangle/(m_\pi c^2 - E_\tau), \tag{11.63}$$

on the model of (9.27). To be considered first will be the only transients $|\tau\rangle$ generated from $|\pi\rangle$ by $V$ which give $\langle 0|H_{N\mu}|\tau\rangle \neq 0$ under the effect of the $V \to H_{N\mu}$ part of the perturbation. These are the neutron-antiproton pair states

$$|\tau\rangle \to |\mathrm{n\bar{p}}\rangle \equiv a^\dagger_{\mathrm{n}}\,c^\dagger_{\mathrm{p}}|0\rangle, \tag{11.64}$$

where $a^\dagger$ and $c^\dagger$ are fermion and antifermion creation operators of the type used in § 9.1. A destruction of the pion is necessary, hence it is the $V \to H(\pi^-)$, the $\pi^-$-destroying part (11.21) of the perturbation, which contributes here

$$\langle\mathrm{n\bar{p}}|V|\pi\rangle = \oint [(d\mathbf{k}_0)/2\omega_0]\langle\mathbf{k}_0|\pi\rangle\langle\mathrm{n\bar{p}}|H(\pi^-)|\mathbf{k}_0\rangle \tag{11.65 a}$$

with

$$\langle\mathrm{n\bar{p}}|H(\pi^-)|\mathbf{k}_0\rangle = 2^{\frac{1}{2}}icG[\hbar/(2\pi)^3]^{\frac{1}{2}} \oint [(d\mathbf{k})/2\omega]\times$$
$$\times \oint (d\mathbf{r})e^{i\mathbf{k}.\mathbf{r}}\langle\mathrm{n\bar{p}}|(\psi^\dagger_{\mathrm{n}}\,\beta\gamma_5\,\psi_{\mathrm{p}})A_{\mathbf{k}}\,A^*_{\mathbf{k}_0}|0\rangle. \tag{11.65 b}$$

All time factors have been eliminated in producing the amplitude expression (11.63). The integration over pion momenta here can also be eliminated, by using (11.61).

The nucleon creation operators of (11.64) enter the formalism through the decomposition of the nucleon fields into modes as in (9.4):

$$\psi_{\mathrm{n,p}} = \sum_N (a_N\,u_N + c^\dagger_N\,u^C_N). \tag{11.66}$$

To take $u$, $u^C$ to be plane wave modes ('bare', non-interacting nucleons) may seem very crude in view of the strong forces known to exist among nucleons. Yet such forces are supposed to stem in large part from the pion-nucleon couplings (footnotes, pp. 301 and 305), and, since these are being neglected in the treatment of the pion state, consistency seems to demand using 'bare' nucleon states. Of course, it cannot be claimed on present grounds that these are at all compensatory approximations. With nucleon plane waves normalized as in (3.4) and (3.6):

$$\sum_N \to \sum_\sigma \oint (d\mathbf{p})V/(2\pi\hbar)^3. \tag{11.67}$$

Substitution of decompositions like (11.66) into the amplitude (11.65), followed with applications of anticommutator relations like (9.5), leaves a spatial integration over plane waves which results in a momentum-conserving delta function. The outcome is

$$\langle \mathrm{n\bar{p}}|H(\pi^-)|\mathbf{k}_0\rangle = 2^{\frac{1}{2}}icG[\hbar/(2\pi)^3]^{\frac{1}{2}}(u_\mathrm{n}^\dagger\beta\gamma_5 u_\mathrm{p}^C)_0\times$$
$$\times(2\pi\hbar)^3\delta(\hbar\mathbf{k}_0-\mathbf{p}_\mathrm{n}-\mathbf{p}_\mathrm{p}), \tag{11.68}$$

with the subscript '0' referring to evaluation of the plane wave modes at $\mathbf{r} = 0$, $t = 0$. The integration over the initial pion state (11.65 a) gives for $\langle \mathrm{n\bar{p}}|V|\pi\rangle$ exactly the same expression (11.68) except for the replacement of the delta function by (see (11.62 b)):

$$(2\hbar^3\omega_0)^{-1}\langle\hbar^{-1}(\mathbf{p}_\mathrm{n}+\mathbf{p}_\mathrm{p})|\pi\rangle = [(2\hbar^3\omega_0)^{-1}\delta(\mathbf{p}_\mathrm{n}+\mathbf{p}_\mathrm{p})]^{\frac{1}{2}}. \tag{11.69}$$

Here $\hbar\omega_0 = m_\pi c^2$ and the indicated vanishing of the total nucleon momentum originates from taking the initial pion to be at rest.

The lepton-production amplitude of the transient neutron-antiproton pair can with similar ease be brought to the form

$$\langle 0|H_{N\mu}|\mathrm{n\bar{p}}\rangle = 2^{\frac{1}{2}}gJ_4^0(u_\mathrm{p}^{C\dagger}\gamma_5 u_\mathrm{n})_0(2\pi\hbar)^3\delta(\mathbf{p}_\mathrm{n}+\mathbf{p}_\mathrm{p}-\mathbf{p}-\mathbf{q}), \tag{11.70}$$

following from $H_{N\mu}$ as given in (11.59). These results for the intermediate amplitudes can now be substituted into the expression (11.63) for the resultant amplitude and the summations over the intermediate states,

$$\sum_\tau \to \sum_{\sigma_\mathrm{n}\sigma_\mathrm{p}} \oint\oint (d\mathbf{p}_\mathrm{p})(d\mathbf{p}_\mathrm{n})V^2/(2\pi\hbar)^6, \tag{11.71}$$

carried out. The delta function of (11.70) serves to reduce the double integration over nucleon momenta here to a single one over $\mathbf{P} \equiv \mathbf{p}_\mathrm{n}$ or $-\mathbf{p}_\mathrm{p}$ and now the delta function of (11.69) is replaced by $\delta(\mathbf{p}+\mathbf{q})$; thus is furnished a factor presupposed to exist in the definition (11.58) of $\langle\gamma_5\rangle_\pi$. Another consequence is that the transient state energy $E_\tau$ of (11.63) becomes $E_\tau = W_\mathrm{n}+W_\mathrm{p} = 2W_P$, with $W_P = c[P^2+M^2c^2]^{\frac{1}{2}}$ if

$M_{\mathrm{p}} = M_{\mathrm{n}} = M$ is taken, as is appropriate for bare nucleons. The summation over intermediate states also involves the nucleon spin sum‡

$$\sum_{\sigma_{\mathrm{n}}\sigma_{\mathrm{p}}} (u_{\mathrm{p}}^{C\dagger}\gamma_5\, u_{\mathrm{n}})_0 (u_{\mathrm{n}}^{\dagger}\,\beta\gamma_5\, u_{\mathrm{p}}^{C})_0 = 2Mc^2/W_P\, V^2, \tag{11.72}$$

obtainable by the same kind of procedure as yielded (11.42), for example.

The results so far may now be gathered into a contribution of the second-order form (11.63) to the $\pi$-decay amplitude. The factors separated out from the latter in the definition of the moment $\langle\gamma_5\rangle_\pi$ in (11.58) need not be rewritten if the result is expressed as

$$\langle\gamma_5\rangle_\pi^{(2)}\Big]_{\mathrm{n}\bar{\mathrm{p}}} = -\frac{i}{2\pi^2}\left[\frac{G^2}{\hbar c}\left(\frac{m_\pi c}{\hbar}\right)\right]^{\frac{1}{2}}\left(\frac{Mc}{\hbar}\right) I_1(m_\pi c^2), \tag{11.73 a}$$

where

$$I_1(m_\pi c^2) = (m_\pi c^2)^{-1}\int\limits_0^\infty (c^3\, dP P^2/W_P^2)(1-m_\pi c^2/2W_P)^{-1}. \tag{11.73 b}$$

The subscription by 'n$\bar{\mathrm{p}}$' is meant to indicate that this is only the contribution via the bare neutron-antiproton pair transient. A reconsideration of the second-order amplitude expression (11.63) shows that the final state can also be reached by the same two steps of interaction, $H(\pi^-)$ and $H_{N\mu}$, acting in reverse order, as corresponds to

$$\pi^- \to \pi^- + (\mathrm{p}+\bar{\mathrm{n}}+\mu^- + \bar{\mu}^0) \to \mu^- + \bar{\mu}^0 \tag{11.74}$$

in place of (11.30). The transient parenthesized here is known as a 'vacuum fluctuation' (leaving the initial pion untouched) induced by the lepton coupling, and the final amplitude it produces must be added to that already calculated, before the sum over transients is complete to second order. The added contribution may be calculated in the same way and has the same result as (11.73), except that $I_1(m_\pi c^2)$ is replaced by $I_1(-m_\pi c^2)$. This sign change is a joint result of the change of transient energy from $E_\tau = 2W_P$ for the (n$\bar{\mathrm{p}}$) state to

$$E_\tau = m_\pi c^2 + 2W_P + W + K = 2(m_\pi c^2 + W_P)$$

for the transient of (11.74), and of a sign change in the nucleon spin sum. The expression (11.72) is obviously to be altered by an interchange $u \leftrightarrow u^C$, corresponding to the replacement of the (n$\bar{\mathrm{p}}$) pair by ($\bar{\mathrm{n}}$p), and this is responsible. The sum of the two contributions becomes

‡ The more general evaluation with the full nucleon current, $u_{\mathrm{p}}^{C\dagger}\beta\gamma_\alpha(1+\gamma_5)u_{\mathrm{n}}$, yields zero for $\alpha \neq 4$ and $\mathbf{p}_{\mathrm{n}} = -\mathbf{p}_{\mathrm{p}}$, $M_{\mathrm{p}} = M_{\mathrm{n}}$, and just the result (11.72) for $\alpha = 4$. This merely bears out conclusions from expected selection rules, already introduced in deriving (11.41).

proportional to $I_0 \equiv I_1(+m_\pi c^2)+I_1(-m_\pi c^2)$ and

$$I_0 \equiv c^3 \int\limits_0^\infty dPP^2/W_P^3[1-(m_\pi c^2/2W_P)^2] \approx \int\limits_0^\infty dPP^2/[P^2+(Mc)^2]^{\frac{3}{2}}, \tag{11.75}$$

the last approximation being justified by the fact that $M^2 \gg \frac{1}{4}m_\pi^2$ This result has involved a near-cancellation of the contributions from the (n$\bar{\text{p}}$) and ($\bar{\text{n}}$p) channels, proportional to $I_1(\pm m_\pi c^2)$ respectively.

The complete result of the second-order evaluation of the moment may now be written as

$$|\langle\gamma_5\rangle^{(2)}|^2 = (G^2/4\pi^4\hbar c)(m_\pi c/\hbar)(Mc/\hbar)^2 I_0^2. \tag{11.76}$$

This supplies no definite value which could be compared with the 'experimental' result (11.57) because the integral $I_0$ diverges, as can be seen from (11.75). Nevertheless it provides a convenient starting-point for the ensuing discussion.

*A 'dispersion-theoretic' result*

The 'perturbation-theoretic' evaluation just reviewed is naturally unsatisfactory. It gives an infinite result because of the divergent number of states available to the virtual nucleon pairs. Moreover, taking into account only the lowest-order effects of as strong an interaction as the pion-nucleon coupling was unsatisfactory *ab initio*.

Goldberger and Treiman‡ avoided the occurrence of any patently divergent integrals, and took into account at least some of the effects of the pion-nucleon coupling to 'all orders', by applying a so-called 'dispersion-theoretic' technique. In essence, this is the formulation of relationships among different physical processes following from generally accepted symmetry principles. These may even lead to the expectation of the same transition amplitude for two different processes, except for the ranges of the variables involved in each. Extrapolations along the variables are performed through the assumption of smooth behaviour ('analytic' except for isolated singularities). Each of the different processes may be as incalculable as the above perturbation evaluation was found to be, but the dispersion relations may allow conclusions about one process to be derived from experimental information about the others. It is held in some quarters that this may be a more fundamental theoretical embodiment of the natural laws than is the description in field-theoretic terms.

‡ M. L. Goldberger and S. B. Treiman, *Phys. Rev.* **110,** 1178 (1958).

Goldberger and Treiman were able to form a dispersion relation between the amplitude with which the $\beta$-decaying $(n\bar{p})$ state is generated and the phase shifts which would arise in a scattering of antiprotons on neutrons. The phase shifts are natural measures of the strong inter-nucleon forces which must exist in the nucleon pair state. The consequent results were expressed in terms of an integral,

$$I = \int_0^\infty dP P^2[P^2+(Mc)^2]^{-\frac{3}{2}} \cos\phi(P) \exp\int_0^\infty dP'\phi(P')\chi(P',P), \tag{11.77}$$

which differs from $I_0$ of (11.75) by the indicated function of the phase-shift, $\phi(P)$; $\chi$ is a well-defined 'propagator' which will not be specified further here because it turns out that the integrals cannot be evaluated anyway, due to lack of information about $\phi$. The important point is that $I$ is a not necessarily divergent quantity which becomes identical with $I_0$ in the limit $\phi \to 0$, i.e. the 'perturbation-theoretic' limit in which the nucleons are treated as free plane waves. In principle, $\phi(P)$ should be determined from observations on neutron-antiproton scattering, but, unfortunately, it is not even clear that any realizable scattering experiment can be of direct help, since the extrapolation from a positive-energy scattering state to the 'bound' state (energy less than $2Mc^2$) forming a pion is a very tenuous one.

Despite the difficulties, Goldberger and Treiman were able to offer a definite conclusion with just the help of the assumption that the unevaluable integral $I$ is not very small. Specifically, they found for the decay rate the same form as the perturbation-theoretic one except for the replacement

$$I_0 \to I/(1+G^2I/2\pi^2\hbar c). \tag{11.78}$$

It is only necessary to suppose that $I \gg 2\pi^2\hbar c/G^2 \approx \frac{1}{2}\pi/15 \approx \frac{1}{10}$, with the value (11.19) of $G$, in order to have $I$ cancel out here and have $I_0 \to 2\pi^2\hbar c/G^2$. On this basis, the expression (11.76) for the $\pi$-decay moment is replaced by

$$|\langle\gamma_5\rangle_\pi|^2 \approx (m_\pi c/\hbar)(Mc/\hbar)^2(\hbar c/G^2) \approx [(4\pi/3)(\hbar/m_\pi c)^3]^{-1}. \tag{11.79}$$

Thus obtained is a theoretical result within 30 per cent of the 'experimental' value quoted in (11.57). Any closer agreement would have no more significance, in view of the drastic approximations required to come to any conclusion.

A more detailed exposition of the Goldberger–Treiman derivation is hardly warranted here. It would require a lengthy digression to develop the underlying dispersion theory from first principles, yet the application to $\pi$-decay is far from straightforward, involving some rather arbitrary technical assumptions. Readers already familiar with dispersion-theoretic procedures may as well be referred to the original paper.

# XII

## MUON DECAY AND THE CONSERVED CURRENT

THE processes considered so far could all be spoken of as generated by nucleonic transformation currents, $J_\alpha(\text{pn})$, yet it is a coupling of two currents, each on the same footing, that provided the successful formulations. A leptonic transformation current, $J_\alpha(\text{e}\nu)$, interacts with $J_\alpha(\text{pn})$ in the coupling $h_\beta$ responsible for nuclear $\beta$-processes; it is $J_\alpha(\mu\mu^0)$ and $J_\alpha(\text{pn})$ that are coupled in $h_{N\mu}$ of (11.31). This suggests postulating that any pair of such transformation currents as exist will interact similarly. A coupling of $J(\mu\mu^0)$ and $J(\text{e}\nu)$ is a remaining possibility,‡ and this would lead to the expectation of muon decay into electrons.

It has long been known that muons do decay into electrons, this being responsible for their finite lifetime as recorded in (11.27). If the processes arise in the way suggested, then they should be represented as

$$\left.\begin{aligned}\mu^- &\rightarrow \text{e}^- + \bar{\nu} + \mu^0\\ \mu^+ &\rightarrow \text{e}^+ + \nu + \bar{\mu}^0\end{aligned}\right\}. \tag{12.1}$$

The evidence for all the assumptions implicit here must come from the observations on $\mu$-decay which have so far been found possible:

(*a*) *The decay rate*, $\tau_\mu^{-1}$. That the measured mean life $\tau_\mu = 2{\cdot}21$ $\mu$sec (11.27) is compatible with the same strength of coupling, $g$, as found in nuclear $\beta$-decay was noticed very early.§

(*b*) *The electron spectrum.* The electrons are found to have a continuous spectrum of energies such as is to be expected of a sharing in an energy release $m_\mu c^2$ with two neutral particles. An end-point electron energy

$$W_0 = (m_\mu^2 + m_\text{e}^2 - m_0^2)c^2/2m_\mu \tag{12.2}$$

is to be expected. The value observed, $W_0 \approx \frac{1}{2}m_\mu c^2$, is consistent with a zero neutretto mass, $m_0 = 0$, within a few per cent. However, an error of only $\Delta W_0 \approx m_\text{e} c^2$ ($\sim$ 1 per cent) would obscure the existence of a neutretto mass as large as $m_0 = (2m_\mu \Delta W_0/c^2)^{\frac{1}{2}} \approx 20m_\text{e}$.

The spectrum shape (Fig. 12.1) shows a continuous rise up to a maximum at about the end-point, corresponding to a 'Michel parameter'

‡ This completes what is sometimes called the 'Puppi Triangle' of couplings (G. Puppi, *Nuovo Cim.* **5**, 505 (1948)).

§ Preceding reference and O. Klein, *Nature, Lond.* **161**, 897 (1948); J. Tiomno and J. A. Wheeler, *Rev. Mod. Phys.* **21**, 144 (1949); T. D. Lee, M. Rosenbluth, and C. N. Yang, *Phys. Rev.* **75**, 905 (1949).

$\rho = 0{\cdot}75 \pm 0{\cdot}03$. The significance of the latter will be the principal concern of the next section.

(*c*) *The electron polarizations.* The product negatrons are found‡ to be polarized left-handedly, the positrons right-handedly, just as in nuclear $\beta$-decay.

(*d*) *The electron's directional distribution.* When observations are made on muons which emerge from $\pi$-decays as sources, then the product electrons are found to be emitted predominantly backwards relative to the muon's direction of motion.§

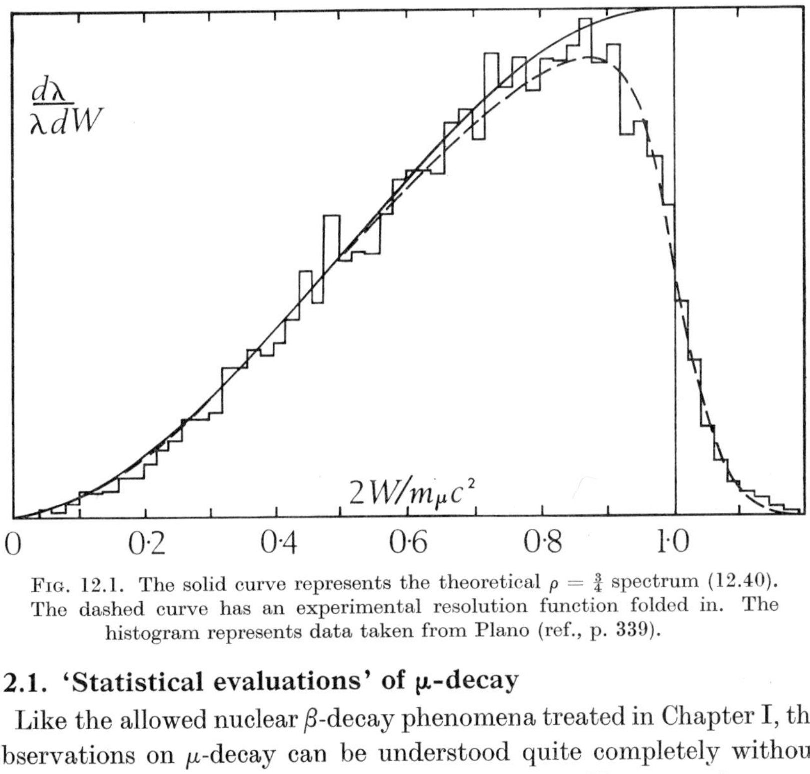


FIG. 12.1. The solid curve represents the theoretical $\rho = \frac{3}{4}$ spectrum (12.40). The dashed curve has an experimental resolution function folded in. The histogram represents data taken from Plano (ref., p. 339).

## 12.1. 'Statistical evaluations' of $\mu$-decay

Like the allowed nuclear $\beta$-decay phenomena treated in Chapter I, the observations on $\mu$-decay can be understood quite completely without the introduction of a field-theoretic formulation. However, the treatment necessary here is a good deal more complicated because it is more essentially a three-body problem, in consequence of the fact that the recoil energy of no one product can be neglected. It will nevertheless be presented here in enough detail to derive the electron spectrum because it furnishes a good way to see the consequences of just the

‡ P. Macq, K. Crowe, and R. Haddock, *Phys. Rev.* **112**, 2061 (1958).

§ R. Garwin, L. Lederman, and M. Weinrich, ibid. **105**, 1415 (1957); J. Friedman and V. Telegdi, ibid., p. 1681.

basic conservation principles, separated from the more special assumptions needed for a complete formulation.

It is particularly appropriate to obtain the electron spectrum to be expected in $\mu$-decay from a 'statistical evaluation' because it has been customary for the observations on it to be reported as measurements of a single parameter, $\rho$, despite the fact that this can characterize only members of a certain restricted family, the 'Michel-parametrized' spectra. It will here be seen that the Michel family of spectra is to be expected on the basis of just energy-momentum conservation, angular momentum conservation among spin-$\frac{1}{2}$ particles, and a 'localized' character of the decay process.

*Energy-momentum conservation*

The 'statistical evaluation' in § 1.3 began with an assumption that the fraction, $d\lambda/\lambda$, of decay events in which the electron receives a momentum in a given interval $(d\mathbf{p}_1) \equiv dp_{1x}\,dp_{1y}\,dp_{1z}$ may be expressed in some such way as

$$d\lambda/\lambda = (d\mathbf{p}_1) \oint\oint (d\mathbf{p}_2)(d\mathbf{p}_3)\delta_4\Big(\sum_{n=1}^{3} p_n - p_\mu\Big)\Big/\Big[\prod_{n=1}^{3} \oint (d\mathbf{p}_n)\Big]\delta_4\big(\sum p_n - p_\mu\big). \tag{12.3}$$

The arguments of the 4-dimensional delta functions here are energy-momentum 4-vectors, $p_n[\mathbf{p}_n, iW_n = i(\mathbf{p}_n^2+m_n^2)^{\frac{1}{2}}]$, of the three product particles, with $p_\mu(0, im_\mu)$ the 4-vector for a muon at rest ($c = \hbar = 1$ will again be assumed). The delta functions vanish unless energy and momentum are conserved,

$$\sum W_n = m_\mu \quad \text{and} \quad \sum \mathbf{p}_n = 0, \tag{12.4}$$

and have the property

$$\oint d^4p_{n'}\,\delta_4\big(\sum p_n - p_\mu\big) \equiv \oint (d\mathbf{p}_{n'})\delta\big(\sum \mathbf{p}_n\big) \int dW_{n'}\,\delta\big(\sum W_n - m_\mu\big) = 1.$$

The energy integration must at least contain the interval in which $\sum W_n = m_\mu$. The insertion of the delta functions into (12.3) serves the same purpose as the restriction of the integration in § 1.3 to regions of the momentum-space consistent with total energy-momentum conservation. The statistical evaluations thus presume that effectively no other correlations among the emission directions $\hat{\mathbf{p}}_n \equiv \mathbf{p}_n/p_n$ will arise except those consequent on the momentum-energy conservation. Unfortunately, the spectrum derived‡ on this assumption is inconsistent§ with *angular* momentum conservation among spinning particles, relativistically described. Deeper correlations are unavoidable on this account.

‡ E. Fermi, *Elementary Particles* (Yale University Press, 1951).
§ N. Karayianis, *Ann. Phys.* **23**, 1 (1963).

The enforcement of angular momentum conservation among spinning particles necessitates introducing spinor descriptions of their motions. For the initial muon state, symbolized by $|\mathrm{i}\rangle$, the representation

$$|\mathrm{i}\rangle \leftrightarrow u_\mu(0)e^{ip_\mu . x}/(2m_\mu V)^{\frac{1}{2}} \tag{12.5}$$

will be adopted, with $p_\mu . x \equiv -m_\mu t$. This representative is a special case of a spinor, $\psi_{\mathbf{p}_n\,\sigma_n}(x_n)$, differently normalized, which will be used in forming a basis

$$|\mathrm{f}\rangle \leftrightarrow \prod_{n=1}^{3} \psi_{\mathbf{p}_n\,\sigma_n}(x_n) \equiv \prod u_{\sigma_n}(\mathbf{p}_n)e^{ip_n . x_n}, \tag{12.6}$$

having $p_n . x_n \equiv \mathbf{p}_n . \mathbf{r}_n - W_n t$, on which the decay state of the product particles may be resolved. The spin descriptions will be taken as

$$u_{\sigma_n}(\mathbf{p}_n) = (W_n + m_n)^{\frac{1}{2}} \begin{pmatrix} 1 \\ \dfrac{\boldsymbol{\sigma} . \mathbf{p}_n}{W_n + m_n} \end{pmatrix} \chi_{\sigma_n}, \tag{12.7}$$

in place of (3.4), because the resulting normalization

$$\oint (d\mathbf{r}_n)\psi^\dagger_{\mathbf{p}_n\sigma_n}\psi_{\mathbf{p}'_n\,\sigma'_n} = (2\pi)^3\delta(\mathbf{p}_n - \mathbf{p}'_n)(2W_n)\delta_{\sigma_n\,\sigma'_n} \tag{12.8}$$

will allow Lorentz-invariant factors to be distinguished more readily.

The decay state may be regarded as the result of some interaction operation‡ $S$ on the initial state:

$$S|\mathrm{i}\rangle = S'|\mathrm{i}\rangle \prod \delta_4(x - x_n), \tag{12.9}$$

with $S'$ to be assumed independent of the space-time variables $x$ and $x_n$. The delta functions serve to 'localize' the interaction at the point of the muon. This will eliminate 'forbidden' spectral contributions which would arise in an interaction of finite range, able to generate orbital momenta. When $S|\mathrm{i}\rangle$ is resolved on the basis $|\mathrm{f}\rangle$ of (12.6),

$$S|\mathrm{i}\rangle = \sum_{\mathrm{f}} |\mathrm{f}\rangle\langle\mathrm{f}|S|\mathrm{i}\rangle \leftrightarrow \left[\prod \sum_{\sigma_n} \oint \frac{(d\mathbf{p}_n)}{(2\pi)^3(2W_n)} \psi_{\mathbf{p}_n\,\sigma_n}\right] \langle\mathrm{f}|S|\mathrm{i}\rangle, \tag{12.10}$$

its square gives the invariant§ count of first-order decay processes

‡ As a concrete example, $S'$ is a tensor in the direct product space of four spinors, with components

$$S'_{abc;d} = 2^{\frac{1}{2}}g[\beta\gamma_\alpha(1+\gamma_5)C]_{ab}[\beta\gamma_\alpha(1+\gamma_5)]_{cd},$$

in the 'V–A Law'. Of course, $S'$ should remain unspecified in the 'statistical evaluation' here.

§ The object of the normalization (12.8) can now be seen fulfilled. Each element of the integration

$$\oint (d\mathbf{p}_n)/2W_n \equiv \oint d^4p_n\,\delta(p_n^2 + m_n^2) \equiv \oint (d\mathbf{p}_n) \int dW_n\,\delta(W_n^2 - \mathbf{p}_n^2 - m_n^2),$$

where $d^4p_n \equiv (d\mathbf{p}_n)dW_n$, is an obvious invariant, as is the product $\lambda T$ formed in any frame. The equivalences here follow from $\int dW_n(2W_n)\delta(W_n^2 - \mathbf{p}_n^2 - m_n^2) = 1$ when only $W_n > 0$ is admitted.

$$\lambda T = \sum_{\mathrm{f}} |\langle \mathrm{f}|S|\mathrm{i}\rangle|^2 = \left[\prod \sum_{\sigma_n} \oint \frac{(d\mathbf{p}_n)}{(2\pi)^3(2W_n)}\right] |\langle \mathrm{f}|S|\mathrm{i}\rangle|^2, \quad (12.11)$$

generated by $S$ out of the single muon initially in the spatial volume $V \to \infty$, at the rate $\lambda$ over an indefinitely long time span, $T \to \infty$.

With the states as represented in (12.5), (12.6) and the 'localized' interaction (12.9), the invariant amplitude becomes

$$\begin{aligned}\langle \mathrm{f}|S|\mathrm{i}\rangle &= (2m_\mu V)^{-\frac{1}{2}} \langle \prod u^\dagger_{\sigma_n}|S'|u_\mu\rangle \oint d^4x\, e^{-i(\Sigma p_n - p_\mu)x} \\ &= (2m_\mu V)^{-\frac{1}{2}} \langle \prod u^\dagger_{\sigma_n}|S'|u_\mu\rangle (2\pi)^4 \delta_4(\textstyle\sum p_n - p_\mu) \\ &\to (2m_\mu V)^{-\frac{1}{2}} \langle \prod u^\dagger_{\sigma_n}|S'|u_\mu\rangle VT, \qquad (12.12)\end{aligned}$$

the last line attaining validity *on* the 'energy shell', where $\sum p_n = p_\mu$. The square of amplitude in the rate expression (12.11) may be evaluated as the product of the last two lines of (12.12), with the result

$$\lambda = \left[\prod \sum_{\sigma_n} \oint \frac{(d\mathbf{p}_n)}{(2\pi)^3(2W_n)}\right] (2\pi)^4 \delta_4(\textstyle\sum p_n - p_\mu)(2m_\mu)^{-1} |\langle \prod u^\dagger_{\sigma_n}|S'|u_\mu\rangle|^2, \quad (12.13)$$

out of which all reference to $V$ and $T$ has been properly eliminated. The product $(2m_\mu \lambda) = 2m_\mu/\tau$ is the expression in the muon's rest-frame of the *invariant* $2W_\mu/\tau'$, where $\tau'$ is the 'dilated' mean lifetime and $W_\mu = (\mathbf{p}^2_\mu + m^2_\mu)^{\frac{1}{2}}$ is the equally 'dilated' muon energy in an *arbitrary* frame. (It is interesting to remark that the relativistic 'time dilatation' has been explicitly observed in comparisons of muon decays at rest and in flight; the expected factor $(1-\beta^2)^{-\frac{1}{2}} = (1-\mathbf{p}^2_\mu/W^2_\mu)^{-\frac{1}{2}} = W_\mu/m_\mu$ was found.) Both the forms (12.11) and (12.12) show that the amplitude $\langle \prod u^\dagger_{\sigma_n}|S'|u_\mu\rangle$ is an invariant, hence may be evaluated in any reference frame with the same result.

A comparison of the rate expression (12.13) to (12.3) shows that the customary 'statistical evaluations', which take into account only the momentum-energy conservation, presume that the factor

$$f(\mathbf{p}_{1,2,3}) = (16 m_\mu W_1 W_2 W_3)^{-1} \tfrac{1}{2} \sum_{\mu\sigma_1\sigma_2\sigma_3} |\langle \prod u^\dagger_{\sigma_n}(\mathbf{p}_n)|S'|u_\mu(0)\rangle|^2 \quad (12.14)$$

will in effect be independent of the individual four-momenta, $p_n$, particularly after the averaging over the muon spin-projections $\mu = \pm\frac{1}{2}$, indicated by $\frac{1}{2}\sum_\mu$. That presumption is plainly possible in a non-relativistic limit, when the spin descriptions become independent of the momenta [$u_{\sigma_n}(\mathbf{p}_n) \to u_{\sigma_n}(0)$ in (12.7), the result being essentially a spin description by the ordinary Pauli spinors, $\chi_{\sigma_n}$]. However, relativistic effects couple the spin to the linear motion (§ 2.4) and it may be that a dependence on the linear momenta $\mathbf{p}_n$ must survive the spin averages in (12.14). Then the factor $f(\mathbf{p}_{1,2,3})$ will describe a correlation of the emission directions compelled by the spin balance.

*Angular momentum conservation*

To make the total angular momentum $I(M)$ of the three product particles explicit, suitably representative eigenstates must be constructed. They must be taken to be descriptions within the muon's rest-frame if the total linear momentum balance already made explicit in the rate expression (12.13) is to be left undisturbed. Suitable eigenstates may be composed out of the individual-particle spherical waves, $\psi_{\kappa_n\mu_n}(x_n)$, given by (3.20), (3.35). These are eigenstates of energy, $W$, of the individual angular momenta $j_n(\mu_n)$ and of $\kappa_n = \pm(j_n+\frac{1}{2})$. Two of the particles must be coupled to form a 'pair' angular momentum, $S(m)$, first, and then the third particle's angular momentum is added. Consequently, there are free choices of $S$, $W_{1,2,3}$ and $\kappa_{1,2,3}$ with which the eigenstate of $I(M)$ may be constructed:

$$|I(M)SW_n\kappa_n\rangle \leftrightarrow \sum_m \Big[\prod \sum_{\mu_n} \psi_{\kappa_n\mu_n}(x_n)\Big]\times$$
$$\times\langle j_1(\mu_1)j_2(\mu_2)|S(m)\rangle\langle S(m)j_3(\mu_3)|I(M)\rangle. \quad (12.15)$$

This set may be introduced into the interaction amplitudes of (12.13) by using the plane to spherical wave transformation (3.47), which leads to:

$$\prod \psi_{\mathbf{p}_n\sigma_n}(x_n) \leftrightarrow \Big[\prod 4\pi(\pi/p_n)^{\frac{1}{2}} \sum_{\kappa_n\mu_n} i^{l_n}\chi^{\dagger}_{\kappa_n\mu_n}(\hat{\mathbf{p}}_n)\cdot\chi_{\sigma_n}\Big]\times$$
$$\times \sum_{IMSm} |I(M)SW_n\kappa_n\rangle\langle j_1(\mu_1)j_2(\mu_2)|S(m)\rangle\langle S(m)j_3(\mu_3)|I(M)\rangle. \quad (12.16)$$

The sixfold summation over $\kappa_{1,2,3}$, $\mu_{1,2,3}$ applies also to the last line. Because $u_{\sigma_n}(\mathbf{p}_n) \equiv \psi_{\mathbf{p}_n\sigma_n}(0)$, according to (12.6), each invariant amplitude of (12.13) is equivalent to

$$\langle\prod \psi^{\dagger}_{\mathbf{p}_n\sigma_n}(0)|S'|u_{\mu}(0)\rangle, \quad (12.17)$$

and the substitution of (12.16) into this will yield a superposition of the amplitudes

$$\langle I(M)SW_n\kappa_n|S'|u_{\mu}(0)\rangle_0, \quad (12.18)$$

to be evaluated for $x_n = 0$ (denoted by the subscript).

It is now physically obvious that all the amplitudes (12.18) must vanish except those for $I = \frac{1}{2}$ and $M = \mu$, and that each surviving amplitude must be independent of the muon's orientation, $\mu$. Formally, all this follows from the rotational invariance which $S'$ must have, as part of its Lorentz invariance, and from the Wigner–Eckart theorem (5.13). Thus, the angular momentum conservation is made explicit as a restriction of the interaction amplitudes to decay states with $I = \frac{1}{2}$, $M = \mu$, matching the muon's spin.

*The 'localization' of the interaction*

The contributing amplitudes are most restricted by their evaluation at $x_n = 0$, which is a consequence of the 'localization' of the interaction at the point of the muon, introduced in (12.9). The individual particles must emanate from a common point and can receive no orbital momentum around that point. The individual angular momenta become restricted to $j_n = \frac{1}{2}$. Moreover, the angular momentum $S$ attributed to any pair of the particles is then restricted to just the singlet and triplet values, $S = 0$ and 1.

All these conclusions are formally the result of evaluating the component states $\psi_{\kappa_n \mu_n}$ which make up the total angular momentum eigenstate (12.15), at $x_n = 0$. Reference to (3.20), (3.35) shows that

$$\psi_{\kappa\mu}(0) = (p/\pi)^{\frac{1}{2}} \begin{pmatrix} \delta_{\kappa,-1}(W+m)^{\frac{1}{2}} \\ i\delta_{\kappa,+1}(W-m)^{\frac{1}{2}} \end{pmatrix} \boldsymbol{\chi}_{-1\mu}, \tag{12.19}$$

vanishing except for $\kappa = \pm(j+\frac{1}{2}) = \pm 1$, as asserted. Here

$$\boldsymbol{\chi}_{-1\mu} = (4\pi)^{-\frac{1}{2}} \boldsymbol{\chi}_{\mu}$$

according to (2.18), where $\boldsymbol{\chi}_{\pm\frac{1}{2}}$ is just the ordinary Pauli spinor. It will be helpful to express $\psi_{\kappa\mu}$ on the basis of the *energy-independent* eigenstates of $\kappa = \mp 1$,

$$w_{-1\mu} = \begin{pmatrix} 1 \\ 0 \end{pmatrix} \boldsymbol{\chi}_{\mu} \quad \text{and} \quad w_{+1\mu} = \begin{pmatrix} 0 \\ 1 \end{pmatrix} \boldsymbol{\chi}_{\mu}. \tag{12.20}$$

Then

$$\psi_{\kappa\mu}(0) = i^l (2\pi)^{-1} [p(W-\kappa m)]^{\frac{1}{2}} w_{\kappa\mu}, \tag{12.21}$$

defined for $\kappa = \pm 1$ only ($l = 1$ and 0, respectively).

The last result permits separating out the energy dependence of the appropriate eigenstates (12.15), hence of the interaction amplitudes (12.18). With $\kappa_n = \pm 1$ only,

$$\langle \tfrac{1}{2}(\mu) S W_n \kappa_n | S' | u_\mu(0) \rangle$$
$$= [(2m_\mu)^{\frac{1}{2}}/(2\pi)^3] A_S(\kappa_1 \kappa_2 \kappa_3) \prod i^{-l_n} [p_n(W_n - \kappa_n m_n)]^{\frac{1}{2}} \tag{12.22}$$

defines sixteen surviving amplitude coefficients, $A_{0,1}(\pm 1, \pm 1, \pm 1)$, which are independent of all energies (including the muon rest-mass, $m_\mu = W_1 + W_2 + W_3$):

$$A_S = \sum_{m\mu_{1,2,3}} \langle \tfrac{1}{2}(\mu_1) \tfrac{1}{2}(\mu_2) | S(m) \rangle \langle S(m) \tfrac{1}{2}(\mu_3) | \tfrac{1}{2}(\mu) \rangle \langle \prod w^\dagger_{\kappa_n \mu_n} | S' | w_{-1\mu} \rangle, \tag{12.23}$$

expressed in terms of eigenstates of the type (12.20). Now the invariant amplitude (12.17) can be written

$$\langle\prod u^{\dagger}_{\sigma_n}|S'|u_{\mu}\rangle = (4\pi)^{\frac{3}{2}}(2m_{\mu})^{\frac{1}{2}}\times$$
$$\times\sum_{Sm\mu_{1,2,3}}\langle\tfrac{1}{2}(\mu_1)\tfrac{1}{2}(\mu_2)|S(m)\rangle\langle S(m)\tfrac{1}{2}(\mu_3)|\tfrac{1}{2}(\mu)\rangle\times$$
$$\times\sum_{\kappa_{1,2,3}}A_S(\kappa_1\kappa_2\kappa_3)\prod(-)^{l_n}(W_n-\kappa_n m_n)^{\frac{1}{2}}\boldsymbol{\chi}^{\dagger}_{\sigma_n}\cdot\boldsymbol{\chi}_{\kappa_n\mu_n}(\hat{\mathbf{p}}_n). \quad (12.24)$$

Only terms with $\kappa_n = \pm 1$ are to be included.

*The invariant correlations*

The spin sum needed in the rate expression (12.13) follows easily from (12.24):

$$\sum_{\sigma_{1,2,3}}|\langle\prod u^{\dagger}_{\sigma_n}|S'|u_{\mu}\rangle|^2$$
$$= (4\pi)^3(2m_{\mu})\left|\left[\prod\sum_{\kappa_n\mu_n}(-)^{l_n}(W_n-\kappa_n m_n)^{\frac{1}{2}}\boldsymbol{\chi}_{\kappa_n\mu_n}(\hat{\mathbf{p}}_n)\right]\times\right.$$
$$\left.\times\sum_{Sm}A_S\langle\tfrac{1}{2}(\mu_1)\tfrac{1}{2}(\mu_2)|S(m)\rangle\langle S(m)\tfrac{1}{2}(\mu_3)|\tfrac{1}{2}(\mu)\rangle\right|^2. \quad (12.25)$$

This still distinguishes the muon spin projections $\mu = \pm\frac{1}{2}$, and can be used to obtain results for polarized muon decay. For unpolarized muons, the expression should still be averaged by applying $\frac{1}{2}\sum_{\mu}$. The result will then be just the correlation factor, $f(\mathbf{p}_{1,2,3})$ of (12.14), multiplied with $16m_{\mu}W_1W_2W_3$.

The invariant intensity (12.25) can be evaluated in terms of the 256 products $A^*_S(\kappa_1\kappa_2\kappa_3)A_{S'}(\kappa'_1\kappa'_2\kappa'_3)$ through the use of techniques demonstrated in Chapter VI. The straightforward calculation is lengthy (see the reference to N. Karaiyinis on p. 330), as is inevitable in dealing with three-particle states, but the character of the result can now be made evident with comparative ease. The entire dependence on the momentum and energy of the $n$th particle is contained in the factors of the type:

$$(-)^{l_n+l'_n}(W_n-\kappa_n m_n)^{\frac{1}{2}}(W_n-\kappa'_n m_n)^{\frac{1}{2}}\boldsymbol{\chi}^{\dagger}_{\kappa_n\mu_n}\cdot\boldsymbol{\chi}_{\kappa'_n\mu'_n}(\hat{\mathbf{p}}_n), \quad (12.26)$$

with $\kappa_n$, $\kappa'_n = \pm 1$ only. Since $\boldsymbol{\chi}_{-1\mu} = (4\pi)^{-\frac{1}{2}}\chi_{\mu}$ and $\boldsymbol{\chi}_{+1\mu} = -\boldsymbol{\sigma}.\hat{\mathbf{p}}\boldsymbol{\chi}_{-1\mu}$ (3.63), such factors can be written

$$(4\pi)^{-1}\chi^{\dagger}_{\mu_n}[\delta_{\kappa'_n\kappa_n}(W_n-\kappa_n m_n)+\delta_{\kappa'_n,-\kappa_n}\boldsymbol{\sigma}^{(n)}.\mathbf{p}_n]\chi_{\mu'_n}. \quad (12.27)$$

Thus, every term of the result for (12.25) must be proportional to either $W_n$, $\mathbf{p}_n$, or $m_n$ for each of the particles.

Consider now the possible invariant forms which the combinations of $m_n$ and $p_n(\mathbf{p}_n, iW_n)$ can take. It is helpful to view them from an arbitrary frame, in which the muon may have the four-momentum

$p_\mu(\mathbf{p}_\mu, i[\mathbf{p}_\mu^2+m_\mu^2]^{\frac{1}{2}})$. Clearly, the proportionality to $m_\mu$ of the rest-frame expression (12.25) can arise from a proportionality to any component of $p_\mu$ in the arbitrary frame. Thus, the most general invariant form which the result for the intensity can take is

$$16\Big\{\sum_n [(a_n(p_\mu\cdot p_n)-b_n m_\mu m_n)(p_{n'}\cdot p_{n''})- \\ -c_n(p_\mu\cdot p_n)m_{n'}m_{n''}]+dm_\mu m_1 m_2 m_3\Big\}, \quad (12.28)$$

containing the scalar products of the 4-momenta, like

$$-(p_1\cdot p_2) = W_1 W_2-\mathbf{p}_1\cdot\mathbf{p}_2.$$

The summation actually runs over the sets of integer labels, $nn'n'' = 123$, 231, and 312, referring to the various product particles. The 10 coefficients $a_n$, $b_n$, $c_n$, and $d$ must be certain linear combinations of the 256 products, $A_S^* A_{S'}$. The reduction of the form (12.28) to the muon's rest frame yields the correlation factor (12.14) in the way discussed in connexion with (12.25):

$$f(\mathbf{p}_{1,2,3}) = \Big\{-\sum_n [(a_n W_n+b_n m_n)(p_{n'}\cdot p_{n''})+c_n W_n m_{n'}m_{n''}]+ \\ +dm_1 m_2 m_3\Big\}/W_1 W_2 W_3. \quad (12.29)$$

Now the interesting finding is that at least one of the coefficients $a_{1,2,3}$ must survive if the interaction $S'$ is to produce any decays at all, hence a directional correlation, $\sim W_{n'}W_{n''}-\mathbf{p}_{n'}\cdot\mathbf{p}_{n''}$, is unavoidable, contrary to the 'statistical' assumption discussed in connexion with (12.14).

The proof of the last point does not require the full evaluation of the expression (12.25); it is only necessary to pick out the terms proportional to $m_\mu W_1 W_2 W_3$, and identify their coefficient with $16(a_1+a_2+a_3)$. It then follows very easily that

$$a \equiv a_1+a_2+a_3 = \tfrac{1}{8}\sum_{S\kappa_1\kappa_2\kappa_3} |A_S(\kappa_1\kappa_2\kappa_3)|^2. \quad (12.30)$$

Every one of whatever amplitude coefficients exist makes a positive definite contribution to this, hence it cannot vanish.

The results here do not nullify the success of the 'statistical evaluation' as applied to the nuclear $\beta$-decay in Chapter I. In the latter processes, one of the decay products is a nucleon with a negligible recoil. Putting $\mathbf{p}_3 = 0$, and $m_2 = 0$ for the neutrino mass, into the correlation factor (12.29) yields

$$f = a+b_3-(a_3+b_3)\mathbf{v}_1\cdot\mathbf{v}_2+(b_1+c_1)m_1/W_1.$$

Values of the coefficients can be chosen which give an arbitrary linear combination of the Fermi (singlet) electron-neutrino correlation,

$$\sim (1+\mathbf{v}_1\cdot\mathbf{v}_2),$$

and the Gamow–Teller (triplet) correlation,

$$\sim (1-\tfrac{1}{3}\mathbf{v}_1.\mathbf{v}_2).$$

There exist choices of the singlet and triplet amplitudes, $A_0$ and $A_1$, in (12.25), which correspond to this. That the correlations here are consistent with the 'statistical evaluation' was shown in Chapter I. Notice that the result here includes a 'Fierz interference' effect of the type shown in (10.11), and to be expected of more general interactions than the 'V–A Law'.

*The Michel-parametrized spectra*

The first expectations for the electron spectra from $\mu$-decay were advanced by Wheeler and Tiomno.‡ They were based on specific interaction forms of the type being tried for nuclear $\beta$-decay. Michel§ generalized the calculations to all interaction forms of the 'even' type (10.1). His results survived the later discovery of parity non-conservation because the spectra observed are averaged over spins. Michel found that all the spectra following from (10.1) could be characterized by a single parameter, $\rho$, in so far as the masses of all the product particles can be neglected. The correlations (12.29) will provide a basis for the same spectra which makes no more special an assumption about the interaction than its 'localization', as defined by the above development.

The primary interest is in expectations neglecting the product particle masses because almost all the muon's rest-energy is found to appear as kinetic energy of the product particles. The electron's rest-mass forms no more than $\frac{1}{2}$ per cent of the total energy release and the neutretto mass may well be zero. With $m_1 = m_2 = m_3 = 0$, the correlation factor (12.29) is simplified to

$$f = a(1-\alpha\hat{\mathbf{p}}_1.\hat{\mathbf{p}}_2-\beta\hat{\mathbf{p}}_1.\hat{\mathbf{p}}_3-\gamma\hat{\mathbf{p}}_2.\hat{\mathbf{p}}_3), \tag{12.31}$$

where $a$ is defined by (12.30) and

$$\alpha+\beta+\gamma = (a_3+a_2+a_1)/a = 1. \tag{12.32}$$

This must be inserted into the rate expression (12.13), with the help of (12.14), in order to obtain the spectrum.

Because of a later need for it, the operation

$$\oint (d\mathbf{p}_2) \oint (d\mathbf{p}_3)\delta_4(\textstyle\sum p_n - p_\mu) = \oint (d\mathbf{p}_2)\delta(\sum W_n - m_\mu) \tag{12.33}$$

in the rate expression will first be discussed with only one of the product masses (the neutrino's) put equal to zero. Moreover, the distinctions

‡ J. A. Wheeler and J. Tiomno, *Rev. Mod. Phys.* **21**, 144 (1949).
§ L. Michel, *Proc. Phys. Soc. Lond.* A, **63**, 514 (1950).

among the particles will be made better evident through the changes in notation: $m_1 \equiv m_e$, $\mathbf{p}_1 \equiv \mathbf{p}$, $W_1 \equiv W$ for the electron; $m_2 = 0$, $\mathbf{p}_2 \equiv \mathbf{q}$, $W_2 \equiv q$ for the neutrino; $m_3 \equiv m_0$, $\mathbf{p}_3 \equiv \mathbf{k}$, $W_3 = K$ for the neutretto. Now, to carry out the operation (12.33), let

$$(d\mathbf{p}_2) \equiv (d\mathbf{q}) = q^2\,dq\,d(\cos\theta_\nu)\,d\phi_\nu$$

with the electron's direction of motion $\hat{\mathbf{p}}$ as polar axis, so that

$$\cos\theta_\nu \equiv \hat{\mathbf{q}}\,.\,\hat{\mathbf{p}}.$$

The conservation relations (12.4) lead to the relation

$$\cos\theta_\nu = (2pq)^{-1}[(m_\mu - W)^2 - p^2 - m_0^2] - (m_\mu - W)/p, \tag{12.34}$$

which enables eliminating the energy-conserving δ-function in (12.33) through integration over $\theta_\nu$, with the result:

$$\oint d\phi_\nu \int dq\,q^2[d(\cos\theta_\nu)/dm_\mu]_{p,q} = p^{-1}\oint d\phi_\nu \int dq\,qK,$$

where $K = m_\mu - W - q$ is the neutretto energy. The limits on the integration over $q$ are set by putting $\cos\theta_\nu = \mp 1$ into (12.34):

$$q_{\min}^{\max} = \tfrac{1}{2}[m_\mu - W \pm p]\{1 - m_0^2/[(m_\mu - W)^2 - p^2]\}. \tag{12.35}$$

With these results, the expression for the electron spectrum following from (12.13) may be written:

$$d\lambda/dW = (d\Omega/4\pi)(4\pi^3)^{-1}W \oint (d\phi_\nu/2\pi) \int dq\,qKf, \tag{12.36}$$

in which a symmetry in the three energies $W$, $q$, $K$ is still evident.

The spectrum (12.36) will now be evaluated in the approximation $m_e = m_0 = 0$, when the correlation factor $f$ is given by (12.31). The various terms of this factor become easy to integrate with the help of

$$\hat{\mathbf{p}}\,.\,\hat{\mathbf{q}} = \cos\theta_\nu = (2W_0/Wq)(W_0 - W) - (2W_0 - W)/W,$$
$$\hat{\mathbf{p}}\,.\,\hat{\mathbf{k}} = -\hat{\mathbf{p}}\,.\,(\mathbf{p}+\mathbf{q})/k = -(W/K) - (q/K)\cos\theta_\nu,$$
$$\hat{\mathbf{q}}\,.\,\hat{\mathbf{k}} = -\hat{\mathbf{q}}\,.\,(\mathbf{p}+\mathbf{q})/k = -(W/K)\cos\theta_\nu - (q/K).$$

The first two of these yield the same integrals (limits now,

$$W_0 - W \leqslant q \leqslant W),$$

because of the symmetry of (12.36) in the neutrino and neutretto when $m_0 = 0$.

The result for the spectrum is

$$d\lambda/dW = (aW_0/2\pi^3)W^2[W_0 - W + \tfrac{1}{2}(1-\gamma)(\tfrac{4}{3}W - W_0)]. \tag{12.37}$$

The correlation coefficients $\alpha$, $\beta$ of (12.31) do not appear explicitly because of the symmetry in the neutral particles when both are treated as massless; this causes $\alpha$ and $\beta$ to appear with equal coefficients and the factor $(\alpha+\beta)$ is replaceable by $(1-\gamma)$ according to (12.32). The terms of the spectrum (12.37) which are proportional to $(1-\gamma)$ have a zero average in the integration over the energy; this yields

$$\lambda = aW_0^5/24\pi^3 \tag{12.38}$$

for the total rate, in terms of the intensity sum $a$ of (12.30).

Michel obtained the same spectrum (12.37) but expressed in terms of a parameter $\rho$ defined in such a way that

$$d\lambda/\lambda\, dW = (12/W_0^4)W^2[W_0 - W + \tfrac{2}{3}\rho(\tfrac{4}{3}W - W_0)], \tag{12.39 a}$$

hence

$$\rho = \tfrac{3}{4}(1-\gamma). \tag{12.39 b}$$

Clearly, $\rho = 0$ corresponds to a spectrum with a vanishing intensity at the end-point, $W = W_0$; the maximum intensity of the $\rho = 0$ spectrum occurs for $W = \frac{2}{3}W_0$. For $\rho > 0$, the maximum shifts closer to the end-point, and the end-point intensity becomes finite. The maximum occurs right at the end-point for $\rho = \frac{3}{4}$.

The Michel parametrization owes its importance to the fact that the experimenters have found that they can consistently fit the theoretical form (12.39) to their observations, and can express their results as simply measurements of $\rho$. All the latest measurements‡ agree with

$$\rho = 0{\cdot}75 \pm 0{\cdot}03.$$

With the value $\rho = \frac{3}{4}$, the spectrum expression (12.39) is simplified to

$$d\lambda/\lambda\, dW = (6/W_0^4)W^2(W_0 - \tfrac{2}{3}W). \tag{12.40}$$

This increases quadratically with energy at low energies and levels off to a maximum at the end-point, $W = W_0$ (Fig. 12.1). More than 80 per cent of the electrons are concentrated in the high-energy end of the spectrum, with $W > \frac{1}{2}W_0$. This fact is important for an understanding of the observed directional distribution of the electrons from polarized muons, as will be seen (12.48).

## 12.2. The V-A Law in μ-decay

Such theoretical arguments as the one offered in the introductory paragraph of this chapter, together with the experimental observations of longitudinal polarizations of the electrons, make it desirable to explore first the interaction form

$$h_\mu = 8^{\frac{1}{2}} g J_\alpha(\mu^0\mu) J_\alpha(e\nu) + \text{h.c.}, \tag{12.41}$$

with

$$J_\alpha(\mu^0\mu) = \phi_{\mu^0}^\dagger \beta\gamma_\alpha \phi_\mu = \psi_{\mu^0}^\dagger \beta\gamma_\alpha \tfrac{1}{2}(1+\gamma_5)\psi_\mu. \tag{12.42}$$

‡ e.g. those of W. Dudziak, R. Sagane, and J. Vedder, *Phys. Rev.* **114**, 336 (1959), of M. Block, E. Fiorini, T. Kikuchi, G. Giacomelli, and S. Ratti, *Nuovo Cim.* **23**, 1114 (1962), and of R. Plano, *Phys. Rev.* **119**, 1400 (1960).

This again is a 'V–A' form of law like (4.10) but here no provision will initially be made, as in (4.63), for possible differences between Vector and Pseudovector coupling strengths. There is no indication that the muon or neutretto are subject to such strong interactions as are nucleons, hence no expectation that an appreciable 'renormalization' of the coupling strengths will be necessary. Of course, it will be a matter of experimental test whether the constant $g$ here is the same as for nuclear $\beta$-decay.

*The* V–A *correlations and the spectrum*

The $\mu$-decay product distributions can be obtained by starting from the general first-order transition rate formula (4.36), but it is immediately evident that this leads to the result (12.13) already used in the preceding section. It is only necessary to make the appropriate identification of the interaction amplitudes $\langle \prod u^{\dagger}_{\sigma_n} | S' | u_\mu \rangle$ with the specific ones

$$\langle h_\mu \rangle_0 = 2^{-\frac{1}{2}} g[u^{\dagger}_{\mu^0}(1 \pm \gamma_5)\beta\gamma_\alpha u_\mu][u^{\dagger}_{\rm e}(1 \pm \gamma_5)\beta\gamma_\alpha u^C_\nu], \qquad (12.43)$$

applying to $\mu^{\mp}$ decays, respectively. The relationship between the two signs follows from considerations like those leading to (4.35). The spinors here must be normalized as in (12.7) if this is to be used in the form (12.13) as it stands.

The techniques for evaluating intensities from amplitudes having forms like (12.43) were amply illustrated in Chapters IV and V. A relatively simple expression results for the following sum over product particle spins:

$$\sum_{\mu^0 e\nu} |\langle h_\mu \rangle|^2 = 64 m_\mu W q K g^2 (1 - \mathbf{v}_{\rm e} \cdot \mathbf{v}_{\mu^0})(1 \pm \boldsymbol{\sigma}_\mu \cdot \hat{\mathbf{q}}) \quad \text{for } \mu^{\mp}. \qquad (12.44)$$

The use of units for which $c = \hbar = 1$ is continued here, hence each velocity $\mathbf{v}$ is in units of $c$; for the neutrino, $\mathbf{v}_\nu = \hat{\mathbf{q}}$ is a unit vector because the particle is taken to be massless. The quantity $\boldsymbol{\sigma}_\mu = \boldsymbol{\chi}^{\dagger}_\mu \boldsymbol{\sigma} \boldsymbol{\chi}_\mu$ is the expectation value of the muon's spin (units $\frac{1}{2}\hbar$) in the state in which it has the projection $\mu$ $(= \pm\frac{1}{2})$; it can thus be treated as a unit vector in the direction of the muon spin. The expression shows that the antineutrino's emission direction is positively correlated with the muon spin direction in $\mu^-$-decay, whereas the neutrino of $\mu^+$-decay tends to emerge in the direction opposite to that pointed out by the muon spin. Since the antineutrino moves right-handedly and the neutrino left-handedly, these particles carry off all the muon's angular momentum in each case. This situation is the same as in neutron decay, discussed in § 1.10.

With the neutrino taking care of conserving the muon's angular momentum effectively by itself, the electron and neutretto should form a singlet spin state. Both are expected to have the same handedness, since both are produced in normal states in $\mu^-$-decay, both in antiparticle states in $\mu^+$-decay, according to the V–A Law. They should therefore be negatively correlated in emission directions (Fig. 12.2), just

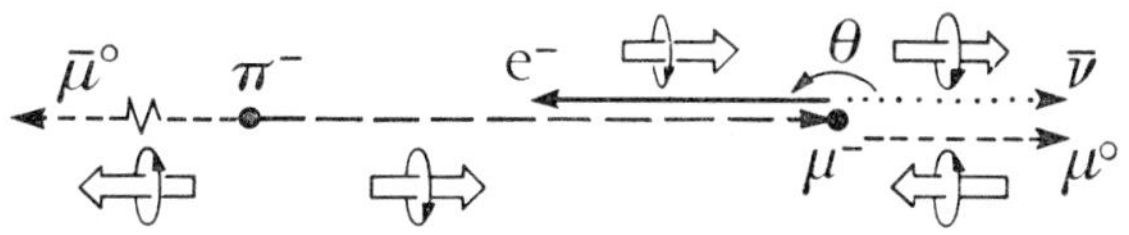


FIG. 12.2. The configuration of maximum occurrence in the decay of a muon emitted by a pion.

as described by (12.44). That the V–A Law leads to a singlet state for the electron and neutretto can be explicitly confirmed by an analysis of the type used in the preceding section. When the singlet and triplet amplitudes $A_S$, of (12.23), are evaluated, it turns out that $A_1 = 0$ and $A_0 \neq 0$ if it is the electron and neutretto which are paired in forming the two-particle angular momentum, $S$. Moreover, the results for $A_0$ properly yield the expression (12.44); the intensity coefficient $a$ of (12.30) attains the value $4g^2$.

The result (12.44) leads to an electron spectrum which is easiest to find through its relation to the corresponding directional correlation factor (12.14). This is just a renormalized average of the intensity (12.44) over the muon orientations:

$$\begin{aligned} f &= (16m_\mu WqK)^{-1}\tfrac{1}{2}\sum_{\mu\mu^0 e\nu}|\langle h_\mu\rangle|^2 \\ &= 4g^2(1-\mathbf{v}_e\cdot\mathbf{v}_{\mu^0}). \end{aligned} \tag{12.45}$$

It is an instance of the general correlation (12.29) with only one of the coefficients ($a_2$) non-vanishing. When the masses $m_e$ and $m_0$ are neglected, as for the form (12.31), then $\alpha = \gamma = 0$ and $\beta = 1$ in this form. The Michel parameter (12.39 b) becomes

$$\rho = \tfrac{3}{4}(1-\gamma) = \tfrac{3}{4}; \tag{12.46}$$

thus the V–A Law leads to the spectrum (12.40), in agreement with experiment.

*The electron's directional distribution*

The angular distribution, relative to the muon spin direction, of the electrons from polarized muons can be obtained by inserting the spin sum (12.44) into the rate expression (12.13), then integrating over the neutrino and neutretto variables, much as this was done in arriving at the spectrum (12.37). When the rest-masses of the product particles are again neglected,

$$4\pi\, d\lambda/dW d\Omega = (g^2/\pi^3)W_0\, W^2[W_0-\tfrac{2}{3}W\mp\tfrac{1}{3}(2W-W_0)\cos\theta], \quad (12.47)$$

for $\mu^{\mp}$-decays, respectively. Here, $\theta$ is the angle of the electron's emission direction to the muon's spin. The coefficient $(2W-W_0)$ is positive for the more than 80 per cent of the electrons which have energies $W > \frac{1}{2}W_0$. Integration over the energy spectrum yields the angular distribution

$$d\lambda/\lambda = (d\Omega/4\pi)(1\mp\tfrac{1}{3}\cos\theta) \quad \text{for } \mu^{\mp}. \quad (12.48)$$

The signs of the correlations here are results of the predominance of the high energy electrons.

Polarized muons are available as products of the $\pi$-decays (11.25). As they emerge from these processes, the muons are expected to be totally longitudinally polarized ($\mathscr{P}_\mu = \pm 1$ for $\mu^{\mp}$) according to (11.48). However, they must first be brought to rest if the above considerations are to apply directly. Muons at rest (i.e. with kinetic energies $\ll m_\mu c^2$) are also the most convenient for experimental observation since the procedures for bringing them to rest tend also to concentrate the processes to a relatively small region of space. The slowing down is accomplished by letting the muons penetrate into some solid material; the slowing-down time is then very much shorter ($\lesssim 10^{-9}$ sec) than the 2·2 $\mu$sec muon lifetime, hence corrections for the few muons which decay in flight are usually negligible. Unfortunately, the slowing-down processes may depolarize the muons to $|\mathscr{P}_\mu| < 1$. Whatever polarization remains at the instant of the muon decay must still have the signs $\mathscr{P}_\mu = \pm|\mathscr{P}_\mu|$ for $\mu^{\mp}$, relative to the muon's direction of motion from its pion source. It then follows from (12.48) that the product electron's (energy-integrated) angular distribution relative to the motion direction of the muon should be

$$d\lambda/\lambda = (d\Omega/4\pi)(1-\tfrac{1}{3}|\mathscr{P}_\mu|\cos\theta_{e\mu}), \quad (12.49)$$

predominantly backwards regardless of the sign of the charge. After comparative studies of the depolarizing effects of various materials,‡ experimental confirmation of this result, within 6 per cent or so, was achieved.§

‡ G. Chadwick, S. Durrais, L. Eisberg, P. Jones, J. Wignall, and D. Wilkinson, *Phil. Mag.* **2,** 684 (1957); D. Wilkinson, *Nuovo Cim.* **6,** 516 (1957).

§ S. Ali-Zade, I. Gurevich, Yu. Dubretsov, B. Nikol'sky, and L. Surkova, *Zh. eksp. teor. Fiz.* **36,** 1327 (1959).

*The muon lifetime*

Besides the $\mu$-decay electron's polarization, spectrum, and angular distribution, only the total decay rate has been observable. The expectation for this which follows from the V–A Law can be obtained by integrating the distribution (12.47). The simple result is

$$\lambda \equiv 1/\tau_\mu = g^2 W_0^5/6\pi^3\hbar^7c^6, \tag{12.50}$$

in which ordinary units have been restored, to prepare for numerical evaluation. (The result naturally coincides with (12.38) with $a = 4g^2$; that the latter characterizes the V–A Law was noted in (12.45), for example.) The rest-masses of the product particles have been neglected here, but this approximation is more than adequate for comparisons with current measurements, as will be demonstrated in the next section.

The evaluation of the rate expression (12.50) reveals a startling fact. When the measured values $\tau_\mu = 2{\cdot}210 \pm 0{\cdot}003$ $\mu$sec (11.27) and

$$W_0 \approx \tfrac{1}{2}m_\mu c^2 = 103{\cdot}38_5 \pm 0{\cdot}01_5 m_e c^2$$

(11.26) are substituted into (12.50), they lead to

$$g = (1{\cdot}428 \pm 0{\cdot}001_5)10^{-49} \text{ erg cm}^3 \tag{12.51}$$

for the coupling constant. This is far more closely the same as $g_V = gC_V$ of (5.89) than was anticipated, on the basis that $g$ is a 'universal' strength for the coupling of any pair of the transformation currents $J_\alpha(\text{pn})$, $J_\alpha(\text{e}\nu)$, and $J_\alpha(\mu\mu^0)$. It leads to $C_V = 0{\cdot}983 \pm 0{\cdot}003$ for the 're-normalization' factor of the nucleonic Vector current, very close to the near-unit value characteristic of a source which, like the muon, is subject to no strong interactions at all. Such an outcome for the nucleon is very difficult to accept, in view of the very sizeable strong-interaction effects exhibited in the general behaviour of nucleons. What has been made of this result will be discussed in § 12.5.

*The electron polarization*

In so far as the product particle masses are negligible (next section), the intensity distribution (12.44) is simply multiplied by the factor

$$\tfrac{1}{2}(1 \mp \boldsymbol{\sigma}_e \cdot \hat{\mathbf{p}}) \quad \text{for } e^{\mp} \tag{12.52}$$

when the summation over electron spins is left off. Such a factor is plainly unmodified in the integrations (12.36) over the unobservable neutral lepton variables, hence the observable electron polarization is expected to be independent of whether the source muons are polarized or not. The result (12.52) corresponds to a complete longitudinal electron polarization, $\mathscr{P} = \mp 1$ for $e^{\mp}$. It may be noted that the $v_e \to c$

electrons from nuclear $\beta$-decay are similarly completely polarized, even from oriented nuclear sources, as reference to the polarization vector expression (5.51 b) shows.

## 12.3. Effects of product-particle rest-mass‡

For the results of the preceding section, the rest-masses of the product particles were ignored. That simplified the formulae considerably and is, on the whole, quite justified for comparisons with measurements of the accuracy currently achieved. Yet there is great interest in seeing to what accuracy the measurements must still be pushed in order to get information about a possible rest-mass of the neutretto, for example.

*On the electron spectrum*

The insertion of the precise V–A correlation factor (12.45) into the integral (12.36) yields the expression for the spectrum:

$$d\lambda/dW = (g^2/\pi^3)\int dq\, q(WK-\mathbf{p}.\mathbf{k}), \tag{12.53}$$

where $W = (p^2+m_e^2)^{\frac{1}{2}}$, $q$ and $K = (k^2+m_0^2)^{\frac{1}{2}}$ are the energies of electron, massless neutrino, and neutretto, respectively. Energy and momentum conservation requires $K = m_\mu - W - q$, $\mathbf{k} = -(\mathbf{p}+\mathbf{q})$, and $\hat{\mathbf{p}}.\hat{\mathbf{q}} = \cos\theta_\nu$ as given by (12.34). The limits on the integration over $q$ are given in (12.35). Then it is straightforward to find

$$d\lambda/dW = (g^2/2\pi^3)m_\mu pW[W_0-\tfrac{2}{3}W-\tfrac{1}{3}(m_e^2/W)+(m_0^2/m_\mu)\delta(W)]D^2(W), \tag{12.54}$$

where $W_0$ is the end-point energy given by (12.2), and

$$\left.\begin{aligned}\delta(W) &= 1+\tfrac{1}{3}p^2/W[W_0-W+(m_0^2/2m_\mu)]\\ D(W) &= (W_0-W)/[W_0-W+(m_0^2/2m_\mu)]\end{aligned}\right\}. \tag{12.55}$$

The result here properly reduces to (12.40) for $m_e = m_0 = 0$.

To see the effect of just the electron mass, as in the most plausible contingency that the neutretto has no rest-mass, the term in $\delta(W)$ should be dropped and $D$ be put equal to unity. The resulting spectrum still has its maximum at its end-point, like the 'massless' spectrum (12.40), and is almost undetectably changed even at low energies, where the rest-energy is the greatest part. For example, the spectrum is depressed from its $m_e = 0$ shape far the most at $W = m_e$, and even here the depression is only by 0·03 per cent of the intensity at the maximum.

‡ J. Bahcall and R. B. Curtis, *Nuovo Cim.* **21**, 422 (1961).

If the neutretto has a non-vanishing rest-mass, $m_0$, then the effect on the electron spectrum is concentrated around its maximum and near its end-point, where $m_e = 0$ is an even better approximation than at the low electron energies. The most striking effect of $m_0 \neq 0$ is that it changes the spectrum from one with its maximum intensity at the end-point to one with a vanishing end-point intensity; this follows from the proportionality to $D^2(W)$, above. The position of the intensity maximum is shifted down from $W = W_0 = \frac{1}{2}m_\mu[1-(m_0/m_\mu)^2]$ to $W_m = \frac{1}{2}m_\mu[1-(m_0/m_\mu)]$, i.e. by about $\frac{1}{2}m_0$. This effect, being nearly linear in the neutretto mass (rather than quadratic like the effect on the position of the end-point itself), may offer one of the best chances for a measure of $m_0$ through observations on $\mu$-decay.

Up to now, the best spectrum measurements have been consistent with a maximum intensity at the end-point, hence $m_0 = 0$. However, the experimental resolution has been such that a shift of the maximum by several times the electron mass could have escaped detection.

*On the decay rate*

Consider first the decay rate obtained by integrating the spectrum (12.54) for the case of zero neutretto mass, $m_0 = 0$:

$$\lambda = (g^2/6\pi^3)(m_\mu/2)^5[1-8\epsilon^2+8\epsilon^6-\epsilon^8-24\epsilon^4\ln\epsilon], \tag{12.56}$$

where $\epsilon \equiv m_e/m_\mu$. This properly agrees with (12.50) for $\epsilon = 0$, when $W_0 = \frac{1}{2}m_\mu$. The net effect of $m_e \neq 0$ is to decrease the rate, as is to be expected since less kinetic energy is then released to the product particles and this decreases the phase space available to them. However, $\epsilon = m_e/m_\mu \approx 1/200$ only, hence there is only about a 0·02 per cent decrease for a given coupling strength.

The same formula (12.56) can be used to represent the effect of a non-vanishing neutretto mass when the electron mass effect is neglected. It is only necessary to redefine the mass ratio as $\epsilon \equiv m_0/m_\mu$. This symmetry in the electron and neutretto masses is obviously to be expected and follows from the symmetry of the correlation factor in (12.45) or (12.53). It now follows that even a neutretto mass five times as great as the electron mass would depress the rate by only $\frac{1}{2}$ per cent for a given coupling strength.

*On the electron polarization*

The precise degree to which the $\mu$-decay electrons will be polarized has so far been ignored, except in the approximation $m_e = m_0 = 0$. A specific evaluation is important because, as was seen in the example of $\pi$-decay (11.47), the restrictions set by linear momentum conservation can influence the observable polarization radically.

The emission rate of electrons with a particle rest-spin orientation, $\boldsymbol{\sigma}_e = \boldsymbol{\chi}_e^\dagger \boldsymbol{\sigma} \boldsymbol{\chi}_e$, is obtained when the summation over $e = \pm\frac{1}{2}$ is left off in the evaluation of the correlation factor (12.45). The result then found is (for $e^\mp$)

$$f_e = 2g^2[1 - \mathbf{v}_e \cdot \mathbf{v}_{\mu^0} \mp \boldsymbol{\sigma}_e \cdot \mathbf{v}_e(1 - \hat{\mathbf{p}} \cdot \mathbf{v}_{\mu^0}) \pm \boldsymbol{\sigma}_e \cdot \mathbf{v}_{\mu^0} m_e/W]. \quad (12.57\,\text{a})$$

This clearly reduces to

$$f_e = \tfrac{1}{2} f(1 \mp \boldsymbol{\sigma}_e \cdot \hat{\mathbf{p}}) \quad \text{for } e^\mp \quad (12.57\,\text{b})$$

when $m_e = 0$, with $f$ the same correlation factor (12.45) already used in the above evaluations of the V–A Law. Thus, all the majority of electrons with speeds negligibly different from the speed of light are expected to be completely polarized, $\mathscr{P}_e \to \mp 1$ as $v_e \to c$, whether or not the neutretto has mass.

The precise result for $m_e$ and $m_0 \neq 0$ is not difficult to obtain, through the integration (12.36) of the correlations $f_e$ (12.57 a), but it is inordinately lengthy because of numerous very small effects. When only corrections linear in $(m_e/m_\mu)$ are retained,

$$\mathscr{P}_e \approx \mp \frac{v}{c}\left\{1 + 2\frac{m_e}{m_\mu}\frac{m_\mu c^2 - W}{3m_\mu c^2 - 4W}\left[1 + 3\frac{m_0^2}{m_\mu}\frac{c^2}{3m_\mu c^2 - 4W} + \cdots\right] + \cdots\right\}. \quad (12.58)$$

The mass-effects are obviously extremely small.

*On the directional distribution*

The effect of finite electron and neutretto rest-masses on the angular distribution of the electrons from polarized muons is obtained by now taking into account the correlation of the neutrino's emission direction with the muon spin, as recorded in (12.44). An integration over the neutrino variables must be performed as in (12.53), but now the integrand has the azimuthal average of the additional factor, $1 \pm \boldsymbol{\sigma}_\mu \cdot \hat{\mathbf{q}}$. This average is simply $1 \pm \cos\theta \cos\theta_\nu$ if $\theta$ is again the angle between the electron's emission direction $\hat{\mathbf{p}}$ and the muon spin, while $\cos\theta_\nu = \hat{\mathbf{p}} \cdot \hat{\mathbf{q}}$ of (12.34). The result for $4\pi d\lambda/dW d\Omega$ can be written as the sum of two terms, the first of which is exactly the isotropic spectrum expression (12.54). Added to that is the anisotropic term

$$\frac{g^2}{2\pi^3} m_\mu p W\left(\mp \frac{1}{3}\frac{p}{W}\cos\theta\right)\left[2W - W_0 - \frac{m_e^2}{m_\mu} + \frac{m_0^2}{m_\mu}\delta'(W)\right] D^2(W), \quad (12.59)$$

for $\mu^{\mp}$ decays, respectively. $D(W)$ is the same function as in (12.55), and

$$\delta'(W) = [W-(m_e^2/m_\mu)]/[W_0-W+m_0^2/2m_\mu]. \quad (12.60)$$

The entire expression properly reduces to (12.47) for $m_e = m_0 = 0$.

The effect of non-vanishing product particle masses on the energy-integrated anisotropy in (12.48) is only quadratic in $\epsilon = m_e/m$ or $m_0/m$, a few hundredths of a per cent. There is an effect linear in the neutretto mass when the observations on the anisotropy are confined to just the high energy electrons which occur with maximum intensity. For them, the effect of the electron mass remains quadratic, hence $m_e$ may be put equal to zero. The energy of the electrons of maximum intensity was found to be $W_m = \frac{1}{2}m_\mu(1-\epsilon)$, with $\epsilon = m_0/m_\mu$, during the consideration of the spectrum (12.54). At this energy,

$$4\pi d\lambda/dWd\Omega = (g^2/3\pi^3)W_m^4[1+4\epsilon+\epsilon^2\mp(1-\epsilon^2)\cos\theta]. \quad (12.61)$$

Most striking is a change of the 'fore-to-aft' ratio from zero to $2\epsilon(1+\frac{1}{2}\epsilon)/(1+2\epsilon)$ by the existence of $m_0 = \epsilon m_\mu$. Establishing experimental limits on this effect may be very difficult since it requires not only a control of the muon polarization but also the attaining of resolution in both energy and angle.

## 12.4. Alternatives for the law of μ-decay

The same V–A form of coupling has been found to account successfully for all the best-established facts about each of the processes considered so far.‡ The 'universality' of form may be implemented by assuming it arises from the interaction of a total neutral ↔ charged-field transformation current,

$$J_\alpha = J_\alpha(e\nu)+J_\alpha(\mu\mu^0)+J_\alpha(np) \quad (12.62)$$

with itself, according to $$h = -8^{\frac{1}{2}}gJ_\alpha^{(*)}J_\alpha \quad (12.63)$$

under a convention that $\mathbf{J}^{(*)} = \mathbf{J}^\dagger$ but $J_4^{(*)} = -J_4^\dagger$. If

$$J_\alpha(ab) = \phi_a^\dagger\beta\gamma_\alpha\phi_b = \psi_a^\dagger\gamma_\alpha\tfrac{1}{2}(1+\gamma_5)\psi_b, \quad (12.64)$$

$h$ contains $h_\beta$ of (4.10), $h_{N\mu}$ of (11.31), and $h_\mu$ of (12.41). It also contains new interactions, leading to processes like $e+\nu \rightarrow e+\nu$ and $e^-+e^+ \leftrightarrow \nu+\bar{\nu}$. All such are extremely difficult to observe and there is no evidence for or against their existence (there have been guesses about their role in stellar evolution).

‡ An exception: the observed weak-magnetic effect discussed in the last subsection of Chapter VII, and to be reconsidered in § 12.5. Moreover, the understanding of the pion decay rate (§ 11.4) cannot be held completely satisfactory in view of the difficulties about its theoretical evaluation.

There would be little point in venturing the hypothesis of the new processes if there were any doubt about the 'universality' in form of the couplings $h_\beta$, $h_{N\mu}$, and $h_\mu$. The renormalized V–A form is best established for $h_\beta$. It appears to be the unique form in the language of 4-fermion interactions (10.9), apart from inconsequential transformations like those of Fierz (§ 10.1) or of Pauli (§ 10.3). Most of the evidence about $h_{N\mu}$ is still to be discussed (next chapter). So far it has been found that, if $h_{N\mu}$ is granted a role in $\pi$-decay, then the V–A form of it is consistent with what is observed and calculable about that process. However, the 'Vector' part of the nucleon current factor played no role ($C_V = 0$ in $h_{N\mu}$ could have been assumed) in the $\pi$-decay, and the 'Pseudovector' part is replaceable by a Pseudoscalar density if the remarkable agreement with the observed muon-to-electron ratio stemming from a universal V–A form is dismissed as accidental. Moreover, arbitrary admixtures of Scalar and Tensor forms into $h_{N\mu}$ would have had no observable effect in the $\pi$-decay. Finally, no alternatives to the V–A form for $h_\mu$ have yet been considered here. Such will be the concern of this section.

*The generalized $\mu$-decay interaction*

A family of alternatives for the $\mu$-decay coupling, $h_\mu$, is provided by the form (10.9), with $(\bar{\psi}_p \Gamma^X \psi_n)$ replaced by $(\bar{\psi}_{\mu^0} \Gamma^X \psi_\mu)$. The consequences are calculable by applying already familiar techniques, hence only end-results‡ will be presented. They will be given only with neglect of the product particle rest-masses, since the interest is now in the interaction form rather than in the obviously small effects of the masses. Moreover, it is not small admixtures into the V–A Law which are of principal interest, but whether the V–A Law may be quite entirely superseded, hence small percentages of uncertainty in the available measurements will be ignored.

To be presented first will be the generalization of the distribution (12.47) of the electrons in energy, and in direction relative to polarized muons:

$$4\pi d\lambda/dW d\Omega = (g^2 Q/8\pi^3) W_0 W^2\{(W_0 - W) + \\ + \tfrac{2}{3}\rho(\tfrac{4}{3}W - W_0) \pm \tfrac{2}{3}\xi \cos\theta[(W_0 - W) + 2\delta(\tfrac{4}{3}W - W_0)]\}, \quad (12.65)$$

for $e^\mp$, respectively. As in the spectrum expression (12.39), parts $\sim (W_0 - W)$ with a vanishing end-point intensity, and parts $\sim (\tfrac{4}{3}W - W_0)$ with a vanishing spectrum average, have been distinguished. Like (12.39), the expression (12.65), with arbitrary parameters $Q$ ($= 4a/g^2$),

‡ e.g. C. Bouchiat and L. Michel, *Phys. Rev.* **106**, 170 (1957).

$\rho$, $\xi$, and $\delta$, can be shown to follow from just the conservation principles and a localization of the interaction.

In the conventional derivations (e.g. reference on p. 348), based on the interaction form (10.9), the parameters naturally depend on the various coupling constants $C_X$ and $C'_X$. These constants can only enter in the combinations (see footnote, p. 289):

$$\left.\begin{aligned} K_{XY} &= C_X^* C_Y + (C'_X)^* C'_Y \\ \text{and} \qquad L_{XY} &= C_X^* C'_Y + (C'_X)^* C_Y \end{aligned}\right\}. \tag{12.66}$$

In terms of these,‡

$$Q = K_{SS} + 4K_{VV} + 6K_{TT} + 4K_{AA} + K_{PP}, \tag{12.67}$$

$$\begin{aligned} Q\rho &= \tfrac{3}{4}[K_{SS} + 2K_{VV} + 2K_{TT} + 2K_{AA} + K_{PP} - \\ &\quad -2(K_{VA} + K_{AV}) - (K_{ST} + K_{TS} + K_{PT} + K_{TP})] \\ &= \tfrac{3}{4}[(2|C_V - C_A|^2 + |C_S - C_T|^2 + |C_P - C_T|^2) + (C_X \to C'_X)], \end{aligned} \tag{12.68}$$

$$Q\xi = [5L_{TT} - 4(L_{VV} + L_{AA}) - 4L_{VA} + 4(L_{ST} + L_{PT}) - L_{SP}] + \text{c.c.}, \tag{12.69}$$

$$Q\xi\delta = \tfrac{3}{4}[-L_{TT} - (L_{VV} + L_{AA}) + 2L_{VA} + (L_{ST} + L_{PT}) - L_{SP}] + \text{c.c.} \tag{12.70}$$

For the V–A Law, only $K_{VV} = K_{AA} = L_{VV} = L_{AA} = 2|C_V|^2$ and $K_{VA} = K_{AV} = L_{VA} = L_{AV} = -2|C_V|^2$ are non-vanishing. Then $\rho = \frac{3}{4}$, $\xi = -1$, $\delta = \frac{3}{4}$ and the distribution (12.65) coincides with (12.47).

The polarization of the electrons from unpolarized muons may be written

$$\mathscr{P} = \pm \frac{\bar{Q}[W_0 - W + \frac{2}{3}\bar{\rho}(\frac{4}{3}W - W_0)]}{Q[W_0 - W + \frac{2}{3}\rho(\frac{4}{3}W - W_0)]} \quad \text{for } e^{\mp}, \tag{12.71}$$

where $\bar{Q}$ and $\bar{\rho}\bar{Q}$ differ from $\rho$ and $\rho Q$ of (12.67) and (12.68) only by the substitutions: $K_{XY} \to L_{XY}$ for $X$ and $Y = $ S, T, or P and $K_{XY} \to -L_{XY}$ when $X, Y = $ V or A. The energy-integrated polarization $\langle\mathscr{P}\rangle$, and the polarization $\mathscr{P}_0$ of the end-point ($W = W_0$) electrons are, respectively:

$$\langle\mathscr{P}\rangle = \pm\bar{Q}/Q \quad \text{and} \quad \mathscr{P}_0 = \pm(\bar{\rho}\bar{Q})/(\rho Q). \tag{12.72}$$

Both of these, as well as the polarization $\mathscr{P}$ of any electron, reduce to just $\mp 1$ for the V–A Law (when $L_{XY} = K_{XY}$!). The same polarization, $\mp 1$, is obtainable with any of the interactions present: it is only neces-

‡ The relations of the coupling constants to the meaningful correlation coefficients $\alpha$, $\beta$, $\gamma$ of (12.31) are:

$$\begin{aligned} Q\alpha &= K_{SS} - 2K_{TT} + K_{PP}, \\ Q(\gamma+\beta) &= 4(K_{VV} + 2K_{TT} + K_{AA}), \\ Q(\gamma-\beta) &= 4K_{VA} + 2(K_{ST} + K_{PT}) + \text{c.c.} \end{aligned}$$

Of course, $\alpha + \beta + \gamma = 1$.

sary that if $C_X$ or $C'_X \neq 0$ for $X = \mathrm{S}$, T, or P, then $C'_X = -C_X$, while for V or A, $C'_X = +C_X$ is necessary. $\langle\mathscr{P}\rangle = \mp 1$ is enough to ensure that $\mathscr{P} = \mp 1$ at every energy. The conditions stated here, as in § 10.1, signify that right-handed antineutrinos will accompany left-handed negatrons generated by V or A couplings, but the antineutrinos will be left-handed when left-handed negatrons are generated by S, T, or P couplings. Under a restriction to a two-component neutrino theory, which allows only right-handed antineutrinos, the V and A couplings must be held to account for left-handed negatrons. The assertions here are not made more definite because the observations on the polarizations of the electrons from $\mu$-decay have not yet been satisfactorily quantitative.

More quantitatively definite have been the experimental conclusions‡ that $\rho \approx \frac{3}{4}$, $\xi \approx -1$, and $\delta \approx \frac{3}{4}$ in the distribution (12.65). Notice that the conclusion $\delta \approx \frac{3}{4}$ in addition to $\xi \approx -1$ required investigating the energy-dependence of the electron's directional distribution. The three data here are not by themselves sufficient to determine the numerous possible coupling constants uniquely; they are consistent with the V–A Law but cannot be said to establish it.

There is less indeterminacy within the framework of the two-component neutrino theory (§ 10.3) and also, perhaps, more urgency that separate evidence be found as to the character of the $\mu$-decay interaction. The two component theory does not rely on a V–A form of interaction to account for the observed left-handedness of the normal neutrinos generated in nuclear $\beta$-decay, but on the hypothesis that no right-handed normal neutrinos exist. Under this hypothesis, only interactions with $C'_X = C_X$, i.e. projections by $\frac{1}{2}(1+\gamma_5)$ of the neutrino states, can exist. Then $K_{XY} = 2C^*_X C_Y = L_{XY}$ in the formulae (12.66)–(12.71). It follows that the data $\rho \approx \frac{3}{4}$, $\xi \approx -1$, $\delta \approx \frac{3}{4}$ are sufficient to exclude only the tensor interaction: $C_\mathrm{T} \approx C'_\mathrm{T} \approx 0$. Besides $C_\mathrm{A} \approx -C_\mathrm{V}$, also $C_\mathrm{S} \approx C_\mathrm{P}$ may exist. The expression (12.72) for the energy-integrated polarization reduces to

$$\langle\mathscr{P}\rangle \approx \mp(4|C_\mathrm{V}|^2 - |C_\mathrm{S}|^2)/(4|C_\mathrm{V}|^2 + |C_\mathrm{S}|^2). \tag{12.73}$$

Thus, granting that only the two-component neutrinos exist, a quantitative measurement of $\langle\mathscr{P}\rangle \approx \mp 1$ would be sufficient to determine the $\mu$-decay interaction as a V–A Law.

‡ R. Plano, *Phys. Rev.* **119,** 1400 (1969); D. Berley, T. Coffin, R. Garwin, L. Lederman, and M. Weinrich, ibid. **106,** 835 (1957); H. Kruger and K. Crowe, ibid. **113,** 341 (1959); J. Cassels, T. O'Keefe, M. Rigby, and J. Wormald, *Proc. Phys. Soc. Lond.* **72,** 781 (1958).

An experimental confirmation of $\langle\mathscr{P}\rangle = \mp 1$, added to the data $\rho \approx \delta \approx \frac{3}{4}$, $\xi \approx -1$, would not be sufficient to establish the V–A Law without the help of the two-component theory. It would still be possible for any amount of $C_S = -C'_S = -C_P = C'_P$ to exist; under such conditions, the Scalar and Pseudoscalar interactions would be producing right-handed neutrinos and left-handed antineutrinos.

*The negative muon as the antiparticle*

It has tacitly been assumed so far that muons should be described exactly like electrons except for the mass change $m_e \to m_\mu$. The negative muons have been described by analogues of the states used for negatrons, relative to their charge-conjugate states for positive muons and positrons. For interactions of muons and electrons, it becomes meaningful to ask whether it is the positive or negative muon which should be treated as the antimuon, to be described by the analogues of the positron states.

The effect of changing from one description to the other is easily seen from considerations like those used to find the relation (4.35) between negatron and positron emissions. It is being proposed that a treatment symbolized by $\mu^- + \nu \leftrightarrow e^- + \mu^0$, when written in terms of the 'normal' particles, and leading to the emission of a normal neutretto in $\mu^-$-decay (12.1), be replaced by the normal particle relationship, $\mu^0 + \nu \leftrightarrow \mu^+ + e^-$, so that‡

$$\left.\begin{aligned} \mu^- &\to e^- + \bar{\nu} + \bar{\mu}^0 \\ \mu^+ &\to e^+ + \nu + \mu^0 \end{aligned}\right\}. \tag{12.74}$$

Now, the current which can be invariantly coupled to $J_\alpha(e\nu) = \phi_e^\dagger \beta\gamma_\alpha \phi_\nu$ of (12.41) must be

$$J_\alpha(\mu\mu^0) = \psi_\mu^\dagger \beta\gamma_\alpha \tfrac{1}{2}(1-\gamma_5)\psi_{\mu^0}, \tag{12.75}$$

in place of (12.42), if this is to give the same results as before. That can be seen from considering $\mu^-$-decay, for which the first factor (with upper sign) of (12.43) will be replaced by

$$\begin{aligned} u_\mu^{C\dagger}(1-\gamma_5)\beta\gamma_\alpha u_{\mu^0}^C &= \tilde{u}_\mu C(1-\gamma_5)\beta\gamma_\alpha C u_{\mu^0}^* \\ &= u_{\mu^0}^\dagger C\gamma_\alpha^* \beta^*(1-\gamma_5^*)Cu_\mu = u_{\mu^0}^\dagger \beta\gamma_\alpha(1+\gamma_5)u_\mu. \end{aligned}$$

Thus, to get the same agreements with experiment as before, a 'V+A' rather than 'V−A' form of interaction law has to be adopted under the assumptions (12.74). Since either of the pictures (12.1) or (12.74) can be formulated so as to give the same physical results, the change from $\mu^+$ to $\mu^-$ as the antimuon can be regarded as an inconsequential trans-

‡ During the period in which neutrettos were believed to be identical with neutrinos, this led to the necessity for antisymmetrizing the product states in the neutral leptons.

formation of the formalism. Of course, it seems preferable to keep the original picture, in which it can be said that the interactions are restricted to the left-handed $\gamma_5 = +1$ components of all normal states.

## 12.5. The conserved vector current

The most reliable measure of the coupling constant $g$ appropriate for the universal 'weak interaction' form (12.63) is expected to be provided by the observed muon decay rate, as in (12.51). The outcome for $g$ obviously depends on the descriptions adopted for the states involved in the measurement, and the pure Dirac spinor descriptions used to arrive at (12.51) are expected to be adequate, within negligible electromagnetic corrections, for the particles involved in the $\mu$-decay process. None of these have been found subject to such strong interactions as are nucleons, which may be pictured as spending substantial fractions of the time in transient states containing pions, for example, as indicated in (11.15). During a phase in which a physical neutron has the properties of a proton plus a negative pion, it cannot be expected to emit negatrons through the interactions (12.63). If only a spinor description is nevertheless employed, as done in the treatment of nuclear $\beta$-decay, then it can at best be expected to approximate only a fraction of the physical state; it should be given some normalization substantially less than unity. This is the basis for having expected the 'renormalization constants', $C_{\mathrm{V}}$ and $C_{\mathrm{A}}$, used in treating nuclear $\beta$-decay, to turn out considerably different from unity.

The finding that after all $C_{\mathrm{V}} \approx 1$, as pointed out in connexion with the $g$ measurement (12.51), has implications which were already anticipated in work by Gershtein and Zeldovitch and were made definitive by Feynman and Gell-Mann.‡ It implies that the physical nucleon does not after all lose any appreciable efficacy as a $\beta$-source despite its fluctuations among its transient components. The proclivity for $\beta$-interaction seems to remain substantially conserved during the strong interactions.

What needs to be described here seems analogous to the conservation of electric charge during strong interaction fluctuations. When a proton fluctuates into $\mathrm{n}+\pi^+$, the charge is merely transferred to the pion and, in general, the strong interactions merely redistribute the charge over a region of order $\hbar/m_\pi c$ in radius. Each nucleon acquires an extended structure which has actually been detected in the scattering of electrons off nucleons, using electrons of sufficiently short wavelength to resolve

‡ S. Gershtein and J. Zeldovitch, *Soviet JETP*, **2**, 576 (1957); R. Feynman and M. Gell-Mann, *Phys. Rev.* **109**, 193 (1958).

distances of order smaller than $\hbar/m_\pi c$. For longer wavelengths, the proton continues to behave (electrically) like a point charge, as if unperturbed by the strong interactions. It now seems appropriate to speak of a '$\beta$-charge' which is likewise merely redistributed by the strong interactions. The result $C_V \approx 1$ for nuclear $\beta$-decay can then be understood as a consequence of the long wavelengths of the leptons involved, incapable of resolving the '$\beta$-charge structure' of the nucleon. All these ideas have been embodied in a hypothesis of a 'Conserved Vector Current', the subject of this section.

Of course, when a fluctuation like $n \to p+\pi^-$ is described as a redistribution of the neutron's negatron-generating '$\beta$-charge', then it is implied that the pion is capable of the direct production of negatrons, without the intervention of its transient decompositions as in (11.23). Processes like $\pi^- \to (e^-+\bar{\nu})+\pi^0$ are to be expected. Such release only $\sim$ 4 MeV of kinetic energy to the leptons, hence may be outcompeted by the pion decay processes considered in Chapter XI, which release about thirty times as much (11.24).

*The isovector current*

When the motion of a charge $+e$ is adequately described by just a Dirac spinor $\psi$, then the conservation of the charge, as expressed in a continuity equation $\partial i_\alpha/\partial x_\alpha = 0$ like (2.76), requires that it be borne by a current $i_\alpha(\mathbf{i}, ic\rho) = iec(\bar{\psi}\gamma_\alpha\psi)$ like (4.5). The corresponding current in a nucleon state described by an isospinor $\Psi$ like (4.11) may be written

$$iec\bar{\Psi}\gamma_\alpha \tfrac{1}{2}(1+\tau_3)\Psi = \tfrac{1}{2}iec[(\bar{\Psi}\gamma_\alpha\Psi)+(\bar{\Psi}\gamma_\alpha\boldsymbol{\tau}\Psi)_3], \qquad (12.76)$$

consisting of an isoscalar part plus the third component of an isovector, $\bar{\Psi}\gamma_\alpha\boldsymbol{\tau}\Psi$. Each part is conserved individually, even in the presence of any given electromagnetic field, and when allowances are made for the nucleon mass differences and for the anomalous magnetic moment of the nucleon (in a covariant manner, stemming from (7.79) for example). However, only the isoscalar part remains conserved when the strong interactions are taken into account.

The last assertion may be demonstrated specifically when the strong interactions are represented by the pseudoscalar pion-nucleon coupling $h_{N\pi} = iG(\bar{\Psi}\gamma_5\boldsymbol{\tau}\Psi).\boldsymbol{\Phi}$ of (11.16). The same kind of procedure which yielded the modification (6.1) of the electron field equation by the weak coupling may then be used to find

$$[\gamma_\alpha \partial/\partial x_\alpha + Mc/\hbar]\Psi = -i(G/\hbar c)\boldsymbol{\Phi}.\boldsymbol{\tau}\gamma_5\Psi \qquad (12.77)$$

as the modification of a nucleon field equation like (2.82) by the strong coupling. $M$ is just the 'bare' nucleon mass, pending the introduction of weaker interactions which can lead to a proton-neutron mass difference. With $\gamma_\alpha \partial\Psi/\partial x_\alpha$ as given by this equation, it is easy to see that the isoscalar $(\bar{\Psi}\gamma_\alpha \Psi)$ has a vanishing 4-divergence and so is separately conserved despite the strong interactions. On the other hand, the isovector current has a non-vanishing divergence,

$$\partial(\bar{\Psi}\gamma_\alpha \boldsymbol{\tau}\Psi)/\partial x_\alpha = -2(G/\hbar c)(\bar{\Psi}\gamma_5 \boldsymbol{\tau}\Psi)\times\boldsymbol{\Phi}, \tag{12.78}$$

where the cross-product notation, $\boldsymbol{\tau}\times\boldsymbol{\Phi}$, is used to represent the way in which the isovector components, $\tau_{1,2,3}$ and $\Phi_{1,2,3}$, occur.

At least the third component of (12.78) must be cancelled by a compensating divergence of pion current if the total charge is to be conserved. Then, in so far as the strong interactions are 'charge-independent' (invariant to rotations in the iso-space), all components of the divergence (12.78) must be similarly compensated. To give these assertions concrete forms, representations of pion currents will be considered next.

The contributions to electric current by any charged pions which may appear depend primarily on the charged-pion fields

$$\Phi = 2^{-\frac{1}{2}}(\Phi_1+i\Phi_2) \quad \text{and} \quad \Phi^*.$$

The appropriate expression for the 4-vector current is

$$j^\pi_\alpha(\mathbf{j}^\pi, ic\rho^\pi) = (ie/\hbar)[\Phi^*(\partial\Phi/\partial x_\alpha)-(\partial\Phi^*/\partial x_\alpha)\Phi], \tag{12.79}$$

in that this is properly conserved by itself in the absence of interactions; a vanishing of its 4-divergence follows from the Klein–Gordon equation (11.12). Aside from the multiplying constant, (12.79) may be recognized as relativistic generalization of the expression for the current familiar from non-relativistic Schrödinger theory. What the multiplier should be depends on the normalizations adopted; the one in (12.79) is appropriate for the field-operator representation (11.4) of $\Phi$. To be used as a field-operator, (12.79), as also all the preceding expressions for currents, must be subjected to the convention that the creation and annihilation operators in it be written in what is called the 'normal order', i.e. with all creation operators placed to the left of the destruction operators. With this, it is easy to check that the expectation value of $\rho^\pi$ in the pion field state $|\pi\rangle$ of (11.62), which describes a single negative pion at rest, properly leads to $\oint (d\mathbf{r})\langle\pi|\rho^\pi|\pi\rangle = -e$.

The bracketed expression in (12.79) is just the third component of the isovector $i\boldsymbol{\Phi}\times\partial\boldsymbol{\Phi}/\partial x_\alpha$, which has as a factor in each of its other two components the neutral pion field $\Phi_3$. Each of the components is conserved, in the absence of interactions, but not when the strong couplings are taken into account. The pion-nucleon coupling, $h_{N\pi}$, being used as representative of the strong interactions here, contributes a source term, $iG(\bar{\Psi}\gamma_5\tau_i\Psi)$, to the right-hand side of the Klein–Gordon equation for $\Phi_i$, as can be confirmed by the procedure outlined in connexion with $H_\pi$ of (11.11). It then follows that the isovector current $(2i/\hbar c)\mathbf{\Phi}\times\partial\mathbf{\Phi}/\partial x_\alpha$ has a 4-divergence which is just the negative of (12.78), the divergence of the nucleonic isovector. Consequently, the total isovector current

$$\boldsymbol{\theta}_\alpha = \tfrac{1}{2}(\bar{\Psi}\gamma_\alpha\boldsymbol{\tau}\Psi)+(i/\hbar c)\mathbf{\Phi}\times\partial\mathbf{\Phi}/\partial x_\alpha \qquad (12.80)$$

is conserved in the presence of the strong coupling $h_{N\pi}$. When its third component is multiplied by $iec$, it gives exactly the isovector part of the nucleon's electric current in (12.76), plus the pion current (12.79); the total is therefore properly conserved during the strong-interaction fluctuations of any nucleon-pion system, as those have been represented.

*The modification of the β-coupling laws*

The nucleon component of the conserved isovector (and 4-Vector) current $\boldsymbol{\theta}_\alpha$ of (12.80) will be recognized as having already been used to help represent the Vector part of the nucleonic transformation current, $J_\alpha(\mathrm{pn})$, which was coupled to the leptons in the $\beta$-interaction forms, e.g. (12.63). As written in (4.18),

$$J_\alpha(\mathrm{pn}) = \tfrac{1}{2}(\bar{\Psi}\gamma_\alpha\tau_+\Psi)+\tfrac{1}{2}(\bar{\Psi}\gamma_\alpha\gamma_5\tau_+\Psi). \qquad (12.81)$$

The first term here is just the bare nucleon current part of $\tfrac{1}{2}[(\theta_\alpha)_1+i(\theta_\alpha)_2]$, where the numerical subscripts refer to isovector components.

With $\Psi$ standing for a Dirac (iso-)spinor field operator, it is clear that the application of (12.81) to a physical neutron state would result in there being no contributions from any component of the physical state which does not contain 'bare' neutrons, described by Dirac spinors. Yet such components exist according to the picture (11.15), and as manifested in the electromagnetic behaviour of nucleons. For the 4-Vector part of the nucleon current, the effects have been formulated in (12.78) as its 'leakage' into pions. There is a corresponding 'leakage' of the Pseudovector part of the current (12.81),

$$\frac{\partial}{\partial x_\alpha}(\bar{\Psi}\gamma_\alpha\gamma_5\tau_+\Psi) = 2^{\frac{1}{2}}\frac{Mc}{i\hbar G}\left[\frac{\partial^2}{\partial x_\alpha^2}-\left(\frac{m_\pi c}{\hbar}\right)^2-\frac{G^2}{Mc^2}(\bar{\Psi}\Psi)\right]\Phi, \qquad (12.82)$$

obtainable in the same way as was (12.78). None of these effects are really calculable in the present stage of strong-interaction theory, hence the practice of describing physical nucleons as bare ones, with states representable by Dirac spinors, was adopted, but factors $C_V$ and $-C_A$ were introduced into the respective terms of (12.81) to represent the effects. Such factors must be understood as some averages over 'internal' variables, including pionic ones, characterizing a physical nucleon's structure, and additional to the variables specifically represented in a Dirac spinor. For allowed nuclear $\beta$-decay, in which nucleonic recoil motions are supposed to be negligible, the factor $C_V$ can be said to have been defined by

$$\langle \mathrm{f}|\bar{\Psi}\gamma_4\tau_+\Psi|\mathrm{i}\rangle \approx C_V\langle \mathrm{p}|\Psi^\dagger\tau_+\Psi|\mathrm{n}\rangle, \tag{12.83}$$

where $|\mathrm{n}\rangle = a_\mathrm{n}^\dagger|0\rangle$ and $|\mathrm{p}\rangle = a_\mathrm{p}^\dagger|0\rangle$ represent bare nucleon states while $|\mathrm{i}\rangle$ and $|\mathrm{f}\rangle$ describe corresponding physical ones. Some mode of contraction (including the 'averaging' mentioned above), $\langle \mathrm{f}|...|\mathrm{i}\rangle$, is being presumed definable, to enable the factorability on the right at least in some approximation. The expression on the right has been used in § 4.4 for evaluating neutron decay; it reduces to

$$C_V\langle \mathrm{p}|\psi_\mathrm{p}^\dagger\psi_\mathrm{n}|\mathrm{n}\rangle = C_V(u_\mathrm{p}^\dagger u_\mathrm{n})$$

if $u_{\mathrm{p,n}}$ denote Dirac spinor modes rather than field operators, as in (11.66).

The experimental outcome $C_V \approx 1$ is interpreted to mean, in the 'Conserved Vector Current' theory, that it is not only the nucleon part of $\frac{1}{2}[(\theta_\alpha)_1+i(\theta_\alpha)_2]$ which is coupled to the leptons in the $\beta$-interactions, but the full conserved current, including its pion part. Just how this would account for $C_V \approx 1$ may be understood from a comparison to the way the electric charge in a physical proton state is conserved. One half of this charge comes from the separately conserved isoscalar charge density, $\frac{1}{2}e(\Psi^\dagger\Psi)$, as follows from (12.76). The remaining half is described by the isovector component $e(\theta_4)_3$. In a bare proton state this has the expectation value

$$\tfrac{1}{2}e\langle \mathrm{p}|\bar{\Psi}\gamma_4\tau_3\Psi+(2/\hbar c^2)[\mathbf{\Phi}\times\dot{\mathbf{\Phi}}]_3|\mathrm{p}\rangle = \tfrac{1}{2}e\langle \mathrm{p}|\bar{\Psi}\gamma_4\tau_3\Psi|\mathrm{p}\rangle = \tfrac{1}{2}e|u_\mathrm{p}|^2, \tag{12.84}$$

with no contribution from the pion current since none exists in a bare proton state (formally, the pion annihilation operators implicit in $\Phi$ have nothing to destroy in $|\mathrm{p}\rangle = a_\mathrm{p}^\dagger|0\rangle$ hence yield nothing, as in (11.10)). There is pion current in a *physical* proton state but its individual contribution is not presently calculable, since a sufficient description of the physical proton has never been developed. However, it is presumed that the same strong interactions which are responsible for converting the bare proton into a physical one also conserve all expectation values of the current $\boldsymbol{\theta}_\alpha$. The result (12.84) is expected to remain unchanged when the bare proton states on the left-hand side are replaced by physical proton states; only the proportions of the nucleon and pion contributions may change. The same argument applies to the neutron-decay matrix element

$$\langle \mathrm{f}|(\theta_4)_1+i(\theta_4)_2|\mathrm{i}\rangle = \langle \mathrm{p}|\bar{\Psi}\gamma_4\tau_+\Psi|\mathrm{n}\rangle = u_\mathrm{p}^\dagger u_\mathrm{n}. \qquad (12.85)$$

In the 'Conserved Vector Current' theory this replaces the left-hand side of (12.83), hence yields $C_\mathrm{V} = 1$.

There is no substantial clue as to whether the Pseudovector part of the $\beta$-coupling should also be modified. The question must be expected to remain ambiguous until a sufficiently detailed characterization of real, physical nucleon states is found. For the present, the best that can be done is to continue using the factor $C_\mathrm{A}$ for representing the difference between proper, physical nucleon contributions and those calculated from a bare nucleon Pseudovector current. Thus, the 'Conserved Vector Current' theory, in its present stage of development, can be said to differ from the $\beta$-coupling law as represented in (12.63), for example, only in a supplementation of the nucleon current expressions with pion currents, such that

$$J_\alpha(\mathrm{pn}) \rightarrow \tfrac{1}{2}[(\theta_\alpha)_1+i(\theta_\alpha)_2]-\tfrac{1}{2}C_\mathrm{A}(\bar{\Psi}\gamma_\alpha\gamma_5\tau_+\Psi)$$
$$= \tfrac{1}{2}\{\bar{\psi}_\mathrm{p}\gamma_\alpha(1-C_\mathrm{A}\gamma_5)\psi_\mathrm{n}+(2^{\frac{1}{2}}/\hbar c)[\Phi(\partial\Phi_3/\partial x_\alpha)-\Phi_3(\partial\Phi/\partial x_\alpha)]\}, \quad (12.86)$$

with $C_\mathrm{A} \neq -1$ to be expected whenever its evaluation in a physical nucleon state is approximated by evaluation in a bare one. Throughout the development of this expression here, it has been emphasized that the specific treatment of the strong interactions being used was only 'representative' of them. It is known that nucleons are subject to other strong interactions besides those with the pion field, hence a sufficiently conserved current $\boldsymbol{\theta}_\alpha$ may not be achievable without supplementations by currents of other quanta than just the pions. Since not even the pion contributions in actual, physical nucleon states are really calculable, it is perhaps sufficient for the present to regard the supplementation exhibited in (12.86) as a surrogate for all the strong interaction effects.

### *Gell-Mann's weak-magnetism*

The evidence for the Conserved Current hypothesis represented as $C_\mathrm{V} \approx 1$ comes from a comparison of muon decay to nuclear $\beta$-decay, hence relies on the validity of the hypothesis that the $\beta$-interactions should be 'universal' in strength. Gell-Mann‡ suggested a way of

‡ See the last subsection of Chapter VII (p. 226).

obtaining independent evidence, from a comparison of nuclear $\beta$-decay to electromagnetic interactions, which relies rather on the 'charge-independence' of the strong couplings. That led to an experimental confirmation of the theory which was particularly impressive because Gell-Mann had made a highly explicit and quantitative prediction of what was to be found.

First it should be clear that the Conserved Current modification of the theory does not change expectations for nuclear $\beta$-decay phenomena in the allowed approximation. It is characteristic of this approximation that the variations of the lepton waves across the nucleon, and even across an entire nucleus, are neglected; the decay amplitudes then become integrals over the conserved current alone, as for its fourth ('$\beta$-charge') component in (12.85), and so are the same as the expectations for the bare nucleons. There is only the identification $g_{\mathrm{V}} = gC_{\mathrm{V}} = g$ to be made. More explicitly, there are effectively no changes to be made in the expectations for the allowed phenomena which have had their Vector contributions adequately represented by the Fermi $\beta$-moment, $\langle 1 \rangle = \int 1$ of (5.3); this amounts to an integral over the entire '$\beta$-charge density' and it makes no difference whether this is described as resident on a point-nucleon or spread out over the entire nucleus. There is similarly no change in the once-parity-forbidden expectations governed by $\langle \boldsymbol{\alpha} \rangle$. Fresh evidence must be sought in effects dependent on variations of the lepton waves over the nucleon's structure, the 'forbidden' effects which measure 'multipoles' arising from the redistribution of the $\beta$-charge.

The situation is much the same as in the effects of the strong interactions on the electromagnetic properties of nucleons. The conserved electric charge being merely redistributed, there is no change in the 'monopole' approximation, which corresponds to the allowed approximation of the Vector interaction in $\beta$-decay. The largest 'multipole' effect of a nucleon, in low energy phenomena, comes in the 'magnetic dipole' approximation as measured by its intrinsic magnetic moments. The well-known anomalies in the latter, represented by $\mu_{\mathrm{p}} - 1 \approx -\mu_{\mathrm{n}}$ in (5.84) and (7.79), are ascribed to effects of charge-independent strong interactions (presumed to arise largely from the pion currents in physical nucleon states). The charge-independence makes it possible to use the observed magnetic moments as measures of the analogous effects arising from the other isovector components of the Vector current as they operate in nuclear $\beta$-decay.

When the magnetic dipole effects are isolated, as in static magnetic moment measurements or by observing magnetic dipole radiation (7.80), it is terms of the total electromagnetic interaction $h_\gamma = -i_\alpha A_\alpha/c$ (4.6) which are proportional to $\mathbf{B} = \nabla \times \mathbf{A}$ that are being gauged. Their effects in non-relativistic physical nucleon states are representable by the modification (7.79) of (7.78) yielding for the intrinsic magnetic moment interaction energy density

$$-(e\hbar/2Mc)\Psi^{\cdot\dagger}[\tfrac{1}{2}(\mu_p+\mu_n)+\tfrac{1}{2}(\mu_p-\mu_n)\tau_3]\boldsymbol{\sigma}\Psi^{\cdot}.(\nabla\times\mathbf{A}). \qquad (12.87)$$

Taking $\mu_p = 1$ and $\mu_n = 0$ gives the 'normal', Dirac magnetic moment effect, obtained in the absence of strong interactions (or in bare nuclear states). The part proportional to $(\mu_p+\mu_n) \approx 1$ is obviously a contribution from the separately conserved isoscalar part of the current (12.76). It is the isovector part, proportional to $(\mu_p-\mu_n) \approx 4{\cdot}7$ which has an analogue in $\beta$-decay.

The analogue referred to is the weak-magnetic effect discussed in the last subsection of Chapter VII. There, only the part corresponding to the normal, Dirac magnetic moment was evaluated. It arises from just the nucleon part of the isovector current $\boldsymbol{\theta}_\alpha$ and should now be supplemented by the remainder of the conserved current. Just as the isovector part of the magnetic moment is multiplied by $(\mu_p-\mu_n)/1$ so the intrinsic weak-magnetic term of (7.82) should be multiplied with $(\mu_p-\mu_n)/C_V$. After all, both arise from isovector currents subject to the same strong-dynamical effects. It is true that different isovector components of $\boldsymbol{\theta}_\alpha$ are involved in the magnetic moment and in the weak-magnetism, but the strong interactions are supposed to be invariant to 'rotations' in the charge-space. Thus, the intrinsic weak-magnetic interaction term of (7.82) is so modified as to yield the energy density

$$2^{\frac{1}{2}}g\Psi^{\cdot\dagger}[-(\hbar/2Mc)(\mu_p-\mu_n)\boldsymbol{\sigma}.(\nabla\times i\mathbf{J})]\tau_+\Psi^{\cdot}, \qquad (12.88)$$

just the transformation of the isovector part of (12.87) according to $\frac{1}{2}\tau_3 \to \tau_+ = \frac{1}{2}(\tau_1+i\tau_2)$, $e \to 2^{\frac{1}{2}}g$, $\mathbf{A} \to i\mathbf{J}$. This is the same transformation which, supplemented with $\phi \to J_4$, gives the Vector interaction part of (7.82) from the isovector part of (7.78).

The contribution to the weak-magnetism by the nucleon's orbital motion, included in the evaluation of the nuclear transition amplitude (7.83), is not expected to be modified in the same approximation (no more than is the orbital contribution to the magnetic moment of (5.84)) because it arises from a 'mass motion' of the nucleon rather than from its internal structure. Thus the total weak-magnetic effect is obtained merely by the replacement of the nuclear matrix element,

$$C_V \int (\mathbf{1}+\boldsymbol{\sigma}) \to \int [\mathbf{1}+(\mu_p-\mu_n)\boldsymbol{\sigma}], \tag{12.89}$$

in (7.83).

For the particular case suggested as an experimental test by Gell-Mann, $B^{12} \to C^{12} \leftarrow N^{12}$, the theoretical expectations for the spectrum shape-factor energy gradients (7.86) are altered to

$$A_{\pm} \approx \pm(4/3|C_A|)\langle l+(\mu_p-\mu_n)\sigma\rangle/\langle\sigma\rangle Mc^2. \tag{12.90}$$

Since $\langle l\rangle \approx -\frac{1}{2}\langle\sigma\rangle$ according to the estimate (7.77) used in evaluating (7.86), the weak-magnetic effect is enhanced by the factor

$$2(\mu_p-\mu_n-\tfrac{1}{2}) \approx 8{\cdot}4$$

as a result of the change to a Conserved Vector Current. This is about the right amount, within experimental error and uncertainties in the treatment of the $\beta$-moments, to account for the discrepancy with the expectations from the unmodified theory, as found in § 7.4.

Gell-Mann reduced the reliance on theoretical estimates of the $\beta$-moments by comparing the $\beta$-transitions of $B^{12}$ and $N^{12}$, to the ground state of $C^{12}$, with the homologous magnetic dipole $\gamma$-transition from the 15·11-MeV excited state of $C^{12}$. All three transitions involve the same isospin and angular momentum changes: $T = 1, I = 1 \to T = 0, I = 0$. With $\Delta T = 1$, the isoscalar part of the electromagnetic current cannot contribute, hence there is a particularly direct comparison of effects from each of the three components of the isovector $\boldsymbol{\theta}_{\alpha}$. The $\gamma$-transition rate is given by (7.80), which here reduces to

$$\hbar\lambda_{\gamma} \approx (9{\cdot}6 \text{ eV})\langle\mu\rangle_{\gamma}^{2}. \tag{12.91}$$

The gamma half-width measurements‡ have given $\hbar\lambda_{\gamma} \approx (50\pm4)$ eV, yielding $|\langle\mu\rangle_{\gamma}| = 2{\cdot}3\pm0{\cdot}1$.

The moment here is just

$$\langle\mu\rangle_{\gamma} = \Big\langle C^{12}\Big| \sum_a [l_z^a+(\mu_p-\mu_n)\sigma_z^a]\tfrac{1}{2}\tau_3^a\Big|(C^{12})^*\Big\rangle. \tag{12.92}$$

The isospin homology of the $(C^{12})^*$ state and the $\beta$-decaying states allows using the ladder relationship $|(C^{12})^*\rangle = 2^{-\frac{1}{2}}T_+|B^{12}\rangle$ based on (5.63). Then, in (12.92):

$$\tfrac{1}{2}\tau_3^a|(C^{12})^*\rangle = 8^{-\frac{1}{2}}\sum_b ([\tau_3^a, \tau_+^b]+\tau_+^b\,\tau_3^a)|B^{12}\rangle = 2^{-\frac{1}{2}}(\tau_+^a+\tfrac{1}{2}T_+\tau_3^a)|B^{12}\rangle.$$

The last term vanishes as a result of the operation, $\langle C^{12}|T_+$, on the

‡ E. Hayward and E. Fuller, *Phys. Rev.* **106**, 991 (1957). See reference to Mayer-Kuckuk and Michel, p. 228, for a summary of others.

$T = 0$ ground state, and the remainder converts (12.92) into an expression for the $\beta$-moment:

$$\langle l+(\mu_p-\mu_n)\rangle = 2^{+\frac{1}{2}}\langle\mu\rangle_{\gamma}, \tag{12.93}$$

having the magnitude $3{\cdot}3\pm0{\cdot}15$ according to the above measurement. For the energy-gradient (12.90), the main, Gamow–Teller moment $\langle\sigma\rangle$ is still needed and this is measured by the comparative half-lives

$$ft = (6140\text{ sec})/C_A^2\langle\sigma\rangle^2 \approx 10^{4\cdot1-4\cdot2}$$

for $B^{12}$, $N^{12}$ respectively. With the value $|C_A|\langle\sigma\rangle = 0{\cdot}66\pm0{\cdot}04$ thus obtained,

$$A_{\pm} = \pm(0{\cdot}71\pm0{\cdot}07)\text{ per cent per MeV}. \tag{12.94}$$

This should still be reduced by $\mp0{\cdot}11$ per cent per MeV because of the coulomb corrections (7.87). The outcome, $A_{\pm} \approx \pm0{\cdot}6$ per cent per MeV, is in complete agreement with the experiments quoted in § 7.4.

*The $\pi \to \pi^0$ $\beta$-decay*

The Conserved Vector Current theory supplements the weak interactions (12.63) with couplings of pion and lepton transformation currents,

$$h_{\pi\beta} = (2g/\hbar c)[\Phi(\partial\Phi_3/\partial x_\alpha)-\Phi_3(\partial\Phi/\partial x_\alpha)]J_\alpha+\text{h.c.} \tag{12.95}$$

as reference to (12.86) shows. Consequently, the processes

$$\left.\begin{aligned}\pi^- &\to \pi^0+e^-+\bar{\nu}\\ \pi^+ &\to \pi^0+e^++\nu\end{aligned}\right\} \tag{12.96}$$

are expected to occur, the energy release

$$(m_\pi-m_\pi^0)c^2 = (9{\cdot}0\pm0{\cdot}3)m_e c^2 \approx 4{\cdot}6\text{ MeV}$$

being available to each. The kinetic energies will be small as compared to a pion mass, hence the recoil of the pion will be practically negligible. The electrons will form a continuous spectrum with the end-point energy $W_0 \approx (m_\pi-m_\pi^0)c^2$, less about 1·6 per cent.

For a transition rate expression of the form (4.36), an amplitude $\langle f|H_{\pi\beta}|i\rangle = \oint (d\mathbf{r})\langle f|h_{\pi\beta}|i\rangle$ will be needed. The initial state may be given the description $|\pi\rangle$ of (11.62), containing the bare pion field state $|\mathbf{k}_0\rangle = A^*_{\mathbf{k}_0}|0\rangle$ or $B^*_{\mathbf{k}_0}|0\rangle$, for $\pi^{\mp}$ respectively. Then the transition amplitude to the neutral pion state $|\mathbf{K}\rangle = C^*_K|0\rangle$ will have as a factor

$$\langle\mathbf{K}|h_{\pi\beta}|\mathbf{k}_0\rangle = -2i[cg/(2\pi)^3]J.(K+k_0)e^{i(k_0-K).x}, \tag{12.97}$$

after substitutions from pion field forms like (11.4). The factor $\hbar(K+k_0)_\alpha$ is the sum of the initial and final pion momentum-energy four-vectors. It is only a straightforward application of methods already illustrated (beginning with the neutron decay, § 4.4) to find the electron spectrum expression

$$\frac{d\lambda}{dp} = \frac{g^2}{2\pi^3\hbar^5}\frac{p^2}{m_\pi}\left\langle \oint \frac{(d\mathbf{q})}{4\pi\hbar\Omega}\,\delta \sum_{e\nu} V^2|(K+k_0)_\alpha J_\alpha|^2\right\rangle. \tag{12.98}$$

The angular brackets here signify an average over all electron directions $\hat{\mathbf{p}}$ while $\delta$ stands for the energy conserving $\delta$-function

$$\delta(\hbar\Omega+W+cq-m_\pi c^2).$$

This also defines the neutral pion energy

$$\hbar\Omega = c\hbar|\mathbf{K}^2+(m_\pi^0 c/\hbar)^2|^{\frac{1}{2}} = c[(\mathbf{p}+\mathbf{q})^2+(m_\pi^0 c)^2]^{\frac{1}{2}}.$$

The formula (12.98) leads to a very simple result when the pion recoil is neglected and so $-i(K+k_0)_\alpha J_\alpha \approx (2m_\pi c/\hbar)J_4$ can be assumed:

$$d\lambda/dp = (g^2/2\pi^3\hbar^7 c).2p^2q^2, \tag{12.99}$$

with $cq = W_0 - W \approx (m_\pi - m_\pi^0)c^2 - W$. The spectrum has a 'statistical shape' just as in allowed nuclear $\beta$-decay where the recoil is also negligible. Indeed the entire expression (12.99) is exactly the same as the nuclear $\beta$-spectrum expression (5.45), for a case of negligible coulomb influence, $F(Z, W) = 1$, and with the 'strength factor' $\xi = 2$. Quite significantly this is also the strength factor (5.39 a) characteristic of the $0 \to 0$ decay of $O^{14}$: $\xi = C_V^2\langle 1\rangle^2 = 2$.

The last point has the consequence that the comparative half-life of the pion $\beta$-decay will be the same as that observed for $O^{14}$: $ft = (3060\pm10)$ sec. Since the latter has been used, in (5.89), to determine the magnitude of the coupling strength $g$, via (5.46), it will be more direct to use the $ft$-value for evaluating the pion $\beta$-decay rate. With the end-point energy $W_0 = (8{\cdot}9\pm0{\cdot}3)$ and $Z = 0$, the formula (1.11) for the 'statistical rate function' gives $f(W_0) = 1860\pm200$. As a result,

$$\lambda_{\pi\beta}^{-1} = (3060 \text{ sec})/0{\cdot}693f(W_0) = (2{\cdot}4\pm0{\cdot}2) \text{ sec} \tag{12.100}$$

is the mean lifetime. It is a straightforward matter to evaluate (12.98) precisely and thus obtain corrections due to recoil effects. The exact result is lengthy but when only terms of no smaller order than $(m_e/m_\pi)$ are retained the correction amounts simply to multiplying the spectrum (12.99) by the factor $(1+2W/m_\pi c^2)$. This leads to a fractional enhancement of the rate by only $\Delta f/f \approx (W_0/m_\pi c^2) \approx 3$ per cent.

When the partial pion decay constant $\lambda_{\pi\beta}$ of (12.100) is compared to the total rate of (11.2) it leads to the branching ratio

$$\frac{\pi \to \pi^0+e+\nu}{\pi \to \mu+\mu^0} = (1{\cdot}1\pm0{\cdot}1)10^{-8}. \tag{12.101}$$

Thus, the $\pi \to \pi^0$ decay mode is even rarer than the $\pi \to e+\nu$ mode (11.44), by a factor $\sim 10^4$. It seems nevertheless to have been observed,‡ being identified by coincidences of the electron with the pair of 67·5 MeV $\gamma$-rays arising from the rapid self-annihilation of the neutral pion. There was a rough resolution of the expected spectrum (12.99) and the observed rate was reported to be consistent with (12.101).

‡ P. Depommier, J. Heintze, A. Mukhin, C. Rubbia, V. Soergel, and K. Warter, *Proceedings* 1962 *CERN Conference*, p. 411 (Geneva, 1962). Also R. Bacastrow, T. Elioff, R. Larsen, C. Wiegand, and T. Ypsilantis, p. 409 of the same publication.

# XIII

# MUON AND NEUTRETTO CAPTURES

THE part of the weak interactions (12.63) which couples the muon-neutretto current to the nucleons should still be given attention. So far, only its role in $\pi$-decay has been considered (Chapter XI), and that involves only the Pseudovector fraction. The full coupling comes into play in captures of muons or neutrettos by nucleons, and some expectations about these processes will be reviewed in this chapter.

There is good reason for leaving consideration of the muon and neutretto capture processes to the last. It was not until $\mu$-decay was compared to nuclear $\beta$-decay that an important point concerning the role of the internal nucleonic structure was learned, the one embodied in the Conserved Vector Current modification of the physical nucleon current (12.86). This has no effect on the present treatments of $\pi$-decay since it throws no light on the Pseudovector fraction. However, it must be expected to have more important effects in the muon and neutretto captures than the relatively minor ones (e.g. $C_V \to 1$ and weak-magnetism, § 12.5) it was found to have in nuclear $\beta$-decay.

The absorption of a muon releases 106 MeV of mass-energy. High energies are also involved in the best-detectable neutretto captures, for which fast pions produced in the high-energy accelerators serve as sources. Thus the muon and neutretto processes lead to much shorter lepton wavelengths, and become much more sensitive to structural variations within nucleons, than is usual in the electron-neutrino processes. The 'monopole' approximation of the physical nucleon, as represented by the 'renormalization constants' $C_V$ and $C_A$, can no longer be expected to be adequate. For this reason, ways of taking into account more details of the internal nucleon structure will be considered first.

## 13.1. Nucleon form-factors

The problem of describing a physical nucleon adequately is already present in a really proper treatment of the neutron decay. This requires forming a transition amplitude which may be written

$$\langle \mathrm{f}|H_\beta|\mathrm{i}\rangle = 8^{\frac{1}{2}} g J_\alpha^0 \oint (d\mathbf{r}) e^{-iQ.x} \langle \mathrm{f}|J_\alpha(\mathrm{pn})|\mathrm{i}\rangle, \qquad (13.1)$$

where $Q[(\mathbf{p}+\mathbf{q}), i(W+q)]$ is a 4-momentum transferred to the leptons and, as before, $J^0_\alpha = J_\alpha(e\bar{\nu})\exp(iQ.x)$ is the lepton current evaluated at $x(\mathbf{r}, it) = 0$. When it was considered in (4.39), the nucleon current was evaluated for bare nucleon states, as when $|i\rangle \to |n\rangle = a^\dagger_n|0\rangle$ and $|f\rangle \to |p\rangle = a^\dagger_p|0\rangle$, and that led to

$$\langle f|J_\alpha(pn)|i\rangle \to \tfrac{1}{2}\bar{\psi}_p\gamma_\alpha(1+\gamma_5)\psi_n, \tag{13.2}$$

with Dirac plane wave spinors $\psi_{p,n}$. When more proper descriptions of the physical nucleon states are contemplated, it can still be expected that the result will be representable as

$$\langle f|J_\alpha(pn)|i\rangle = \tfrac{1}{2}\bar{\psi}_p(V_\alpha+A_\alpha)\psi_n, \tag{13.3}$$

with $V_\alpha$ and $A_\alpha$ appropriate Vector and Pseudovector operators, respectively. Up to the introduction of the Conserved Vector Current modifications in § 12.5, $V_\alpha = C_V\gamma_\alpha$ and $A_\alpha = -C_A\gamma_\alpha\gamma_5$ were taken, in partial recognition of the difference between a bare and a physical nucleon.

That the result (13.3) should be representable by the indicated projections on Dirac spinors is expected because, according to current ideas, a physical nucleon state may be regarded as one generated in operations on a bare state by the strong interactions. Then $V_\alpha+A_\alpha$ is a resultant of those operations combined with $\gamma_\alpha(1+\gamma_5)$ of (13.2). Arriving at the resultant must involve integrations and contractions over a complex of 'internal variables' (including virtual pion distributions), with only the dependence on the variables still explicit in the Dirac spinors $\psi_{p,n}$ remaining 'unaveraged'. Thus, $V_\alpha$ and $A_\alpha$ may still depend explicitly on the Dirac operators, $\gamma_\alpha$, and on the resultant (barycentric) four-momenta, $P_i$ and $P_f$, of the initial and final physical-nucleon states. The possibilities for these dependences are considered next.

*P, T, and C invariances*

First there are restrictions arising from the covariances of $V_\alpha$ and $A_\alpha$, characteristic of a vector and pseudovector respectively. Each may be a linear combination of the five Dirac covariants, like (2.84) or (2.91), in so far as these are reducible to a vector or a pseudovector through combinations with the 4-vectors

$$Q_\alpha = (P_i-P_f)_\alpha \quad \text{and} \quad \bar{P}_\alpha = \tfrac{1}{2}(P_i+P_f)_\alpha. \tag{13.4}$$

Any explicit dependence on $\bar{P}_\alpha$, which measures a 'convection' of the physical nucleon system as a body, can be eliminated with the help of the Dirac equations satisfied by $\psi_{\mathrm{n}}(P_{\mathrm{i}})$ and $\psi_{\mathrm{p}}(P_{\mathrm{f}})$,

$$[\gamma_\alpha(P_{\mathrm{i}})_\alpha - iM_{\mathrm{i}}]\psi_{\mathrm{n}} = 0 \quad \text{and} \quad \bar{\psi}_{\mathrm{p}}[\gamma_\alpha(P_{\mathrm{f}})_\alpha - iM_{\mathrm{f}}] = 0, \tag{13.5}$$

which follow from (2.82) for example. These jointly lead to the expressions for 4-vectors,

$$\left.\begin{aligned} 2\bar{P}_\alpha &= i(M_{\mathrm{i}}+M_{\mathrm{f}})\gamma_\alpha - i\sigma_{\alpha\beta}Q_\beta \\ 2\sigma_{\alpha\beta}\bar{P}_\beta &= (M_{\mathrm{i}}-M_{\mathrm{f}})\gamma_\alpha + iQ_\alpha \end{aligned}\right\}, \tag{13.6}$$

allowing for the elimination of $\bar{P}_\alpha$ in favour of $Q_\alpha$. Then the most general Vector combination of the $\gamma_\alpha$'s and $Q_\alpha$ may be written

$$V_\alpha = f_{\mathrm{V}}\gamma_\alpha + f_{\mathrm{T}}\sigma_{\alpha\beta}Q_\beta + if_{\mathrm{S}}Q_\alpha, \tag{13.7}$$

where each scalar 'form-factor' $f_X$ is some invariant function of the momentum transfer $Q_\alpha$, hence contains the invariant $Q^2$ only. For similar reasons, the Pseudovector form

$$A_\alpha = [f_{\mathrm{A}}\gamma_\alpha + f'_{\mathrm{T}}\sigma_{\alpha\beta}Q_\beta + if_{\mathrm{P}}Q_\alpha]\gamma_5 \tag{13.8}$$

can be expected. The factors $i$ made explicit in these forms enable them to give results invariant to time reversal with *real* functions $f_X(Q^2)$. That can be proved quite straightforwardly by the methods exhibited in § 10.2. It is only necessary to make the appropriate replacements $C_{\mathrm{V}}\gamma_\alpha \to V_\alpha$ and $-C_{\mathrm{A}}\gamma_\alpha\gamma_5 \to A_\alpha$ in the form for the coupling energy density $h_\beta$, and to remember that $Q_\alpha \to -Q_\alpha^*$ in a time reversal of momenta.

The strong interactions must be expected to generate the modifications $\gamma_\alpha \to V_\alpha$ and $\gamma_\alpha\gamma_5 \to A_\alpha$ independently, since they conserve parity and cannot blur the Vector-Pseudovector distinction. Together with their space-inversion and time-reversal invariances, the strong interactions are invariant to charge-conjugation, hence $V_\alpha$ and $A_\alpha$ must be expected to display the same symmetries upon substitutions of charge-conjugates as do $\gamma_\alpha$ and $\gamma_\alpha\gamma_5$, respectively:

$$\bar{\psi}^C_{\mathrm{p}}\gamma_\alpha\psi^C_{\mathrm{n}} = -\bar{\psi}_{\mathrm{n}}\gamma_\alpha\psi_{\mathrm{p}} \quad \text{and} \quad \bar{\psi}^C_{\mathrm{p}}\gamma_\alpha\gamma_5\psi^C_{\mathrm{n}} = \bar{\psi}_{\mathrm{n}}\gamma_\alpha\gamma_5\psi_{\mathrm{p}}, \tag{13.9}$$

according to the transformation by $C$ of (3.76) and (3.77). The resultant signs given here arise when $\psi_{\mathrm{p}}$ and $\psi_{\mathrm{n}}$ are treated as anticommuting field operators, as is necessary for such strong interaction forms as $h_{N\pi}$ of (11.16) to show explicit invariance (with $\Phi^C = \Phi^*$). It may also be checked that the entire isovector current $\boldsymbol{\theta}_\alpha$ of (12.80) exhibits the same symmetry, $[(\theta_\alpha)_1 + i(\theta_\alpha)_2]^C = -[(\theta_\alpha)_1 - i(\theta_\alpha)_2]$, as does $(\bar{\psi}_{\mathrm{p}}\gamma_\alpha\psi_{\mathrm{n}})$; this is important in view of its role in the $\beta$-coupling (12.86) as modified by the Conserved Vector Current theory. Under these conditions, it must be expected that

$$\bar{\psi}_{\mathrm{p}}^{C} V_{\alpha} \psi_{\mathrm{n}}^{C} = -\bar{\psi}_{\mathrm{n}} V_{\alpha} \psi_{\mathrm{p}} \quad \text{and} \quad \bar{\psi}_{\mathrm{p}}^{C} A_{\alpha} \psi_{\mathrm{n}}^{C} = \bar{\psi}_{\mathrm{n}} A_{\alpha} \psi_{\mathrm{p}}, \tag{13.10}$$

yet a check will show that this will be so only if $f_{\mathrm{S}} = 0$ in $V_{\alpha}$ and $f'_{\mathrm{T}} = 0$ in $A_{\alpha}$ (the terms in $f_{\mathrm{S}}$ and $f'_{\mathrm{T}}$ acquire wrong signs in the transformation). The argument for assuming $f_{\mathrm{S}} = f'_{\mathrm{T}} = 0$ has customarily been based on the expected invariance of the strong interactions to '$G$-conjugation', for which the charge-conjugation is supplemented‡ with a rotation by $\pi$ around the '$y$-axis' of the isospace ($\Phi_{1,3} \to -\Phi_{1,3}$ and $\Phi_2 \to +\Phi_2$ while $\psi_{\mathrm{p}} \to \psi_{\mathrm{n}}$ and $\psi_{\mathrm{n}} \to -\psi_{\mathrm{p}}$). This supplementation is justified by the charge-symmetry of the strong interactions, and the $G$-transformation thus defined compares states of the same electric charge, rather than of opposite charges such as arise in the charge-conjugation by itself. The eventual conclusion, $f_{\mathrm{S}} = f'_{\mathrm{T}} = 0$, is unaffected by the change of viewpoint.

*The Vector form-factors*

The invariance to *arbitrary* rotations in the isospace, i.e. the charge-independence which is supposed to characterize the strong interactions, makes possible comparisons to electromagnetic currents, such as have already been utilized for evaluating Conserved Vector Current effects in § 12.5. Only the Vector part of the nucleon current (13.3) is involved in the comparisons; it is a component of an isovector, $\frac{1}{2}(\bar{\Psi} V_{\alpha} \boldsymbol{\tau} \Psi)$, which can represent, in the form of its third component multiplied by $ie$, the isovector part of the electromagnetic current (12.76) as modified by the strong interactions. The comparability is complete, with unchanged form-factors $f_{\mathrm{V}}(Q^2)$ and $f_{\mathrm{T}}(Q^2)$, according to the Conserved Vector Current theory; then $\frac{1}{2}(\bar{\Psi} V_{\alpha} \boldsymbol{\tau} \Psi)$ ought to be the result of evaluating an isovector field-operator like $\boldsymbol{\theta}_{\alpha}$ of (12.80) in a physical-nucleon state.

The connexions to the electromagnetic data are best made explicit by examining the coupling (4.6) of the isovector current to an electromagnetic field, $\mathscr{A}_{\alpha}$:

$$h'_{\gamma} = -\tfrac{1}{2} ie \mathscr{A}_{\alpha} (\bar{\Psi} V_{\alpha} \tau_3 \Psi) = -\tfrac{1}{2} ie \mathscr{A}_{\alpha} \bar{\Psi} (f_{\mathrm{V}} \gamma_{\alpha} + f_{\mathrm{T}} \sigma_{\alpha\beta} Q_{\beta}) \tau_3 \Psi. \tag{13.11 a}$$

The momentum transfer $Q_{\beta} = (P_{\mathrm{i}} - P_{\mathrm{f}})_{\beta}$ here can be represented as the result of operations $Q_{\beta} = -i(\partial/\partial x_{\beta} + \widetilde{\partial/\partial x_{\beta}})$, where the tilde denotes a 'backward' application of the derivative, to $\bar{\Psi} \sim \exp(-iP_{\mathrm{f}}.x)$.

‡ A. Pais and R. Jost, *Phys. Rev.* **87**, 871 (1952).

Because the 4-divergence, $(\partial/\partial x_\beta)[\mathscr{A}_\alpha(\overline{\Psi}\sigma_{\alpha\beta}\tau_3\Psi)]$ vanishes in an integration over all space-time, (13.11 a) may be replaced by

$$h'_\gamma = -\tfrac{1}{2}ie\overline{\Psi}[f_V\gamma_\alpha\mathscr{A}_\alpha + if_T\sigma_{\alpha\beta}(\partial\mathscr{A}_\alpha/\partial x_\beta)]\tau_3\Psi$$
$$= \tfrac{1}{2}e\Psi^\dagger[f_V(\phi-\boldsymbol{\alpha}.\mathscr{A})-f_T\beta\boldsymbol{\sigma}.\mathbf{B}+if_T\beta\boldsymbol{\alpha}.\mathscr{E}]\tau_3\Psi, \quad (13.11\,\text{b})$$

into which the magnetic field, $\mathbf{B} = \boldsymbol{\nabla}\times\mathscr{A}$, and the electric field, $\mathscr{E} = -\boldsymbol{\nabla}\phi-\partial\mathscr{A}/\partial t$, have been introduced.

The implications of low-energy (hence $Q_\alpha \to 0$) electromagnetic data were already brought out in § 12.5. Re-expressed in terms of the form-factors, they give

$$f_V(0) = 1 \quad \text{and} \quad 2Mf_T(0) \approx \mu_p-\mu_n-1 \approx 3{\cdot}7. \qquad (13.12)$$

This is easily seen from the non-relativistic limit of (13.11 b), obtained as for the electromagnetic effects of (7.78),

$$h'_\gamma \approx \tfrac{1}{2}e\Psi^\dagger\{f_V(0)\phi-[(2M)^{-1}f_V(0)+f_T(0)]\boldsymbol{\sigma}.\mathbf{B}\}\tau_3\Psi, \qquad (13.13)$$

when only the largest, electric monopole and magnetic dipole, effects are kept. The best information about the form-factors $f_V(Q^2)$ and $f_T(Q^2)$ for higher momentum transfers has been obtained from the Stanford electron scattering experiments,‡ which have revealed something of the internal charge structure of the nucleon. In so far as this has been determined, the results for $f_V(Q^2)$ and $f_T(Q^2)$ seem to be representable by§

$$f_V \approx 2Mf_T/(3{\cdot}7) \approx [1+\tfrac{5}{4}Q^2/M^2]^{-1}, \qquad (13.14)$$

corresponding to a root-mean-square nucleon radius of about $0{\cdot}8(10)^{-13}$ cm.

*The induced Pseudoscalar*

The Pseudovector part of the nucleon current, represented by $A_\alpha$ of (13.8) with $f'_T = 0$, is only known to be directly involved in the weak interactions of nucleons, and any information about the form-factors $f_A$ and $f_P$ must come from those. The low momentum-transfer nuclear $\beta$-decay can be presumed to have $f_P Q_\alpha \to 0$ so that it furnishes the measure:

$$f_A(0) \to -C_A \approx +1{\cdot}19, \qquad (13.15)$$

according to the result for $C_A/C_V = C_A$ given in (5.90). The pion decay rate furnishes another number, but this serves to measure the practically incalculable degree to which a nucleon current is generated in the transformation of a pion, rather than measuring the differences between the bare and physical nucleon currents. It is the capture pro-

‡ R. Hofstadter, F. Bumiller, and M. Yearian, *Rev. Mod. Phys.* **30,** 482 (1958).

§ As used in extensive numerical evaluations of $\mu^0$-capture by Y. Yamaguchi, *CERN Report* 61–2 (Geneva, 1961).

cesses to be reviewed in this chapter which must be relied on for more experimental information about the nucleon form-factors.

The effect measured by $f_P$ is known as the 'induced Pseudoscalar' since it simulates the Pseudoscalar couplings of (10.9) or (11.50). This can be seen from a consideration of just that part of the transition matrix (13.1) which is proportional to $f_P$. Expressed in terms of the nucleon current forms (13.3), (13.8) and the lepton current

$$J_\alpha = \tfrac{1}{2}\bar{\psi}_e \gamma_\alpha(1+\gamma_5)\psi_\nu,$$

it is
$$\langle f|H_\beta|i\rangle_P = 2^{\frac{1}{2}} g i f_P Q_\alpha \oint (d\mathbf{r}) J_\alpha(\bar{\psi}_p \gamma_5 \psi_n). \tag{13.16 a}$$

Considerations like those just below (13.11 a), or simply noting the effect of a derivative operation $\partial/\partial x_\alpha$ on $J_\alpha = J_\alpha^0 \exp(-iQ.x)$, lead to

$$-iQ_\alpha J_\alpha = \tfrac{1}{2}[(\partial\bar{\psi}_e/\partial x_\alpha)\gamma_\alpha(1+\gamma_5)\psi_\nu + \bar{\psi}_e(1-\gamma_5)\gamma_\alpha(\partial\psi_\nu/\partial x_\alpha)].$$

The lepton fields here obey the Dirac equations $\gamma_\alpha(\partial\psi_\nu/\partial x_\alpha) = 0$ and $(\partial\bar{\psi}_e/\partial x_\alpha)\gamma_\alpha = +m_e\bar{\psi}_e$, hence

$$\langle f|H_\beta|i\rangle_P = 2^{\frac{1}{2}} g(-m_e f_P) \oint (d\mathbf{r})(\bar{\psi}_p \gamma_5 \psi_n)[\bar{\psi}_e \tfrac{1}{2}(1+\gamma_5)\psi_\nu]. \tag{13.16 b}$$

This is just the transition matrix which would follow from a Pseudoscalar coupling to *bare* nucleons of the type measured by $C_P$ and $C'_P$ in (10.9); the effective coupling constant for the 'induced Pseudoscalar' interaction here is $C_P = C'_P = -m_e f_P$ and it will be $C_P = C'_P = -m_\mu f_P$ in the coupling $H_{N\mu}$ to the muon-neutretto current (11.31).

This Pseudoscalar effect, induced in Pseudovector currents by the strong couplings, cannot alter the electron-to-muon ratio (11.44) in the $\pi$-decay. That was independent of the moment $\langle\gamma_5\rangle_\pi$, which is the only factor through which the strong coupling effects can enter into the determination of the rates. The point can be confirmed explicitly by considering the ratio of the induced Pseudoscalar to bare Pseudovector amplitudes following from (11.51),

$$-[C_P\langle\beta\gamma_5\rangle_\pi/C_A\langle\gamma_5\rangle_\pi][(1+v/c)/(1-v/c)]^{\frac{1}{2}}, \tag{13.17}$$

when the moments are evaluated for bare nucleon constituents. The square-root factor is just $m_\pi/m_e$ for the electron mode, and $m_\pi/m_\mu$ for the muon mode, of the $\pi$-decay. Thus, effective coupling constants $C_P = -m_e f_P$ for the one mode and $C_P = -m_\mu f_P$ for the other make the ratio (13.17) independent of the mode.

Theoretical attempts‡ to predict a size for the induced Pseudoscalar effect have been made on the basis that it arises primarily from the

‡ L. Wolfenstein, *Nuovo Cim.* **8**, 889 (1958); M. Goldberger and S. Treiman, *Phys. Rev.* **111**, 354 (1958).

decay of the pseudoscalar pion during a fluctuation of the nucleon into a transient containing a pion. Wolfenstein made a field-theoretic estimate of the fluctuation and used the observed pion decay rate. Goldberger and Treiman used the same dispersion-theoretic formulation which had enabled them to calculate the pion lifetime (last subsection of Chapter XI), hence could offer an analytic expression,

$$C_{\mathrm{P}} = -m_\mu f_{\mathrm{P}} \approx [2m_\mu M/(m_\pi^2+m_\mu^2)]C_{\mathrm{A}}, \tag{13.18}$$

for the induced Pseudoscalar coupling to the muon-neutretto current. Both approaches led to about the same estimate

$$C_{\mathrm{P}} \approx 8C_{\mathrm{A}}. \tag{13.19}$$

The constant $(-m_{\mathrm{e}} f_{\mathrm{P}})$ which is effective in nuclear $\beta$-decay should be smaller in the ratio $m_{\mathrm{e}}/m_\mu \approx 1/207$. Since much larger Pseudoscalar couplings have already been shown (§ 10.1) undetectable in the electron processes, their existence can be ignored for nuclear $\beta$-decay.

## 13.2. Muon capture

The occurrence of the muon capture processes (11.28) is inferred from the disappearance of muons during their passage through matter, without the simultaneous appearance of the electrons characteristic of $\mu$-decay. The relative proportions of the captures and the decays may be determined simply by counting the electrons emerging from a thin sample of material per muon stopped in it. The most accurate measurements are made by counting delayed $(\mu, \mathrm{e})$ coincidences. As the time between entry of the muon into the material and the attempt to detect a product electron is increased, the coincidence rate naturally decreases since fewer source muons will have survived. The significant finding is that the decrease with delay time is measurably steeper for negative muons than it is for $(\mu^+, \mathrm{e}^+)$ coincidences, which exhibit just the rate expected of free muon decay.

That the extra disappearances of the negative muons should indeed be attributed to capture processes is supported by the fact that the disappearance rate can be increased strongly by using material containing heavier atomic nuclei. Negative muons can be expected to approach the nuclei much more closely than positively charged muons can and 'muonic atoms' are actually formed, as the appearance of characteristic X-rays makes evident. The nuclei are playing an essential role in the absorption of the muons and the analogue, (11.28),

$$\mathrm{p}+\mu^- \rightarrow \mathrm{n}+\mu^0, \tag{13.20}$$

of the electron capture process must be taking place in competition with the $\mu^-$-decay. If $\lambda_C$ is the rate of the $\mu$-capture in the material, while $\lambda_\mu$ is the material-independent decay rate, then the number of electrons appearing in the coincidence experiments should be given by

$$\lambda_\mu N_\mu(t) = \lambda_\mu N_\mu(0)\exp\{-(\lambda_\mu+\lambda_C)t\}, \tag{13.21}$$

where $N_\mu(t)$ is the number of muons present at the moment $t$. This makes explicit the fact that it is the total muon disappearance rate, $\lambda_\mu+\lambda_C$, which is measured by the observed fall-off with delay time, $t$.

The neutrettos presumed to arise in the $\mu$-captures (13.20) have naturally not been directly observed. Their occurrence was initially rendered plausible by the fact that muon-to-neutretto transformations were already known from the $\mu$-decay processes. Now they help account for the muon-to-electron ratio (11.44) in the $\pi$-decay, and for the production of muons upon captures of the neutral products of $\pi$-decay (§ 13.3).

*The nuclear hamiltonian effective in $\mu$-capture*‡

In dealing with the interaction of muons with entire nuclei, it is convenient to formulate it as a contribution $H_{A\mu}$ to the nuclear hamiltonian, analogous to the $H_\beta$ of (4.67) used for nuclear $\beta$-decay:

$$H_{A\mu} = 2^{\frac{1}{2}}g\sum_a J_\alpha(\mu^0\mu)\beta^a(V_\alpha^a+A_\alpha^a)\tau_-^a+\text{h.c.}, \tag{13.22 a}$$

in which the form-factors $f_\text{V}$, $f_\text{T}$, $f_\text{A}$, and $f_\text{P}$ of (13.7), (13.8) are implicit. This may be considered in four parts (aside from their hermitian conjugates):

$$H_{A\mu} = H_{A\mu}(V')+H_{A\mu}(\text{wm})+H_{A\mu}(A')+H_{A\mu}(P)+\text{h.c.} \tag{13.22 b}$$

The first term consists of the contributions proportional to $f_\text{V}$ after the 'non-anomalous' part of the 'weak-magnetism' has been separated off. By this is meant a leaving off, and incorporation into $H_{A\mu}(\text{wm})$ instead, of the term proportional to $\sigma_{\alpha\beta}$ which arises when the relation (13.6) is used to eliminate $f_\text{V}\gamma_\alpha$ of $V_\alpha$ (13.7). In consequence,

$$H_{A\mu}(V') = 2^{\frac{1}{2}}g(f_\text{V}/2iM)\sum_a J_\alpha(P_\text{p}^a+P_\text{n}^a)_\alpha\beta^a\tau_-^a, \tag{13.23}$$

where $(P_\text{p}+P_\text{n})_\alpha \equiv -i(\partial/\partial x_\alpha-\widetilde{\partial/\partial x_\alpha})$ in the notation discussed below (13.11 a). The remainder of the contributions by the nucleon Vector current operators $V_\alpha^a$ are represented by

$$H_{A\mu}(\text{wm}) = 2^{\frac{1}{2}}gf_\text{V}[(\mu_\text{p}-\mu_\text{n})/2M]\sum_a J_\alpha\beta^a\sigma_{\alpha\beta}^a(P_\text{p}^a-P_\text{n}^a)_\beta\tau_-^a, \tag{13.24}$$

‡ The treatment here will parallel that of H. Primakoff, *Rev. Mod. Phys.* **31**, 802 (1959). Some of the earliest explorations were made by J. A. Wheeler, ibid. **21**, 133 (1949).

where advantage has been taken of the fact that the ratio

$$f_{\mathrm{T}}/f_{\mathrm{V}} = (\mu_{\mathrm{p}}-\mu_{\mathrm{n}}-1)/2M$$

(13.12) is supposed to hold to high momentum transfers. The primary Pseudovector contribution, proportional to $f_{\mathrm{A}}$, may be written (compare (5.1)):

$$H_{A\mu}(A') = 2^{\frac{1}{2}} g f_{\mathrm{A}} \sum_{a} [J_4 \gamma_5^a + i\mathbf{J}.\boldsymbol{\sigma}^a]\tau_{-}^a. \tag{13.25}$$

This leaves the 'induced Pseudoscalar',

$$H_{A\mu}(P) = 2^{\frac{1}{2}} g m_{\mu} f_{\mathrm{P}} \sum_{a} [\psi_{\mu^0}^{\dagger}\tfrac{1}{2}(1-\gamma_5)\psi_{\mu}]\beta^a\gamma_5^a\tau_{-}^a, \tag{13.26}$$

implicit in the hermitian conjugate of (13.16 b) with $\mathrm{e} \to \mu$ and $\nu \to \mu^0$.

In adapting the hamiltonian expressions to practical cases of $\mu$-capture, it is essential to retain a fully relativistic treatment only for the neutretto:

$$\psi_{\mu^0} = 2^{-\frac{1}{2}}\begin{pmatrix} 1 \\ \boldsymbol{\sigma}.\hat{\mathbf{q}} \end{pmatrix}\boldsymbol{\varphi}_{\mu^0}, \qquad \boldsymbol{\varphi}_{\mu^0} = \boldsymbol{\chi}_{\mu^0} e^{iq.x}/V^{\frac{1}{2}}, \tag{13.27}$$

according to (3.4), with a massless neutretto of 4-momentum $q(\mathbf{q}, iq)$. The muon is captured almost exclusively from an atomic $s$-orbit of zero average momentum, and may be treated non-relativistically,

$$\psi_{\mu} = \begin{pmatrix} 1 \\ 0 \end{pmatrix}\boldsymbol{\varphi}_{\mu}. \tag{13.28}$$

A more accurate treatment would be justified only if the finite spread of the charge on the nucleus were taken into account, but this can scarcely be done satisfactorily without machine computation.‡ Here, the expressions following from (13.28),

$$\left.\begin{aligned} \mathbf{J} &= i\psi_{\mu^0}^{\dagger}\boldsymbol{\sigma}\tfrac{1}{2}(1+\gamma_5)\psi_{\mu} = 2^{-\frac{3}{2}}\boldsymbol{\varphi}_{\mu^0}^{\dagger}(1-\boldsymbol{\sigma}.\hat{\mathbf{q}})i\boldsymbol{\sigma}\boldsymbol{\varphi}_{\mu} \\ J_4 &= 2^{-\frac{3}{2}}\boldsymbol{\varphi}_{\mu^0}^{\dagger}(1-\boldsymbol{\sigma}.\hat{\mathbf{q}})\boldsymbol{\varphi}_{\mu} = \bar{\psi}_{\mu^0}\tfrac{1}{2}(1-\gamma_5)\psi_{\mu} \end{aligned}\right\}, \tag{13.29}$$

will be put for the lepton current and densities.

The energy $m_{\mu}-B \approx m_{\mu}[1-\frac{1}{2}(\alpha Z)^2]$ becomes nominally available for exciting the nucleus, but even in a momentum balance with an individual nucleon, $\mathbf{P}_{\mathrm{p}}^a = \mathbf{P}_{\mathrm{n}}^a+\mathbf{q}$, the neutretto would take most of the energy; nucleons bound to a heavy structure might be expected to take even less recoil energy than a free nucleon. Consequently, the fourth component of the total nucleon 4-momentum occurring in (13.23) may be approximated as $(P_{\mathrm{p}}^a+P_{\mathrm{n}}^a)_4 \approx 2iM$. Such procedures for treating the momentum transfer as were exhibited in the preceding section can be used to justify putting $\mathbf{P}_{\mathrm{p}}^a+\mathbf{P}_{\mathrm{n}}^a = 2\mathbf{P}_{\mathrm{p}}^a-(\mathbf{P}_{\mathrm{p}}^a-\mathbf{P}_{\mathrm{n}}^a) = 2\mathbf{P}_{\mathrm{p}}^a-\mathbf{q}$. This occurs in (13.23) in scalar product with $\mathbf{J}$ of (13.29), hence the operation

‡ See e.g. K. Ford and J. Wills, *Nuc. Phys.* **35**, 295 (1962), for computations of $\mu$-atomic wave functions.

$(1-\boldsymbol{\sigma}.\hat{\mathbf{q}})\boldsymbol{\sigma}.\mathbf{q} = -(1-\boldsymbol{\sigma}.\hat{\mathbf{q}})q$ is involved. Finally, since $\beta^a \approx 1$ for non-relativistic nucleons, treated to order $M^{-1}$,

$$H_{A\mu}(V') \approx \tfrac{1}{2}gf_{\mathrm{V}} \sum_a \tau_-^a \boldsymbol{\varphi}_{\mu 0}^{\dagger}(1-\boldsymbol{\sigma}.\hat{\mathbf{q}})[1+(q/2M)+\boldsymbol{\sigma}.\mathbf{P}_{\mathrm{p}}^a/M]\boldsymbol{\varphi}_{\mu} \tag{13.30}$$

may be written for (13.23).

In $H_{A\mu}(\mathrm{wm})$ of (13.24), the operators $\beta^a\boldsymbol{\alpha}^a$ occur, but may be neglected since they will lead to results of only the order $M^{-2}$. The remainder is approximately

$$H_{A\mu}(\mathrm{wm}) \approx 2^{\frac{1}{2}}gf_{\mathrm{V}}[(\mu_{\mathrm{p}}-\mu_{\mathrm{n}})/2M] \sum_a \tau_-^a[-\mathbf{J}.(\boldsymbol{\sigma}^a \times \mathbf{q})]. \tag{13.31 a}$$

Since $-i\boldsymbol{\sigma}.(\boldsymbol{\sigma}^a \times \mathbf{q}) = (\boldsymbol{\sigma}.\mathbf{q})(\boldsymbol{\sigma}.\boldsymbol{\sigma}^a)-\boldsymbol{\sigma}^a.\mathbf{q}$, the last square bracket may be written

$$-2^{-\frac{3}{2}}\boldsymbol{\varphi}_{\mu 0}^{\dagger}(1-\boldsymbol{\sigma}.\hat{\mathbf{q}})\boldsymbol{\sigma}^a.(\mathbf{q}+q\boldsymbol{\sigma})\boldsymbol{\varphi}_{\mu}. \tag{13.31 b}$$

For (13.25), the approximation $\gamma_5^a \approx -\boldsymbol{\sigma}^a.(\mathbf{P}_{\mathrm{p}}^a+\mathbf{P}_{\mathrm{n}}^a)/2M$ is needed, obtainable by such methods as were used for (7.69). Then

$$H_{A\mu}(A') \approx -2^{\frac{1}{2}}gf_{\mathrm{A}} \sum_a \tau_-^a[-i\mathbf{J}.\boldsymbol{\sigma}^a+J_4\,\boldsymbol{\sigma}^a.(2\mathbf{P}_{\mathrm{p}}^a-\mathbf{q})/2M], \tag{13.32 a}$$

and the square bracket may be written in more detail as

$$2^{-\frac{3}{2}}\boldsymbol{\varphi}_{\mu 0}^{\dagger}(1-\boldsymbol{\sigma}.\hat{\mathbf{q}})\boldsymbol{\sigma}^a.(\boldsymbol{\sigma}+\mathbf{P}_{\mathrm{p}}^a/M-\mathbf{q}/2M)\boldsymbol{\varphi}_{\mu}. \tag{13.23 b}$$

Finally, (13.26) becomes

$$H_{A\mu}(P) \approx -\tfrac{1}{2}gm_{\mu}f_{\mathrm{P}} \sum_a \tau_-^a[\boldsymbol{\varphi}_{\mu 0}^{\dagger}(1-\boldsymbol{\sigma}.\hat{\mathbf{q}})\boldsymbol{\varphi}_{\mu}](\boldsymbol{\sigma}^a.\mathbf{q})/2M, \tag{13.33}$$

as a result of similar treatment.

Putting together the findings (13.30)–(13.33) yields Primakoff's effective hamiltonian:

$$H_{A\mu} = \tfrac{1}{2} \sum_a \tau_-^a \boldsymbol{\varphi}_{\mu 0}^{\dagger}(1-\boldsymbol{\sigma}.\hat{\mathbf{q}})[G_{\mathrm{V}}+G_{\mathrm{A}}\,\boldsymbol{\sigma}.\boldsymbol{\sigma}^a+G_{\mathrm{P}}\,\boldsymbol{\sigma}^a.\hat{\mathbf{q}}]\boldsymbol{\varphi}_{\mu}, \tag{13.34}$$

designed to be approximately correct to order $M^{-1}$ in the nucleon mass. For consistency with this, a unit value should be taken for the form-factor (13.14). Using (13.15) and (13.19) for the other form-factors leads to

$$\left.\begin{aligned} G_{\mathrm{V}} &\equiv g(1+q/2M) \\ G_{\mathrm{A}} &\equiv g[C_{\mathrm{A}}-(\mu_{\mathrm{p}}-\mu_{\mathrm{n}})q/2M] \\ G_{\mathrm{P}} &\equiv g[C_{\mathrm{P}}-C_{\mathrm{A}}-(\mu_{\mathrm{p}}-\mu_{\mathrm{n}})]q/2M \end{aligned}\right\}. \tag{13.35}$$

Here, $C_{\mathrm{A}} = -1{\cdot}19$, $C_{\mathrm{P}} \approx 8C_{\mathrm{A}}$ according to (13.19), and $\mu_{\mathrm{p}}-\mu_{\mathrm{n}} \approx 4{\cdot}7$. Terms

$$(\boldsymbol{\sigma}+C_{\mathrm{A}}\,\boldsymbol{\sigma}^a).\mathbf{P}_{\mathrm{p}}^a/M \tag{13.36}$$

have been left out of the square bracket in (13.34). This corresponds to retaining in part one of the two steps taken in forming the 'allowed approximation' (5.4) for the nuclear $\beta$-decay. Plainly, $\mathbf{P}_{\mathrm{p}}^a/M$ and $-\boldsymbol{\sigma}^a.\mathbf{P}_{\mathrm{p}}^a/M$ are just the non-relativistic equivalents of the operations in the nuclear $\beta$-moments $\langle\alpha\rangle$ and $\langle\gamma_5\rangle$ when nucleonic recoils from the leptons are ignored. The effects of $\langle\alpha\rangle$ and $\langle\gamma_5\rangle$ were found to be completely negligible in allowed $\beta$-decay and this can be expected to be true also in the muon captures except for the extra nucleonic momenta $\mathbf{P}_{\mathrm{n}}^{a}-\mathbf{P}_{\mathrm{p}}^{a} = -\mathbf{q}$ generated by recoil from the neutretto. The latter effects are additional to (13.36) and have already been incorporated in the factors $G_{\mathrm{V}}$ and $G_{\mathrm{A}}$ (terms $\sim q/2M$). Nothing further of the 'allowed approximation' can be taken over for the $\mu$-captures because the lepton momenta become too large and the corresponding wavelengths may be of nuclear dimensions and less.

*Formulation of the capture rate*

The capture of a muon by a nucleus in a given (ground) state $|\mathrm{i}\rangle$ will generally result in various final nuclear states $|\mathrm{f}\rangle$. Corresponding to each nuclear energy change $\Delta_{\mathrm{f}} = E_{\mathrm{f}}-E_{\mathrm{i}}$, there will be a different emitted neutretto energy,

$$q_{\mathrm{f}} = m_{\mu}-B+\Delta_{\mathrm{f}}, \tag{13.37}$$

even when all the muons are captured from the same atomic orbit, of binding energy $B$. Corrections proportional to $m_{\mu}/AM$, arising from nuclear recoil and reduced mass effects, may still be made but are usually small compared to the precision with which $B$ and $\Delta_{\mathrm{f}}$ are known. An expression for the capture rate which then follows from the general formula (4.36) may be written:

$$\lambda = \sum_{\mathrm{f}\mu^0} (q_{\mathrm{f}}^2/\pi) \oint [(d\hat{\mathbf{q}})/4\pi]V\,|\langle\mathrm{f}|H_{A\mu}|\mathrm{i}\rangle|^2, \tag{13.38}$$

where $\mu^0 = \pm\frac{1}{2}$ labels a summation over the neutretto spins. Averages over the muon spin and initial nuclear orientations may be regarded as implicit here.

The muon is captured out of an atomic $K$-orbit and its state is representable by a spherically symmetric function

$$\boldsymbol{\varphi}_{\mu} = \boldsymbol{\chi}_{\mu}\,\phi_K(r)/(\pi a_{\mu}^3)^{\frac{1}{2}}, \tag{13.39}$$

where $\boldsymbol{\chi}_{\mu}$ is a Pauli eigenspinor and

$$a_{\mu} = 1/m_{\mu}\,\alpha Z \tag{13.40}$$

is the Bohr radius of the muon's orbit (units $\hbar/m_{\mathrm{e}}c$). When the nucleus can be treated as a point-charge, $\phi_K(r) = \exp(-r/a_{\mu})$ simply, and $1/\pi a_{\mu}^3$ is just the muon density at the point-charge (it can be identified as $g_K^2(0)/4\pi$, suitably adapted from (8.3)). However, $\phi_K(r)$ is more properly to be computed for an extended charge distribution, since already for $Z \gtrsim 45$ the muon Bohr radius $a_{\mu}$ lies within the nuclear radius. Now the transition matrix element of the hamiltonian $H_{A\mu}$ of (13.34) may be given the form

$$\langle \mathrm{f}|H_{A\mu}|\mathrm{i}\rangle = \tfrac{1}{2}(\pi a_\mu^3 V)^{-\frac{1}{2}}\Big\{\chi_{\mu^0}^\dagger(1-\boldsymbol{\sigma}.\hat{\mathbf{q}})\Big[G_\mathrm{V}\int\limits_\mu 1+(G_\mathrm{A}\boldsymbol{\sigma}+G_\mathrm{P}\hat{\mathbf{q}}).\int\limits_\mu \boldsymbol{\sigma}\Big]\chi_\mu\Big\}, \tag{13.41}$$

where

$$\left.\begin{aligned}\int\limits_\mu 1 &\equiv \Big\langle \mathrm{f}\Big|\sum_a \tau_-^a e^{-i\mathbf{q}.\mathbf{r}^a}\phi_K(r^a)\Big|\mathrm{i}\Big\rangle\\ \int\limits_\mu \boldsymbol{\sigma} &\equiv \Big\langle \mathrm{f}\Big|\sum_a \tau_-^a e^{-i\mathbf{q}.\mathbf{r}^a}\phi_K(r^a)\boldsymbol{\sigma}^a\Big|\mathrm{i}\Big\rangle\end{aligned}\right\}. \tag{13.42}$$

The latter forms would reduce to just the Fermi and Gamow–Teller matrix elements (5.3) of nuclear $\beta$-decay if only the variations of the lepton waves across the nucleus could be neglected.

When the square of the transition matrix element (13.41) is summed and averaged over the lepton spins, the result is easily seen to be

$$\tfrac{1}{2}\sum_{\mu\mu^0}|\langle \mathrm{f}|H_{A\mu}|\mathrm{i}\rangle|^2 = (2\pi a_\mu^3 V)^{-1}\Big\{\Big|G_\mathrm{V}\int\limits_\mu 1+G_\mathrm{P}\hat{\mathbf{q}}.\int\limits_\mu \boldsymbol{\sigma}\Big|^2+$$
$$+G_\mathrm{A}^2\Big|\int\limits_\mu \boldsymbol{\sigma}\Big|^2-\Big[\Big(G_\mathrm{V}\int\limits_\mu 1+G_\mathrm{P}\hat{\mathbf{q}}.\int\limits_\mu \boldsymbol{\sigma}\Big)G_\mathrm{A}\Big(\int\limits_\mu \boldsymbol{\sigma}\Big)^*.\hat{\mathbf{q}}+\mathrm{c.c.}\Big]\Big\}. \tag{13.43}$$

The interferences proportional to $G_\mathrm{V}\,G_\mathrm{A}$ and $G_\mathrm{V}\,G_\mathrm{P}$ which are implicit here will not survive the averages and sums over nuclear orientations, and the integration over neutretto directions, needed for the rate (13.38). The nuclear matrix elements become independent of any direction, hence the interferences odd in $\hat{\mathbf{q}}$ will have a vanishing directional average. As a result

$$\lambda = (2\pi^2 a_\mu^3)^{-1}\sum_\mathrm{f} q_\mathrm{f}^2\oint[(d\hat{\mathbf{q}})/4\pi]\Big\{G_\mathrm{V}^2\Big|\int\limits_\mu 1\Big|^2+G_\mathrm{A}^2\Big|\int\limits_\mu \boldsymbol{\sigma}\Big|^2+$$
$$+(G_\mathrm{P}^2-2G_\mathrm{A}\,G_\mathrm{P})\Big|\int\limits_\mu \boldsymbol{\sigma}.\hat{\mathbf{q}}\Big|^2\Big\}. \tag{13.44}$$

The major task which remains is to come to some conclusion about the contributions from the various nuclear matrix elements here.

*Primakoff's closure approximation*‡

With the high nuclear excitation possible in each case of muon capture, it can be hoped that enough final nuclear states are energetically available for approximate 'closure' in operations of the type

$$\sum_\mathrm{f}|\langle \mathrm{f}|\mathcal{O}|\mathrm{i}\rangle|^2 = \sum_\mathrm{f}\langle \mathrm{i}|\mathcal{O}^\dagger|\mathrm{f}\rangle\langle \mathrm{f}|\mathcal{O}|\mathrm{i}\rangle \approx \langle \mathrm{i}|\mathcal{O}^\dagger\mathcal{O}|\mathrm{i}\rangle, \tag{13.45}$$

‡ Compare the application of the same idea to double $\beta$-decay in (9.42), also initiated by Primakoff.

even when $\sum_{\text{f}}$ is restricted to the available states. It can well be that $\langle \text{f}|\mathcal{O}|\text{i}\rangle$ is small for the 'unavailable' states, because of poor 'overlap' with the ground state $|\text{i}\rangle$.

To apply closure in the rate expression (13.44) it is necessary to ignore the differences among the various possible neutretto energies $q_{\text{f}}$ (13.37), and replace them with some plausible average, $q$. Then, for example,

$$\sum_{\text{f}}\left|\int_{\mu} 1\right|^2 = \left\langle \text{i}\left|\sum_{a,b} \tau_+^a\, \tau_-^a\, e^{i\mathbf{q}\cdot\mathbf{r}_{ab}}\phi_K(r^a)\phi_K(r^b)\right|\text{i}\right\rangle, \tag{13.46}$$

where $\mathbf{r}_{ab} = \mathbf{r}^a - \mathbf{r}^b$. The result for $\sum_{\text{f}}\left|\int_{\mu} \boldsymbol{\sigma}\right|^2$ is the same except for containing the extra factors $\boldsymbol{\sigma}^a.\boldsymbol{\sigma}^b$ while $\sum_{\text{f}}\left|\int_{\mu} \boldsymbol{\sigma}.\hat{\mathbf{q}}\right|^2$ contains $(\boldsymbol{\sigma}^a.\hat{\mathbf{q}})(\boldsymbol{\sigma}^b.\hat{\mathbf{q}})$. The latter factors will be replaced by $\frac{1}{3}(\boldsymbol{\sigma}^a.\boldsymbol{\sigma}^b)$ after the averaging over neutretto directions; this is exactly correct in the main, $a = b$, terms and an approximation when $a \neq b$. This affects only contributions which are at most of order $q/M$.

In the average over neutretto directions,

$$\oint [(d\hat{\mathbf{q}})/4\pi]\exp(i\mathbf{q}.\mathbf{r}_{ab}) = \sin qr_{ab}/qr_{ab},$$

and the closure approximation of the rate expression (13.44) may be written

$$\lambda = \frac{G_{\text{V}}^2\, q^2}{2\pi^2 a_\mu^3}\left\langle \text{i}\left|\sum \tau_+^a\, \tau_-^b\, \frac{\sin qr_{ab}}{qr_{ab}}\, \phi_K^a\, \phi_K^b(1+\eta\boldsymbol{\sigma}^a.\boldsymbol{\sigma}^b)\right|\text{i}\right\rangle, \tag{13.47}$$

where $\eta$ is the combination of effective coupling constants,

$$\eta = [G_{\text{A}}^2 + \tfrac{1}{3}(G_{\text{P}}^2 - 2G_{\text{A}}\, G_{\text{P}})]/G_{\text{V}}^2. \tag{13.48}$$

The terms $a \neq b$ represent exchanges, in the nuclear configuration, of the transforming nucleon with others, equivalent to interferences among the individual nucleon waves. If only the terms $a = b$ were kept, the result would represent a sum of the independent transformations of the individual nucleons which could contribute to the capture rate. It will be convenient to examine this 'independent-nucleon' rate, $\lambda_{\text{ind}}$, first, and later its correction by the 'exchange' ($a \neq b$) terms.

If only the $a = b$ terms of (13.47) are kept, the simplifications $\boldsymbol{\sigma}^a.\boldsymbol{\sigma}^a = 3$ and $\tau_+^a\, \tau_-^a = \frac{1}{2}(1+\tau_3^a)$ may be used, with the result:

$$\lambda_{\text{ind}} = [(m_\mu\, \alpha Z)^3/2\pi^3]q^2 G_{\text{V}}^2(1+3\eta)\left\langle \text{i}\left|\sum_a \tfrac{1}{2}(1+\tau_3^a)|\phi_K(r^a)|^2\right|\text{i}\right\rangle. \tag{13.49}$$

Here, the expression $a_\mu = (m_\mu\, \alpha Z)^{-1}$ has been introduced for the muon's Bohr radius in order to make its dependence on the nuclear charge $Z$

explicit. The matrix element here is plainly just a count of the protons in the capturing nucleus, each weighted in proportion to the muon density at its site. This count, which becomes as great as $Z$ for $|\phi_K|^2 \to 1$ (a muon spread uniformly over a volume $\pi a_\mu^3 > \pi R^3$), together with the factor $Z^3$ arising from the muon density, $1/\pi a_\mu^3$, led Wheeler to define a $Z_{\text{eff}}$ which is given by

$$(Z_{\text{eff}}/Z)^4 \equiv \Big\langle \mathrm{i}\Big|\sum_a \tfrac{1}{2}(1+\tau_3^a)|\phi_K(r^a)|^2\Big|\mathrm{i}\Big\rangle \Big/ Z \tag{13.50}$$

in the terms used here. Averaging by $(2I+1)^{-1}\sum_M$ is to be understood if $|\mathrm{i}\rangle$ is defined for specific eigenvalues $I$, $M$ of the nuclear spin. Comparison with the comparative half-life of the neutron

$$(ft)_{\mathrm{n}} = 2\pi^3 \ln 2/g^2(1+3C_{\mathrm{A}}^2) = 1180 \pm 35 \text{ sec}$$

permits the evaluation

$$\begin{aligned}\lambda_{\text{ind}} &= (272 \text{ sec}^{-1}) Z_{\text{eff}}^4 \left(\frac{q}{m_\mu}\right)^2 \frac{G_{\mathrm{V}}^2(1+3\eta)}{g^2(1+3C_{\mathrm{A}}^2)} \\ &= (290 \pm 10) Z_{\text{eff}}^4 (q/m_\mu)^2 \text{ sec}^{-1}.\end{aligned} \tag{13.51}$$

The uncertainty in the last line corresponds to evaluating the effective coupling constants of (13.35) for neutretto energies ranging from about $0{\cdot}75m_\mu$ to $0{\cdot}9m_\mu$. With such values, $\eta \approx 1{\cdot}4$, which is about the same as the GT-to-Fermi ratio, $C_{\mathrm{A}}^2 = C_{\mathrm{A}}^2/C_{\mathrm{V}}^2$, by mere coincidence.

Next, attention must be given to the 'exchange' fraction,

$$\frac{\lambda - \lambda_{\text{ind}}}{\lambda_{\text{ind}}} = \frac{\Big\langle \mathrm{i}\Big|\sum_{a \neq b} \tau_+^a \tau_-^b (1+\eta \boldsymbol{\sigma}^a . \boldsymbol{\sigma}^b)[\sin q r_{ab}/q r_{ab}]\phi_K^a \phi_K^b\Big|\mathrm{i}\Big\rangle}{(1+3\eta)\Big\langle \mathrm{i}\Big|\sum_a \tfrac{1}{2}(1+\tau_3^a)|\phi_K^a|^2\Big|\mathrm{i}\Big\rangle} \tag{13.52}$$

which follows from the $a \neq b$ terms of (13.47).

Without detailed nuclear state descriptions, about the best that can be done in evaluating the ratio (13.52) is to make use of the fact that the nucleons are fairly uniformly distributed within the nuclear radius, $R$. Then the relatively simple denominator matrix element may be written

$$\int (d\mathbf{r})|\phi_K(r)|^2 \Big\langle \mathrm{i}\Big|\sum_a \tfrac{1}{2}(1+\tau_3^a)\delta(\mathbf{r}-\mathbf{r}^a)\Big|\mathrm{i}\Big\rangle \approx \int_R (d\mathbf{r})|\phi_K(r)|^2[Z/\tfrac{4}{3}\pi R^3]. \tag{13.53}$$

The bracket on the left amounts to the expectation value of the proton density at $\mathbf{r}$, and the subscript $R$ on the right indicates that the volume integration is to be restricted to the region within the nuclear radius, where the average proton density $Z/(\frac{4}{3}\pi R^3)$ can be said to exist. This procedure should be adequate for estimating the ratio (13.52) if the numerator matrix element is averaged in a comparable way. Somewhat better procedures have sometimes been used for computing $Z_{\text{eff}}$ of (13.50). For example, Sens‡ replaced the sharply bounded nucleus with a parametrized proton distribution determined from electron-nucleus scattering data. Once a nuclear charge distribution is settled on, it is straightforward to compute (numerically) the corresponding muon wave function, $\phi_K$.

Before the same type of space-averaging can be applied to the numerator matrix element of (13.52), an important precaution must be observed. Consider the contributions of a given nucleon-pair $(a, b)$ to the sum, $\sum_{a \neq b}$. Clearly, those stemming from the part of the state $|\mathrm{i}\rangle$ which is symmetric in the exchange of the positions $\mathbf{r}^a$, $\mathbf{r}^b$ should not be lumped together, in the space averaging, with the contributions from the antisymmetric part. The two parts may be separated, for each pair $(a, b)$, with the help of a position-exchange operator, $X_{ab}$, defined by $X_{ab} f(\mathbf{r}^a, \mathbf{r}^b) = f(\mathbf{r}^b, \mathbf{r}^a)$. Then, whatever the state description $|\mathrm{i}\rangle$, the expression

$$|\mathrm{i}\rangle = \tfrac{1}{2}(1+X_{ab})|\mathrm{i}\rangle + \tfrac{1}{2}(1-X_{ab})|\mathrm{i}\rangle \tag{13.54}$$

distinguishes the symmetric and antisymmetric parts, as desired. With this, the numerator matrix element of (13.52) may be viewed as the sum of the two double-volume integrals

$$\int (d\mathbf{r}) \int (d\mathbf{r}') \frac{\sin q|\mathbf{r}-\mathbf{r}'|}{q|\mathbf{r}-\mathbf{r}'|} \phi_K(r)\phi_K(r') F_{\mathrm{i}}^{\pm}(\mathbf{r}, \mathbf{r}') \mathscr{M}_{\mathrm{i}}^{\pm}, \tag{13.55}$$

where

$$F_{\mathrm{i}}^{\pm} = \frac{\left\langle \mathrm{i} \middle| \sum_{a\neq b} \tau_+^a \tau_-^b (1+\eta \boldsymbol{\sigma}^a . \boldsymbol{\sigma}^b) \delta(\mathbf{r}-\mathbf{r}^a) \delta(\mathbf{r}-\mathbf{r}^b) \tfrac{1}{2}(1 \pm X_{ab}) \middle| \mathrm{i} \right\rangle}{\left\langle \mathrm{i} \middle| \sum_{a\neq b} \tau_+^a \tau_-^b (1+\eta \boldsymbol{\sigma}^a . \boldsymbol{\sigma}^b) \tfrac{1}{2}(1 \pm X_{ab}) \middle| \mathrm{i} \right\rangle}, \tag{13.56}$$

and

$$\mathscr{M}_{\mathrm{i}}^{\pm} = \left\langle \mathrm{i} \middle| \sum_{a\neq b} \tau_+^a \tau_-^b (1+\eta \boldsymbol{\sigma}^a . \boldsymbol{\sigma}^b) \tfrac{1}{2}(1 \pm X_{ab}) \middle| \mathrm{i} \right\rangle. \tag{13.57}$$

Separating off the final matrix-element factors, $\mathscr{M}_{\mathrm{i}}^{\pm}$, in (13.55), enabled the definition of 'nucleon pair-correlation functions', $F_{\mathrm{i}}^{\pm}$, having relatively clear effects in the space-integration (13.55). Each function is a ratio which, in the absence of the differences caused by the exchange operations $X_{ab}$, could be treated as the product of an average nucleon-density, $1/(\frac{4}{3}\pi R^3)$, with itself, in the type of procedure used for (13.53). However, it is just the differences arising from the exchanges $X_{ab}$ which the introduction of these operations was designed to bring out. The

‡ J. C. Sens, *Phys. Rev.* **113**, 679 (1959).

form these give to the two functions $F_i^{\pm}$ makes it plausible to treat them as

$$F_i^{\pm}(\mathbf{r},\mathbf{r}') \approx (\tfrac{4}{3}\pi R^3)^{-2}\tfrac{1}{2}[1\pm f(|\mathbf{r}-\mathbf{r}'|)], \tag{13.58}$$

where $f$ is some 'short-ranged' function of the nucleon-pair separations. This function arises from the exchange operations $X_{ab}$ and receives contributions only from pairs of nucleons which overlap in position. Thus, $f$ should be near-vanishing outside some range $d$ which is of the order of the average distance apart, $r_0$, of nucleons in nuclei:

$$d \approx r_0 = R/A^{\frac{1}{3}} \approx 1{\cdot}2(10)^{-13}\ \text{cm} \approx 0{\cdot}65/m_\mu. \tag{13.59}$$

It is also clear that $f(0) = 1$ in order that $F_i^-(\mathbf{r},\mathbf{r}')$ properly vanish for $\mathbf{r}' = \mathbf{r}$. The assumption

$$f(\rho \leqslant d) = 1 \quad \text{and} \quad f(\rho > d) = 0 \tag{13.60}$$

will be a suitable representation of those facts. The consequence for the sum of the two double integrals (13.55) is that it will have a term independent of $f(\rho)$,

$$(\tfrac{4}{3}\pi R^3)^{-2}\int (d\mathbf{r})\phi_K(r)\int (d\boldsymbol{\rho})\frac{\sin q\rho}{q\rho}\phi_K(|\mathbf{r}-\boldsymbol{\rho}|)(\mathscr{M}_i^+ + \mathscr{M}_i^-), \tag{31.61 a}$$

and a term proportional to it,

$$(\tfrac{4}{3}\pi R^3)^{-2}\int (d\mathbf{r})|\phi_K(r)|^2\int (d\boldsymbol{\rho})\frac{\sin q\rho}{q\rho}f(\rho)(\mathscr{M}_i^+ - \mathscr{M}_i^-). \tag{13.61 b}$$

In the last line, $\phi_K(|\mathbf{r}-\boldsymbol{\rho}|)$ has been approximated by $\phi_K(r)$ because of the short-ranged character of $f(\rho)$. The same property enables replacing $\sin q\rho$ by its power series, with the result

$$\int (d\boldsymbol{\rho})\frac{\sin q\rho}{q\rho}f(\rho) \approx \tfrac{4}{3}\pi d^3(1-\tfrac{1}{10}q^2d^2+\ldots). \tag{13.62}$$

The corrections to the first term may be neglected, particularly since $q \approx m_\mu$ varies little, and can be absorbed into the definition of $d^3$.

There remains the task of evaluating $(\mathscr{M}_i^+ \pm \mathscr{M}_i^-)$ with the matrix elements as defined in (13.57). The contributions of the various operators to these can be separated into parts which are cumulative in the summations over the nucleon pairs, and parts to which the various nucleon pairs give mostly cancelling contributions. The latter may be expressed in terms of the operators

$$\mathbf{T} = \sum_a \tfrac{1}{2}\boldsymbol{\tau}^a, \qquad \mathbf{S} = \sum_a \tfrac{1}{2}\boldsymbol{\sigma}^a, \quad \text{and} \quad \mathbf{Y}_k = \sum_a \tfrac{1}{2}\tau_k^a\boldsymbol{\sigma}^a. \tag{13.63}$$

Then, for example,

$$\sum_{a\neq b}\tfrac{1}{4}\boldsymbol{\tau}^a.\boldsymbol{\tau}^b = \Big(\sum_a \tfrac{1}{2}\boldsymbol{\tau}^a\Big).\Big(\sum_b \tfrac{1}{2}\boldsymbol{\tau}^b\Big) - \sum_a (\tfrac{1}{2}\boldsymbol{\tau}^a)^2 = \mathbf{T}.\mathbf{T} - \tfrac{3}{4}A, \tag{13.64}$$

and
$$\sum_{a\neq b} \tfrac{1}{4}\tau_k^a \tau_k^b \boldsymbol{\sigma}^a.\boldsymbol{\sigma}^b = \mathbf{Y}_k.\mathbf{Y}_k - \tfrac{3}{4}A, \tag{13.65}$$
where $A$ is the total number of nucleons ($a, b = 1,..., A$). These relations, together with
$$\tau_+^a \tau_-^b = \tfrac{1}{4}(\tau_1^a \tau_1^b + \tau_2^a \tau_2^b) = \tfrac{1}{4}(\boldsymbol{\tau}^a.\boldsymbol{\tau}^b - \tau_3^a \tau_3^b), \tag{13.66}$$
are sufficient to yield
$$\mathscr{M}_{\mathrm{i}}^+ + \mathscr{M}_{\mathrm{i}}^- = -\tfrac{1}{2}(1+3\eta)A + \langle \mathrm{i}|\mathbf{T}^2 - T_3^2 + \eta(\mathbf{Y}_1^2 + \mathbf{Y}_2^2)|\mathrm{i}\rangle. \tag{13.67}$$
Nuclear ground states tend to have low values for such quantum numbers as are given by the last bracket, hence this is negligible for any nucleus with a respectable number of nucleons, $A$.

For evaluating $\mathscr{M}_{\mathrm{i}}^+ - \mathscr{M}_{\mathrm{i}}^-$, the position exchange operator $X_{ab}$ will be expressed in terms of operations on spin and isospin. This is made possible by the fact that any nuclear state must be antisymmetric in the exchange of any pair of nucleons; the state description must change sign when the space, spin, and isospin variables of the pair are exchanged simultaneously. Now, it is well known that $\frac{1}{2}(1+\boldsymbol{\sigma}^a.\boldsymbol{\sigma}^b)$ can be used as a spin-exchange operator; it properly reduces to factors $\pm 1$, respectively, when applied to the symmetric (triplet) and antisymmetric (singlet) descriptions of spin pairs because $\boldsymbol{\sigma}^a.\boldsymbol{\sigma}^b = +1$ for parallel, and $\boldsymbol{\sigma}^a.\boldsymbol{\sigma}^b = -3$ for antiparallel, spins. The isospin descriptions have like properties, hence
$$X_{ab} = -\tfrac{1}{4}(1+\boldsymbol{\sigma}^a.\boldsymbol{\sigma}^b)(1+\boldsymbol{\tau}^a.\boldsymbol{\tau}^b). \tag{13.68}$$
It follows for the operators of interest here that
$$\tau_+^a \tau_-^b (1+\eta\boldsymbol{\sigma}^a.\boldsymbol{\sigma}^b)X_{ab} = -\tfrac{1}{8}(1-\tau_3^a\tau_3^b)[1+3\eta+(1-\eta)\boldsymbol{\sigma}^a.\boldsymbol{\sigma}^b],$$
when relations like $(\boldsymbol{\sigma}^a.\boldsymbol{\sigma}^b)^2 = 3-2\boldsymbol{\sigma}^a.\boldsymbol{\sigma}^b$ are used. The expression vanishes for $a = b$, hence the restriction $a \neq b$ in the sums over pairs implicit in $\mathscr{M}_{\mathrm{i}}^+ - \mathscr{M}_{\mathrm{i}}^-$ can be ignored. The isospin operation in the expression can be analysed into proton and neutron counting operations,
$$\tfrac{1}{4}(1-\tau_3^a\tau_3^b) = \tfrac{1}{2}(1+\tau_3^a)\tfrac{1}{2}(1-\tau_3^b) + \tfrac{1}{4}(1-\tau_3^a) - \tfrac{1}{4}(1-\tau_3^b).$$
This provides sufficient guidance for obtaining
$$\mathscr{M}_{\mathrm{i}}^+ - \mathscr{M}_{\mathrm{i}}^- = -\tfrac{1}{2}(1+3\eta)ZN - 2(1-\eta)\langle \mathrm{i}|\mathbf{S}_{\mathrm{p}}.\mathbf{S}_{\mathrm{n}}|\mathrm{i}\rangle, \tag{13.69}$$
where $N = A-Z$ is the number of neutrons and
$$\mathbf{S}_{\mathrm{p,n}} = \sum_a \tfrac{1}{2}(1\pm\tau_3^a)\tfrac{1}{2}\boldsymbol{\sigma}^a \tag{13.70}$$
are resultant spins of all the protons and neutrons, respectively.

Of all the contributions to $\mathscr{M}_{\mathrm{i}}^+ \pm \mathscr{M}_{\mathrm{i}}^-$, the one proportional to $ZN$ in (13.69) is expected to stand out in any general survey of capture rates as functions of atomic or mass number, not including nuclei which are too light. Even for as light a nucleus as $C^{12}$, $ZN = 36$ as against $A = 12$ in the next largest term of (13.67), and $ZN \approx \frac{1}{4}A^2$ grows much more rapidly with $A$ than any other contribution. When all the terms of (13.67), (13.69) are neglected except $\mathscr{M}_{\mathrm{i}}^{+} - \mathscr{M}_{\mathrm{i}}^{-} \approx -\frac{1}{2}(1+3\eta)ZN$, then the 'exchange' fraction (13.52) becomes

$$(\lambda - \lambda_{\mathrm{ind}})/\lambda_{\mathrm{ind}} \approx -\tfrac{1}{2}N(d/R)^3, \tag{13.71}$$

the results (13.53), (13.61 b), and (13.69) having been used here. The capture rate formula following from this and (13.51) is

$$\lambda = (290\ \mathrm{sec}^{-1})Z_{\mathrm{eff}}^4(q/m_\mu)^2[1-\delta(A-Z)/2A], \tag{13.72}$$

where $\delta \approx (d/r_0)^3$ with $r_0 = R/A^{\frac{1}{3}} \approx 1{\cdot}2(10)^{-13}$ cm. Because of the uncertainties about the average neutretto energy, $q$, and the range $d$ over which there is substantial spatial overlap of the average nucleon pair in the nucleus, the comparison of the rate formula (13.72) with observations‡ has been used to determine $q$ and $\delta$. The quantity $Z_{\mathrm{eff}}$ was calculated (ref. p. 378) and $\lambda/Z_{\mathrm{eff}}^4$ plotted against the neutron fraction $N/A = (A-Z)/A$, for capturing nuclei ranging from $C^{12}$ to $U^{238}$. The expected linear decrease was found, with fluctuations in individual cases as is to be expected. The absolute values and the average rate of decrease with $N/A$ were consistent with expectations for the very reasonable values $q \approx 0{\cdot}8m_\mu$ and $\delta \approx 3{\cdot}15$.

Just as the proportionality $\lambda \sim Z^4$ can be understood as arising from the number of capturing protons multiplied by the muon density, $\sim a_\mu^{-3}$, at each, so the decrease of $\lambda/Z^4$ with neutron fraction, $N/A$, can be regarded as arising from the inhibition of capture by protons which must turn into neutrons in already filled states. The last effect is proportional to the 'spatial overlap' volume, $\sim d^3$, because this also measures the volume around each nucleon from which other nucleons in identical states are excluded by the Pauli principle, as reference to the lower sign in the correlation forms (13.58) bears out. Measures of the exclusion volume are implicit in other data about nuclei. Thus, the ratio $(d/r_0)^3$ is explicitly involved in the so-called exchange corrections to the total coulomb energies in nuclei. The data on coulomb energy differences between mirror pairs of nuclei (see discussion on p. 143) lead to $d/r_0 \approx 1{\cdot}47$, in good consistency with the value $\delta \approx (d/r_0)^3 \approx 3{\cdot}15$ fitting the muon data.

‡ The first definitive survey of the capture rate as a function of atomic number was made by Sens, Swanson, Telegdi, and Yovanovitch, *Phys. Rev.* **107**, 1464 (1957).

*Muon capture in light nuclei*

The final results of the preceding subsection are appropriate only for rather heavier nuclei than ones with $A \approx 12$ or so. However, the steps in the closure approximation procedure were given in sufficient detail so that adaptations needed for lighter nuclei may be introduced. These call for specialized treatments, each suited to some individual case, and to what is known concerning details of the nuclear description in that case.

Primakoff (ref. p. 371) presented results for the four nuclei $H^1$, $H^2$, $He^3$, and $He^4$, a family distinguished by having spatial descriptions which are symmetric in interchanges of nucleon positions, and thus $F_i^-(\mathbf{r},\mathbf{r}') = 0$ in (13.55). Moreover, the nuclei are small and low in charge, so that the muon density at a point-charge ($\phi_K = 1$) and $Z_{\text{eff}} = Z$ (1 or 2) can be taken for them. It then follows from (13.50)–(13.55) that

$$\lambda = (272\ \text{sec}^{-1})Z^4(q/m_\mu)^2_{\text{eff}}[G_V^2(1+3\eta)/g^2(1+3C_A^2)]\times$$
$$\times\{1+[\mathscr{M}_i^+/Z(1+3\eta)]\iint (d\mathbf{r})(d\boldsymbol{\rho})F_i^+\sin q\rho/q\rho\}, \quad (13.73)$$

for the four cases, with $F_i^+ = 0$ in the case of the single-nucleon hydrogen nucleus. A complication in dealing with any very light nuclei arises from the relatively greater importance of the various recoil effects; the new quantity $(q/m_\mu)^2_{\text{eff}}$ is defined to include all these. In the first place, the neutretto energy as calculated from (13.37) must be decreased by the fraction $m_\mu/2(AM+m_\mu)$ in order to take into account the kinetic energy taken by the product nucleus, as it recoils with the momentum $q$. Second, the available phase space is decreased by the factor $(dW_f/dq)^{-1}$, where $W_f = q+[(MA)^2+q^2]^{\frac{1}{2}}$. Third, the muon Bohr radius implicit in (13.73), as reference to (13.47) shows, should be computed with the reduced mass: $m_\mu \to m_\mu(AM)/(AM+m_\mu)$. Consequently,

$$(q/m_\mu)^2_{\text{eff}} = (q/m_\mu)^2[1+q/(M^2A^2+q^2)^{\frac{1}{2}}]^{-1}(1+m_\mu/AM)^{-3}, \quad (13.74)$$

if the $q$ value on the right-hand side is the actual neutretto energy.

To complete the evaluation of (13.73), a detailed description of each nuclear state is still needed. The spin and isospin descriptions for the hydrogen and helium nuclei are quite simple and it is easy to find that $\mathscr{M}_i^+$, as given by (13.67) and (13.69), has the values

$$\mathscr{M}_i^+ = -(1+\eta), \qquad -(1+3\eta), \qquad -2(1+3\eta), \quad (13.75\,\text{a})$$

for $H^2$, $He^3$, and $He^4$, respectively. For the spatial descriptions, Primakoff assumed 'simple variational trial forms', such as are customary in nuclear binding energy calculations; his results for the dimensionless double integral of (13.73) were 0·64, 0·66, and 0·80 in the $H^2$, $He^3$, and $He^4$ cases respectively. These numbers will be referred to as 'spatial overlap fractions'; each would reach a unit value if all the nucleons of each nucleus occupied exactly the same positions, in a region small compared to the neutretto wavelength. The final outcome for the evaluations was:

$$\left.\begin{aligned} \lambda(H^1) &= 169\ \text{sec}^{-1}, & \lambda(H^2) &= 135\ \text{sec}^{-1} \\ \lambda(He^3) &= 2500\ \text{sec}^{-1}, & \lambda(He^4) &= 470\ \text{sec}^{-1} \end{aligned}\right\}. \qquad (13.75\,\text{b})$$

These results may be understood roughly as follows. First, there are differences among them because of the different neutretto energy in each case: $(q/m_\mu) = 0{\cdot}94$, 0·90, 0·95, and 0·75 for $H^1$, $H^2$, $He^3$, and $He^4$, respectively (the low value for $He^4$ arises primarily from its large binding, which requires a great excitation before a new nuclear configuration can be formed). The $H^1$ case is naturally subject to the biggest additional recoil effects (13.74): $(q/m_\mu)^2_{\text{eff}} = 0{\cdot}58$, 0·65, 0·78, 0·50. Then there is the large jump by the factor $2^4$ in going from hydrogen to helium because of the doubling of the capturing protons and the greater concentration of the muon on the nucleus arising from the charge doubling. Finally, there are the inhibitions caused by the initial presence of neutrons; since the 'neutron wave' to be formed must overlap well on the 'source proton', the prior occupation of the overlapping state tends to inhibit the process. The size of the effect may be judged from the proportionality of the process to the difference $Z(1+3\eta)-|\mathscr{M}_{\text{i}}^{+}|$ obtaining when the 'spatial overlap' is complete; the first term is the comparable contribution from an uninhibited ('independent-nucleon') process (13.49). According to (13.75 a), the difference in question decreases only from $1+3\eta$ to $2\eta$ when the deuteron's neutron is added to the proton; this is because there is room for a second neutron of opposite spin. The one neutron of $He^3$ tends to inhibit the spin-dependent ($\sim \eta$) part of the two protons' contributions just as much as the spin-independent part, $2(1+3\eta)$ being decreased by

$$|\mathscr{M}_{\text{i}}^{+}| = 1(1+3\eta),$$

because the neutron's spin is parallel to that of one of the protons, antiparallel to the other's. Finally, $2(1+3\eta)-|\mathscr{M}_{\text{i}}^{+}| \to 0$ for $He^4$ because of its 'saturated' neutron configuration. The $He^4$ capture rate is saved from vanishing because the 'spatial overlap' is only 80 per cent complete.

The closure approximation need not be relied on to get definite results when the muon capture can be assumed to produce just the ground state of the final nucleus most of the time. This assumption has the best chance of validity among the lightest nuclei, with their widely spaced energy levels. Even for a nucleus with as many as $A = 12$ nucleons, it has been determined experimentally that no more than 10 per cent of the bound states formed in the $C^{12}+\mu^- \to B^{12}+\mu^0$ process are excited‡ states of $B^{12}$. In any case, the production of the ground-state nucleus may become directly detectable, as through a measurement of its $\beta$-radioactivity unaccompanied by $\gamma$-rays. Examples for which calculations have been performed§ are captures which generate the nuclear transitions $He^3 \to H^3$ and $Li^6 \to He^6$, as well as $C^{12} \to B^{12}$; each product then undergoes the reverse transition, with emissions of $\beta$-negatrons. The rate of producing the $\beta$-decaying state is to be obtained from the capture rate formula (13.44) with the summation $\sum_{\mathrm{f}}$ over other final nuclear states left off. That is to be compared with the $\beta$-decay rate as given by (5.46),

$$\lambda_\beta = (g^2/2\pi^3)f(Z,W_0)\left(\left|\int_\beta 1\right|^2 + C_{\mathrm{A}}^2\left|\int_\beta \boldsymbol{\sigma}\right|^2\right). \tag{13.76}$$

The calculations are directed toward gauging the differences between the corresponding $\mu$-capture and $\beta$-decay nuclear matrix elements for each specific case.

A relatively superficial difference between the nuclear matrix element expressions as they occur in (13.44) and (13.76) stems from the summations and averages over nuclear orientations implicit in each. Thus, in the $\mu$-capture rate (13.44),

$$\left|\int_\mu 1(\boldsymbol{\sigma})\right|^2 \equiv (2I_{\mathrm{i}}+1)^{-1}\sum_{M_{\mathrm{i}}M_{\mathrm{f}}}\left|\left\langle \mathrm{f}\left|\sum_a \tau_-^a e^{-i\mathbf{q}\cdot\mathbf{r}^a}\phi_K(r^a)(\boldsymbol{\sigma}^a)\right|\mathrm{i}\right\rangle\right|^2, \tag{13.77}$$

for a $I_{\mathrm{i}}(M_{\mathrm{i}}) \to I_{\mathrm{f}}(M_{\mathrm{f}})$ transition. For the reverse, $\beta$-decay, transitions given by (13.76),

$$\left|\int_\beta 1(\boldsymbol{\sigma})\right|^2 \equiv (2I_{\mathrm{f}}+1)^{-1}\sum_{M_{\mathrm{i}}M_{\mathrm{f}}}\left|\left\langle \mathrm{i}\left|\sum_a \tau_+^a(\boldsymbol{\sigma}^a)\right|\mathrm{f}\right\rangle\right|^2$$

$$= (2I_{\mathrm{f}}+1)^{-1}\sum_{M_{\mathrm{i}}M_{\mathrm{f}}}\left|\left\langle \mathrm{f}\left|\sum_a \tau_-^a(\boldsymbol{\sigma}^a)\right|\mathrm{i}\right\rangle\right|^2. \tag{13.78}$$

‡ This was done by measuring the effect of excluding from the counts of the capture processes those which were accompanied by de-excitation $\gamma$-rays of $B^{12}$. H. Argo, F. Harrison, H. Kruse, and A. McGuire, *Phys. Rev.* **114**, 626 (1959).

§ A. Fujii and H. Primakoff, *Nuovo Cim.* **12**, 327 (1959).

The chief difference is made explicit by writing

$$\left\langle \mathrm{f}\left|\sum_a \tau_-^a e^{-i\mathbf{q}.\mathbf{r}^a}\phi_K(\boldsymbol{\sigma}^a)\right|\mathrm{i}\right\rangle = \left\langle \mathrm{f}\left|\sum_a \tau_-^a(\boldsymbol{\sigma}^a)\right|\mathrm{i}\right\rangle \int (d\mathbf{r})e^{-i\mathbf{q}.\mathbf{r}}\phi_K(r)\mathscr{D}(\mathbf{r}), \quad (13.79\,\mathrm{a})$$

where
$$\mathscr{D}(\mathbf{r}) \equiv \left\langle \mathrm{f}\left|\sum_a \tau_-^a \delta(\mathbf{r}-\mathbf{r}^a)(\boldsymbol{\sigma}^a)\right|\mathrm{i}\right\rangle \Big/ \left\langle \mathrm{f}\left|\sum_a \tau_-^a(\boldsymbol{\sigma}^a)\right|\mathrm{i}\right\rangle \quad (13.79\,\mathrm{b})$$

is an effective nucleon density. Now the ratio of the $\mu$-capture to $\beta$-decay rates may be written

$$\frac{\lambda_{\mu c}}{\lambda_\beta} = \frac{\pi}{a_\mu^3} \frac{(q^2)_{\mathrm{eff}}}{f(Z, W_0)} \frac{G_\mathrm{V}^2}{g^2} \frac{2I_\mathrm{f}+1}{2I_\mathrm{i}+1} \frac{\langle 1\rangle^2+\eta\langle\sigma\rangle^2}{\langle 1\rangle^2+C_\mathrm{A}^2\langle\sigma\rangle^2}.\mathscr{R}, \quad (13.80)$$

for which it has been assumed that, as in the closure approximation, $\left|\int_\mu \boldsymbol{\sigma}.\hat{\mathbf{q}}\right|^2 \approx \frac{1}{3}\left|\int_\mu \boldsymbol{\sigma}\right|^2$ after the spin and neutretto-direction averages (see the discussion following (13.46)). The new factor $\mathscr{R}$ arises essentially from the different radial integrations needed in the $\mu$-capture nuclear matrix elements:

$$\mathscr{R} \equiv \oint [(d\hat{\mathbf{q}})/4\pi]\left|\int (d\mathbf{r})e^{-i\mathbf{q}.\mathbf{r}}\phi_K(r)\mathscr{D}(\mathbf{r})\right|^2. \quad (13.81)$$

It is being presumed that the presence or absence of the operations $\boldsymbol{\sigma}^a$ in the numerator and denominator of the ratio in (13.79 b) make no essential difference, when both $\int 1$ and $\int \boldsymbol{\sigma}$ exist.

It is for the evaluation of the effective nucleon density $\mathscr{D}(\mathbf{r})$ that the most detailed descriptions of the specific nuclear states are needed. Fujii and Primakoff took advantage of the fact that in the parity-preserving, $\Delta I \leqslant 1$ transitions in which $\int_\beta 1(\boldsymbol{\sigma})$ exist, only $s$ and $d$ neutretto waves can be generated; moreover, their calculations indicated that the $d$-wave contributions are relatively small despite the short neutretto wavelength (apparently because of misfits between the $d$-wave, with its several nodes, and the fairly simple radial distributions of the nucleons). Thus, only the $s$-wave part of the plane wave

$$\exp(-i\mathbf{q}.\mathbf{r}) \rightarrow j_0(qr) = \sin(qr)/(qr)$$

is important for $\mathscr{R}$ of (13.81). Moreover, it provides the chief one of the effects responsible for making $\mathscr{R}$ less than unity; the variation of $\phi_K \approx \exp(-r/a_\mu)$ over the relatively small nuclei with $A \lesssim 12$ is much less, and any nucleon density $\mathscr{D}(\mathbf{r})$ is likely to be still more uniform. Very crudely then,

$$\mathscr{R} \approx \langle \sin qr/qr\rangle^2 \approx 1-\tfrac{1}{3}q^2\langle r\rangle^2+\tfrac{2}{45}q^4\langle r\rangle^4-...,$$

where $\langle r\rangle$ is some average of the order of the nuclear radius, $R$. Taking $\langle r\rangle = R = 1{\cdot}2A^{\frac{1}{3}}(10)^{-13}$ cm and $q/m_\mu = 0{\cdot}975$, $0{\cdot}95$, $0{\cdot}86$ for $He^3$, $Li^6$, and $C^{12}$, respectively, gives $\mathscr{R} \approx 0{\cdot}73$, $0{\cdot}62$, $0{\cdot}56$. These crude figures are given only to furnish some understanding of Fujii and Primakoff's much more carefully calculated results: $\mathscr{R} = 0{\cdot}74$, $0{\cdot}57$, and $0{\cdot}57$.

With the measure $\mathscr{R}$ of the ratio between $\mu$-capture and $\beta$-decay matrix elements evaluated, the formula (13.80) can be used to determine expected $\mu$-capture rates from observed $\beta$-decay rates. For the $\frac{1}{2} \leftrightarrow \frac{1}{2}$ transitions of the $He^3 \leftrightarrow H^3$ case, both the Fermi and Gamow–Teller $\beta$-moments, $\langle 1 \rangle$ and $\langle \sigma \rangle$, exist. Their ratio differs little from $\langle \sigma \rangle^2/\langle 1 \rangle^2 = 3$ according to the observed comparative half-life, $ft(H^3)$, listed in Table 5.1. The calculation is otherwise straightforward and yields

$$\lambda_{\mu c}(He^3 \to H^3) = 1460 \text{ sec}^{-1}, \tag{13.82 a}$$

based on the measured $\beta$-decay rate $\lambda_\beta(H^3) = 1{\cdot}77(10)^{-9}$ sec$^{-1}$. Direct observations‡ on $\mu$-captures yielding tritons have given $(1410 \pm 140)$ sec$^{-1}$ and $(1520 \pm 50)$ sec$^{-1}$. For the $0 \to 1$ $\beta$-transition $He^6 \to Li^6$, and the $1 \to 0$ decay $B^{12} \to C^{12}$, the Fermi moment $\langle 1 \rangle$ vanishes and the Gamow–Teller moment $\langle \sigma \rangle$ cancels out of (13.80). The observed $\beta$-decay rates then lead to

$$\left. \begin{aligned} \lambda_{\mu c}(Li^6 \to He^6) &= 1790 \text{ sec}^{-1} \\ \lambda_{\mu c}(C^{12} \to B^{12}) &= 7860 \text{ sec}^{-1} \end{aligned} \right\} \tag{13.82 b}$$

for the $\mu$-capture rate expectations. Numerous experiments§ with carbon indicate that the $B^{12}$ ground state is produced at a rate (6 to 9)$10^3$ sec$^{-1}$, in agreement with the expectation here.

It will be noted that the closure approximation, which counts all the $\mu$-captures, leading not only to the $\beta$-decaying states but also to ejections of nucleons (e.g. $\mu^- + He^3 \to H^2 + n + \mu^0$), properly leads to total rates higher than (13.82). Thus, the total $He^3$ capture rate expectation (13.75) is nearly twice as large as (13.82 a); the products other than the $H^3$ $\beta$-emitter do not seem to have been well enough measured to check on this as yet. The closure formula (13.72) leads to a total capture rate 50 800 sec$^{-1}$ for $C^{12}$, in rough accord with a value $(44 \pm 10)10^3$ sec$^{-1}$ deduced from the observed muon disappearance rate, reported in connexion with the experiments quoted as checking (13.72). Overestimates by the closure formulae should perhaps be expected, since they may be counting some final states which are not energetically available.

‡ I. Falomkin, A. Filippov, M. Kulyukin, B. Pontecorvo, Yu. Scherbakov, R. Sulyaev, V. Tsupko-Sitnikov, and O. Zaimidoroga, *Phys. Letters*, **3**, 229 (1963); L. Auerbach, R. Esterling, R. Hill, D. Jenkins, J. Lach, and N. Lipman, *Phys. Rev. Letters*, **11**, 23 (1963).

§ T. Godfrey, *Phys. Rev.* **92**, 512 (1953), made the initial experimental and theoretical comparisons of the $C^{12} \leftrightarrow B^{12}$ processes.

*Hyperfine effects and capture in hydrogen*

When a muon falls into an atomic $s$-orbit, preliminary to its absorption by the nucleus, it may form a state with the total angular momentum $F = I+\frac{1}{2}$, or one with $F = I-\frac{1}{2}$, together with the nuclear spin $I$. The two states should be populated with the relative weights $2(I+\frac{1}{2})+1 = 2I+2$ and $2(I-\frac{1}{2})+1 = 2I$, from the total of $2(2I+1)$ orientations possible to the randomly formed muon-nucleus system. The capture rates calculated in the preceding subsections, having been averaged over the initial muon and nuclear orientations, consist of weighted sums,

$$\lambda = \frac{I+1}{2I+1}\lambda(I+\tfrac{1}{2})+\frac{I}{2I+1}\lambda(I-\tfrac{1}{2}), \tag{13.83}$$

of capture rates $\lambda(I\pm\frac{1}{2})$ from the individual $F = I\pm\frac{1}{2}$ states.

The magnetic interaction of muon with nucleus makes the $F = I-\frac{1}{2}$ member of the 'hyperfine doublet' of states more stable than the other. However, the muon spin flip needed for the $I+\frac{1}{2} \to I-\frac{1}{2}$ conversion, if left to occur spontaneously within the atom, is very slow in comparison to the muon's lifetime. Consequently both the $F = I\pm\frac{1}{2}$ states tend to persist, and in the initial weights given in (13.83), so that the averaged formulae of the preceding subsections continue to apply. If a discrimination of the two rates $\lambda(I\pm\frac{1}{2})$ is desired, special measures of preparation or detection must usually be taken. In the case of hydrogen, no more special measure than preparing it in sufficient density seems to be required for converting all the atoms to the stabler, singlet state ($F = \frac{1}{2}-\frac{1}{2}$). The $p+\mu^-$ atom is neutral without a protective 'coating' of outer orbital electrons, hence is particularly vulnerable to conversion into its stablest form through interatomic collisions. Gershtein and Zeldovitch‡ have estimated the collisional conversions to be frequent enough already at a density of only $\sim 10^{20}$ atoms/cm$^3$, for practically all the $p+\mu^-$ systems to be in singlet states by the time the muon decays or is captured.

A discrimination of the two rates§ $\lambda(I\pm\frac{1}{2})$ is desirable as a check on the spin-dependence of the capture interaction. How direct this will be depends on how well correlated are the spins of the capturing proton and of the nucleus as a whole. Thus, in complex nuclei, any differences between the two rates $\lambda(I\pm\frac{1}{2})$ will mostly serve as a check on ideas about

‡ Their article in *Soviet Physics—Usp.* **3**, 593 (1961) sums up much work on this and related problems (below).

§ First considered by J. Bernstein, T. D. Lee, C. N. Yang, and H. Primakoff, *Phys. Rev.* **111**, 313 (1958).

how the nuclear states should be described. A much more direct test of the interaction (13.34) believed effective in $\mu$-capture is offered in the case of hydrogen. Here the spin of the capturing proton is the entire nuclear spin and the hyperfine effects should be particularly significant.

A direct evaluation of the capture rate following from the effective interaction (13.44) for the case of the hydrogen atom is quite simple, and gives the same results as the closure procedure (13.47)–(13.70). The latter is not an approximation in this case, since the sum over the final neutron's orientations is enough to complete the closure. It remains simple to forgo the averages over the initial muon and proton orientations which led to (13.75 b), and then the result can be written

$$\lambda = (169\ \mathrm{sec}^{-1})[1-\langle \boldsymbol{\sigma}_\mu . \boldsymbol{\sigma}_\mathrm{P} \rangle \zeta/(1+3\eta)], \tag{13.84}$$

where $\langle \boldsymbol{\sigma}_\mu . \boldsymbol{\sigma}_\mathrm{P} \rangle$ stands for the expectation value of the indicated projection of the muon and proton spin operators on each other. The correlation coefficient is a ratio to the coupling constant combination $(1+3\eta)$, which measures the rates (13.73)–(13.75 b) for the case of $\langle \boldsymbol{\sigma}_\mu . \boldsymbol{\sigma}_\mathrm{P} \rangle = 0$. The quantity $\zeta$ is the new coupling constant combination

$$\zeta = 2[G_\mathrm{A}(G_\mathrm{A}-\tfrac{2}{3}G_\mathrm{P})-G_\mathrm{V}(G_\mathrm{A}-\tfrac{1}{3}G_\mathrm{P})]/G_\mathrm{V}^2. \tag{13.85}$$

Primakoff has demonstrated how this arises from a specialization of the closure procedure to the hydrogen atom. It is equally easy to obtain the results directly from (13.34), using $\phi_K \approx 1$ in (13.39):

$$\sum_{\mathrm{n}\mu^0} |\psi_\mathrm{n}^\dagger H_{A\mu} \psi_\mathrm{P}|^2 = (4\pi a_\mu^3 V)^{-1} \sum_{\mathrm{n}\mu^0} |\chi_\mathrm{n}^\dagger \chi_{\mu^0}^\dagger (A+\boldsymbol{\sigma}.\mathbf{B})\chi_\mathrm{P}\chi_\mu|^2$$

$$= (4\pi a_\mu^3 V)^{-1} \chi_\mathrm{P}^\dagger \chi_\mu^\dagger (A^\dagger+\boldsymbol{\sigma}.\mathbf{B}^\dagger)(A+\boldsymbol{\sigma}.\mathbf{B})\chi_\mathrm{P}\chi_\mu,$$

where

$$A = G_\mathrm{V}-(G_\mathrm{A}-G_\mathrm{P})\boldsymbol{\sigma}^a.\hat{\mathbf{q}},$$

$$\mathbf{B} = G_\mathrm{A}\,\boldsymbol{\sigma}^a-\hat{\mathbf{q}}(G_\mathrm{V}+G_\mathrm{P}\,\boldsymbol{\sigma}^a.\hat{\mathbf{q}})+iG_\mathrm{A}\,\boldsymbol{\sigma}^a\times\hat{\mathbf{q}}$$

are results of the linearization of $H_{A\mu}$ in the muon spin, $\boldsymbol{\sigma}$. Now

$$\oint [(d\hat{\mathbf{q}})/4\pi](A^\dagger A+\mathbf{B}^\dagger.\mathbf{B}) = 2G_\mathrm{V}^2(1+3\eta),$$

and, since $(\boldsymbol{\sigma}.\hat{\mathbf{q}})(\boldsymbol{\sigma}^a.\hat{\mathbf{q}})$ becomes $\tfrac{1}{3}(\boldsymbol{\sigma}.\boldsymbol{\sigma}^a)$ upon averaging over the neutretto directions,

$$\oint [(d\hat{\mathbf{q}})/4\pi][i\boldsymbol{\sigma}.(\mathbf{B}^\dagger\times\mathbf{B})+\boldsymbol{\sigma}.(A^\dagger\mathbf{B}+\mathbf{B}^\dagger A)] = -2\zeta G_\mathrm{V}^2(\boldsymbol{\sigma}.\boldsymbol{\sigma}^a).$$

The bracket in (13.84) is the expectation value of the sum of the last two results in ratio to the first of them.

In the singlet configuration of the $\mathrm{p}+\mu^-$ atom, $\langle \boldsymbol{\sigma}_\mu . \boldsymbol{\sigma}_\mathrm{P} \rangle = -3$ and

$$\lambda(\tfrac{1}{2}-\tfrac{1}{2}) = (169\ \mathrm{sec}^{-1})[1+3(\eta+\zeta)]/(1+3\eta) = 636\ \mathrm{sec}^{-1}, \tag{13.86}$$

while in the triplet configuration $\langle \boldsymbol{\sigma}_\mu . \boldsymbol{\sigma}_p \rangle = +1$ and

$$\lambda(\tfrac{1}{2}+\tfrac{1}{2})$$
$$= (169\,\text{sec}^{-1})\{(G_V+G_A)^2+G_P[G_P-\tfrac{2}{3}(G_A+G_V)]\}/G_V^2(1+3\eta) \approx 13\,\text{sec}^{-1}. \quad (13.87)$$

It is easy to check that $\frac{1}{4}(636)+\frac{3}{4}(13) \approx 169$ as it should be according to (13.83). The triplet form has been written in more detail because this helps demonstrate that the triplet capture rate is saved from vanishing only by the internal nucleon structure effects. In the absence of the latter $G_V+G_A \rightarrow g(1+C_A) \rightarrow 0$ and $G_P \rightarrow 0$.

The great difference between the capture rates from the singlet and triplet states is easy to understand as a consequence of the left-handedness impressed on all the normal particles by the V–A forms of interaction. The product neutron and neutretto must recoil into opposite directions from each other. If they need bear away no resultant angular momentum, as in processes from a singlet state, they have opposite spins and both can move away left-handedly. However, their spins must be parallel in the triplet processes and then the neutron must recoil right-handedly.

The experiments on $\mu$-capture by the proton are usually done in liquid hydrogen, which has about $4(10)^{22}$ atoms/cm$^3$. This is a much more than great enough density to ensure the depopulation of the triplet hyperfine level so that any atom undergoing $\mu$-capture must be in the singlet state. However, the collision frequency responsible for this also encourages the formation of $[p\mu^- p]^+$ molecular ions, which have a much tighter bonding, by the muon, than do ordinary hydrogen molecules, with their electron bonds. In the molecular ion, the muon 'belongs' equally to either of the two protons, and the second proton cannot be considered a mere 'spectator' of an otherwise 'atomic' capture process, involving only the other proton. It becomes important to know the relative proportions in which the atomic and molecular combinations exist when either may be serving as the sources of whatever $\mu$-capture events may be detected.

The rate of the molecule formation has been measured experimentally‡ by adding known amounts of heavier nuclei, e.g. deuterons, to the liquid hydrogen. There ensues a measurable competition with the $[p\mu p]$ molecule formation of a $[d\mu p]$ molecule formation. The latter forms a link in chains of events like

$$[p\mu] \rightarrow [d\mu] \rightarrow [d\mu p] \rightarrow [He^3\mu]+\gamma.$$

‡ With greatest definition by E. Bleser, E. Anderson, L. Lederman, S. Meyer, J. Rosen, J. Rothberg, and I. T. Wang, *Phys. Rev.* **132**, 2679 and 2664 (1963).

The nuclear 'fusion' reaction‡ which produces the $He^3$ atom is what makes the prior [d$\mu$p] formation directly detectable, through the 5·8 MeV $\gamma$-ray which accompanies it. An analysis of what was observed, as to the time distribution of the $\gamma$-rays as well as the effect on the muon disappearances of the different deuterium concentrations, makes possible the discrimination of the various rates involved in the competing chains of events. The rate of the [p$\mu$] $\rightarrow$ [p$\mu$p] link in the muon disappearances was thus found to be $(1{\cdot}9\pm0{\cdot}2)10^6\ \text{sec}^{-1}$. This means that, upon coming to a stop in pure liquid hydrogen, the muon can be expected to have become part of a molecule after 0·5 $\mu$sec.

The last circumstance makes it possible to give the most definite experimental value to the rate of muon capture in the [p$\mu$p] molecule,

$$\lambda(\mathrm{p}\mu\mathrm{p}) = 460\pm40\ \text{sec}^{-1}, \tag{13.88}$$

this being obtained by accepting only those $\mu$-capture events (detected through the characteristic 5·2 MeV neutron produced in $\mu$-capture by a proton) which occur more than 0·5 $\mu$sec after the stoppage of the muon. The result here seems to be consistent with observations in hydrogen bubble chambers.§

For comparison to the experimental result (13.88), the theoretical capture rate (13.84) must be adapted to the conditions in a molecule. The latter is formed when a second proton attaches itself to a *singlet* [p$\mu$] atom, hence a structure with the total angular momentum $J = \frac{1}{2}$ results (ref. p. 387):

$$\langle J^2\rangle = \tfrac{3}{4} = \langle[\tfrac{1}{2}\boldsymbol{\sigma}+\tfrac{1}{2}(\boldsymbol{\sigma}_1+\boldsymbol{\sigma}_2)]^2\rangle = \tfrac{3}{4}+\langle S_\mathrm{p}^2\rangle+\langle\boldsymbol{\sigma}.\mathbf{S}_\mathrm{p}\rangle, \tag{13.89}$$

on the assumption that the $J = \frac{1}{2}$ is a resultant of the muon spin $\frac{1}{2}\boldsymbol{\sigma}$ and the total proton spin $\mathbf{S}_\mathrm{p} = \frac{1}{2}(\boldsymbol{\sigma}_1+\boldsymbol{\sigma}_2)$. Of the two possibilities $S_\mathrm{p} = 0$ and 1, corresponding to the so-called *para* and *ortho* states of the molecule, it is almost exclusively the *ortho* ($S_\mathrm{p} = 1$) form which is expected.‖ It can result from an electric dipole collisional transition, as against an 'electric monopole' transition, $\sim 10^{-4}$ as probable, needed for the para-hydrogen formation. With the proton spins parallel,

$$\langle\boldsymbol{\sigma}.\boldsymbol{\sigma}_1\rangle = \langle\boldsymbol{\sigma}.\boldsymbol{\sigma}_2\rangle = -\langle S_\mathrm{p}^2\rangle = -2 \tag{13.90}$$

‡ J. D. Jackson, *Phys. Rev.* **106,** 330 (1957).

§ R. Hildebrand and J. Doede, *Report of the* 1962 *CERN Conference* (*Geneva*), p. 418; E. Bertolini, A. Citron, G. Gianianella, S. Focardi, A. Mukhin, C. Rubbia, and S. Saporetti, p. 421.

‖ S. Weinberg, *Phys. Rev. Letters,* **4,** 575 (1960). This author also considered the introduction of orbital momenta into the molecule and found it to have no appreciable effect on the conclusions presented here.

follows from (13.89). Then the capture rate by the two protons of the molecule which follows from (13.84) is

$$\lambda_{\text{theo}}(\text{p}\mu\text{p}) = 2\gamma(169\,\text{sec}^{-1})[1+2\zeta/(1+3\eta)]$$
$$= 2\gamma[\tfrac{3}{4}\lambda(\tfrac{1}{2}-\tfrac{1}{2})+\tfrac{1}{4}\lambda(\tfrac{1}{2}+\tfrac{1}{2})]. \qquad (13.91)$$

The last form shows the degree to which the singlet and triplet atom rates (13.86), (13.87) are effective in the molecular process. The new coefficient $\gamma$ represents the ratio of the muon density at each proton of the molecule to the central muon density in the atom. Weinberg derived the number $\gamma = 0{\cdot}583$ from numerically computed‡ wave functions for the molecule; it turns out that $\gamma > \frac{1}{2}$ because the nearness of the second proton which shares the muon tends to concentrate the 'half-muon' more than in an atom. The consequent theoretical expectation is $\lambda_{\text{theo}}(\text{p}\mu\text{p}) = 560\ \text{sec}^{-1}$, considered to be accurate to 10 per cent if the correctness of the conventional values for the effective coupling constants (13.35) is granted.

The experimentally observed value (13.88) is large enough to help confirm the role of the 'handedness' discussed in connexion with the large difference (13.86)–(13.87) it makes to the proton $\mu$-capture from singlet and triplet combinations with the muon. The deviation from the quantitative theoretical expectation may not be entirely significant, in view of both the experimental and theoretical uncertainties. However, other data§ seem to indicate the same kind of deviations. Since the weakest point in the theoretical considerations may well be the estimate (13.19) of the induced Pseudoscalar coupling, the experimental finding should perhaps be treated as a measurement of it. Then the difference between the experimental and theoretical capture rates, 460 and 560 $\text{sec}^{-1}$, could be accounted for by adopting $C_{\text{P}} \approx 16C_{\text{A}}$ instead $C_{\text{P}} \approx 8C_{\text{A}}$, as in (13.19).

## 13.3. Neutretto capture

The detection of the antineutrinos emitted in nuclear $\beta$-decay (§ 8.2) was enabled by the large currents of them which emerge from nuclear reactors. The available currents of neutrettos are not nearly so large, the best sources being pion decays (11.30). On the other hand, pions are most copiously produced in high energy accelerators, and the decay in flight of the fast pions can yield neutrettos with energies of the order

‡ S. Cohen, D. Judd, and R. Riddell, *Phys. Rev.* **119**, 384 (1960).

§ e. g. V. Evseev, V. Roganov, V. Chernogovova, M. Szymczak, and Chang Run-Hwa, *Report of* 1962 *CERN Conference* (*Geneva*), p. 425; R. Cohen, S. Devons, and A. Kanaris, *Phys. Rev. Letters*, **11**, 134 (1963).

1 GeV and more. Since the neutretto capture cross-sections are expected to grow roughly as the square of the energy (8.37), a factor of a thousand in the energy can compensate for a decrease by a factor of a million in the incident current.‡

*The capture cross-sections*§

Only the neutretto capture by 'isolated' nucleons,

$$\left.\begin{array}{l}\mu^0+\mathrm{n}\rightarrow \mathrm{p}+\mu^-\\ \bar{\mu}^0+\mathrm{p}\rightarrow \mathrm{n}+\mu^+\end{array}\right\}, \tag{13.92}$$

will be considered here. The nucleons may be treated as 'isolated' even when they are parts of nuclei for neutrettos which have wavelengths much smaller than internucleonic distances within nuclei, $1{\cdot}2(10)^{-13}$ cm. Such wavelengths correspond to momenta greater than $q \approx \frac{1}{6}$ GeV/$c$.

Relations arising from momentum-energy conservation may be represented by the equation of the alternative expressions for the 4-momentum transfer,

$$Q_\alpha = (P_\mathrm{i}-P_\mathrm{f})_\alpha = (p-q)_\alpha, \tag{13.93}$$

where $P_{\mathrm{i,f}}$, are the initial and final nucleonic 4-momenta, while $p_\alpha$, $q_\alpha$ are the muon and neutretto 4-momenta. The result for the unique energy of a muon ejected at an angle $\theta$ to a given incident neutretto momentum, $\mathbf{q}$, is simple to express when the rest-masses of the leptons are neglected:

$$W = cp = cq/[1+(2q/Mc)\sin^2\tfrac{1}{2}\theta], \tag{13.94}$$

valid for $q^2 \gg (m_\mu c)^2 \approx (\frac{1}{10}\ \mathrm{GeV}/c)^2$. The corresponding 4-momentum transfer is given by $Q^2 = (\mathbf{p}-\mathbf{q})^2-(p-q)^2$, or:

$$Q^2 = 4pq\sin^2\tfrac{1}{2}\theta = (2q\sin\tfrac{1}{2}\theta)^2/[1+(2q/Mc)\sin^2\tfrac{1}{2}\theta]. \tag{13.95}$$

This will furnish a natural 'unit' for expressing the angular distribution of the muons.

When the differential cross-section is obtained by such procedures as yielded (8.27), it may be written

$$\begin{aligned}\frac{d\sigma}{d\Omega} &= \frac{2\pi}{\hbar}\int\frac{dpp^2V}{(2\pi\hbar)^3}\oint(d\mathbf{P}_\mathrm{f})\delta_4[(P_\mathrm{i}-P_\mathrm{f})_\alpha-(p-q)_\alpha]\tfrac{1}{2}V^2\sum_{\mathrm{spins}}|h_{N\mu}|^2\\ &= [p^2/(2\pi)^2\hbar^4][d(W+E_\mathrm{f})/dp]^{-1}\tfrac{1}{2}V^3\sum_{\mathrm{spins}}|h_{N\mu}|^2,\end{aligned} \tag{13.96}$$

‡ The consequent feasibility of detecting neutretto capture was pointed out by B. Pontecorvo, *Soviet JETP*, **10,** 1236 (1960), and by M. Schwartz, *Phys. Rev. Letters*, **4,** 306, (1960).

§ T. D. Lee and C. N. Yang, *Phys. Rev. Letters*, **4,** 307 (1960); Y. Yamaguchi, *Progr. Theoret. Phys.* **6,** 1117 (1960); N. Cabibbo and R. Gatto, *Nuovo Cim.* **15,** 304 (1960).

where $W+E_{\mathrm{f}} = -i(p+P_{\mathrm{f}})_4$ is the final total energy and

$$\frac{d}{dp}(W+E_{\mathrm{f}}) = c^2\left[\frac{p}{W}+\frac{p-q\cos\theta}{E_{\mathrm{f}}}\right] \to \frac{cq(Mc^2)}{pE_{\mathrm{f}}}, \tag{13.97}$$

with the last form valid for $m_\mu \to 0$. The cross-section expression (13.96) is predicated on normalizations to unit neutretto current-density, and to unity in $V$ for the other particles. By adopting instead the invariant normalizations (12.7) for all the fields occurring in the transformation currents $J_\alpha(\mathrm{pn})$ and $J_\alpha(\mu\mu^0)$ of (13.3) and (11.31), a relativistically invariant factor is isolated in:

$$|h_{N\mu}|^2 = (g^2/2V^3WqE_{\mathrm{f}}Mc^4)|J_\alpha(\mathrm{pn})J_\alpha(\mu\mu^0)|^2. \tag{13.98}$$

Now $$d\sigma/d\Omega = [g^2/(4\pi)^2\hbar^4c^8](p/Mq)^2 \sum_{\mathrm{spins}} |J_\alpha(\mathrm{pn})J_\alpha(\mu\mu^0)|^2 \tag{13.99}$$

for $m_\mu \to 0$.

To the degree that the muon mass may be neglected, the induced pseudoscalar effect $\sim C_{\mathrm{P}} = -m_\mu f_{\mathrm{P}}$ may be adjudged negligible and

$$J_\alpha(\mathrm{pn}) \approx \tfrac{1}{2}\bar\psi_{\mathrm{p}}[(f_{\mathrm{V}}+2Mf_{\mathrm{T}}-f_{\mathrm{A}}\gamma_5)\gamma_\alpha+if_{\mathrm{T}}(P_{\mathrm{i}}+P_{\mathrm{f}})_\alpha]\psi_{\mathrm{n}} \tag{13.100}$$

taken for (13.3). Here, the first of the relations (13.6) has been used to eliminate $\sigma_{\alpha\beta}Q_\beta$ of (13.7). With the neutron-proton mass difference neglected ($M_{\mathrm{n}} = M_{\mathrm{p}} = M$), the distinction between neutron and proton may be disregarded in comparing the two processes (13.92). However, there still remains an effect of the non-invariance to charge-conjugation which is taken into account when the current expressions

$$J_\alpha(\mu\mu^0) = \tfrac{1}{2}\bar\psi_\mu\gamma_\alpha(1\pm\gamma_5)\psi_{\mu^0} \tag{13.101}$$

are respectively used for the $\mu^-$ and $\mu^+$ production. Then the invariant result for the spin sum‡ becomes (with $c = 1$):

$$\begin{aligned}\tfrac{1}{2}\sum_{\mathrm{spins}}|J_\alpha(\mathrm{pn})J_\alpha(\mu\mu^0)|^2 &= 2M^2[(f_{\mathrm{V}}+2Mf_{\mathrm{T}})^2-f_{\mathrm{A}}^2](q\cdot p)+\\ &\quad +2[(f_{\mathrm{V}}+2Mf_{\mathrm{T}})^2+f_{\mathrm{A}}^2][(q\cdot P_{\mathrm{i}})(p\cdot P_{\mathrm{f}})+(q\cdot P_{\mathrm{f}})(p\cdot P_{\mathrm{i}})]+\\ &\quad +[f_{\mathrm{T}}^2(M^2-P_{\mathrm{i}}\cdot P_{\mathrm{f}})-2Mf_{\mathrm{T}}(f_{\mathrm{V}}+2Mf_{\mathrm{T}})][2q\cdot(P_{\mathrm{i}}+P_{\mathrm{f}})p\cdot(P_{\mathrm{i}}-P_{\mathrm{f}})-\\ &\quad -(q\cdot p)(P_{\mathrm{i}}+P_{\mathrm{f}})^2]\pm 2f_{\mathrm{A}}(f_{\mathrm{V}}+2Mf_{\mathrm{T}})\textstyle\sum,\end{aligned} \tag{13.102}$$

where $\sum$ is the invariant contraction of antisymmetrical tensors,

$$\textstyle\sum = \sum_{\alpha\beta}(q_\alpha p_\beta - q_\beta p_\alpha)[(P_{\mathrm{i}})_\alpha(P_{\mathrm{f}})_\beta-(P_{\mathrm{i}})_\beta(P_{\mathrm{f}})_\alpha].$$

Notice that in the limit of 'localized' interaction (here represented by $f_{\mathrm{T}} = 0$), each term is linear in either the 4-momentum or the mass of each particle, as expected from such considerations as in § 12.1. For an initial nucleon at rest, $P_{\mathrm{i}}(0, iMc)$, the expression (13.102) can be put

‡ See § 8.2 for the treatment of the polarized incident beam.

entirely in terms of the neutretto energy $cq$ and the momentum transfer $Q$, with the help of the relations

$$\left.\begin{array}{c}(q.p) = (q.Q) = -\tfrac{1}{2}(Q^2+m_\mu^2 c^2), \quad (p.Q) = \tfrac{1}{2}(Q^2-m_\mu^2 c^2) \\ Q_0 \equiv (Mc^2-E_\mathrm{f})/c = (W-cq)/c = -Q^2/2Mc\end{array}\right\}, \qquad (13.103)$$

which follow from definitions and from the conservation laws.

A reasonably simple expression can be written for the differential cross-section when the muon mass is neglected:

$$\frac{d\sigma}{d\Omega} = \frac{g^2q^2}{2\pi^2\hbar^4c^2}\cos^2\tfrac{1}{2}\theta\left(\frac{p}{q}\right)^3\{f_\mathrm{V}^2+f_\mathrm{A}^2(1+2\tan^2\tfrac{1}{2}\theta)+f_\mathrm{T}^2\,Q^2/c^2+$$
$$+[(f_\mathrm{V}+2Mf_\mathrm{T}\mp f_\mathrm{A})^2Q^2/2M^2c^2\pm 4f_\mathrm{A}(f_\mathrm{V}+2Mf_\mathrm{T})q/Mc]\tan^2\tfrac{1}{2}\theta\}, \qquad (13.104)$$

for $\mu^\mp$ production, respectively. More explicit forms of $p/q$ and $Q^2$ were given in (13.94) and (13.95). It should be remembered that the form-factors may also be functions of $Q^2$, e.g. as in (13.14).

Yamaguchi‡ has presented extensive numerical evaluations of the cross-section (13.104), using the form-factors

$$f_\mathrm{A} = +1{\cdot}25f_\mathrm{V}, \qquad 2Mf_\mathrm{T} = 3{\cdot}7f_\mathrm{V}, \qquad f_\mathrm{V} = [1+\tfrac{5}{4}Q^2/M^2c^2]^{-1} \qquad (13.105)$$

indicated by (13.14) and (13.15). Some of the results for the integrated cross-section in units of $10^{-38}$ cm$^2$ are:

| $q/Mc$ | $\sigma(\mu^0+\mathrm{n}\to\mathrm{p}+\mu^-)$ | $\sigma(\bar{\mu}^0+\mathrm{p}\to\mathrm{n}+\mu^+)$ |
|---|---|---|
| 0·25 | 0·36 | $0{\cdot}10_5$ |
| 0·50 | 0·70 | 0·19 |
| 0·75 | 0·82 | 0·27 |
| 1·00 | 0·86 | 0·33 |
| 1·50 | 0·85 | 0·42 |
| 2·00 | 0·84 | 0·48 |

Detailed angular distributions were computed first; they exhibited near-isotropy for $q \approx \frac{1}{4}Mc$ but a forward peaking develops as the energy increases. At $q \approx Mc$, the ratio of forward to lateral ejections becomes $\sigma(0)/\sigma(\frac{1}{2}\pi) \approx 27$ and 316, for the $\mu^-$ and $\mu^+$ products, respectively.

The large difference between the $\mu^-$ and $\mu^+$ cross-sections shown by the above table arises from the Vector-Pseudovector interference in (13.104). Thus, accurate measurements of the differential $\mu^\mp$ production rates should yield particularly direct evidence about the Pseudovector form-factor, $f_\mathrm{A}(Q^2)$.

‡ Y. Yamaguchi, *CERN Report* 61–2, Geneva (1961).

The effect of the finite muon mass remains quite negligible in the range of energies tabulated above even for the induced Pseudoscalar contributions measured by $C_{\mathrm{P}} = -m_{\mu} f_{\mathrm{P}}$, if the large ratio $C_{\mathrm{P}}/C_{\mathrm{A}} \approx 8$ indicated in (13.19) is taken. The induced Pseudoscalar interaction adds the term $\frac{1}{2} i f_{\mathrm{P}} Q_{\alpha} \beta\gamma_5$ to the nucleon current operator of (13.100), as reference to $A_{\alpha}$ of (13.8) shows. It leads to a supplementation of the invariant expression (13.102) by

$$[2Mf_{\mathrm{A}} f_{\mathrm{P}} + f_{\mathrm{P}}^2(M^2 + P_{\mathrm{i}} . P_{\mathrm{f}})][(q . p)Q^2 - 2(q . Q)(p . Q)]. \quad (13.106)$$

The consequence for the differential cross-section expression (13.104) is a supplementation of its curly bracket by the terms

$$(m_{\mu}/2M)^2[f_{\mathrm{P}}^2 Q^2 - 4Mcf_{\mathrm{A}} f_{\mathrm{P}}]. \quad (13.107)$$

Yamaguchi evaluated this for $m_{\mu} f_{\mathrm{P}} = 8f_{\mathrm{A}} = 10f_{\mathrm{V}}$ with $f_{\mathrm{V}}(Q^2)$ as in (13.105). He thus found an increase in the total cross-sections by $0{\cdot}17(10)^{-38}$ cm$^2$ at $q = Mc$. The contribution turns out to become rapidly smaller with increasing energy and, of course, is also negligible at low energies.

The production of muons in the capture by nuclei of high energy neutrettos was successfully detected in large-scale experiments.‡ The number of the rare events which were found appear to be consistent with the above expectations.

*Neutretto vs. neutrino*

There was great interest in the outcome of the neutretto capture experiment because it is presumed to test whether the neutretto is identifiable with the neutrino.

*A priori*, there need be no expectation that the neutral partner in the muon transformation current is the same as in the electron-neutrino current. However, should the neutretto turn out to be as massless as the neutrino, then a possible identification of the two particles acquires some urgency. In another known case of mass and spin degeneracy (the '$\tau$' and '$\theta$' particles), an eventual identification proved possible.

If the neutral particles accompanying the muons of $\pi$-decay were ordinary neutrinos, then about equal numbers of electrons and muons should have been observed in the capture experiment. Indeed, with the mass of the charged lepton neglected, the cross-section expression for the $\nu \rightarrow \mathrm{e}$ processes is identical with the $\mu^0 \rightarrow \mu$ formula (13.104). Yet the experimenters could not find that any electrons were produced among

‡ G. Danby, J. M. Gaillard, K. Goulianos, L. Lederman, N. Mistry, M. Schwartz, and J. Steinberger, *Phys. Rev. Letters*, **9**, 36 (1962).

the muons which they observed. It seems clear that the neutretto is not identical with the ordinary, left-handed neutrino, and the antineutretto is not the same as the right-handed antineutrino.

The last statement suggests that it may still be possible‡ to identify the neutretto with the neutrino in those two states which play no role in the electron-neutrino current (see the last subsection of Chapter X). The neutretto could be just a *right*-handed normal neutrino, while the antineutretto is a *left*-handed antineutrino.

The latter picture would fit handsomely into the 'V+A' alternative (12.75) for the muon transformation current, in which it is $\mu^+$ that is treated as the normal muon while $\mu^-$ is the antimuon (i.e. described by analogues of the positron states). The change to that current affects no observable result, as was shown in connexion with (12.75). The neutral lepton which is capturable by neutrons to produce negative muons must still be left-handed, as in (13.92) and the 'V−A' current, but is now treated as an antiparticle ($\bar{\mu}^0+\mathrm{n}\rightarrow\mathrm{p}+\mu^-$ and $\mu^0+\mathrm{p}\rightarrow\mathrm{n}+\mu^+$ replace (13.92)).

The replacement of a massless neutretto by a neutrino in the 'V+A' current (12.75), yielding

$$J_\alpha(\mu\nu) = \psi_\mu^\dagger\beta\gamma_\alpha\tfrac{1}{2}(1-\gamma_5)\psi_\nu, \tag{13.108}$$

changes none of the physical results because only the neutrinos of opposite helicity, $\frac{1}{2}(1+\gamma_5)\psi_\nu$, are involved in the 'V−A' electron-neutrino current. The capture reactions (13.92) are now replaced by

$$\left.\begin{aligned}\bar{\nu}_\mathrm{L}+\mathrm{n}&\rightarrow\mathrm{p}+\mu^-\\ \nu_\mathrm{R}+\mathrm{p}&\rightarrow\mathrm{n}+\mu^+\end{aligned}\right\}. \tag{13.109}$$

Subscripts L (left-handed) and R (right-handed) are appended in order to emphasize that the neutrino states involved here are not the ones ($\nu_\mathrm{L}$ and $\bar{\nu}_\mathrm{R}$) which are involved in the electron-producing captures (8.25) and $\nu_\mathrm{L}+\mathrm{n}\rightarrow\mathrm{p}+\mathrm{e}^-$ of (1.21). With (13.109), the representations (11.30) of the $\pi$-decays are replaced by

$$\left.\begin{aligned}\pi^+&\rightarrow\mathrm{p}+\bar{\mathrm{n}}\rightarrow\mu^++\bar{\nu}_\mathrm{L}\\ \pi^-&\rightarrow\mathrm{n}+\bar{\mathrm{p}}\rightarrow\mu^-+\nu_\mathrm{R}\end{aligned}\right\}. \tag{13.110}$$

The neutral products here can induce the muon-producing reactions (13.109), as observed experimentally, but not electron production in captures by nucleons. Only the rare (fraction $\sim 10^{-4}$) $\pi$-decays into electrons, $\pi^+\rightarrow\mathrm{e}^++\nu_\mathrm{L}$ and $\pi^-\rightarrow\mathrm{e}^-+\bar{\nu}_\mathrm{R}$, provide neutral leptons which can induce electron production by nucleons.

‡ S. Bludman, *Nuovo Cim.* **27**, 751 (1963).

It should still be mentioned that the neutretto-neutrino identification under discussion here changes the procedure for calculating $\mu$-decay, yet makes no change in results. The processes are now represented by

$$\left.\begin{aligned} \mu^+ &\rightarrow e^+ + \nu_L + \nu_R \\ \mu^- &\rightarrow e^- + \bar{\nu}_R + \bar{\nu}_L \end{aligned}\right\}, \qquad (13.111)$$

instead of (12.1) or (12.74). With two product particles which are identical except for the states of their spins, their description should properly be antisymmetrized. It will emerge automatically from the field-operator formalism that the transition amplitude (12.43) is replaced by

$$\langle h_\mu \rangle_0 = 2^{-\frac{1}{2}} g\{[u_1^\dagger(1-\gamma_5)\beta\gamma_\alpha u_\mu][u_2^\dagger(1+\gamma_5)\beta\gamma_\alpha u_e^C] - \\ -[u_2^\dagger(1-\gamma_5)\beta\gamma_\alpha u_\mu][u_1^\dagger(1+\gamma_5)\beta\gamma_\alpha u_e^C]\},$$

in the case of $\mu^+$-decay. The spinors $u_{1,2}$ describe neutrinos with momenta $\mathbf{q}_{1,2}$ respectively. This leads to the same expectations as (12.43) because of the finding discussed in connexion with (12.75), and because the opposite helicity neutrinos cannot interfere. Such an intensity expression as (12.44) is just doubled, but then a factor $\frac{1}{2}$ must be introduced into the otherwise unrestricted summation over the neutral particle states; this is because a mere interchange of the momenta and spins of the two neutrinos in their antisymmetrized state does not produce a new state.

There remains no objection to identifying the neutretto with the 'other two components' of the neutrino (on the presumption of equal masses) except the rather formal one that the chiralities involved in the muon transformation current would be the opposite ($\gamma_5 = -1$) of those involved in the electron-neutrino and nucleon currents ($\gamma_5 = +1$). There is a switch from a 'V$-$A' to a 'V$+$A' current.

## 13.4. The outlook for the weak interactions

The high-energy neutretto capture problem called attention‡ to a theoretical difficulty of long standing, anent the formulations of the weak couplings as 'direct contact' or 'point' interactions among four fermions, as in (12.63) or (10.9). The difficulty is manifested by such results as the proportionalities to the squared energy, of the capture cross-sections (8.37) or (13.104). They imply that the cross-sections would increase indefinitely with energy were it not for essentially extraneous effects. Thus, the cross-section (13.104) levels off with increasing energy only because of such strong-coupling effects as are represented by the form-factors (13.105). If lepton capture by muons or electrons

‡ T. D. Lee and C. N. Yang, *Phys. Rev. Letters*, **4**, 307 (1960).

were considered, there need enter no strong-couplings at all to put a limit on the cross-section. Yet infinite cross-sections plainly contradict expectations from 'unitarity' (the conservation of particles). For example, there is a 'unitarity limit' on any $s$-wave cross-section given by $\sigma \leqslant 4\pi\lambda\!\!\!^{-2} = 4\pi\hbar^2/q^2$, having a typical *decrease* with energy.

The situation could be saved through the occurrence of appropriate form-factors even in the absence of any stronger couplings, ones characteristic of the weak interactions themselves. In general, form-factors are manifestations of incomplete localizations of the interaction, just as the spreading of the '$\beta$-charge' by the strong couplings gave rise to the form-factors (13.105). Comparable form-factors would arise in every type of weak interaction if the four-fermion, 'point' couplings were replaced by unlocalized interactions such as were briefly alluded to in § 10.1. If the interacting transformation currents of (12.63) were to be evaluated at separated points, a propagation in an 'intermediary field' would be formulated by any procedure adopted for integrating the contributions of various separations between the points. There would be an exchange of 'virtual quanta' of an intermediate field, so that the interaction (1.21), for example, would be replaced by some two-step process like $p+e^- \rightarrow W \rightarrow n+\nu$. The name 'W-boson' for the intermediate field quantum was suggested by Yang and Lee,‡ who offered speculations about its character.

Properties which must be attributed to the W-boson follow from the functions it is asked to perform and from the fact that, despite its putative intrusion in various processes, it has escaped detection through them. Unfortunately, such considerations seem to require several types of W-boson (or a large variety of 'internal' configurations in a single quantum). The conclusions about the intermediate boson are far from unique as yet and any present attempt to summarize them is bound to have only the most transitory validity. It seems quite clear that for all the processes considered in this treatise, the introduction of an intermediate boson constitutes an unnecessary complication, producing no detectable effects on them. The weak interactions take place within a region so nearly a point that the four-fermion coupling forms yield adequate descriptions up to energies of more than 1 GeV. The non-localizations generated by the strong couplings are the more important so far, and these are still so ill-formulated that considerable progress in their treatment may well be necessary before any very definite conclusions about any intermediate bosons can be distilled.

‡ T. D. Lee and C. N. Yang, *Phys. Rev.* **119**, 1410 (1960).

The scope of this treatise has been restricted in still another respect. It has been found that various 'strange' particles ($\Lambda$, $\Sigma$, $\Xi$, K,...) undergo weak interactions resulting in leptonic products. Sometimes a pion substitutes for a pair of leptons ($\pi \leftrightarrow \mu+\mu^0 \leftrightarrow e+\nu$). The rarity of the lepton-producing events has made the evidence about them extremely fragmentary. Some progress in reducing the observations to order has been made by assuming various analogies with the interactions of the 'Puppi Triangle' represented in (12.63). However, the conclusions are as yet far from unique and only too likely to be transitory. Their consideration has therefore been omitted here.

In summary, this treatise can be said to have been restricted to the 'strangeness-conserving' processes, and even these have been considered only in so far as the four-fermion 'point' couplings form an adequate representation of them.

# INDEX

PRINTED IN GREAT BRITAIN
AT THE UNIVERSITY PRESS, OXFORD
BY VIVIAN RIDLER
PRINTER TO THE UNIVERSITY